CRANDALL, KEITH

EX 2-3

W9-ALN-362

CONSULTING EDITOR

BENJAMIN A. WHISLER

HEAD, DEPARTMENT OF CIVIL ENGINEERING
PENNSYLVANIA STATE UNIVERSITY

Elementary Surveying

By

RUSSELL C. BRINKER

Formerly Head, Department of Civil Engineering
Virginia Polytechnic Institute

and

WARREN C. TAYLOR

Professor Emeritus of Civil Engineering
Union College

THIRD EDITION

INTERNATIONAL TEXTBOOK COMPANY
Scranton, Pennsylvania

Fourth Printing, February, 1958

Copyright, 1955, by International Textbook Company. All rights reserved.
Printed in the United States of America by The Haddon Craftsmen, Inc., at
Scranton, Pennsylvania. Library of Congress Catalog Card Number: 55–10890.

PREFACE

This third edition of ELEMENTARY SURVEYING has been considerably expanded, to conform with the actual content of surveying courses now being given to students in geology, forestry, and all engineering curricula other than civil engineering. Ample material is also included for the courses offered to civil engineering students at many colleges and universities.

The book has been completely rewritten and extensively rearranged. Greater emphasis is placed upon the theory of errors and optics, the use of significant figures, and practical field methods.

All chapters presuppose that essentially engineering and surveying involve practical operations, not theoretical and academic manipulations of numbers. Proper field procedures to obtain a desired precision are stressed. Although little time is available in most modern curricula for drill on techniques, the classroom work must be supplemented by demonstrations on the part of the instructor, and student practice in the field.

Engineers, architects, geologists, and foresters must be able to make measurements and to analyze the precision and accuracy of the results obtained by other people. They should also be qualified to properly locate and set machinery; to lay out houses, buildings, and other common structures; and to understand and prepare simple topographic maps. Each of these skills is discussed in this edition.

Considerations of economy are introduced in the text in order that the student will be more likely to associate this important factor with the theory learned in later courses. All surveying is a constant fight to eliminate or isolate errors and mistakes. In each chapter the student is reminded of this point, through lists of typical errors and mistakes. Also, methods of checking field and office work are accented.

The chapters are arranged in the order found most convenient at the various colleges with which the authors are familiar. Fundamental material is collected in the first sixteen chapters comprising Part I. There the theory and use of the four fundamental surveying instruments—the tape, level, transit, and plane table—are described in detail, and new types of equipment are noted briefly. Any chapter

v

following Chapter 11 can be omitted without loss of continuity, but many of those chapters are short enough to be suitable for a single assignment.

Limited coverage of such subjects as photogrammetry, field astronomy, boundary surveys, and industrial applications of surveying methods is given in Part II to fit the programs offered at some colleges. For example, the brief chapter on boundary surveys is intended to make students aware of a few of the problems involved in the survey and transfer of property, and the legal requirements of professional registration. Some instructors give broad survey-type courses and want their students to get an over-all view of the many facets of the profession. It is believed that the arrangement and scope of material presented herein will meet that need.

Taping, leveling, and transit work are taken up in that order because students find it easier to acquire some facility with the equipment in that sequence, and because this arrangement permits the start and continuation of field work with a minimum of lecture time. The suggested order of field assignments given in Appendix A makes it possible to begin effective computation and drafting-room problems after just a few periods in the field if bad weather is encountered.

The difficulty in getting through all of the preliminary material (basic conceptions of the profession, history, theory of errors, and methods of notekeeping) before commencing field work during the first week is recognized. Nevertheless the authors feel that these topics must precede the theory of instruments.

The subject of notes and noteforms—an important part of surveying and engineering—is discussed in a separate chapter. Most of the sample noteforms are collected in Appendix A instead of being scattered throughout the text.

A large number of problems are available at the end of each chapter, to illustrate theory and practice and to offer a wide choice in the selection of assignments.

Suggestions and criticisms will be greatly appreciated.

R. C. B.
W. C. T.

Acknowledgment

The authors wish to acknowledge the use of material from Professors Emeritus A. S. Cutler, O. S. Zelner, and L. F. Boon (University of Minnesota); Professor Emeritus C. B. Andrews (University of Hawaii); Professor P. P. Rice (Rutgers University); and Professor D. F. Griffin (University of Southern California). Many helpful suggestions were offered by Professor A. S. Chase (Alabama Polytechnic Institute), Professor Lawrence Perez (Pennsylvania State University), and Lt. Col. Wyley L. Baxter (United States Military Academy). Professors L. G. Rich and D. V. Smith (Virginia Polytechnic Institute), Professors E. C. Wagner and H. E. Kallsen (University of Wisconsin), Professor G. B. Lyon (Cornell University), Mr. W. C. Wattles of Glendale, California, Mr. R. B. Irwin of Los Angeles, and others, gave assistance or provided useful material. The chapter on photogrammetry was written by Professor J. O. Eichler of Georgia Institute of Technology. The noteforms in Appendix A were lettered by Mr. J. H. Bell.

Illustrative material has been freely supplied by the U. S. Bureau of Land Management, the U. S. Geological Survey, and the U. S. Coast and Geodetic Survey. Manufacturers of surveying equipment who furnished illustrations include the Keuffel and Esser Company, W. and L. E. Gurley, Kern Instruments, Inc., Wild Heerbrugg Instruments, Inc., Abrams Aerial Survey Corporation, Wallace and Tiernan, and Bausch and Lomb.

CONTENTS

PART I

PART II

PART I

Chapter 1

INTRODUCTION

1-1. Definition of surveying. Surveying is the science or art of making the measurements necessary to determine the relative positions of points above, on, or beneath the surface of the earth, or to establish such points.

The work of the surveyor, which largely consists of making such measurements, can be divided into three parts:

FIELD WORK—Taking and recording measurements in the field.

MAPPING—Plotting the measurements and drawing a map.

COMPUTING—Making the necessary calculations to determine locations, areas, and volumes.

1-2. Importance of surveying. Surveying is one of the oldest arts practiced by man, because from the earliest times it has been found necessary to mark boundaries and divide land. It is now indispensable in all branches of engineering. For example, surveys are required prior to and during the planning and construction of highways, railroads, buildings, bridges, tunnels, canals, irrigation ditches, dams, drainage works, and water-supply and sewerage systems. They are also essential in laying out pipelines and mine shafts. The use of surveying or surveying methods has become common in the layout of assembly lines and jigs, the fabrication of aeroplanes, and the placement of equipment, and in many related tasks in aeronautical, agricultural, chemical, electrical, mechanical, and mining engineering, and in geology and forestry. Optical tooling represents an application of surveying in shop practice.

1-3. Training for all engineers. All engineers must know the limits of accuracy possible in construction, plant design and layout, and manufacturing processes, even though someone else does the actual surveying. This knowledge is best obtained by making measurements with the equipment employed in practice.

1

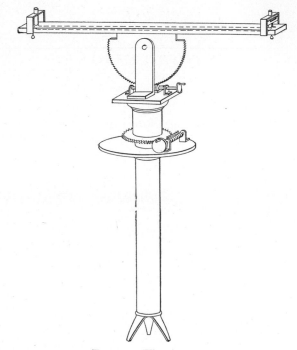

FIG. 1–1.   The diopter.[1]

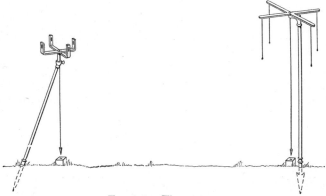

FIG. 1–2.   The groma.

[1] Figures 1–1, 2, 3, and 4 are shown through the courtesy of Professor Edward Noble Stone.

In addition to stressing the need for reasonable limits of accuracy, surveying emphasizes the value of significant figures. An engineer must know when to work to hundredths of a foot instead of to tenths or thousandths, or perhaps the nearest foot, and what precision in field data is necessary to justify carrying out computations to the desired number of decimal places. With experience, he learns how the equipment and personnel available govern procedures and results.

Neat sketches and computations are the mark of an orderly mind, which in turn is an index of sound engineering background and competence. Taking field notes under all sorts of conditions is excellent preparation for the kind of recording and sketching expected of engineers. Additional training having a carry-over value is obtained in arranging computations properly.

1–4. History of surveying. The oldest historical records in existence today which bear directly on the subject of surveying state that this science had its beginning in Egypt. Herodotus says Sesostris (about 1400 B.C.) divided the land of Egypt into plots for the purpose of taxation. The annual floods of the Nile River swept away portions of these plots, and surveyors were appointed to replace the bounds. These early surveyors were called *rope-stretchers*. Their measurements were made by means of ropes with markers at unit distances.

As a consequence of this work the early Greek thinkers developed the science of geometry. Their advance, however, was chiefly along the lines of pure science. Heron stands out prominently for applying science to surveying, about 120 B.C. He was the author of several important treatises of interest to engineers, including one called *The Dioptra*, which related the methods of surveying a field, drawing a plan, and making calculations. This treatise also described one of the first pieces of surveying equipment recorded, the *diopter* (Fig. 1–1). For many years Heron's work was the most authoritative among Greek and Egyptian surveyors.

Real development in the art of surveying came through the practical-minded Romans, whose best-known treatise on surveying was by Frontinus. Although the original manuscript disappeared, copied portions have been preserved. This noted Roman engineer and surveyor, who lived in the first century, was a pioneer in the field and his treatise remained the standard for many years.

The engineering ability of the Romans was demonstrated by their extensive construction work throughout the Empire. The surveying necessary for this construction resulted in the organization of a surveyors' guild. Ingenious instruments were developed and used. Among these were the *groma* (Fig. 1–2), used for sighting; the *libella* (Fig. 1–3), an A frame with a plumb bob, used for leveling; and the *chorobates* (Fig. 1–4), a horizontal straightedge about 20 ft long, with supporting legs and with a groove on top for water to serve as a level.

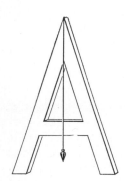

One of the oldest Latin manuscripts in existence is the *Codex Acerianus*, written about the sixth century. It contains an account of surveying as practiced by the Romans and includes several pages from Frontinus' treatise. The manuscript was found in the tenth century by Gerbert and served as the basis for his text on geometry, which was largely devoted to surveying.

FIG. 1–3. The libella.

During the Middle Ages, Greek and Roman science was kept alive by the Arabs. Little progress was made in the art of surveying, and the only writings pertaining to it were called "practical geometry."

In the thirteenth century Von Piso wrote *Practica Geometria*, which contained instructions on surveying. He also wrote *Liber Quadratorum*, dealing chiefly with the *quadrans*, a square brass frame having a 90° angle and other scales marked off on it. A movable pointer was used for sighting. Other instruments of the period were the *astrolabe*, a metal circle with a pointer hinged at its center and held by a ring at the top, and the *cross staff*, a wooden rod about 4 ft long with an adjustable crossarm at right angles to it. The known lengths of the arms of the cross staff permitted distances to be measured by proportion and angles.

In the eighteenth and nineteenth centuries the art of surveying advanced more rapidly. The need for maps and the location of national boundaries caused England and France to make extensive surveys requiring accurate triangulation. Thus geodetic surveying began. The United States Coast and Geodetic Survey was established by an act of Congress in 1807.

Increased land values and the importance of exact boundaries, along with the demand for public improvements in the turnpike, canal, and railroad eras, brought surveying into a prominent position.

More recently, the large amount of general construction has entailed an augmented surveying program. Surveying is still the sign of progress.

During world wars I and II, surveying in its many branches played an important part because of the stimulus provided to improve instruments and speed the methods of making measurements and maps. As a result a new era has opened for the surveying profession.

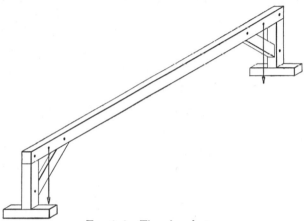

FIG. 1–4. The chorobates.

The four basic surveying instruments of today—the transit, level, plane table, and steel tape—are shown in Fig. 1–5. In the field of mapping, aerial surveying has become a valuable supplement to ground surveying but has not replaced it. Ground surveying is still essential for accurate horizontal and vertical control.

1–5. Types of surveys. There are many types of surveys, each so specialized that a man proficient in one branch may have little contact with the other branches. The more-important classifications will be described briefly:

Plane surveying. Surveying in which the curvature of the earth is neglected. It is applicable for small areas.

Geodetic surveying. Surveying in which the curvature of the earth is considered. It is applicable for large areas and long lines and is used to precisely locate basic points suitable for controlling other surveys.

Land or boundary surveys. Surveys to establish property corners

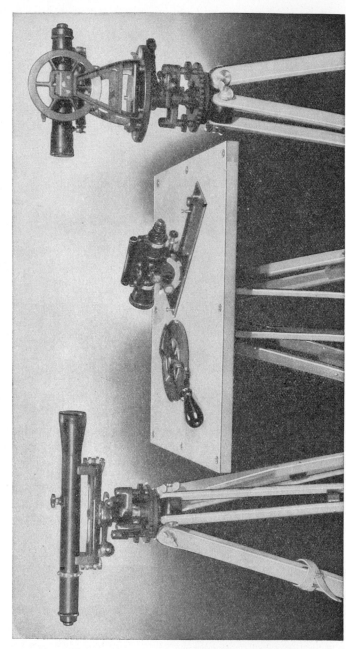

FIG. 1-5. Level, steel tape, plane table and alidade, and transit. (Courtesy of W. & L. E. Gurley.)

and land lines. Usually closed surveys (surveys which start at one corner and end at the same corner).

Topographic surveys. Surveys made for the purpose of preparing maps showing locations of natural and artificial features, and elevations of points on the ground.

Route surveys. Surveys of and for highways, railroads, pipelines, transmission lines, canals, and other projects which do not close upon the starting point.

Hydrographic surveys. Surveys of lakes, streams, reservoirs, and other bodies of water.

Construction surveys. Surveys to provide locations and elevations of structures.

Photogrammetric surveys. Surveys in which photographs, either terrestrial or aerial, are used.

1–6. Present status of surveying. There is an increasing demand for good maps in the United States, and various governmental agencies, although handicapped by insufficient funds and personnel, are attempting to provide them. A common misconception is that the entire country has been adequately mapped. Actually, about thirty-seven per cent of the United States is covered now (1956) by reasonably up-to-date topographic maps. At the present rate of new map production and periodic revision of satisfactorily mapped areas, at least two ot three decades will be required to complete the job.

Three United States Government departments do mapping on a large scale:

a) The Coast and Geodetic Survey was organized to map the coast. Its activities now include triangulation, precise leveling, preparation of nautical and aeronautical charts, photogrammetric surveys, tide and current studies, and collection of magnetic data. The basic control points established by this organization are the foundation for all large-area surveying.

b) The General Land Office, established in 1812, has directed the public-lands surveys. Lines and corners have been set for most of the public lands. The Bureau of Land Management now has jurisdiction over the survey and sale of these lands.

c) The United States Geological Survey, established in 1888, will ultimately map the entire country. Its standard $7\frac{1}{2}$- and 15-minute quadrangle sheets show topography and physical features and are suitable for use by the general public and on engineering projects. These maps are sold by the United States Geological Survey, Washington 25, District of Columbia, for twenty cents per copy.

In addition, units of the Army Corps of Engineers have made extensive surveys for emergency and military purposes. Some of these surveys provide data for engineering projects, such as those connected with flood control. The Army Map Service, operated by the Corps of Engineers, is primarily concerned with the production and supply of military topographic maps and allied data for the Department of Defense. One of its relatively new products is the plastic three-dimensional terrain model.

Extensive surveys have also been conducted for special purposes by the Forest Service, National Park Service, International Boundary Commission, Bureau of Reclamation, Tennessee Valley Authority, Mississippi River Commission, United States Lake Survey, and United States Hydrographic Office.

1–7. The surveying profession. Surveying is classified as a learned profession because the modern practitioner needs a background of technical training and experience, and because he must exercise independent judgment. A registered (licensed) professional surveyor must have a knowledge of mathematics—particularly geometry and trigonometry—and of law as it pertains to land and boundaries. He should be accurate in computations and field operations, and be able to do neat drafting. Above all, he is governed by a professional code of ethics.

The personal qualifications of a private surveyor are as important as his technical ability. He must be patient and tactful in dealing with clients and their hostile neighbors. Few people are aware of the painstaking search of old records that is required before field work is done. Diligent, time-consuming effort may be needed to locate corners on nearby tracts, for checking purposes, and to find the marks for the property in question.

Permission to trespass on private property or to cut obstructing branches and shrubbery must be obtained through a proper approach. These privileges are not conveyed by a surveying license, or by employment in a state highway department.

All forty-eight states, as well as Hawaii and Alaska and the provinces of Canada, now have registration laws for professional engineers, and many have separate registration for surveyors. In general, a surveyor's license is required for making boundary surveys, but construction and route surveying can be done by registered civil engineers. To qualify for registration as either a professional engineer or a surveyor, it is usually necessary to have a college degree (or an equivalent number of years of experience) plus four years of practical work, and to pass appropriate written examinations. The standard registration law makes it a misdemeanor "to practice or offer to practice land surveying" without a license. Technical considerations alone should discourage anyone other than an experienced surveyor from setting property corners. As in all professions, scholastic training is merely the first step toward the goal of every surveyor and engineer—true professional status denoted by registration.

PROBLEMS

1-1. List the requirements for registration as a land surveyor in your state.

1-2. What are the advantages of having subdivision laws which specify the accuracy required for surveys?

1-3. Describe a method for measuring right angles to lay out the walls of a house 24 ft by 35 ft.

1-4. Devise a simple instrument which could be used for leveling a basement floor 15 ft by 18 ft.

1-5. List ten uses for surveying in activities other than construction.

1-6. Describe how surveying might be used in charting the shore line and water depths of a lake covering four acres.

1-7. List the difficulties encountered in using as a map a vertical photograph taken from an aeroplane.

1-8. Why are surveys needed in connection with the transfer of property?

1-9. List the reasons for making a survey prior to and during the laying of a 36-in. city sewer and an 8-in. water main.

1-10. How is surveying used in connection with the construction of a new highway?

1-11. Explain how surveying methods are applicable in building an aeroplane having a wing span of 200 ft.

1-12. What applications of astronomy might be used in surveying?

1-13. List some of the applications of surveying in forestry work and in geology.

1-14. Why is it necessary to make surveys of underground mines?

Chapter 2

THEORY OF MEASUREMENTS
AND ERRORS

2-1. Measurements in general. The process of making measurements in surveying requires a combination of human observation and mechanical equipment. Experience and good physical condition improve the human factor; superior equipment enables good operators to do better work.

2-2. Types of measurements made in surveying. In plane surveying, linear measurements are made on, or reduced to, the horizontal plane, with some few exceptions. For small areas this neglect of the effect of curvature of the earth causes little error. In mapping a state, however, it is necessary to consider the spherical shape of the earth and to use geodetic methods.

Elevations—distances above a reference (datum) plane—are measured in a vertical plane or reduced to vertical distances. Angles are determined automatically as projections in the vertical or horizontal planes, when measured with a transit in correct adjustment.

Points are located in horizontal or vertical planes by determining their positions with respect to established points or lines. Four kinds of measurements form the basis of all plane surveying: (a) horizontal angles, (b) horizontal distances, (c) vertical angles, and (d) vertical distances.

2-3. Units of measurement. The units of measurement in surveying are those for *length* and *angle*. The length unit in the English system, the *foot*, bears a definite relation to the *meter*, which was legally established in 1866 to be 39.37 in. in the United States. A committee representing nineteen nations worked for nineteen years to agree upon an international standard. A standard metal bar, 90% platinum and 10% iridium, with marks upon it indicating the length of one meter, was adopted. This bar was deposited in a vault in the

International Building near Paris.   Several copies of the bar were made, two of which were brought to the United States.   One of these was adopted by the Bureau of Weights and Measures as its standard and is now kept in the archives of the National Bureau of Standards in Washington.

In route surveys, decimals of a foot are universally used, whereas in building construction, inches and fractions of an inch are more common.

Units of length used in past surveys in the United States include the following:

$$1 \text{ foot} = 12 \text{ inches}$$
$$1 \text{ yard} = 3 \text{ feet}$$
$$1 \text{ meter} = 39.37 \text{ inches} = 3.2808 \text{ feet}$$
$$1 \text{ rod} = 1 \text{ pole} = 1 \text{ perch} = 16\tfrac{1}{2} \text{ feet}$$
$$1 \text{ vara} = 33 \text{ inches in California} = 33\tfrac{1}{3} \text{ inches in Texas}$$
$$1 \text{ Gunter's chain} = 66 \text{ feet} = 100 \text{ links} = 4 \text{ rods}$$
$$1 \text{ mile} = 5280 \text{ feet} = 80 \text{ Gunter's chains}$$
$$1 \text{ engineer's chain} = 100 \text{ feet} = 100 \text{ links}$$

The unit of angle used in surveying is the *degree*, which is defined as $\frac{1}{360}$ the total angle around a point.   One degree equals 60 minutes, and one minute equals 60 seconds.

In France the circle is divided into 400 *grads*.   Military maps in the United States may use the *mil*.   There are 6400 mils in the total angle around a point.

The *radian* is an angle subtended by an arc of a circle having a length equal to the radius of the circle.   Obviously 2π radians = $360°$, 1 radian = $57° \ 17' \ 44.8''$, and 0.01745 radians = 1 degree.

2–4. Direct and indirect measurements.   Measurements may be made directly or indirectly.   A *direct measurement* is obtained by applying a tape to a line, or a protractor to an angle, or by turning an angle with a transit.

An *indirect measurement* is secured when it is not possible to apply the unit of measure directly to the distance or angle to be measured. The quantity is therefore determined by its relation to some other measured quantity.   Thus the distance across a river can be found by measuring an angle from each end of a base line of known length on one side of the river to a point on the other side.   The desired distance is then computed by one of the standard trigonometric formulas.   Since many indirect measurements are made in surveying, a thorough knowledge of geometry and trigonometry is essential.

2–5. Errors in measurements. Every measurement contains an *error*, since no measurement is exact. For example, a distance scaled with a rule divided into tenths of an inch requires interpolation for hundredths. If a better rule graduated in hundredths of an inch is available, the same distance might be estimated to thousandths of an inch. As better equipment is developed, recorded measurements will more closely approach their true values.

The surveyor's task is to keep errors in measurements within prescribed limits. In order to do so, he must know sources of errors, types of errors, and the effects of errors, and how to evaluate his results.

A *mistake* is caused by a misunderstanding of the problem, by carelessness, or by poor judgment. Mistakes are not considered in the succeeding discussion of errors. They are detected by systematic checking of all work.

2–6. Sources of errors in making measurements. Errors in measurements fall into three classes:

Natural errors. These are caused by variations in wind, temperature, humidity, refraction, gravity, and magnetic declination. For example, the length of a steel tape varies with changes in temperature.

Instrumental errors. These result from any imperfection in the construction or adjustment of instruments, and from the movement of individual parts. For example, the painted graduations on a rod may not be perfectly spaced, or the rod may be warped. The effect of most instrumental errors can be reduced by observing proper surveying procedures and by applying computed corrections.

Personal errors. These arise from limitations of the human senses of sight, touch, and hearing. For example, there is a small error in the measured value of an angle when the vertical cross hair in a transit is not aligned perfectly on the target sighted.

2–7. Types of errors. Errors in measurements are of two types: systematic errors and accidental errors.

Systematic errors. These errors conform to known mathematical and physical laws. They always have the same sign, but their magnitude may be constant or variable, depending upon conditions. Systematic errors, also known as *cumulative errors*, can be computed and their effects eliminated by applying corrections. For example, a 100-ft steel tape which is 0.02 ft too long introduces a plus 0.02-ft error each time it is used. The change in length of a steel tape resulting from a given temperature differential can be computed by a simple formula, and the correction can be easily made.

Accidental errors. These are the errors which remain after mistakes and systematic errors have been eliminated. They are caused by factors beyond the control of the observer and they obey the law of probability.

The magnitude and algebraic sign of an accidental error are matters of chance. There is no absolute way to compute accidental errors or to eliminate them. Accidental errors are also known as *compensating errors,* since they tend to partially cancel themselves in a series of measurements. For example, a tapeman interpolating to hundredths of a foot on a tape graduated only to tenths will estimate too high on some lengths and too low on others. Individual personal characteristics may nullify such partial compensation, however, since some people are inclined to interpolate high, others to interpolate low. It will be shown in section 2–10 that *the number of accidental errors remaining after cancellation of some of the plus and minus values is the square root of the number of opportunities for error.*

It is evident that systematic errors are more important than accidental errors. Their sources must therefore be scrutinized carefully.

2–8. Magnitude of errors. *Discrepancy* is the difference between two measured values of the same quantity. It is also the difference between the measured value and the known value of a quantity. A small discrepancy between two measured values indicates that there are no mistakes, and that accidental errors are small. It does not reveal the magnitude of systematic errors.

Precision denotes relative or apparent nearness to the truth and is based upon the refinement of the measurements and the size of the discrepancies. The degree of precision attainable is dependent upon the sensitiveness of the equipment and upon the skill of the observer. In surveying, precision should not be confused with *accuracy,* which denotes absolute nearness to the truth.

Agreement between two values for the same quantity implies accuracy, as well as precision, but does not assure it. For example, two measurements of a distance made with a tape assumed to be 100.000 ft long but actually 100.020 ft long might give results of 453.270 and 453.272 ft. These values are precise, but they are not accurate since there is an error of approximately 0.090 ft in each measurement.

2–9. Elimination of errors. All field operations and office computations are governed by the constant fight to eliminate or at least reduce errors.

Mistakes can be corrected only if discovered. Comparing several measurements of the same quantity is one of the best ways to isolate mistakes and errors. Making a common-sense estimate and analysis is another.

As an example, assume that five measurements of a line are recorded as follows: 567.91, 576.95, 567.88, 567.90, and 567.93. The second value disagrees with the others, apparently because of a transposition of figures in reading or recording. This mistake can be eradicated (a) by repeating the measurement, (b) by casting out the doubtful value, or (c) by rectifying the questionable figure.

When a mistake is detected it is usually best to repeat the measurement. If a sufficient number of other measurements of the quantity are available and in agreement, as in the foregoing example, the widely divergent result may be discarded. Serious consideration must be given to the effect on the average before discarding a value. It is seldom safe to change a measurement, even though there appears to be a simple transposition of numbers. Tampering with physical data is always bad practice and will surely cause trouble, even though done infrequently.

Since systematic errors result from known causes, their values can be calculated and proper corrections applied to the measurements, or a procedure can be used which will automatically eliminate the errors. For example, the error due to the sag of a tape supported at the ends only can be computed and subtracted from each measurement. If, however, the tape is supported throughout its length or at short intervals, the sag error is zero or negligible. A leveling instrument which is out of adjustment gives incorrect differences of elevation unless all sights are made the same length to cancel the error of adjustment.

2–10. Probable error. Since no measurement is exact, the correct value of a quantity is never known and the actual difference between the measured value and the true value is always in doubt. Investigations of observations of various types, however, show that accidental errors follow a definite law, the *law of probability*. This law defines the occurrence of errors and can be expressed in the form of an equation which is used to compute the *most probable error* in a series of measurements. It is the basis for the *method of least squares* used in the adjustment of observations.

The algebraic difference between the mean (average) value of a series of measurements and any individual measurement is called its *residual error*, or *residual*. Thus in illustration 2–1 (page 17) the average length of a line determined from five measurements is 952.47 ft. The first observation gave a length of 952.52 ft, and therefore its residual is 0.05 ft.

If a large number of measurements of the same quantity are made and all of the residuals are determined, the *probability-of-error curve* shown in Fig. 2–1 can be plotted. The value of each residual becomes the abscissa, and the number of times the residual occurs is the ordinate. Thus in Fig. 2–1, 45 of the hundreds of measurements made agreed exactly with the computed mean; 25 had residuals of +0.5 and −0.5; and only 5 measurements differed from the mean by +1.0 and −1.0 units. A smooth curve is drawn through the plotted points of all residuals versus their frequency to obtain Fig. 2–1. A large number of observations are necessary to develop or apply such a typical curve.

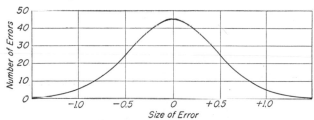

FIG. 2–1.   Probability-of-error curve.

A true error curve is symmetrical about the vertical axis and has a peak at the center. It approaches the horizontal axis as an asymptote. The curve demonstrates the following assumptions regarding the occurrence of accidental errors in a large number of observations of a single quantity (the effects of mistakes and systematic errors having been eliminated from the measured values):

a. Small errors occur more often than large ones; that is, they are *more probable*.

b. Large errors occur infrequently and are therefore *improbable*. Usually they are classified as mistakes rather than accidental errors.

c. Positive and negative errors of the same size happen with equal frequency; in other words, they are *equally probable*.

The probability curve has wide application in statistics and other fields. It is used by some teachers in distributing grades among several hundred students in the same course. The relative values of the ordinates at $+1.0$, $+0.5$, 0.0, -0.5, and -1.0 fit the proper distribution of grades A, B, C, D, and F, respectively, in a large class.

The principle of least squares, developed from the law of probability, is that *the most probable value of an observed quantity available from a given set of observations is the one for which the sum of the squares of the errors (residuals) is a minimum.*

The method of least squares is useful (a) in adjusting the results of a set of observations to find the most probable value of a quantity, and (b) in investigating the precision of a set of observations and estimating the effect of errors upon the results.

The *probable error* of a measured quantity may be defined as the middle error of all the errors arranged in numerical order, with each value written as many times as it occurs. The theory of least squares developed in various texts permits calculation of the probable error in accordance with the following assumptions:

a. The average of a series of measurements is the *most probable value*.

b. The probable error E_m contained in this mean value is

$$E_m = \pm 0.6745 \sqrt{\frac{\Sigma d^2}{n(n-1)}} \tag{2-1}$$

where d = residual, or difference between each single measurement and the average;

n = number of measurements.

c. The probable error E_s in a single measurement is

$$E_s = E_m \sqrt{n} \tag{2-2}$$

An example at this point will clarify the definition and calculation of probable error. A series of measurements, with their residuals and the squares of the residuals, is shown in illustration 2-1. The com-

Illustration 2–1

PROBABLE ERRORS

Length (ft)	d (ft)	d²
952.52	0.05	0.0025
952.48	0.01	0.0001
952.38	0.09	0.0081
952.56	0.09	0.0081
952.41	0.06	0.0036

Avg. = 952.47   Σ = 0.0224

$$E_m = \pm 0.6745\sqrt{\frac{0.0224}{5 \times 4}} = \pm 0.02 \quad \text{ft}$$

$$E_s = \pm 0.023\sqrt{5} = \pm 0.05 \quad \text{ft}$$

putations for determining the probable errors by means of the standard formulas are shown below the tabulation.

From the computed value of $E_m = \pm 0.02$ ft, it can be concluded that if the average distance of 952.47 ft is accepted as the most probable value, then there is just as much chance that the true length is between 952.45 and 952.49 as there is that it falls outside this range. The most probable value and the probable error are usually expressed by the notation 952.47 ± 0.02 ft. This does *not* mean that the true value is either 952.45 or 952.49 ft.

The probable error $E_s = \pm 0.05$ ft indicates that if an additional measurement is made, it has a 50–50 chance of being within 0.05 ft of the most probable value.

Sometimes two quantities A and B are measured independently and it is necessary to find their sum or their product. If E_a and E_b represent the probable errors of the independent measurements, then the probable error E_t of the sum of A and B is

$$E_t = \sqrt{E_a^2 + E_b^2} \tag{2-3}$$

Likewise, the probable error E_p of the product of quantities A and B is

$$E_p = \sqrt{A^2 E_b^2 + B^2 E_a^2} \tag{2-4}$$

As an example, if a base line is measured in three sections and the probable errors of the sections are ±0.012, ±0.028, and ±0.020 ft, respectively, then the probable error of the total length is

$$E_t = \sqrt{0.012^2 + 0.028^2 + 0.020^2} = 0.036 \text{ ft}$$

Again, if the sides of a rectangular lot are 50.00 ft $\pm$ 0.01, and 100.00 ft $\pm$ 0.02, the probable error of the computed area is

$$E_p = \sqrt{50^2 \times 0.02^2 + 100^2 \times 0.01^2} = 1.4 \text{ sq ft}$$

Knowledge of these relationships is helpful in determining the precision required to bring the results of measurements or computations within specified limits.

Some measurements are more accurate than others because of the use of better equipment and improved techniques, or because of advantageous atmospheric conditions. It may therefore be desirable to assign *weights* to individual observations. For example, four measurements of a distance recorded as 482.16, 482.17, 482.20, and 482.18 ft might be given weights of 1, 2, 2, and 4, respectively. The *weighted mean* is found by multiplying each measurement by its weight and dividing by the sum of the weights. In this case the weighted mean is

$$\frac{482.16 + 482.17 \times 2 + 482.20 \times 2 + 482.18 \times 4}{1 + 2 + 2 + 4} = 482.18 \text{ ft}$$

It must be noted that the method of least squares is valid only for observations of equal reliability or for those which can be weighted as to reliability. It is misleading and a waste of time to use least squares if systematic errors and mistakes have not been cancelled by the employment of proper procedures, equipment, and calculations.

2–11. Significant figures. In making calculations involving field measurements, there is a tendency to carry out the results to digits beyond the accuracy inherent in the measurements. The number of significant digits in computations should be consistent with the recorded values. If a line is measured as 875.63 ft long, the result has five significant figures; but the last one may be estimated, as would be the case if a tape divided only in tenths of a foot were used for the measurement. Four of the digits are certain, and one is an estimate. Significant figures include all those digits which are certain, plus one that is estimated.

The accuracy of computations involving a measurement depends upon the certainty of the digits. If several values are added, the sum is accurate only to the least number of certain digits following any decimal point. Thus if three distances are measured with a tape graduated only to tenths of a foot, and are recorded as 268.1 ft, 34.23 ft, and 2.7 ft, the total distance should be taken as 305.0 ft.

If measurements are multiplied or divided, the results cannot be more accurate than any one factor. This condition limits the certainty of the product or quotient to the number of significant figures in any one measurement.

The computed product of 362.56 and 2.13 is 772.2528. But if the last digit in each factor is an estimated one, the product should be rounded off to 772. The accuracy of surveying computations is governed by the number of significant figures in any one field measurement rather than by the number of digits that can be read from a ten-bank calculating machine.

The number of significant figures to be sought in making a measurement in the field is determined by the precision desired. The sides of waste land worth only one dollar per acre cannot be measured to the nearest 0.01 ft economically. In a large city, however, the value of property justifies greater precision and higher costs for surveys.

2–12. Rounding off numbers. Rounding off a number is the process of dropping one or more digits so that the answer contains only those digits which are significant or necessary in subsequent computations. When rounding off numbers to any required degree of accuracy in this text, the following procedure will be observed:

a. When the digit to be dropped is less than 5, the number is written without the digit. Thus 78.374 becomes 78.37.

b. When the digit to be dropped is exactly 5, the nearest even number is used for the preceding digit. Thus 78.375 becomes 78.38.

c. When the digit to be dropped is greater than 5, the number is written with the preceding digit increased by one. Thus 78.376 becomes 78.38.

The procedures in (a) and (c) are standard practice. When rounding off the value 78.375 in (b), however, some computers always take the next-higher hundredth, whereas others invariably use the next-lower hundredth. Using the nearest even digit produces better-balanced results in a series of computations. An exception occurs in the case of taped distances, where recorded measurements tend to be larger than the true values and therefore always rounding off to the next-lower digit is reasonable.

2–13. Methods of computation. Elementary surveying computations require only arithmetic, simple geometry, and trigonometry. Logarithms were universally used some years ago but have limited application now.   Most surveying offices employ calculating machines and natural functions of angles, for speed and accuracy.

Traverse tables expedite certain computations.   They consist of tabulations of the products of distances from 1 to 100 and the sines and cosines of angles from 0° to 90°.

Slide rules do not provide a sufficient number of significant figures for important surveying computations.   They are therefore used mainly for checking purposes.   Special slide rules are manufactured for stadia-reduction work and yield satisfactory results since normally not more than three significant figures are required.

PROBLEMS

2-1. A measured distance is expressed as 12 ch. 40 lk. (here, ch. is the abbreviation for Gunter's chain, and lk. is the abbreviation for link).   What is the distance in feet?

2-2. What is the distance 22 ft $7\frac{5}{8}$ in. in feet and a decimal of a foot?

2-3. A certain line measures 6.4 miles.   What is the length in kilometers?

2-4. A rectangular field 25 ch. 50 lk. by 41 ch. 80 lk. contains how many acres?

2-5. What is the number of significant figures in the sum of the three numbers 1.6, 65.48, and 581.027?

2-6. What is the number of significant figures in the quotient obtained by dividing 2.84 by 736.152?

2-7. The adjusted angles of a triangle ABC are $A = 47° 52' 21''$; $B = 82° 34' 16''$; and $C = 49° 33' 23''$.   Determine the values of the angles in radians, and check the results.

2-8. A circle whose diameter is 450.00 ft is divided into arcs $AB = 212.4$, $BC = 375.1$, $CD = 547.0$, and $DA = 279.2$.   Determine the angles subtending these arcs at the center of the circle.

2-9. Compute the elevation of a point X above a horizontal reference plane if the vertical angle and stadia slope distance to it are $+10° 15'$ and 210 ft, respectively.

2-10. Using Fig. 2-1, ascertain the normal number of A, B, C, D, and F grades for a class of 100 students in a given subject.

2-11. The observed values of an angle X are $24° 18'$, $24° 19'$, $24° 19'$, $24° 18' 30''$, $24° 20'$, and $24° 19' 30''$.   What is the most probable value of the angle?

2-12. A distance AB is measured six times with the following results in feet: 731.46, 731.48, 731.41, 731.38, 731.37, and 731.42.   Determine the most probable value of the length, the probable error of the mean, and the probable error of a single measurement.

2-13. Values of the elevation of a point P found by running different circuits are 360.420, 360.425, 360.419, 360.416, and 360.421.   Compute the most probable elevation of the point, the probable error of the mean elevation, and the probable error of a single measurement.

2–14. In reciprocal leveling (discussed in Chapter 5), successive observations on a rod gave the following results in feet: 5.268, 5.263, 5.264, and 5.269. What is the probable error of the mean value, and that of a single measurement?

2–15. If the probable error in a measurement of 100 ft is ±0.10 ft, what is the probable error per mile from the same cause?

2–16. The probable error in locating a machined surface used as a reference for a machine part is ±0.002 in. The probable error in locating the center of a hole in the part is ±0.004 in. What is the probable error of the dimension from the reference surface to the center of the hole?

2–17. Determine the weighted mean of the following angles: 47° 28′ 27.5″, wt. 2; 47° 28′ 37.5″, wt. 1; 47° 28′ 45.0″, wt. 2; and 47° 28′ 50″, wt. 2.

2–18. The measured angles of a certain triangle are $A = 49° 51′ 15″$, wt. 1; $B = 60° 32′ 08″$, wt. 2; and $C = 69° 36′ 33″$, wt. 3. Adjust the angles and find the probable error of the adjusted value of A.

2–19. List three kinds of cumulative errors and three kinds of accidental errors that might occur in measuring an angle with a transit.

2–20. List three kinds of compensating errors and three kinds of cumulative errors that might occur in measuring a line with a steel tape.

Chapter 3

SURVEYING FIELD NOTES

3–1. General. Surveying field notes are the permanent record of work done in the field. If the notes are incomplete, incorrect, or destroyed, much or all of the time spent in making accurate measurements may be lost. Hence, the notekeeper's job is frequently the most difficult one in the party. A field book containing information gathered over a period of weeks is worth thousands of dollars, assuming that it costs $100 to $125 per day to maintain a party of four men in the field. Every field book should therefore have the name and address of the owner lettered with India ink on the cover and inside.

The data in field notes are normally used by office personnel to make a map or computations. It is therefore essential that the notes be intelligible to others without verbal explanations. The Reinhardt system of slope lettering is generally employed, for clarity and speed.

Property surveys are subject to court review under some conditions, in which case the field notes become an important factor in the litigation. Also, because survey notes may be used as references in land transactions for generations, it is necessary to properly index and preserve them. The salable "good will" of a surveyor's business depends largely upon his library of field books. Cash receipts may be kept in an unlocked desk drawer, but field notes are stored in a fireproof safe.

Original notes are those taken while measurements are being made. All other sets are copies and must be so marked. Copied notes may not be accepted in court. They are always subject to suspicion because of the possibility of errors and omissions. The value of a distance or an angle placed in the field book from memory, half an hour after the observation, is definitely unreliable.

Students are tempted to scribble notes on scrap sheets of paper for later transference in neat form to the regular field book. This practice defeats the purpose of a surveying course, which is to provide experience in taking notes under job conditions. On practical work, a surveyor is not likely to spend his own time at night transcribing scribbled notes. Certainly his employer will not pay him for this evidence of incompetence.

Notes should be lettered with a pencil of at least 3-H hardness so that an indentation is made in the paper. Books so prepared will withstand damp weather in the field (or even a soaking) and still be legible, whereas graphite from a soft pencil will leave an undecipherable smudge under such circumstances.

Erasures are not permitted in field books. If a number has been recorded incorrectly, a line is run through it without destroying its legibility, and the correct value is noted above. If an entire page is to be deleted, diagonal lines are drawn from opposite corners and VOID is lettered prominently.

3–2. Requirements of good notes. Five points are considered in appraising a set of field notes:[1]

Accuracy. This is the most important quality in all surveying operations.

Integrity. A single omitted measurement or detail may nullify use of the notes for plotting or computing. If the field party is far from the office, it may be time-consuming and expensive to obtain the missing data. Notes should be checked carefully for completeness before leaving the survey site.

Legibility. Notes can be used only if they are legible. Also, a professional-looking set of notes is likely to be professional in quality of measurements.

Arrangement. Noteforms appropriate to the particular survey contribute to accuracy, integrity, and legibility.

Clarity. Advance planning and proper field procedures are necessary to insure clarity of sketches and tabulations, and to make errors and omissions more evident. Mistakes in drafting and computing are the end results of ambiguous notes.

3–3. Types of field books. Since field books contain valuable data, must take hard wear, and must be permanent in nature, it is poor economy to use anything but the best book for practical work. Various types of field books are available.

The *bound book*, a standard for many years, has a sewed binding

[1] Material in this chapter has been partly abstracted from *Engineers Field Notes*, by Roth and Rice, privately published in 1940. By permission of the authors.

and a hard stiff cover of impregnated canvas, leather, or imitation leather, and contains 80 leaves.

The *bound duplicating book* permits copies of notes to be made through carbon paper. Alternate pages are perforated for easy removal.

The *loose-leaf book* has come into wide use because of many advantages, which include (a) assurance of a flat working surface, (b) simplicity of filing individual project notes, (c) ready transfer of partial sets of notes between field and office, (d) provision for carrying pages of printed tables and diagrams, (e) the possibility of using different rulings in the same book, and (f) a saving in sheets (since none are wasted by filing partially filled books).

The *stapled, sewed, or spiral-bound books* are not suitable for practical work. They may be satisfactory for abbreviated surveying courses having only a few field periods, because of the limited service required and the low cost.

Special column and page rulings provide for particular needs in leveling, transit work, topographic surveying, and cross-sectioning.

3–4. Kinds of notes. Four types of notes are kept in practice: (a) sketches, (b) tabulations, (c) descriptions, and (d) combinations of these. The most common type is a combination form, but an experienced recorder selects the version best fitted to the job at hand. Appendix A contains a set of typical noteforms illustrating some of the field problems covered in this text.

In a simple survey, such as one for measuring the distances between hubs on a series of lines, a sketch showing the lengths is sufficient. See Plate A–1.[2] The proverb about one picture being worth 10,000 words might well have been written for notekeepers.

In measuring the length of a line forward and backward, a tabulation properly arranged in columns is adequate, as on Plate A–1.

The location of a reference point may be difficult to identify without a sketch, but often a few lines of description are enough. Bench marks usually are so described, as on Plate A–3.

In notekeeping, this axiom is always pertinent: When in doubt about the need for recording any information, include it and make a sketch.

---

[2] Plates A-1 to A-12 are full-size pages of typical field notes and are grouped in Appendix A for convenience in referring to them in the office or in the field.

3–5. Arrangement of notes. The arrangement of notes depends upon departmental standards and individual preference. Highway departments, mapping agencies, and other organizations engaged in surveying furnish field men with sample noteforms. These specimens aid in preparing uniform and complete records which can be checked quickly.

It is desirable for students to have an expertly designed set of noteforms covering their first field work, to set high standards and save time. Opportunities to devise appropriate variations are always present, particularly in topographic work.

The noteforms shown in Appendix A are a composite of several models. They stress the open style, in which some lines or spaces are skipped for clarity. Thus angles measured at a point X are placed opposite X in the notes, but distances measured between points X and Y on the ground are recorded on the line between points X and Y in the field book.

The left- and right-hand pages are always used in pairs and therefore they carry the same number. A complete title should be lettered across the top of the left page and may be extended over the right page. Titles may be abbreviated on succeeding pages for the same survey project. The location and type of work is placed beneath the title on the left or right page.

The left page is ruled in six columns and normally is reserved for tabulations only. Column headings are placed between the first two horizontal lines at the top of the page and should follow from left to right in the anticipated order of recording.

The upper right-hand corner of the right page should contain four items:

a) *Date, time of day* (A.M. *or* P.M.), *starting and finishing time.* These entries are necessary to document the notes and furnish a time table. Precision, troubles encountered, and other facts may be gleaned from the time required for the survey.

b) *Weather.* Wind velocity, temperature, and other weather conditions, such as rain, snow, sunshine, and fog, have a decided effect upon accuracy in surveying operations. A chainman is unlikely to do the best possible work at a temperature of minus 20 F or with rain pouring down his neck. Hence weather details are important in reviewing field notes.

c) *Party.* The names and initials of members of the party, and their duties, are necessary for documentation and possible future reference. Jobs may be shown by symbols, such as $\barwedge$ for instrumentman, ϕ for rodman, N. for notekeeper, H.C. for head chainman, and R.C. for rear chainman.

d) *Instrument type and number.* The type of instrument used, and its adjustment, affect the accuracy of a survey. Identification of the particular equipment employed aids in isolating errors in some cases.

Each field book must have an index to permit ready location of desired data. In practice, surveyors cross-index their notes on days when field work is impossible.

3–6. Suggestions on recording notes. Observing the points listed here will eliminate some of the common mistakes in notekeeping:

a. Begin a new day's work on a new page.

b. Always record directly in the field book, rather than on a scrap sheet of paper for copying later.

c. Carry a straightedge for ruling lines, and a small protractor for laying off angles.

d. Run notes down the page except in route surveys, where they progress upward to conform with the sketches.

e. Place north at the top, or left side, of all sketches, if possible. A meridian arrow must be shown.

f. Keep tabulated figures inside the column rulings, with the decimal points and digits in line vertically.

g. Make a mental estimate of all measurements before receiving and recording them, to eliminate large errors.

h. Repeat aloud values given for recording. For example, before recording a distance 124.68, call out "one, two, four, point, six, eight" for verification by the tapeman who submitted the measurement.

i. Place a zero before the decimal point for numbers less than one. For example, record 0.37 instead of .37.

j. Reduce the size of figures for the decimal part of a number and elevate them for clarity. The decimal portion may also be underscored. Examples are $276.^{45}$ and $276.^{\underline{45}}$.

k. Show the precision of measurements by recording significant zeroes. For example, show 3.80 instead of 3.8 if the reading was actually determined to hundredths.

l. Do note write one figure over another.

m. Use sketches instead of tabulations when in doubt.

n. Make sketches to general proportions, rather than exactly to scale or without plan.

o. Exaggerate details on sketches if clarity is thereby improved.

p. Line up descriptions and sketches with corresponding numerical data. For example, the beginning of a bench-mark description should be placed on the same line as its elevation, as on Plate A–3 in Appendix A.

q. Avoid crowding. If it is helpful to do so, use several right-hand pages of descriptions and sketches for a single left-hand page of tabulation. Similarly, use any number of pages of tabulation for a single sketch.

r. Use explanatory notes when they are pertinent.

s. Employ conventional symbols and signs, for compactness.

t. Make all possible arithmetic checks on the notes, and record them before leaving the field, as shown on Plate A–3.

u. Record essential computations made in the field, so that they can be checked later.

v. Compute all closures and ratios of error before leaving the field. On large projects where daily assignments are made for several parties, completed work is shown by the satisfactory closures.

w. Sign surname and initials in the lower right-hand corner of the right page on all original notes. Letter COPY in large letters on copied notes, but do not obscure the sketch or any figures in so doing.

PROBLEMS

3-1. Sketch in plan view an H-shaped building which is 80 ft by 80 ft and which has all wings 20 ft wide. The bottom of the H is parallel with, but offset 15 ft from, a street 40 ft wide. The building is centered on a lot 120 ft wide and 110 ft deep. Show the dimensions required to locate and lay out the building.

3-2 Prepare a set of notes covering the measurement of all three angles and all three sides of a triangle.

3-3. Prepare a set of survey notes for a rectangular lot 50 ft by 100 ft, in which the angle at one corner is 89° 57′.

3-4. List any special information which might appear on a set of field notes taken on a survey of a valley and a stream for a proposed reservoir.

3-5. Why are sketches in field notes usually drawn to general proportions only?

3-6. Prepare a set of survey notes for an irregular pentagon, assuming that the lengths of the sides were obtained by pacing and that the directions of the sides were found by compass bearings.

Chapter 4

LINEAR MEASUREMENTS

4-1. General.   Linear measurement is the basis of all surveying. Even though angles may be read precisely with elaborate equipment, the length of at least one line must be measured to supplement the angles in locating points.

Standard taping procedure is so simple that beginners in professional survey parties are traditionally assigned this work.   As a result, the importance of correct techniques may be overlooked. Nevertheless, an energetic head chainman is probably more important than a fast instrumentman in keeping a field party moving.

In plane surveying the distance between two points means the horizontal distance.   If the points are at different elevations, the distance is the horizontal length between plumb lines at the points.

Lines may be measured directly by applying a unit of length to them.   The unit generally used in plane surveying in the United States and Canada is the foot, decimally divided.   In architectural and machine work it is the foot divided into inches and fractions of an inch.   The meter is commonly employed in geodetic surveying. Chains, varas, rods, and other units have been, and still are, utilized in some localities and for special purposes.

4-2. Methods of making linear measurements.   In surveying, direct linear measurements are obtained by (a) speedometer readings, (b) pacing, (c) taping, (d) stadia, and (e) electronic devices.

Triangulation and other methods of computing distances from known lengths and angles have been developed.   In triangulation, all the angles and one or more lines (the base lines) are measured accurately and the remaining distances computed.   See Fig. 4-1.

4-3. Speedometer readings.   Distances measured by speedometer are suitable for some preliminary surveys in route-location work. They also serve as a rough check on measurements made by other methods.

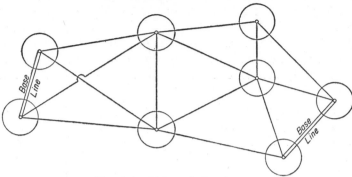

FIG. 4–1. Triangulation figures.

4–4. Pacing. Distances obtained by pacing are sufficiently accurate for many purposes in surveying, engineering, geology, agriculture, forestry, and military field sketching. Pacing is also used to detect large errors if they occur in taping or in stadia readings.

The process of pacing consists in counting the number of steps or paces in a required distance. The length of an individual's pace must first be determined. This is best done by walking with natural steps back and forth over a measured level course at least 300 ft long, and averaging the number of steps taken. For short distances the length of each pace is needed, but the number of steps taken per 100 ft is desirable for checking long lines. Plate A–2 in Appendix A gives the notes for a field problem on pacing.

It is possible to adjust one's pace to an even 3 ft, but a person of average height finds such a step tiring if maintained very long. The length of an individual's pace shortens when going uphill, lengthens when going downhill, and changes with age. For long distances, a pocket instrument called a *pedometer* can be carried to register the number of paces.

Some surveyors prefer to count *strides*. A stride is the distance between the place where one foot is lifted and where it is put down again. A stride equals two paces.

Pacing is one of the most valuable things learned in surveying, since it has practical applications for everybody and requires no equipment. Experienced pacers can measure distances of 100 ft or longer with a maximum error of 1 or 2 per cent, if the terrain is open and reasonably level.

4–5. Taping.   The most common method of measuring lengths in surveying is taping.   Two types of problems arise: (a) measuring a distance between fixed points, such as two stakes in the ground, and (b) laying out a distance with only the starting mark in place.   In either case the procedure consists in applying the tape length a number of times.

Taping is performed in six steps: (a) lining in, (b) pulling the tape, (c) plumbing, (d) marking tape lengths, (e) reading the tape, and (f) recording the distance.   Sections 4–9 and 4–10 detail the application of these steps in taping on level and sloping ground.

Various types of equipment have been used in the United States to measure lengths.   Early surveyors struggled with braced wooden panels, wood and metal poles (which resulted in the term *pole* as a unit of measurement), and other devices.   The 100-ft steel tape and the 50-ft metallic tape are now standard, but other kinds of tapes and chains are important because of their present or past use.

Surveyor's tapes.   Surveyor's tapes are made of steel $\frac{1}{4}$ to $\frac{3}{8}$ in. wide and $\frac{1}{50}$ in. thick, and weigh from 2 to 3 lb per 100 ft.   For convenience when not in use, a steel tape may be done up in loops 5 ft long making a figure eight, and may then be *thrown* into a circle with a diameter of $9\frac{1}{2}$ in.   Graduations are placed at every foot and they are marked from 0 to 100.   The last foot at each end is subdivided into tenths, and on some tapes into hundredths.   As a variation, tapes having an extra graduated foot at one end are manufactured. Surveyor's tapes are also made in lengths of 200 ft, 300 ft, and 500 ft.

Reel or ribbon tapes.   Reel tapes, made of steel, have a thickness of $\frac{1}{64}$ to $\frac{3}{64}$ in. and a width of $\frac{1}{8}$ to $\frac{1}{4}$ in., and they weigh from $\frac{3}{4}$ to $1\frac{1}{2}$ lb per 100 ft.   They are graduated in feet, tenths, and hundredths throughout their length.   A metal ring or loop at the ends allows a handle or leather thong to be attached.   The tapes are wound upon open reels or into a box.   Similar tapes varying in length from 5 ft to 1000 ft are manufactured.

Wires.   Before thin flat steel could be produced efficiently, wires were utilized for measuring lengths.   Recent experiments indicate the possibility of their return to use.

Builder's tapes.   Builder's tapes have smaller cross sections and are lighter in weight than surveyor's tapes.   Since most plans for buildings as prepared by engineers and architects carry dimensions in feet and inches, the builder's tape is graduated in those units.

Shop equipment. Shop equipment will be discussed in Chapter 25.

Invar tapes. Invar tapes are made of a special nickel steel (35% nickel and 65% steel) to reduce length variations caused by differences in temperature. The thermal coefficient of expansion and contraction is only about $\frac{1}{30}$ to $\frac{1}{60}$ that of an ordinary steel tape. The metal is soft and easily damaged. This weakness of invar tapes, along with their cost of perhaps ten times that of ordinary steel tapes, makes them suitable only for precise geodetic work.

Lovar tapes. A somewhat newer version, the lovar tape, has properties and a cost roughly midway between those of steel and invar tapes.

Metallic tapes. Metallic tapes are actually made of high-grade linen with fine copper wires running lengthwise to give additional strength and to prevent excessive elongation. The type of metallic tape commonly used is 50 ft long and it comes in a leather case. Longer ones are available. Although not adapted to precise work, metallic tapes are convenient and practical for many purposes.

Glass-fiber tapes. Glass-fiber tapes can be used for the same types of work as the metallic tapes.

Gunter's chain. The Gunter's chain was the best measuring device available for many years in the United States and is referred to in old field notes and deeds. It is 66 ft long and has 100 *links*, each link therefore being equal to 7.92 in. The links are made of heavy wire, have a loop at each end, and are joined together by rings. The outside ends of the handles fastened to the end links are the 0 mark and the 66-ft mark. Successive tags, having 1, 2, 3, or 4 teeth, mark every tenth link from each end. The center tag is plain.

Distances measured with chains are recorded either in chains and links or in chains and decimals of chains. For example, a certain distance would be 7 ch. 94.5 lk. or 7.945 ch. Decimal parts of links are estimated.

The 66-ft length of the Gunter's chain was selected because of its relationship to the mile and acre. Thus 1 chain = $\frac{1}{80}$ mile, and 10 square chains = 10×66^2 square feet = 1 acre.

Engineer's chain. The engineer's chain is constructed in the same manner as the Gunter's chain, but it is 100 ft long and each of its 100 links has a length of 1 ft.

Chains are used sparingly if at all today, although a steel tape graduated like a Gunter's chain is manufactured. Nevertheless, the many chain surveys on record oblige the modern practitioner to understand the limits of accuracy possible with this equipment. The term chaining continues to be used interchangeably with taping, even though tapes are employed exclusively.

Accessories. Chaining pins (surveyor's arrows) are used to mark tape lengths. Most chaining pins are made of number 12 steel wire and are 10 to 15 in. long. They are sharply pointed at one end, have a round loop at the other end, and are painted with alternate red and white bands. Sets of eleven pins carried on a steel ring are standard.

Poles. Range poles (flags or lining rods) are made of wood or steel and are about 1 in. thick and 6 to 10 ft long. They are round or hexagonal in cross section and are marked with alternate red and white bands 1 ft long which can be used for rough measurements. A wooden range pole has a metal shoe at the base. The main utility of range poles is in marking the alignment.

Plumb bobs. Plumb bobs for taping should weigh a minimum of 8 oz and have a fine point. At least 6 ft of fish-line cord free of knots is necessary. Plumb-bob points are now standardized to simplify replacement.

Full equipment for a chaining party consists of one 100-ft steel tape; one 50-ft metallic tape; two range poles; 11 chaining pins on a ring;

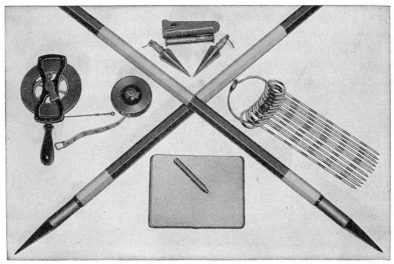

FIG. 4-2. Taping equipment for a field party. (Courtesy of W. & L. E. Gurley.)

two plumb bobs; one hand level or clinometer; keel (colored crayon); and a field book. This equipment is shown in Fig. 4-2.

4-6. Stadia. Stadia is a method of measuring distances by sighting through a telescope equipped with two or more horizontal cross hairs at a known spacing, and noting the apparent intercepted length between the top and bottom hairs on a rod held vertically. The distance from telescope to rod is found by proportional relationships in similar triangles. A detailed explanation of the method is given in Chapter 12.

4-7. Electronic devices. One of the major advances in surveying following World War II has been the development of electronic devices for measuring distance. Basically the process consists in determining the time required for an induced wave to reach a reflector and return to the sender. Automatic equipment converts the time interval to distance. An advantage of the electronic method is that both long distances (hundreds of miles) and short lengths can be measured with approximately the same total error.

Shoran is an electronic system by means of which distances up to about 600 miles can be measured. The *loran* system, used for surface navigation, has an effective range at night up to 1400 miles.

A different type of instrument now being developed is the *geodimeter*. This electronic optical device is used to measure distances up to 50 miles by means of a fundamental constant, the speed of light. Test measurements made over special short lines gave results having probable errors of one part in 1,500,000. Since errors are largely constant rather than proportional to distance for this type of equipment, the accuracy should be improved on longer lines.

The geodimeter consists of two basic units—the measuring unit, and the light-conductor unit. The measuring unit contains the necessary electronic equipment. The light-conductor unit includes two spherical mirrors with the necessary optics to project and receive the light beam. A plane mirror placed at the opposite end of the line being measured returns the projected light beam to the geodimeter. The plane mirror is equipped with a collimated telescope, and horizontal and vertical mechanisms, to permit precise pointing and plumbing. The plane mirror will probably be replaced by retrodirective mirrors and prisms, which eliminate pointing problems and do not require a rigid support.

The complex nature and high cost of the equipment make the electronic methods applicable only to large-scale geodetic surveying at the present time.

4–8. Care of equipment. The following points are pertinent in the care of tapes and range poles:

a. The cross-sectional area of a surveyor's steel tape is $\frac{1}{4} \times \frac{1}{50}$ in. = 0.005 sq in. At a permissible stress of 20,000 lb per sq in., a pull of $20,000 \times 0.005 = 100$ lb will do no damage. If the tape is kinked, however, a pull of less than 1 lb will break it. A check must be made to be certain that all loops and kinks are eliminated before any tension is applied.

b. Tapes should be wiped first with a dry rag and then with an oily rag, if they get wet.

c. Tapes should either be kept on a reel or be thrown, but should not be handled both ways. Double throwing is not recommended.

d. Each tape should have an individual number or tag to identify it.

e. Broken tapes can be mended by riveting and/or a sleeve device, but a mended tape should not be used on important work.

f. Range poles are made with the metal shoe and the point in line with the section above. This alignment may be lost if the pole is used improperly.

4–9. Taping on level ground. The six steps in the process of taping on level ground will now be described in some detail:

Lining in. The line to be measured should be definitely marked at both ends, or at intermediate points, to insure unobstructed sights. Range poles are ideal for this purpose. The forward tapeman is lined in by the rear tapeman (or by the transitman, for greater accuracy). Directions are given by vocal or hand signals.

Pulling the tape. The 100-ft end of the tape is held over the first (rear) point by the rear tapeman while the forward tapeman, holding the zero end, is lined in. For accurate results the tape must be straight and the two ends must be at the same elevation. A specified tension, generally 10, 12, or 15 lb, is applied. In order to maintain a steady pull, each tapeman wraps the leather thong at the end of the tape around his right hand, keeps his right forearm against his body, and faces at right angles to the line. In this position he is off the line of sight. Also, he need only tilt his body to hold, decrease, or increase the pull. Sustaining a constant tension with outstretched arms is difficult, if not impossible, for a pull of 15 lb or more.

Plumbing. Weeds, brush, obstacles, and surface irregularities usually make it undesirable to lay the tape on the ground. Instead, each end point of a measurement is marked by placing the plumb-bob string over the proper tape graduation and securing it with the left thumb. The rear tapeman continues to hold a plumb bob over the fixed point while the forward tapeman marks the length. In measuring a distance shorter than a full tape length, the forward tapeman moves the plumb-bob string to a point on the tape over the ground mark.

Marking tape lengths. When the tape has been lined in properly, tension has been applied, and the rear tapeman is over the point, the forward tapeman places a pin from his set of ten (one is in the ground at the rear point) exactly opposite the zero mark of the tape. If the point is being plumbed and the ground is soft, the plumb bob is released by raising the left thumb. A chaining pin is then carefully set in the hole made by the plumb-bob point. The pin should form a right angle with the tape but approximately a 45° angle with the ground. The point where the pin enters the ground is checked by repeating the measurement.

After checking the measurement, the forward tapeman signals that he is finished, the rear tapeman pulls up the pin beside him, and they move ahead. The forward tapeman drags the tape. Just before the 100-ft end reaches the point which has been set, the rear tapeman calls "tape" to notify the forward tapeman that he has gone 100 ft. The process is repeated until a partial tape length is needed at the end of the line.

When a surveyor is working on pavement, the plumb bob is eased to the surface, and the position of the point is marked by a scratch, a spike, keel, a bottle top, or other means.

Reading the tape. With a full-foot graduation held at the last chaining pin set, the graduated section of the tape between the zero mark and the 1-ft mark should straddle the closing point, as indicated in Fig. 4–3. Assume that the 88-ft mark is being held on the last chaining pin and that the tack marking the end of the line is opposite 0.32 ft read from the zero end. The partial tape length is then 88.00 − 0.32 = 87.68 ft. The quantity 0.32 ft is said to be *cutoff.* To insure subtraction of a foot, the following field procedure and calls

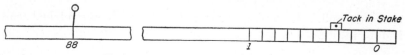

FIG. 4–3. Reading partial tape length.

are recommended: Rear tapeman calls "88"; forward tapeman says "0.32" (point three-two); rear tapeman answers "87.68"; forward tapeman replies "check."

Subtraction of the decimal of a foot is avoided if the forward tapeman reads 0.68 ft backward from the 1-ft graduation. Calls of 88, 0.68, 87.68, and check are made in this procedure.

The same routine should be used throughout all taping by a party, and the results should be tested in every possible way. A single failure to subtract the one foot in the measurement of a partial tape length will destroy the precision of a hundred other measurements. The extra foot on some tapes eliminates this potential mistake.

It is customary to have the 100-ft end of the tape ahead in route surveys, where stationing along the line is continuous. Some surveyors prefer this arrangement in other work also, when setting intermediate points or when measuring partial tape lengths.

Recording the distance. Accurate field work may be cancelled by careless recording. After the partial tape length is obtained at the end of a line, the rear tapeman determines the number of full 100-ft tape lengths by counting the pins he has collected from the original set of eleven. For distances longer than 1000 ft, a notation is made in the field book when the rear tapeman has ten pins and one remains in the ground. The forward tapeman starts out again with ten pins and the process is repeated.

Taping is a skill that can best be taught and learned by field demonstrations and practice.

4–10. Horizontal measurements on uneven ground. In taping on uneven or sloping ground, it is standard practice to hold the tape horizontal and to plumb at one or perhaps both ends. It is difficult to keep the plumb line steady for heights above the chest. Wind exaggerates this problem and may make accurate work impossible.

Where a 100-ft length cannot be held horizontal without plumbing from above shoulder level, shorter distances are measured and accumulated to total a full tape length. This procedure is called *breaking tape.*

As an example of this operation, assume that when the zero end of the tape is held at the rear point, the forward tapeman can advance only 30 ft without being forced to plumb from above his chest. A pin is therefore set beneath the 30-ft mark, as in Fig. 4–4. The rear tapeman moves ahead to this pin and holds the 30-ft graduation while another pin is set at, say, 75 ft. Then, with the 75-ft graduation over the second pin, the 100-ft distance is marked.

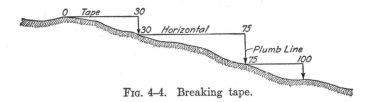

FIG. 4–4. Breaking tape.

Note that the partial tape lengths are added mechanically to make a full 100 ft by holding the proper graduations. No mental arithmetic is required. The rear tapeman returns the pins set at the intermediate points to the forward tapeman, to keep the tally clear on the number of full tape lengths established. In all cases the tape is leveled by eye or by instrument, the tapeman keeping in mind the natural tendency to have the downhill end of the tape too low. Practice will develop the knack of holding the tape at right angles to the plumb-bob string.

Taping downhill is preferable to measuring uphill, since in taping downhill the rear point is held steady on a fixed object while the other end is plumbed. In taping uphill, the forward point must be set while the other end is wavering somewhat.

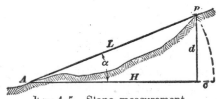

FIG. 4–5. Slope measurement.

4-11. Slope measurements. In measuring the distance between two points on a steep slope, it may be desirable to tape along the slope and to determine the angle of inclination by means of a clinometer, rather than to break tape every few feet. Long tapes, 200 to

500 ft in length, are advantageous for measuring along slopes (as well as across rivers and ravines).

In Fig. 4–5 the horizontal distance between points A and B can be computed from the relation

$$H = L \cos \alpha \qquad (4\text{–}1)$$

where H = horizontal distance between the points;
L = slope distance between the points;
α = vertical angle from the horizontal.

The horizontal projection of the slope distance can also be computed by subtracting a correction, c, from the slope distance. This correction is obtained from the equation

$$c = L(1 - \cos \alpha) = L \text{ vers } \alpha \qquad (4\text{–}2)$$

On base-line work, the difference in elevation, d, between the ends of the tape is found by leveling, and the horizontal projection is computed. Thus in Fig. 4–5,

$$c = L - H$$

$$d^2 = L^2 - H^2 = (L - H)(L + H) = c(L + H)$$

and

$$c = \frac{d^2}{L + H} \qquad (4\text{–}3)$$

or

$$c = \frac{d^2}{2L} \qquad [\text{approximately}] \qquad (4\text{–}4)$$

The error in using the approximate formula for a 100-ft length on a slope of 10 per cent is only 0.001 ft. More-precise results are obtained for slopes steeper than 10 per cent by using the partial series formula

$$c = \frac{d^2}{2L} + \frac{d^4}{8L^3} \qquad (4\text{–}5)$$

4–12. Stationing. In route surveying, stationing is carried along continuously from a starting point designated as station $0 + 00$. The term *station* is applied to each 100-ft length, where a stake is normally set, and also to any point whose position is given by its total distance from the beginning hub. Thus station $7 + 84.9$ is a unique point 784.9 ft from the starting mark, this distance being measured along the survey line. The partial length beyond a full station, in this example 84.9 ft, is termed a *plus*.

Taping in stations is done most conveniently by carrying the 100-ft end of the tape ahead. Since stakes are driven at every change in direction (*angle point*) of a route survey as well as at each full station, it is necessary to follow each plus station with a full one. A special procedure for *determining the plus* at a stake and for *getting off a plus* with the least chance of making an arithmetic error will now be described.

To determine the plus station of an angle point, for example at station 7 + 84.9, the 100-ft end of the tape is pulled beyond the angle point and the forward tapeman then walks back to hold a full foot mark graduation on the stake (in this case the 85-ft graduation). Meanwhile the rear tapeman reads the number of tenths of a foot from the 1-ft mark (in this illustration 0.9 ft).

To get off the plus and establish the next full station, 8 + 00, the rear tapeman holds the 84-ft graduation at the plus station, and the forward tapeman sets a pin 0.9 ft back from the 100-ft mark. Note that all subtractions are eliminated by holding the foot mark corresponding to the plus station at that station, and by reading the decimal part of the plus from the 100-ft graduation. This method, like others to be discussed, exemplifies the advantage of systematizing field procedures to reduce the possibility of errors.

4-13. Sources of error in taping. There are three sources of error in taping:

a. *Instrumental errors.* The tape may be different in length from its nominal length because of a defect in its manufacture or repair, or as a result of kinks.

b. *Natural errors.* The horizontal distance between the end graduations of a tape varies because of the effects of temperature, wind, and the weight of the tape itself.

c. *Personal errors.* The tapemen may be careless in setting pins, reading the tape, and/or manipulating the equipment.

Errors in taping may be classified another way, under the following nine headings:

1. Incorrect length of tape.
2. Temperature other than the standard 68 F.
3. Pull (tension) not consistent.
4. Sag due to weight and wind.
5. Poor alignment.

6. Tape not horizontal.

7. Improper plumbing.

8. Faulty marking.

9. Incorrect reading or interpolation.

Some of the nine classifications produce cumulative errors; others yield compensating errors.

4–14. Incorrect length of tape. Incorrect length of tape always increases, or always decreases, individual measurements and is the most important of any of the errors. It is a cumulative error.

Tape manufacturers do not guarantee steel tapes to be exactly their nominal length, for example 100.00 ft. The true length of a tape is obtained by comparing it with a standard tape or distance. The National Bureau of Standards in Washington, D.C., will make such a comparison for a nominal fee and will certify the exact distance between the end graduations under given conditions of temperature, tension, and manner of support.

One-hundred-foot steel tapes usually are standardized for each of two sets of conditions: 68 F, a 10-lb pull, and the tape fully supported throughout; and 68 F, a 12-lb pull, and the tape supported at the ends only. Schools and surveying offices normally have at least one standardized tape which is used only to check other tapes subjected to wear.

A taping error due to incorrect length of tape occurs each time the tape is laid down. If the true length of a tape is known by standardization, the correct length of a line measured with the tape can be determined from the formula

$$T = MC \qquad (4\text{–}6)$$

where T = true length of the line;

  M = measured (recorded) length with given tape;

  C = a constant for the given tape.

For a particular tape, C is the ratio of the actual length of the tape to its assumed length. If the length of tape is assumed to be 100.00 ft but when it is compared with a standardized tape its length is found to be 100.02 ft, then $C = 100.02/100.00 = 1.0002$. A line which measured 565.75 ft with this tape has a true length of 565.75×1.0002 = 565.86 ft. For a tape 99.98 ft long and a measured length of 565.75 ft, the true distance is $565.75 \times 99.98/100.00 = 565.64$ ft. This

computation is simplified if arranged in the form
$$565.75 - 0.02(5.6575) = 565.64 \text{ ft}$$

From a practical standpoint, the effect of all errors is to make the tape length incorrect.

4–15. Temperature. Steel tapes are standardized for 68 F in the United States. A temperature greater or less than this value causes a change in length which must be considered.

The coefficient of thermal expansion and contraction of steel is approximately 0.0000065 per unit length per degree F. Then

$$C_t = 0.0000065(T_t - T)L \qquad (4\text{--}7)$$

where C_t = correction in length of line due to nonstandard temperature;

T_t = temperature of tape at time of measurement;

T = temperature of tape when it has standard length;

L = measured length of line.

The error due to temperature changes may be eliminated in either of two ways:

a) The correction to the measured length of the line may be calculated by formula 4–7. For example, assume that the recorded length of a line measured at 30.5 F with a steel tape that is 100.00 ft long at 68 F is 872.54 ft. The change in the recorded length of the line due to temperature is

$$0.0000065(30.5 - 68)872.54 = -0.21 \text{ ft}$$

The correct length of the line is

$$872.54 - 0.21 = 872.33 \text{ ft}$$

b) An invar tape whose coefficient of thermal expansion and contraction is 0.0000001 or 0.0000002, or a lovar tape with a coefficient of perhaps 0.0000022, can be used. The temperature effect on the length of an invar tape is negligible for most practical work.

Errors due to temperature may be either cumulative or compensating, but they are more likely to be cumulative. On a day when the temperature is always above 68 F, or always below 68 F, they will be cumulative. If the temperature is above 68 F during part of the time occupied in measuring a long line, and below 68 F for the remainder of the time, the errors will be partially compensating.

Temperature effects are the most difficult to correct for in taping. The air temperature read from a thermometer may be quite different from the temperature of the tape to which the thermometer is attached. Sunshine, shade, wind, evaporation from a wet tape, and other conditions make the tape temperature uncertain. Recent experiments prove that temperatures on the ground or in the grass may be 10 to 25 deg higher or lower than those at shoulder height because of a 6-in. "layer of weather" (microclimate) on top of the ground. Since a 1-deg error in the temperature of the tape is significant in measuring a long line, the importance of large variations is obvious.

Shop measurements made with steel scales and other devices likewise are subject to temperature effects. The precision required in fabricating a large aeroplane can be lost by this one cause alone.

4–16. Pull. When a tape is pulled with a tension greater than the standard amount, it elongates in an elastic manner. The modulus of elasticity of a material is the ratio of the unit stress to the unit elongation, or

$$E = \frac{\text{unit stress}}{\text{elongation per unit length}} = \frac{P/A}{e/L}$$

Also, the correction for pull is

$$C_p = e = \frac{(P_1 - P)L}{AE} \tag{4-8}$$

where $C_p = e$ = total elongation in one tape length due to increase in pull, in feet;
P_1 = pull applied to the tape, in pounds;
P = standard pull for the tape, in pounds;
L = length of tape, in feet;
A = cross-sectional area of the tape, in square inches;
E = modulus of elasticity of steel, in pounds per square inch.

The average value of E is 29,000,000 lb per sq in. for the kind of steel used in tapes.

Errors due to incorrect pull may be either cumulative or compensating. The pull applied by an experienced tapeman is sometimes greater than the desired amount, and sometimes less. An inexperienced person, particularly one who has not used a spring balance on a tape, is likely to apply less than the standard tension consistently.

Errors resulting from incorrect tension can be eliminated by three methods:

a) A spring balance can be used to measure and maintain the standard pull.

b) The elongation caused by pull can be calculated. Assume that a steel tape is 100.000 ft long under a pull of 12.0 lb, and has a cross-sectional area of 0.005 sq in. The increase in the length of the tape for a pull of 20.0 lb is

$$\frac{(20 - 12)100}{29,000,000 \times 0.005} = 0.0055 \text{ ft or } 0.006 \text{ ft}$$

A line measuring 872.54 ft with this tape and tension requires a correction of $8.7254 \times 0.0055 = 0.048$ ft.

c) Sag can be decreased by greater tension; therefore these factors may be adjusted to offset each other. The following formula can be solved by trial to obtain a balanced value:

$$P_t = \frac{0.2W\sqrt{AE}}{\sqrt{P_t - P}} \tag{4-9}$$

where P_t = total pull on the tape, in pounds;
$\quad P$ = pull for the standardized tape, in pounds;
$\quad W$ = weight of the tape, in pounds;
$\quad A$ = cross-sectional area of the tape, in square inches;
$\quad E$ = modulus of elasticity of steel, in pounds per square inch.

The cross-sectional area of a steel tape can be obtained by measuring its width and thickness with calipers (1 lb of steel occupies 3.526 cu in.), or it can be determined from the total weight of the tape and the unit weight of steel of 490 lb per cu ft.

The pull required to balance sag for a tape having a cross-sectional area of 0.005 sq in. and a weight of 1.6 lb is found by trial to be 29.0 lb. Thus

$$29 = \frac{0.2(1.6)\sqrt{0.005 \times 29,000,000}}{\sqrt{29 - 12}}$$

The pull required to make the distance between end graduations exactly 100.00 ft under given conditions of temperature and end support is called the *normal tension*. Normal tension is not commonly used, because it may be too large for convenient application and it changes with temperature variations.

4-17. Sag. A steel tape not supported along its entire length sags in the form of a catenary. A good example of the catenary is the cable of a suspension bridge. Sag shortens the horizontal (chord) distance between end graduations, since the tape length remains the same. Sag can be diminished (by greater tension) but not eliminated, unless the tape is supported throughout.

The actual sag of a tape (for example, 6 in. below the horizontal) is not important. The reduced chord distance between the end graduations is the critical factor.

For a small deflection v at the center of the length of a tape, the equation of a parabola can be used to investigate the sag effect. Thus

$$L - d = \frac{8v^2}{3d}$$

Also, by mechanics,

$$Pv = \frac{wd^2}{8}$$

Combining these two relations, and assuming that $L = d$ approximately, the following equation is obtained:

$$C_s = L - d = \frac{L}{24}\left(\frac{W}{P}\right)^2 = \frac{W^2 L}{24 P^2} = \frac{w^2 L^3}{24 P^2} \tag{4-10}$$

where C_s = correction for sag (difference between length of curve and straight line from one support to the next), in feet;

L = length of curved tape between supports, in feet;

d = chord distance between supports, in feet;

w = weight of tape per foot of length, in pounds;

$W = wd$ = total weight of tape between supports, in pounds;

P = pull on tape, in pounds.

Errors due to sag may be either cumulative or compensating since they are dependent upon the tension applied.

Three methods can be used to eliminate errors caused by sag. These are as follows:

a. Support the tape at short intervals or throughout.

b. Increase the pull to make the tape stretch an amount equal to the sag correction required.

c. Calculate the sag correction for each measurement and apply it to the recorded length.

As an example of method c, assume that a steel tape 100.000 ft long weighs 1.50 lb and is supported at its ends only. If a 12-lb pull is applied, the correction for sag is $100(1.5)^2/24(12)^2 = 0.065$ ft. This correction is proportional to the cube of the unsupported length, since w and P are constants in a given case. For an unsupported length of 50 ft, the correction would be $0.065/2^3 = 0.008$ ft.

On slopes where measurements less than 100 ft are used in breaking tape, it may be desirable to vary the pull or compute special sag corrections.

4–18. Alignment. If one end of a tape is off line, or if the tape is snagged on an obstruction, an accidental error is introduced. The size of this type of error can be calculated from the formula

$$C_a = \frac{d^2}{2L} \qquad (4\text{–}11)$$

where C_a = correction for offset from alignment;
d = distance the tape is off line;
L = length of tape involved.

If a pin marking the end of a 100-ft length is set 1.4 ft off line, the error in that measurement is $1.4^2/200 = 0.01$ ft. A similar error enters the next tape length when the succeeding pin is set correctly on line.

If the center of a 100-ft tape catches on brush and is 1.0 ft off line, the error produced in the two 50-ft lengths is

$$\frac{2 \times 1^2}{2 \times 50} = 0.02 \text{ ft}$$

Errors resulting from poor alignment are cumulative and always make the recorded length longer than the true length. They may be reduced (but never eliminated) by care in setting pins, lining in properly, and keeping the tape straight. Snapping the tape while applying tension will straighten it. A moderate amount of field practice enables a rear tapeman to keep the forward tapeman within much less than a foot of the correct line.

4–19. Tape not horizontal. The error caused by a tape being inclined in the vertical plane is similar to that caused by the tape being out of line in the horizontal plane. Its value can be determined by the formula

$$C_g = \frac{h^2}{2L} \qquad (4\text{–}12)$$

where C_g = grade correction;
    h = difference in elevation between the ends of the tape;
    L = length of tape.

Errors due to the tape not being horizontal are cumulative and always make the recorded length longer than the true length. They are reduced by using a hand level to check elevations of the tape ends, or by running differential levels over the taping points. The errors cannot be completely eliminated since the tape is certain to be out of level on some measurements despite the best efforts of a tapeman.

4–20. Plumbing. Practice and steady nerves are necessary to hold a plumb bob still for a period long enough to mark a point or permit an instrument sight. The plumb bob moves around, even in calm weather. On very light slopes, and on smooth surfaces such as pavements, inexperienced tapemen obtain better results by laying the tape on the ground instead of plumbing. Experienced tapemen plumb most measurements.

Errors due to improper plumbing are partially compensating, since they may make distances either too long or too short. The errors would be cumulative, however, when taping directly against or in the direction of a strong wind.

Touching the plumb bob on the ground, or steadying it with one foot, decreases its swing. Practice in plumbing will reduce errors.

4–21. Incorrect marking. Chaining pins should be set perpendicular to the taped line but inclined 45° to the ground. This position permits plumbing to the point where the pin enters the ground without interference from the loop.

Brush, stones, and roots deflect a chaining pin and may increase the effect of incorrect marking. Errors from these sources tend to be compensating and are kept small by carefully locating a point and then checking it.

4–22. Interpolation. The process of reading to hundredths on tapes graduated only to tenths is called interpolation. This process is readily learned and can be applied in many branches of engineering. Some individuals tend to interpolate high; others tend to interpolate low. Also, some people are inclined to favor certain digits; for example, they read 3 rather than 4 or 5, or perhaps 7 instead of 6 or 8.

Errors due to interpolation are partially compensating over the length of a line. They can be reduced by care in reading; by using a small scale to determine the last figure; and by correcting any disposition toward particular values. Tabulating the number of times each digit from 0 through 9 is interpolated in work covering a period of several days will expose any predilection for a few numerals.

4-23. Summary of effects of taping errors. An error of 0.01 ft is significant in many surveying measurements. Table 4-1 lists the nine sources of errors, classifies them as cumulative or compensating, and gives the departure from normal that will produce an error of 0.01 ft. The summary verifies practical experience that recorded lengths of lines are more often too long than too short.

TABLE 4-1

TYPES OF ERRORS

Type of Error	Cumulative or Compensating	Departure from Normal to Provide 0.01-Foot Error for a 100-Foot Tape
Tape length....	Cum.	0.01 ft
Temperature...	Cum. (or Comp.)	15 F
Pull...........	Cum. (or Comp.)	15 lb
Sag...........	Cum.	$7\frac{3}{8}$ in. at center for 100-ft tape standardized by support throughout
Alignment......	Cum.	1.4 ft at one end of 100-ft tape or $8\frac{1}{2}$ in at midpoint
Tape not level..	Cum.	1.4 ft
Plumbing......	Comp.	0.01 ft
Marking.......	Comp.	0.01 ft
Interpolation...	Comp.	0.01 ft

The accepted method of reducing errors is to make several measurements of the same line with various tapes and at different times of the day. This procedure is used on precise work.

4-24. Mistakes. Careless manipulation of equipment results in personal errors so large they are classified as mistakes. Examples are:

a. Reading the tape incorrectly.

b. Miscounting the number of full tape lengths.

c. Using the end mark as zero on a tape having an extra foot.

d. Transposing figures, or otherwise recording a distance improperly.

e. Failing to subtract one foot in making a measurement covering a partial tape length.

Mistakes are not compensating in nature. They are reduced or eliminated by standard field procedures, and by measuring lines in both directions.

4–25. Tape problems. All tape problems develop from the fact that a nominal 100-ft tape is longer or shorter than 100.00 ft. There are four versions of the problem: A line can be either measured or laid out with a tape that is either too long or too short. The solution of a particular problem is simplified by drawing a sketch.

Assume that the distance AB in Fig. 4–6 is measured with a tape that is later found to be 100.03 ft long. Then (the conditions are greatly exaggerated) the first tape length would stretch to point *1*; the next, to point *2*; and the third to point *3*. Since the distance remaining from *3* to B is less than the correct distance from the 300-ft mark to B, the recorded length AB is too small and must be increased by a correction. If the tape had been too short, the recorded distance would be too large.

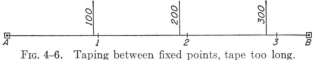

FIG. 4–6. Taping between fixed points, tape too long.

In laying out a distance from one fixed point, the reverse is true. The correction must be subtracted for tapes longer than the nominal value, and must be added for tapes shorter than the assumed length.

4–26. Laying out a right angle with a tape. Many problems arising in the field can be solved by taping. For example, a right angle is

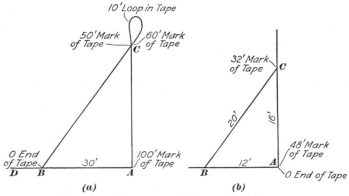

FIG. 4–7. Laying out right angle with tape.

laid out readily by the 3–4–5 method. In Fig. 4–7a, to erect a perpendicular to AD at A, measure 30 ft along AD and set point B. Then with the zero graduation of the tape at B and the 100-ft mark at A, form a loop in the tape by bringing the 50- and 60-ft graduations together and pull each part of the tape taut to locate point C. One person can make the layout alone by tying the tape thongs to stakes beyond A and B.

If a 50-ft metallic tape is used, a possible procedure is indicated in Fig. 4–7b. The zero mark can be held at A, the 12-ft mark at B, the 32-ft mark at C, and the 48-ft mark at A. Any other distances in the proportions of 3, 4, and 5 may be used.

4–27. Measuring an angle with a tape by the chord method. If all three sides of a triangle are known, the angles can be computed. To find angle A, Fig. 4–8, measure any definite lengths along AM and AN, such as AB and AC. Also measure BC. Then

$$\sin \tfrac{1}{2}A = \sqrt{\frac{(s-b)(s-c)}{bc}} \tag{4–13}$$

where a, b, and c are the sides of the triangle ABC, and where $s = \frac{1}{2}(a + b + c)$.

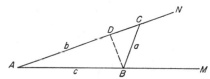

FIG. 4–8. Measuring an angle with tape.

For $b = 30.0$ ft, $c = 25.0$ ft, and $a = 21.5$ ft, angle A is found to be equal to 24° 08′.

An isoceles triangle is formed by making AB equal to AC. Then

$$\sin \tfrac{1}{2}A = \frac{a}{2c} \tag{4–14}$$

Selecting a value of 50 ft for AB and AC simplifies the arithmetic. Thus if $AB = AC = 50.0$ ft, and BC measures 20.90 ft, then $\sin \tfrac{1}{2}A = 0.2090$ and angle $A = 24°\ 08′$.

4–28. Measuring an angle with a tape by the tangent method. If AD and a perpendicular BD are measured (Fig. 4–8), $\tan A = BD/AD$. By making AD equal to 50 or 100 ft, the tangent can be easily computed.   To illustrate, if AD = 100.00 ft and BD measures 44.80 ft, then tan A = 0.4480 and angle A = 24° 08′.

4–29. Laying off angles.   An angle can be laid off by reversing the tangent method just described.   Along the initial side of the angle, a unit distance of 10, 20, 50, or 100 ft is laid off, as AB in Fig. 4–9. A perpendicular BC is erected, and its length is made equal to 100 times the natural tangent of the desired angle A.   Points A and C are connected to give the required angle at A.   This method is used in the drafting room, as well as in the field.

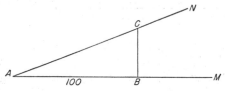

FIG. 4–9.   Laying off angle by tangent
method.

4–30. Tape survey of a field.   A field may be completely surveyed by taping.   In fact this was the only method available before instruments for measuring angles were built.

The procedure consists in dividing the area into a series of triangles and measuring the sides of each one.   For small areas, one corner of the field is selected as the apex, and the distances to all other corners and the perimeter are measured.   In Fig. 4–10, if corner G is chosen as the reference point, the distances GA, AB, BC, CD, DE, EF, and FG

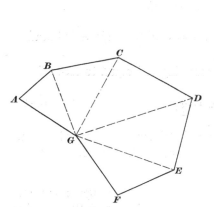

FIG. 4–10.   Survey of field by tape.

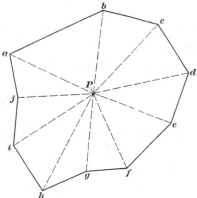

FIG. 4–11.   Survey of field using
central point.

along the perimeter and the diagonal distances *GB*, *GC*, *GD*, and *GE* locate all corners of the field.

For larger areas it is better to establish a central point, such as *P* in Fig. 4–11, and to measure the perimeter and all lines radiating from *P* to the corners. The field can be plotted and the area then calculated from these data. The central-point method may appear to require more work, but the short lengths of the interior distances compensate for their greater number. Also, all corners are more likely to be visible from a selected point within the field.

4–31. Solution of a taping problem. The reduction of a typical base-line measurement will illustrate the method of making tape corrections. Data taken in the field are shown in the first four columns of Table 4–2. The tape ends were supported on *chaining bucks* (tripods).

TABLE 4–2

BASE-LINE TAPING ON BUCKS

Section	Measured Distance (ft)	Temperature (deg F)	Difference in Elevation (ft)	Inclination Correction (ft)
A–1.........	100.000	58	1.26	0.0079
1–2.........	100.000	58	0.98	0.0048
2–3.........	100.000	59	0.60	0.0018
3–4.........	100.348	59	0.81	0.0033
4–5.........	100.000	59	1.22	0.0074
5–6.........	100.000	60	2.06	0.0212
6–7.........	100.000	60	2.54	0.0323
7–8.........	100.000	60	2.68	0.0359
8–B.........	70.216	61	1.87	0.0249
Sum or avg....	870.564	59.3	....	0.1395

The properties of the tape are as follows:

Tape NBS 5269

Standardization by the National Bureau of Standards when supported on a horizontal flat surface:

Tension, 15 lb   Interval 0 mark to 100 mark, 100.008 ft

Standardization when supported at ends only:

Tension, 15 lb   Interval 0 mark to 100 mark, 99.963 ft

Four corrections will be applied: (a) inclination (slope) correction, (b) temperature correction, (c) standard-length correction for full tape length, and (d) standard-length and sag corrections for partial tape length.

In geodetic work, a fifth correction is made to reduce the measurement to sea level in order to have all lengths throughout the country comparable regardless of the elevations at which they are determined.

Inclination correction. Individual corrections for each tape measurement are shown in the last column of Table 4–2. Each is computed by formula 4–12, which is $C_g = h^2/2L$, and their total is -0.140 ft. The adjusted length becomes $870.564 - 0.140 = 870.424$ ft.

Temperature correction. Using the average temperature and substituting in formula 4–7, we find that the total correction is

$$C_t = (59.3 - 68) \times 0.0000065 \times 870.424 = -0.049 \text{ ft}$$

Standard-length correction for full tape lengths. The standard distance between the 0 mark and the 100-ft mark (tape supported at the ends only) differs from the nominal length by $100.000 - 99.963 = 0.037$ ft. For eight full tape lengths the correction is $8 \times 0.037 = -0.296$ ft.

Standard-length and sag correction for partial tape length. If the tape is supported throughout, the distance between the 0 mark and the 100-ft mark is 100.008 ft. The interval separating other graduations is assumed to be increased proportionately. The length correction for 70.216 ft is therefore $70.216 \times 0.008/100 = +0.006$ ft.

According to formula 4–10, the correction C_s for sag is proportional to L^3 when the weight per foot of tape and the tension are constant, as in this example. The sag correction from the standardization data is $100.008 - 99.963 = 0.045$ ft. Then the correction for approximately a 70-ft span is $(70/100)^3 \times 0.045 = -0.015$ ft.

The true length of the base line is $870.564 - 0.140 - 0.049 - 0.296 + 0.006 - 0.015 = 870.564 - 0.494 = 870.070$ ft.

Field data and corrections for this base-line computation have been carried out consistently. Ordinary taping precision does not justify working in thousandths of a foot, but the procedure is the same.

It is immaterial whether the inclination correction is made before or after the temperature adjustment. The temperature correction for the partial tape length should be computed separately if the temperature deviates considerably from the average.

PROBLEMS

4–1 A distance recorded as 2468.2 ft is measured with a 100-ft tape which later is found to be 100.04 ft long. What is the correct length of the line?

4–2. What distance should be laid out with a tape 99.97 ft long to set two points 2468.2 ft apart?

4–3. A line is measured with a 100-ft steel tape having an extra graduated foot, and by mistake the 101-ft length is used to obtain a recorded value of exactly six tape lengths. What is the correct distance?

4–4. A distance of 376.48 ft is measured on a slope between two points A and B having a difference of elevation of 23.50 ft. (a) What is the correct horizontal distance AB? (b) What is the vertical angle between the two points?

4–5. A standardized steel tape (100.13 ft long at 68 F) is used to measure a line recorded as 874.32 ft when the temperature is 14 F. What is the true length of the line?

4–6. The recorded length of a line measured with a Gunter's chain is 19.60 ch. The same line is measured later with a steel tape 100.00 ft long under standard conditions and is found to be 1274.62 ft, but the temperature at the time of taping is 80 F. What is the correct length of the line and the Gunter's chain? Assuming there are no errors other than the length of the chain, what is the area of a field measured with the chain and computed to be 17.90 acres?

4–7. A 100-ft steel tape is known to be 99.992 ft long at 68 F when supported throughout. What is the true distance between two points if the recorded length measured at 40 F with the tape laid on the ground is 63.428 ft?

4–8. A 100-ft tape is $\frac{1}{2}$ in. wide and $\frac{1}{32}$ in. thick. If the tape is standardized for a pull of 12 lb but a 15-lb pull is mistakenly used, what error is made in a line 1800 ft long?

4–9. A tension of 20 lb is applied while measuring a line with a tape that is 100.04 ft long under a standard 12-lb pull. The tape is $\frac{1}{64}$ in. thick and $\frac{3}{8}$ in. wide. The recorded length is 576.34 ft. What is the true length?

4–10. What is the normal tension for a steel tape having a cross-sectional area of 0.0030 sq in. and supported at the ends only, at 68 F, if the tape is 99.985 ft long at the same temperature when supported at the ends only and subjected to a 15-lb pull?

4–11. A 100-ft steel tape weighing 1 lb has a cross-sectional area of 0.0025 sq in. It is 100.02 ft long under the following standard conditions: supported at the ends only, 15-lb tension, and 68 F. What is the distance between the end marks for a 25-lb pull at 53 F, tape supported at the ends only?

4–12. A surveyor's tape $\frac{1}{4}$ in. wide by $\frac{1}{32}$ in. thick is 100.07 ft long when supported throughout its length under a tension of 14 lb. What is the length between end graduations if the same tension is applied but the tape is supported at the ends only? If it is supported at the 0-. 25-, 50-, 75-, and 100-ft points?

4–13. A steel tape weighing 0.025 lb per lineal foot is 99.98 ft long at a temperature of 60 F, when under a tension of 10 lb and supported throughout its length. A distance of 80.00 ft is to be laid out when the temperature is 40 F by supporting the tape at the 0- and 100-ft marks only. What reading on the tape corresponds to the required distance of 80.00 ft?

4–14. What is the error caused by having one end of a 90-ft length of tape off line by 1.6 ft and too low by 2.2 ft?

4–15. Determine the most probable length of the line, and the probable error of a single measurement, for the following recorded series of measurements of the line AB: 745.34, 745.38, 745.45, 745.39, and 745.41 ft.

4–16. To determine the angle between two intersecting fences, a distance of 80.00 ft is measured along each fence from the corner. If the distance between the established points is 75.4 ft, what is the intersection angle?

4–17. A tape survey of a field with a central point P and corners A, B, C, and D furnishes the following distances in feet: $PA = 210.0$; $PB = 316.2$; $PC = 393.2$; $PD = 273.1$; $AB = 360.5$; $BC = 471.7$; $CD = 583.1$; and $DA = 269.3$. Compute the angles APB, BPC, CPD, and DPA around the center point, and the angles ABC, BCD, CDA, and DAB at the corners of the field.

4–18. A cloth tape, nominally 50 ft long, has stretched to a length of 50.4 ft after hard usage. What dimensions should be laid out with the tape to locate the corners of a house 42 ft 6 in. by 34 ft 9 in?

4–19. A 4-ft 6-in. steel scale in a shop is actually 4 ft $6\frac{1}{4}$ in. long at 68 F. What distance should be measured with this scale at 85 F to obtain a correct length of 3 ft $4\frac{1}{32}$ in.?

4–20. Assuming that the electromagnetic waves used in the shoran system have a velocity through the atmosphere of 186,218 miles per second at a standard barometric pressure of 29.92 in. of mercury, what time lag in the equipment will produce an error of 50 ft in the distance measured to a target 200 miles away?

4 21. A tape when standardized is 100.02 ft long at 68 F, under a 12 lb pull, supported at the ends only. Using this tape, with the same pull and method of support, but at a temperature of 52 F, a surveyor records the perimeter of a farm to be 6274.5 ft. When measured a second time in the opposite direction and at a temperature of 61 F, the recorded length of the perimeter is 6258.8 ft. What is the ratio of error of the measurements (the difference between the two measurements divided by the average and reduced to the form $1/x$)? Is this ratio suitable for farm land worth $50 per acre?

Chapter 5

LEVELING

5-1. General. Leveling is a relatively simple process but a vital one in all construction work, in setting machinery and equipment, and in the fabrication of large objects such as aeroplanes. Leveling has its own special terms and these will be defined in the following topic as an introduction to the subject.

5-2. Definitions. The basic terms in leveling defined below are illustrated in Fig. 5-1.

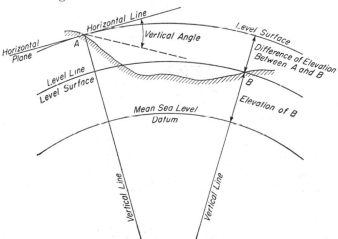

Fig. 5-1. Leveling terms.

Vertical line. A line to the center of the earth from any point. It is commonly considered to be the line defined by a plumb line.

Level surface. A curved surface which at every point is perpendicular to the plumb line (the direction in which gravity acts). Level surfaces are approximately spheroidal in shape. A body of still water is the best example. In the survey of a limited area, a level surface is sometimes treated as a plane surface.

Level line. A line in a level surface, therefore a curved line.

Horizontal plane. A plane perpendicular to the plumb line.

Horizontal line. A straight line perpendicular to the vertical.

Datum. Any level surface to which elevations are referred (for example, mean sea level). Also called datum plane, although not actually a plane.

Mean sea level. The average height of the sea for all stages of the tide. At any particular place it is derived by averaging the hourly tide heights over a long period of time. The standard for the United States was determined by correlating observed mean sea level elevation at Galveston, Texas, with that at a number of other stations.

Elevation. The vertical distance from a datum, usually mean sea level, to a point or object.

Bench mark. A relatively permanent material object, natural or artificial, bearing a marked point whose elevation above or below an adopted datum is known or assumed.

Leveling. The process of finding the difference in elevation between two points by measuring the vertical distance between the level surfaces through the points.

If the elevation of a point X is 802.56 ft, X is 802.56 ft above some datum. Mean sea level is the nation-wide reference surface made available for the use of local surveyors by the United States Coast and Geodetic Survey through its establishment of thousands of bench marks. Locations and elevations of these marks can be obtained by writing to its Director, Washington 25, D.C.

Many organizations have their own arbitrarily selected datums. Hence it is necessary to state the datum on which an elevation is based.

5–3. Curvature and refraction. From the definitions of a level surface and a horizontal line, it is evident that a horizontal line departs from a level surface because of the *curvature* of the earth. In Fig. 5–2 the departure DB from a horizontal line through point A is expressed approximately by the formula

$$C = 0.667M^2 = 0.024F^2 \tag{5-1}$$

where C is the departure, in feet, of a level surface from a horizontal line, M is the distance in miles, and F is the distance in thousands of feet.

Since points A and B are on a level line, they have the same elevation. Curvature of the earth therefore causes a rod held on B to be
read too high by an amount BD.

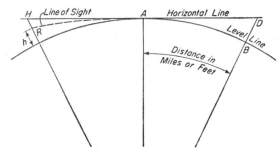

FIG. 5–2. Curvature and refraction.

Light rays passing through the earth's atmosphere are bent or
refracted toward the earth's surface as shown in Fig. 5–3. Thus a
theoretically horizontal line of sight, as AH in Fig. 5–2, is bent to the
curved form AR. The result is that an object at R appears to be at
H, and the reading on a rod held at R is diminished by the distance
RH.

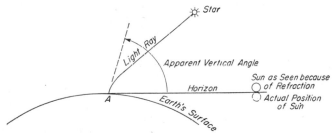

FIG. 5–3. Refraction.

The effect of *refraction* in making objects appear higher than they
really are (and thus rod readings smaller), can be remembered by
considering what happens when the sun is on the horizon, as in Fig.
5–3. At the moment the sun has just passed below the horizon, it
is seen just above the horizon. The sun's diameter of approximately
32 min is roughly equal to the average refraction on a horizontal
sight.

The angular displacement resulting from refraction is variable. It
depends upon atmospheric conditions and the angle the line of sight

makes with the vertical. For a horizontal sight it is expressed
approximately by the formula

$$R = 0.09M^2 = 0.003F^2 \tag{5-2}$$

This is closely one-seventh of the effect of curvature of the earth, but
in the opposite direction.

The formula for the combined effect of curvature and refraction is
approximately

$$h = 0.574M^2 = 0.0206F^2 \tag{5-3}$$

For sights of 100, 200, and 300 ft, h equals 0.00021 ft, 0.00082 ft,
and 0.0019 ft, respectively.

5-4. Methods of determining differences in elevation. Differences in elevation are determined directly by taping, by a leveling
instrument or a barometer, and indirectly by trigonometric leveling.

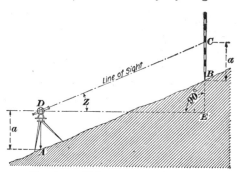

FIG. 5-4. Trigonometric leveling.

Taping method. Application of a tape to the vertical line between
two points is sometimes possible. This method is used in determining the depths of mine shafts and in the layout and construction of
multistory buildings. When a water or sewer pipe is being laid, a
graduated rod or pole may replace the tape.

Leveling instrument. A horizontal plane of sight tangent to the
level surface at any point is readily established by means of a level
vial. If a sighting device (telescope) and level vial are combined,
vertical distances can be measured by observing on graduated rods.
This is the method commonly used by engineers.

Barometer, or altimeter. This instrument measures air pressure and
converts the readings to elevations in feet. Readings taken at
critical points provide relative elevations.

Trigonometric leveling. The difference in elevation between two points can be determined by measuring (a) the inclined distance between them and (b) the vertical angle to one point from a horizontal plane through the other. Thus in Fig. 5–4 if the slope distance AB or DC and the vertical angle EDC are measured, then the difference in elevation between A and B is $EC = DC \sin EDC$.

Trigonometric leveling is commonly used in topographical work where inclined distances and vertical angles are obtained by means of a transit or alidade.

5–5. Types of leveling instruments. The types of levels used by most surveyors are the American-type engineer's level (wye and dumpy), shown in Figs. 5–9 and 5–10; the tilting level, Fig. 5–11; the European-type engineer's level, Fig. 5–12; and the self-leveling level, Fig. 5–13. For less-accurate work, the hand level, Fig. 5–14, is often used.

The principal parts of the engineer's level are the level vial, telescope, level bar, and leveling head. A hand level, as the name implies, is a hand-held instrument consisting of a telescope and level vial.

5–6. Level vials. A level vial is a glass tube which is sealed at both ends and contains a sensitive liquid and a small air bubble. The liquid must be nonfreezing, quick-acting, and relatively stable in length for normal temperature variations. A mixture of alcohol and ether is generally specified. Uniformly spaced graduations are etched on the exterior surface of the tube to show the exact position of the bubble. These divisions may provide spaces of 0.01 ft, 0.1 in., or 2 mm.

The *axis* of a level vial is the longitudinal line tangent to the upper inside surface at the mid-point. When the bubble is in the center of its run, the axis should be a horizontal line, as in Fig. 5–5.

The sensitivity of a level vial is determined by the radius of curvature provided in the grinding. The larger the radius, the more sensitive the bubble. A highly sensitive bubble is necessary for precise work but may be a handicap in rough surveys because of the longer time required to center it.

A properly designed instrument has the sensitivity of the level vial correlated with the magnification of the telescope. A slight movement of the bubble should be accompanied by a minute change in the observed rod reading at a distance of perhaps 200 ft. Sensitiveness of a level vial is expressed in two ways: (a) by the angle, in seconds, subtended by one division on the scale, and (b) by the radius of curvature of the tube.

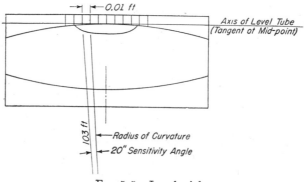

FIG. 5-5. Level vial.

If one division subtends an angle of 20 sec at the center, it is called a 20-sec bubble. Because of the variable lengths of divisions used, this is not always a fair comparison. A 20-sec bubble on a vial having 0.01-ft divisions has a radius of 103 ft. The angles of level vials used on America-made instruments range from about 10 sec to 1 min, the usual value for a level being 15 to 20 sec for 0.1-in. or 2-mm divisions.

FIG. 5-6. Coincident type of level bubble. Correctly set in left view; twice the deviation of the bubble shown in right view. (Courtesy of Kern Instruments, Inc.)

Figure 5-6 illustrates the *coincident* type of level bubble used on precise equipment. The bubble is centered by bringing the two ends together to form a smooth curve. A prism splits the bubble and makes the two ends visible simultaneously.

A noncoincident type of bubble can be centered with an accuracy of about one-tenth of its sensitivity. A coincident bubble, because of the opposite motions of the two ends and the magnification provided in an optical-reading instrument, can be centered with an accuracy of perhaps one-fortieth of its sensitivity. Thus the precision possible in centering, as well as the sensitivity of the bubble, must be considered in estimating the results to be obtained.

5–7. Telescopes. The telescope on an engineer's level, Fig. 5–7, is a metal tube containing three main parts—objective lens, cross-hair ring, and eyepiece.

Objective lens. The objective lens is a compound lens through which rays of light from objects are brought to a focus on the cross hairs by means of the focusing screw. If the object sighted is at an infinite distance, for example a star, the image would be formed at a distance from the lens called its focal length, denoted by f. Practically, a sight distance of several thousand feet reproduces this condition. Surfaces of lenses on modern instruments are coated to increase their light-transmission, since some illumination is lost at every contact between air and glass.

Cross-hair ring. Spider webs or fine platinum wires arc used for cross hairs and are mounted on one side of a heavy brass annular ring. Many of the newer instruments utilize a glass reticule with fine lines etched on one surface. The usual arrangement consists of a vertical and a horizontal hair which intersect at the exact center of the ring. For stadia and precise leveling work, two additional horizontal hairs are spaced equidistant from the center. If a glass reticule is used, the stadia lines are extended over only part of the width, to differentiate them from the middle hair. The hairs and reticule are accurately set by the manufacturer, but adjustment may be necessary later. Capstan screws, v in Fig. 5–7, hold the cross-hair ring in the telescope barrel and permit accurate centering.

Eyepiece. The eyepiece end of the telescope is a microscope, u in Fig. 5–7, composed of a set of lenses which magnify the image focused on the plane of the cross-hair ring by the objective lens. Magnification by the eyepiece varies from about 10 to 30 diameters. Since the image on the cross-hair ring is inverted, an eyepiece which simply magnifies leaves the image inverted. To erect this image for the eye, another set of lenses must be introduced.

Both types of eyepieces, inverting and erecting, are used. The erecting eyepiece utilizes more lenses, and therefore some loss of light results. An inverting eyepiece is troublesome for beginners but is preferable on precise instruments.

Focusing. Telescopes may be either internal-focusing or external-focusing. Movement of the objective lens is visible in the latter type. Dust and wear affect the slide and may disturb the optical axis (the line connecting the optical center of the objective lens and the intersection of the cross hairs) of an external-focusing telescope.

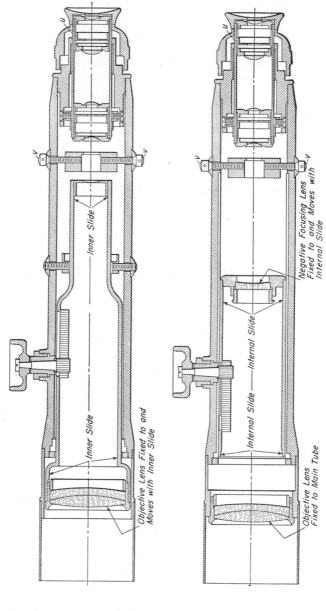

FIG. 5-7. Types of telescopes. Top: external-focusing. Bottom: internal-focusing. (Courtesy of W. & L. E. Gurley.)

As shown in Fig. 5–7, an internal-focusing telescope has a fixed objective lens and an additional sliding, focusing, compound lens inside the telescope tube. This type of telescope is dust-resistant and will probably be used almost exclusively in the future.

The fundamental principle of lenses is given by the formula

$$\frac{1}{f_1} + \frac{1}{f_2} = \frac{1}{f} \tag{5–4}$$

where f_1 = distance from lens to image at plane of cross hairs;
$\quad\quad f_2$ = distance from lens to object, as on Plate A–8 in Appendix A;
$\quad\quad f$ = focal length of lens.

The focal length is a constant for any particular set of lenses. Therefore, as the distance f_1 changes, f_2 must also change. The distance f_2 between the objective lens and the cross-hair ring is varied by turning the focusing screw to move the objective lens. This is the process of focusing.

Since the cross-hair ring remains fixed in the telescope tube, the distance between the ring and the eyepiece must be adjusted to suit the eye of an individual observer. This is done by bringing the cross hairs to a clear focus, that is, making them appear as black as possible when sighting at the sky or a distant, light-colored object. Once this has been accomplished, the adjustment need not be changed for the same observer, regardless of the length of sight.

After the eyepiece has been adjusted, objects are brought to sharp focus at the plane of the cross hairs by moving the objective lens. If the cross hairs appear to travel over the object sighted when the eye is shifted slightly in any direction, parallax exists. Either the objective lens or the eyepiece, or both, must be adjusted to eliminate this effect if accurate work is to be done.

The rule *near-far, far-near* may be helpful to beginners using an external-focusing telescope. If the object is near the observer, the objective lens is run far out. When the object is far away, the objective lens is brought nearer to the observer's eye.

The level vial is attached to the telescope tube in such a manner that the axis of the level bubble is exactly parallel to the line of sight through the center of the telescope. Centering the level bubble therefore makes the line of sight horizontal.

5–8. Optics.[1]   A brief discussion of the optics of surveying instruments and optical tooling equipment (see Chapter 25) is desirable before leaving the subject of telescopes.

The purpose of a telescope is to create for the observer a picture that shows the position of the cross hairs on the target with the greatest possible clarity and precision.   This end is attained by skillful design and perfection in manufacture to secure the combination of optical qualities best suited to a particular application.   Optical factors include resolving power, magnification, definition, eye distance, size of pupil, and field of view.

Specifications alone can seldom indicate the true qualities of one telescope as compared with those of another.   The most important test for a telescope, and in fact the only true test, is a simultaneous comparison with another telescope, under the same conditions.

Some of the important optical terms will be explained.

Resolving power.   The ability of a lens to show detail is termed resolving power.   It is measured by the smallest angular distance, expressed in seconds of arc, between two points that are just far enough apart to be distinguished as separate.

The maximum resolving power that theoretically can be attained with a telescope when the optical parts are perfectly designed, and exactly placed, depends entirely on the diameter of that part of the objective lens actually used (the effective aperture).   The resolving power of an objective lens is independent of magnification.   It can be computed by the formula

$$R = \frac{5.5''}{D} \tag{5-5}$$

where R is the angle that can be resolved, in seconds, and D is the diameter of the effective aperture of the lens, in inches.   For example, the objective lens of the jig transit shown in Fig. 25–7 has an effective aperture 1.18 in. in diameter.   The resolving power is therefore 4.6 sec.

The accepted standard for the resolving power of the human eye is 60 sec.   Hence the resolving power of the telescope has to be brought at least to this limit by magnification.   If the angular distance resolved by the telescope is 4.67 sec, this resolving power must

---

[1] This section on optics includes some material from *Optical Tooling Equipment*, published by Keuffel and Esser Company and reprinted here by permission.

be magnified 13 times. Since the eyesight of different observers varies, more magnification is invaribly used.

Magnification. The value of magnification (power) is the ratio of the apparent size of an object viewed through a telescope to its size as seen by the unaided eye from the same distance. Magnification varies slightly when the focus of the telescope is changed. Therefore it is affected somewhat by the distance to the object. For any telescope, the greatest magnification occurs at infinite focus, and this is the value used to describe the property.

Although telescopic magnification must be greater than $60/R$, there is a limiting point beyond which it is impossible to increase magnification without sacrificing definition. This point is reached when the magnification becomes greater than two or three times $60/R$. For larger values the quality of the image seen is impaired, and the accuracy with which the line of sight can be made to coincide with a target is reduced.

Certain disadvantages result from the use of too high a magnification, even when the objective lens is large enough to give the necessary resolution. With high magnification the field of view is reduced, and any heat waves, turbulence, or vibration cause the image of an object to move over the cross hairs too fast for accurate observation. The magnifying power of the telescopes on modern engineer's levels ranges from 26 to 41 diameters, and averages perhaps 32 diameters. The levels shown in Figs. 5–11 and 5–12 have variable-power eyepieces.

Definition. Definition is a term used to define the over-all results produced by a telescope. Better definition permits objects to be seen more clearly through the telescope. It depends upon a number of optical features and is the quality that gives the greatest pointing accuracy.

Since definition is a relative term, it can be determined best by comparing the appearance of the same object when viewed through the telescope to be tested and a telescope with which the observer is familiar.

Pointing accuracy. The exactness with which the line of sight can be directed toward a target, or a target can be placed on the line of sight, is called pointing accuracy. It depends upon magnification, definition, the arrangement of the cross hairs, and the design of the target or scale sighted. The general relationship between magnification and pointing accuracy for telescopes having the same definition is shown in Fig. 5–8. Other tests show that the standard 1-min transit can be pointed within 5 sec of arc consistently in the field.

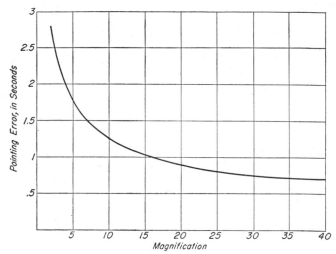

FIG. 5–8. Relation between magnification and pointing error. (Courtesy of Keuffel and Esser Company.)

5–9. Level bar and supports. The telescope of a level rests upon vertical supports at each end of a horizontal bar called the level bar. The level bar in turn is centered on a vertical spindle which is accurately machined and rests in a conical socket of the leveling head. The spindle insures that the level bar will revolve in a horizontal plane when the instrument is properly adjusted.

The vertical supports for the telescope may be wyes which are adjustable in height and have clamps to hold the telescope tube, or they may be rigid and integral parts of the level bar as in the dumpy level. The wye and dumpy levels, shown in Figs. 5–9 and 5–10 respectively, differ primarily in the method of supporting the telescope.

5–10. Leveling head. The conical socket into which the vertical axis of the level bar fits is supported by four large thumbscrews called leveling screws. These rest upon a plate which is screwed on top of the tripod. The four leveling screws are in two pairs, those of each pair being directly opposite each other. The level vial is placed alternately over each pair of leveling screws, which are adjusted by

FIG. 5–9a. Wye level. (Courtesy of W. & L. E. Gurley.)

turning them until the bubble remains in the center of the vial for a complete revolution. The line of sight will then generate a horizontal plane.

Most precise equipment has three rather than four leveling screws. The three-screw arrangement is faster and not subject to the rocking which takes place in the four-screw type when two opposite screws are turned up or down slightly more than the other two. The disadvantage of the three-screw type is that a slight difference in elevation of the line of sight results if all three screws are turned up or all are turned down. Manipulation of the four-screw head does not change the elevation of the telescope. Also, after the threads become worn on a three-screw leveling head, there is some loss of rigidity which must be eliminated by replacing the screws. Tightening one screw of each pair in the four-screw arrangement results in a clamping action and produces a stable setup.

5–11. Wye level. The wye level, Fig. 5–9a, has a telescope tube A resting in supports B, called *wyes* because of their shape. Curved clips C, hinged at one end and pinned at the other, fasten the telescope in place. If the clips are raised, the telescope can be rotated in the wyes, or removed and turned end for end as part of the adjustment procedure. The sunshade X should always be used when observing,

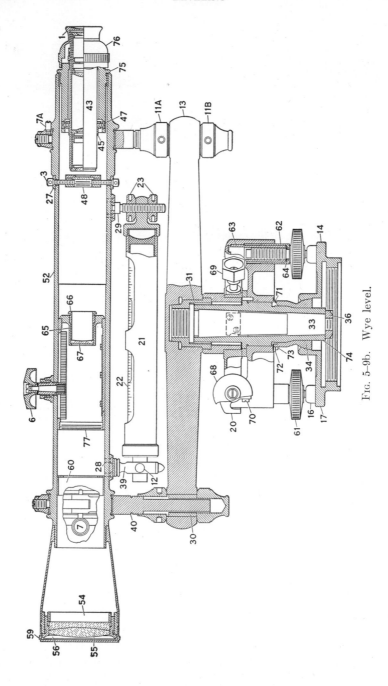

FIG. 5–9b. Wye level.

1. eyepiece cap
3. capstan screw—adj. reticle
6. obj. focussing pinion
7. wye pin
7A. stop pin
11A. wye capstan nuts (upper)
11B. wye capstan nuts (lower)
12. level lateral adjusting screw
13. wye bar
14. leveling head
16. leveling screw cup
17. bottom plate
20. leveling head clamp
21. telescope level complete
22. telescope level vial
23. vertical adjusting capstan nuts for telescope level
27. collet—reticle centering screws
28. screws for telescope level hanger and post
29. telescope level post
30. spline
31. spindle head
33. spindle
34. half ball
36. nut—end of spindle
39. hanger for telescope level
40. wye complete

43. eyepiece
45. eyepiece centering ring
47. eyepiece centering screw
48. recticle
52. main tube
54. inner ring—obj. setting
55. objective lens
56. outer ring—obj. setting
59. objective cap
60. diaphragm in telescope
61. leveling screw
62. dust cap
63. leveling screw bushing
64. neoprene washer
65. negative lens setting
66. negative lens retaining ring
67. negative lens
68. tangent screw
69. clamp screw
70. tension screw for tangent screw
71. lock washer
72. clamp washer
73. washer clamp screw
74. shell
75. eyepiece body
76. eyepiece focussing ring
77. objective slide

even in cloudy weather. A cap covers the objective lens when the instrument is not being used.

The level tube *D* is attached to the telescope but can be adjusted in the horizontal and vertical planes by the capstan-headed screws *Z*. The wyes are supported by the *level bar E* which can be adjusted vertically by means of the capstan nuts *F*.

The *spindle* (visible only in the cutaway view, Fig. 5–9b) is constructed at right angles to the level bar and rotates in a socket *G* (Fig. 5–9a) in the leveling head *H*. A collar *L* turning on the socket can be secured by the *clamp screw M* to hold the telescope in any vertical plane. *Tangent screw N*, also called the *slow-motion screw*, is operative only when the clamp screw is tightened. The tangent screw rotates the telescope through a small angle for precise settings.

Four *leveling screws O*, resting in cups *P* upon the bed or *foot plate Q*, control the leveling head. A ball-and-socket joint at the lower end of the spindle provides a flexible connection to the bed plate and a means of rotation as the leveling screws are raised or lowered. Threads on the inside of the bed plate fasten the head of the instrument to the tripod.

FIG. 5–10. Dumpy level. (Courtesy of W. & L. E. Gurley.)

The wye level is simpler to adjust than the dumpy level because the telescope can be lifted from the wyes and turned end for end. This feature permits one man to make all adjustments by himself. Although more adjustments are required for the wye level, they are thus easier to make. The advantage is lost if the collars on the telescope, or the bearings of the wyes on which they rest, become worn. The instrument then must be adjusted in the same way as the dumpy level.

5–12. Dumpy level. In the dumpy level, Fig. 5–10, the telescope is rigidly attached to, and parallel with, the level bar. The level vial is set in the level bar and thereby protected somewhat. The level vial always remains in the same vertical plane as the telescope, but screws at each end permit vertical adjustment or replacement of the vial. Other construction details are similar to those of the wye level.

The advantages of the dumpy level over the wye level are (a) simpler construction with fewer movable parts, (b) fewer adjustments to be made, and (c) probably longer life for the adjustments. A disadvantage is that one of the adjustments requires a second man (rodman) and is more time-consuming. This difficulty can be eliminated if two points of known elevation are established and fixed targets set up on them.

The dumpy level is used almost exclusively in precise work and is replacing the older wye type in most fields.

5–13. Tripods. Several types of tripods are available. The legs may be fixed or adjustable in length, and solid or split. All types are shod with metallic conical points, and hinged at the top where they connect to a metal head. The adjustable-leg tripod is advantageous for setups in rough terrain or in a shop, but the type with a fixed-length leg may be slightly more rigid. The split-leg model is lighter than the solid type but less rugged. A wide-framed tripod, used for many years on European instruments, is now being adopted by some American manufacturers. A sturdy tripod in good condition is necessary to obtain the best results from a fine instrument.

In the past, many different thread types were used on tripods. The standard now adopted by all American manufacturers is eight threads per inch on a cap $3\frac{1}{2}$ in. in diameter.

5–14. Tilting level. A tilting dumpy level, Fig. 5–11, is gaining favor for general use. Originally it was employed only on high-precision work. A bull's-eye (circular spirit) level (on the far side of the telescope and not visible in the figure) is mounted on the leveling

Fig. 5–11.   Tilting level.   (Courtesy of Keuffel and Esser Company.)

head for quick approximate leveling by means of the four leveling screws. Exact level is obtained by tilting or rotating the telescope slightly in a vertical plane about a fulcrum at the vertical axis of the instrument. A micrometer screw under the eyepiece controls this movement.

The tilting feature saves time and increases accuracy, since only one screw need be manipulated to keep the line of sight horizontal as the telescope is turned about a vertical axis. The telescope bubble is viewed through a system of prisms from the observer's normal position behind the eyepiece. The prism arrangement splits the bubble image into two parts. Centering the bubble is accomplished by making the images of the two ends coincide.

An internal-focusing telescope, high magnification, and a glass

FIG. 5–12. European tilting level. (Courtesy of Kern Instruments, Inc.)

reticule with etched stadia lines are standard on this type of instrument.

5–15. European instruments. European levels, one of which is shown in Fig. 5–12, are characterized by short telescopes, streamlined construction, small size, and light weight. Most such levels are of the dumpy type and include a tilting arrangement with a three-screw leveling head. Sensitivity of the level vial ranges from 6 to 40 sec for 2-mm graduations. Magnification ranges from 18 to 36 diameters. Horizontal circles of glass are available on some instruments for measuring angles.

One type, Fig. 5–13, incorporates a self-leveling feature. If the instrument is set up reasonably level, an air-damped prism automatically levels the line of sight and keeps it precisely level.

Fig 5–13. Self-leveling level. (Courtesy of Keuffel and Esser Company.)

Packaging is one of the outstanding innovations in European surveying equipment. Smoothly curved metal containers protect the instrument and make carrying convenient. Gasket seals are no longer used on the container because in humid climates trapped moisture may damage the optical system. European instruments compete in price with American equipment.

5-16. Hand level. The hand level, Fig. 5-14, is a hand-held instrument used on low-precision work and for checking purposes. It consists of a brass tube 5 or 6 in. long having a plain glass objective and a peep-sight eyepiece. A small level vial mounted above a slot in the tube is viewed through the eyepiece by means of a prism or a 45°-angle mirror. A horizontal hair extends across the tube.

FIG. 5-14. Hand level. (Courtesy of Keuffel and Esser Company.)

The prism or mirror occupies only one half of the inside of the tube, the other half being open to provide a clear sight through the objective. Thus the rod sighted and the reflected image of the bubble are visible beside each other, with the cross hair superimposed.

The instrument is held in one hand and leveled by raising or lowering the objective end until the cross hair bisects the bubble. The tube can be steadied by making a tripod with the thumb on a cheekbone, the first finger on the forehead, and the eyepiece against the brow. Holding the level against a staff, or better still, resting it in a Y-shaped stick, increases the accuracy.

FIG 5-15. Abney hand level and clinometer. (Courtesy of Keuffel and Esser Company.)

Stadia hairs reading 1 : 10 may be included. Magnification of $1\frac{1}{2}$ diameters is usually provided for observing the bubble and the cross hair, but the rod is seen through plain glass. The length of sight possible is limited, therefore, to the distance at which a rod can be read with natural vision.

The *Abney hand level and clinometer*, shown in Fig. 5–15, has limited application in measuring vertical angles and slopes, and for direct leveling. It has an arc graduated in degrees up to 90°, a vernier reading to 10 min, and several scales for slopes ranging from a ratio of 1 to 1 to a ratio of 1 to 10.

5–17. Leveling rods. Rods used in most leveling work are made of wood and are marked with graduations in feet and decimals or in meters and decimals. There are two main classes of rods:

a. Self-reading rods which can be read by the levelman as he sights through the telescope and notes the apparent intersection of the horizontal cross hair with the rod.

b. Target rods which contain a movable target that is set by the rodman at the position indicated by signals from the levelman.

A wide choice of patterns, colors, and graduations on single-piece, two-section, and three-section leveling rods is available. The varied types, usually named for cities or states, include the Philadelphia, New York, Boston, Troy, Chicago, Florida, and California rods.

Rods for general leveling, and for special purposes such as slope staking, can be made by fastening a flexible ribbon of treated fabric to a wooden strip. Such strips, graduated in diverse ways, can be purchased from manufacturers.

A self-reading rod consisting of a wooden frame and an invar strip graduated in decimals of meters is used for precise work, to eliminate the effects of humidity and temperature changes. The invar strip is attached only at the ends and is free to slide in grooves on each side of the wooden frame.

The Philadelphia rod is a combination self-reading and target rod, and is the most popular type for all but precise leveling. The 7-ft by 13-ft model will be described in detail. Other lengths are also made, the 6.5-ft by 12-ft rod being common.

5–18. Philadelphia rod. The Philadelphia rod shown in Fig. 5–16 consists of two sliding sections graduated in hundredths of a foot and joined by brass sleeves *a* and *b*. The rear section can be locked in position by a clamp screw *c* to provide any length from a *short rod* for readings of 7 ft or less, up to a *long rod*, or *high rod*, of 13 ft when fully extended. The graduations on the front faces of the two sections

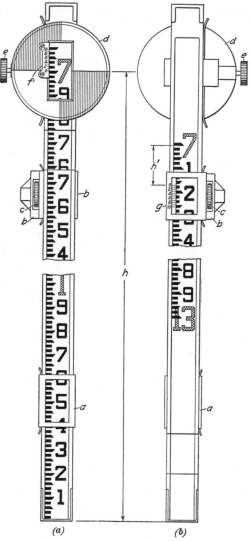

(a)   *(b)*

FIG. 5–16. Philadelphia rod.

read continuously from zero at the base to 13 ft at the top for the high-rod setting.

The rod graduations are accurately-painted alternate black and white spaces 0.01 ft wide. The 0.1- and 0.05-ft graduations are emphasized by spurs extending the black markings. Tenths are designated by black numbers, and foot marks by red numbers. The figures straddle the proper graduation. A Philadelphia rod can be read accurately through the engineer's level at distances up to 300 ft.

On long sights, or when readings to the nearest 0.001 ft are desired, a target d is used. Circular, oval, and angular targets are made. All are approximately 5 in. high and painted red and white in alternate quadrants. A clamp e and a vernier scale f are part of the target. For readings of less than 7 ft, the target is set at the proper elevation in accordance with directions given by the instrumentman. When the rod is extended, the target is clamped at 7.000 ft and the rear section raised to bring the target to the correct height. Divisions on the back of the rod are marked from 7 to 13 ft in a downward direction. As the rod is extended, a fixed vernier scale g attached to sleeve b shows the target height.

Leveling rods are made of carefully selected, kiln-dried, well-seasoned hardwood, and are graduated in accordance with rigid specifications. They should not be used as seats, or for pole vaulting, or in any other way that will bend them or mar the painted graduations. Letting the rod down "on the run" batters both sections and may change the vernier reading to less than 7.000 ft, for example to 6.998 ft. If this happens, the target must be set to the same reading, as 6.998 ft, for high rods.

5–19. Verniers. The fractional part of the smallest division of a scale or rod can be measured without interpolation by means of an auxiliary scale called a vernier. Figure 5–17 shows the simple type of direct vernier used on leveling rods.

As illustrated in Fig. 5–17a, the vernier has n divisions in a space covered by $(n - 1)$ of the smallest divisions on the scale. Then

$$(n - 1)d = nv \qquad (5\text{–}6)$$

where d = the length of a scale division;
v = the length of a vernier division.

This is the fundamental basis for all vernier construction. For leveling-rod verniers, $n = 10$, $d = 0.01$ ft, and $v = 0.09/10 = 0.009$ ft.

In Fig. 5–17a the reading is 0.300. If the vernier is moved so that its first graduation from zero coincides with the first graduation

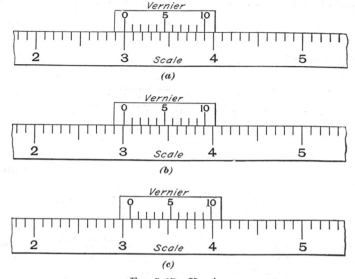

FIG. 5–17.   Vernier.

of the scale, Fig. 5–17b, the vernier index has moved a distance equal to

$$d - v = 0.010 - 0.009 = 0.001 \text{ ft}$$

The reading is therefore 0.301 ft.

If the vernier is moved so that the second graduation on the vernier is coincident with the graduation representing 0.32 on the scale, the movement from the position in Fig. 5–17a has been $2(d - v) = 0.002$ ft.   Thus the fractional part of a scale division from the preceding scale graduation to the vernier index is read by determining the number of the vernier line which is coincident with any scale graduation. The reading for the decimal part of a foot in Fig. 5–17c is 0.308 ft.

From formula 5–6,

$$nv = (n - 1)d$$

or

$$nv = nd - d$$

and

$$(d - v) = \frac{d}{n} \tag{5–7}$$

The expression $(d - v)$ or d/n is termed the *least count* of a vernier. It represents *the value of the smallest division on the scale divided by the number of divisions on the vernier.*   The least count of a vernier

can also be defined as the smallest reading obtainable without interpolating.   An observer cannot be certain he is reading a scale and
vernier correctly until he has determined the least count.

In selecting the vernier line which is coincident with a scale division,
an observer must assume a position directly behind the lines, or over
them, to avoid parallax.   The second graduation on each side of the
apparently coincident lines should be checked to see that a symmetrical pattern is formed about them.   In Fig. 5–17c, vernier
graduations 6 and 10 fall inside (toward division 8) the scale lines by
equal distances.

5–20. Setting up the level.   The safest way to carry an engineer's
level in a car is to keep the head in its box.   The box closes properly
only when the instrument is set perfectly in the padded supports.

A level should be removed from its box by lifting on the level
bar or base, *not* by grasping the telescope.   The head must be
screwed snugly on the tripod.   If the head is too loose, the instrument
is unstable; if too tight, it may freeze on the tripod.   A grain of sand,
roughness in the threads, or a change in temperature makes the head
stick.   Spreading the tripod legs until the head of the instrument
almost touches the ground often helps to release the head in case it
freezes.

The legs of a tripod must be tightened correctly.   If each leg
falls slowly of its own weight after being placed in a horizontal position, it is properly adjusted.   Clamping the legs too tightly strains
the plate and screws.   If the legs are loose, the setup is wobbly.

Unlike the transit, the level is not set up over any particular point.
It is inexcusable, therefore, to have the base plate badly out of level
before using the leveling screws.   Moving one leg radially, or circum-
ferentially, will level the instrument.   On side-hill setups, placing one
leg on the uphill side and two on the downhill slope eases the problem.
The most convenient height of setup is one which enables the observer
to sight through the telescope without stooping or stretching.

In leveling the four-screw head, the telescope is turned until it is
over two opposite screws.   The bubble is approximately centered by
using the thumb and first finger of each hand to adjust the opposite
screws.   The procedure is repeated with the telescope over the other
two leveling screws.   Time is wasted by centering the bubble exactly
on the first try, since it will be thrown off during the cross-leveling.

Working with each pair of screws about three times should complete the job.

The leveling screws are turned in opposite directions at the same speed by both hands, unless the intention is to tighten or loosen the leveling head. A simple rule is that the bubble follows the left thumb. This is illustrated in Fig. 5–18.

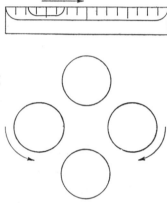

FIG. 5–18. Use of leveling screws.

If one hand turns faster than the other, the screws loosen and the head rocks on two screws, or the screws bind. Final precise adjustment may be made with one hand only. Leveling screws should be snug, not wrench-tight, to save time and avoid damage to the threads and base plate. A good instrumentman senses the proper setting of the leveling screws to permit ready movement without jamming the threads.

5–21. Holding the rod. The duties of a rodman are relatively simple. Like a chainman, however, the rodman can nullify the best efforts of the observer if he fails to follow a few simple rules.

The level rod must be held plumb to give a correct reading. In Fig. 5–19, point A is below the line of sight by a distance equal to AB. If the rod is tilted to position AD, an erroneous reading AE is obtained. It can be seen that the smallest reading possible, AB, is the correct one and this reading is secured only when the rod is plumb.

Formula 4–4 of section 4–11 can be applied to determine approximately the error in reading caused by the rod not being plumb. For example, if $AB = 10$ ft and $EB = 6$ in. in Fig. 5–19, the error is

$$c = \frac{d^2}{2L} = \frac{0.5^2}{2 \times 10} = 0.012 \text{ ft}$$

Errors of this magnitude are serious, whether results are being carried to hundredths or thousandths, and make careful plumbing necessary for high rod readings.

On still days the rod can be plumbed by letting it balance of its own weight while lightly supported by the finger tips. The instru-

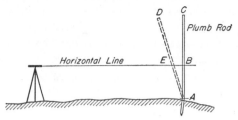

FIG. 5-19. Plumbing rod.

mentman makes certain the rod is plumbed in the lateral direction by checking its coincidence with the vertical cross hair and signaling for any adjustments necessary. The rodman can save time by squinting along the side of the rod to line it up with a telephone pole, a tree, or the side of a building. Plumbing on the line toward the instrument is more difficult, but holding the rod against the toes, stomach, and nose will bring it close to the plumb position.

A rod level of the type shown in Fig. 5-20 insures fast and correct rod plumbing. Its L shape is designed to fit the rear and side faces of the rod while the bull's-eye bubble is centered to plumb the rod in both directions. The simplicity and reasonable cost of a rod level should encourage greater use of this accessory.

FIG. 5-20. Rod level. (Courtesy of Keuffel and Esser Company.)

5-22. Theory of leveling. Leveling is the process of determining the elevations or differences in elevation of points. Figure 5-21 illustrates the procedure in its basic form.

A level is set up approximately halfway between B.M. Rock and point X. Assume that the elevation of B.M. Rock is known to be 820.00 ft. After leveling the instrument, a plus sight taken on a rod held on the B.M. gives a reading of 8.42 ft. A *plus sight* (+S), also termed *backsight* (B.S.), is the reading on a rod held on a point of known or assumed elevation. This reading is used in computing the height of instrument. The direction of the sight—whether forward, backward, or sideways—is not important. The term plus sight is preferable to backsight, but both are used.

Adding the plus sight 8.42 ft to the elevation of B.M. Rock, 820.00, gives the *height of instrument* (H.I.) as 828.42 ft.   Height of instrument is defined as the vertical distance from the datum to the line of sight of the instrument.

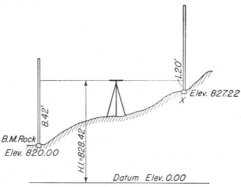

FIG. 5–21.   Theory of leveling.

Turning the telescope to bring into view the rod held on point X, a *minus sight* $(-S)$, also called *foresight* (F.S.), of 1.20 ft is obtained. A minus sight is defined as the reading on a rod held at a point whose elevation is to be determined.   The term minus sight is preferable to foresight, but both are used.

Subtracting the minus sight 1.20 ft from the H.I., 828.42, gives the elevation of point X as 827.22 ft.

All leveling theory and applications can thus be expressed by two equations which are repeated over and over:

$$\text{Elev.} + \text{B.S.} = \text{H.I.} \tag{5-7}$$

$$\text{H.I.} - \text{F.S.} = \text{Elev.} \tag{5-8}$$

Note that if a backsight is taken on a bench mark located on the roof of a tunnel, or on the ceiling of a room, with the instrument at a lower elevation, the backsight must be subtracted to obtain the height of instrument.   For similar conditions, a foresight would be added.

5–23. Types of leveling.   The following types of leveling are performed in surveying: (a) differential leveling, (b) reciprocal leveling, (c) profile leveling, (d) barometric leveling, (e) trigonometric leveling, and (f) borrow-pit or cross-section leveling.

Each type has special applications or advantages under given conditions.

5–24. Differential leveling. Differential leveling is the process of determining the difference in elevation of two points. When the points are far apart, it may be necessary to set up the instrument several times. Figure 5–22 illustrates the procedure followed in differential leveling. Field notes for the work are shown in Plate A–3, Appendix A.

The points on which the rod is held to carry the line from one setup to the next are called *turning points* (T.P.). A turning point is defined as a solid point on which both a plus and a minus sight are taken on a line of direct levels. Horizontal distances for the plus and minus sights should be made approximately equal by pacing, by stadia measurements, by counting lengths of rails if working along a track, or by some other easy method. The effects of refraction, curvature of the earth, and lack of adjustment of the instrument are thereby eliminated. On slopes, a zigzag path may be taken to utilize the longer rod length available on the downhill sights.

Bench marks are described the first time used, and are thereafter referred to by noting the page number on which detailed. The description should give the general location first and include enough particulars to enable a person unfamiliar with the area to find the mark readily. Bench marks are usually named for some prominent object which is nearby, to aid in describing their location, one word being preferable. Examples are B.M. River, B.M. Tower, B.M. Corner, and B.M. Bridge. On some surveys, bench marks are given numbers. These have the advantage of giving relative positions along a line, but the numbers are more subject to mistakes in recording. Turning points are numbered consecutively along a line of levels but need not be described since they are merely a means to an end and will seldom have to be relocated.

Before a party leaves the field, all possible note checks must be made to detect any mistakes in arithmetic. The algebraic sum of the plus and minus sights applied to the first elevation should give the last elevation. This computation checks the values of all H.I.'s and T.P.'s unless compensating errors have been made.

Important work is checked by leveling forward and backward between end points. The difference between the *rod sum* (algebraic total of plus and minus sights) on the run out and the rod sum on the run back is called the *loop closure*. Specifications, or the purpose of

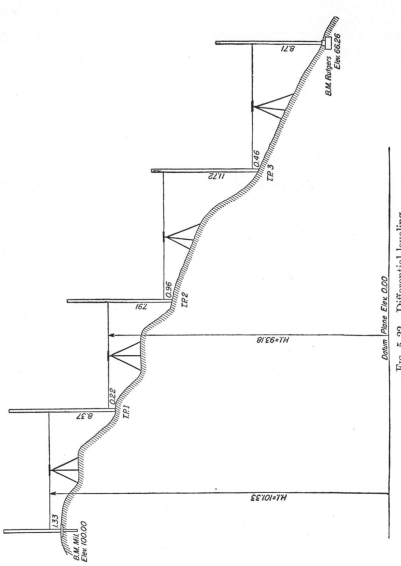

FIG. 5-22. Differential leveling.

the survey, fix the permissible loop closure.   For surveys of moderate precision, it is satisfactory to use the formula

$$\text{Permissible closure in feet} = 0.10\sqrt{M} \qquad (5\text{–}9)$$

where M is the distance in miles.   If the permissible closure is exceeded, one or more additional runs must be made.

The difference in elevation between the end points is considered to be the average of the rod sums on the runs out and back.   True elevations can be obtained by starting from a bench mark whose elevation above mean sea level is known.   If this is not possible, an assumed elevation may be used, and later all values can be converted to true elevations by application of a constant.

Double-rodded lines of levels are sometimes used on important work.   Plus and minus sights are taken on two rods from each setup of the instrument and carried in separate noteform columns.

Flying levels may be run at the end of the work day, to check the results of an extended line run in one direction only.   Longer sights and fewer setups are used, the purpose being to detect any large mistakes.

Three-wire leveling, formerly used mainly in precise work, now is employed on projects requiring only ordinary precision.   Readings of the upper, middle, and lower cross hairs are averaged to obtain a better value.   A check on the work is obtained by noting the difference between the middle and upper hairs, and the difference between the middle and lower hairs. The intercept between the upper and lower hairs gives the sight distance for checking the lengths of plus and minus sights.

5–25. Reciprocal leveling.   Topographic features such as rivers, lakes, and canyons make it difficult or impossible to keep plus and minus sights short and equal.   Reciprocal leveling is employed at such locations.

As shown in Fig. 5–23, the level is set up on one side of a stream

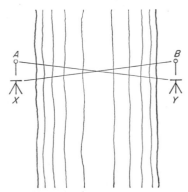

Fig. 5–23.   Reciprocal leveling.

at X, and rod readings are taken on points A and B.   Since the sight XB is very long, several readings are secured for averaging.

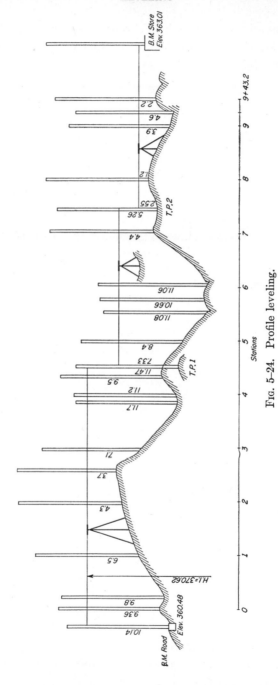

FIG. 5-24.   Profile leveling.

This is done by reading, turning the leveling screws to throw the instrument out of level, and then releveling and reading again. The process is repeated two, three, four, or more times. The instrument is now moved to Y and the same procedure followed.

The differences in elevation between A and B determined with the instrument at X and Y may differ because of curvature and refraction and instrumental errors. The average of the two differences in elevation is accepted as the correct value. Plate A–4 in Appendix A is a sample set of field notes for reciprocal leveling.

5–26. Profile leveling. On a route survey for a highway or a pipeline, elevations are required at every 100-ft station, at breaks in the slope of the ground surface, and at such critical points as roads, bridges, and culverts. These elevations when plotted show a *profile*—a vertical section of the surface of the ground along any fixed line. For most engineering projects the profile is taken along the center line, which is staked out in 100-ft stations.

Profile leveling, like differential leveling, requires the establishment of turning points on which both plus and minus sights are taken. In addition, any number of *intermediate sights* (minus sights) may be obtained on points along the line from each setup of the instrument, as shown in Fig. 5–24. Plate A–5 is a sample set of level notes covering the profile shown in Fig. 5–24.

As shown in the notes, a plus sight is taken upon a bench mark, and intermediate sights are read on the stations, at breaks in the ground surface, and at critical points, until the limit of accurate sighting distance is reached. A turning point is selected, the instrument moved ahead, and the process repeated. The level itself is set up off the center line so that sights of more uniform length can be procured. Bench marks out of the way of future construction are established along the route on a long line.

It is evident that when the "page check" is made on arithmetic computations, only the minus sights taken on turning points can be used. For this reason, and to isolate the points to be plotted, a separate column is necessary for the intermediate sights.

Readings on paved surfaces, such as concrete roadways, curbs, and sidewalks, can be taken to 0.01 ft. Readings on the ground closer than 0.1 ft are not practical.

A modern development in highway surveys is the *Johnson elevation meter*. This device is towed behind a car or truck and produces a profile of the line traversed.

5–27. Drawing and use of the profile. Profiles are usually plotted on a special paper called *Plate A profile paper*, which is ruled as shown in Fig. 5–25. Vertical lines are spaced $\frac{1}{4}$ in. apart, with every tenth line heavier. Horizontal lines are $\frac{1}{20}$ in. apart, with every fifth line heavier and every fiftieth line still heavier.

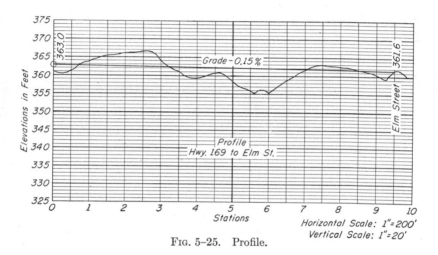

FIG. 5–25. Profile.

The vertical scale of a profile is generally exaggerated with respect to the horizontal scale in order to make differences of elevation more pronounced. A ratio of 10 to 1 is frequently used. Thus for a horizontal scale of 1 in. = 100 ft, the vertical scale would be 1 in. = 10 ft. The heavy lines of Plate A paper make blocks $2\frac{1}{2}$ in. by $2\frac{1}{2}$ in. and are best suited to a scale of 1 in. = 40 ft (or 400 ft) horizontally, and 1 in. = 4 ft (or 40 ft) vertically. The scale actually used should be plainly marked.

Curves, or in some cases straight lines, are drawn to connect the plotted elevations.

The plotted profile is used for many purposes, such as (a) determination of the depth of cut and fill on a proposed highway or airport, (b) study of grade-crossing problems, (c) investigation of the most economical location and depth for sewers and tunnels, and (d) selection of grades for irrigation ditches, pipelines, and other projects.

Rate of grade (or *gradient*, or just *grade*) is the rise or fall in feet per 100 feet. Thus a grade of 2.5 per cent means a 2.5-ft difference in elevation per 100 ft horizontally. Ascending grades are plus, descending grades are minus. A grade line selected to give somewhat equal cuts and fills is shown in Fig. 5–25. The process of staking out grades is described in Chapter 24.

The term "grade" is also employed to denote the elevation of the finished surface of an engineering project.

5–28. Barometric leveling. The *barometer*, an instrument which measures air pressure, can be used to find relative elevations of points on the surface of the earth. Figure 5–26 shows a modern surveying *altimeter*. Calibration of the scale on different models is in multiples of 2 to 10 ft.

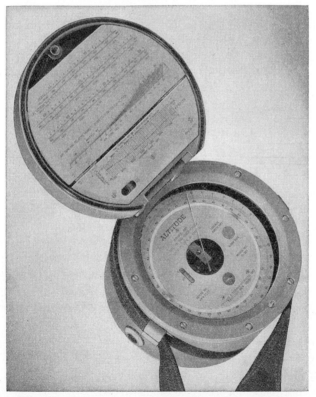

FIG. 5–26. Surveying altimeter. (Courtesy of Wallace and Tiernan.)

Air pressures are affected by conditions other than difference in elevation—for example, sudden changes in temperature and changing weather conditions due to storms. Also, there is during each day a normal variation in barometric pressure amounting to perhaps 100 ft difference in elevation and known as the diurnal range.

In barometric leveling, one or more control barometers remain on a bench mark (base) while the *roving* instrument is taken to points whose elevations are desired. The controls on the bases are read at stated intervals of time, perhaps every 10 min, and the elevations are recorded along with the temperature and time. Readings of the roving barometer are taken at critical points and adjusted later in accordance with changes observed at the control points. Several methods of making field surveys by barometer have been developed in which one base, two bases, or leapfrog techniques of control are used.

The barometric method is particularly suited for work in rough country where a high order of accuracy is not necessary.

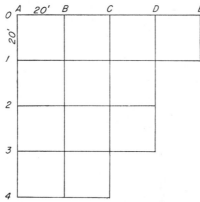

FIG. 5–27. Borrow-pit leveling.

5–29. Borrow-pit or cross-section leveling. The amount of earth, gravel, rock, or other material excavated or filled on a construction project may be determined by borrow-pit leveling. The quantities computed form the basis for payment to the contractor or materials supplier. The number of cubic yards of coal or other loose materials in stockpiles can be found in the same way.

As an example, assume the area shown in Fig. 5–27 is to be graded to an elevation of 358.0 for a building site. Notes for the field work are shown in Plate A–6.

The area to be covered is staked in squares of 10, 20, 50, 100, or more feet, the choice depending upon the size of the project and the accuracy desired. A transit and/or tape may be used for the layout. A bench mark of known or assumed elevation is established outside the area in a place not likely to be disturbed.

The level is set up at any convenient location from which a plus sight can be taken on the bench mark and minus sights are read on the corners of the squares. If the terrain is not too rough, it may be possible to select a point near the center of the area and take sights on all the corners from the same setup, as in this example.

Corners of the squares are designated by letters and numbers, such as *A–1, C–4,* and *D–2.* Since the site is to be graded to an elevation of 358.0, the amount of cut or fill at each corner can be obtained by subtracting 358.0 from its elevation. For each square, then, the average height of the four corners of the prism of cut or fill is determined and multiplied by the base area, 20 ft × 20 ft = 400 sq ft, to get the volume. The total volume is found by adding the individual values for each block and dividing by 27 to obtain a result in cubic yards.

As a simplification, the cut at each corner multiplied by the number of times it enters the volume computation can be shown in a separate column, a total secured, and divided by 4. The result multiplied by the base area of one block gives the volume. This procedure is shown in the sample noteform.

5–30. Use of the hand level. A hand level can be used for some types of work, such as differential leveling, when a high order of precision is not required. The instrumentman takes a plus and a minus sight while standing in one position, then moves ahead to repeat the process.

In hilly country it may be most convenient to locate contours without using the leveling rod. A *contour* is a line that passes through points having the same elevation. The observer first measures his H.I.—the height of his eye above the ground. The H.I. above a datum plane is obtained by taking a plus sight on a point of known elevation, as in differential leveling. The point at which a level line of sight strikes the ground will have the same elevation as the observer's H.I. After identifying this point on the ground, the instrumentman moves there and uses the elevation to compute a new H.I.

In leveling downhill, the observer finds by trial the point where he must stand to make a backsight strike the ground at the previously occupied position. The elevation of the trial point is then found by subtracting the observer's H.I., and the process is repeated. In locating 5-ft contours, adoption of an exact 5-ft H.I. by using a rod or forked stick is desirable to speed the work and simplify the arithmetic.

Cross-section leveling for a route survey is discussed in Chapter 24.

5–31. Size of field party. Ordinary differential leveling can be done efficiently by a two-man party. The instrumentman keeps notes if a self-reading rod is used; the rodman records if a target rod is employed. On precise leveling, an observer, an umbrellaman, a note-keeper, and two rodmen are required.

A self-reading rod is practically always used on borrow-pit and profile leveling, hence a party of two men is sufficient. Using a third man to keep notes relieves the observer of this task, however, and permits the party to move faster.

5–32. Signals. The distance between personnel, and noise from traffic or other sources, make it necessary to communicate by hand signals on many surveys. Some typical signals used in leveling will be listed in the following paragraphs of this section. Special signals to fit unusual requirements may be invented for a particular job. They should simulate as closely as possible the action to be taken. The instrumentman must remember that he has the advantage of telescopic magnification and give clear signals which cannot be mis-understood by a rodman using only natural vision. Equipping the rodman with a small telescope is helpful.

Plumb rod. If the rod is to the right of a plumb position, the instrumentman extends his right arm full length upward and inclined to the vertical. This position is maintained until the rod is plumb.

Give or take a T.P. Either the instrumentman or the rodman may give this signal by holding one arm straight up and moving it in a horizontal circle.

High rod. Instrumentman extends both arms horizontally and sideways, palms up, and brings them together over his head.

Raise for red. Instrumentman holds one arm straight forward, palm up, and raises the arm slowly to a position about 45° above the horizontal.

Raise target. Instrumentman raises an extended arm above his shoulder, holding it high if considerable movement is required. The arm is moved toward the horizontal position as the target approaches the desired setting.

Lower target. Same as "raise target," but the extended arm is held below the shoulder and moved up.

Clamp target. Instrumentman waves one hand in a vertical circle with his arm in a horizontal position.

T.P. or B.M. Rodman holds the rod horizontally above his head, then places it on the T.P. or B.M. Used in profile leveling to differentiate between intermediate sights and T.P.'s or B.M.'s for the benefit of the instrumentman and notekeeper.

All right. Arms are extended sideways, palms forward, and waved up and down several times. Used by any member of the party in all types of surveying.

Signals for numbers. One of the systems used is shown in Fig. 5–28.

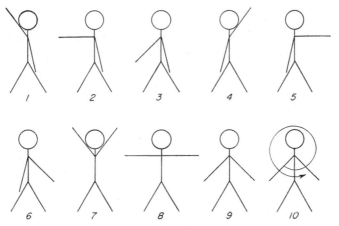

FIG. 5–28. Signals for numbers.

5–33. Precision. Precision in leveling, as in taping, is determined by repeating the measurement or tying in to control points. The elevation of a bench mark may be obtained by leveling over two different routes, or by a closed circuit of levels returning to the point of beginning. If an accurately established bench mark is available at or near the end of the line run, a check can be made upon it.

Closures are compared with permissible values on the basis of either the number of setups or the distance covered in miles. The type of formula generally used to compute the allowable closure is

$$C = k\sqrt{M} \tag{5–10}$$

where C is the allowable closure;
  k is a constant;
  M is the distance in miles.

The United States Coast and Geodetic Survey specifies constants of 0.017, 0.035, and 0.050 for its three classes of leveling now designated as first, second, and third order, respectively. For ordinary leveling a coefficient of 0.10 might be used.

If sights of 300 ft are taken, thereby spacing instrument setups at 600 ft, approximately nine setups per mile will be used. For ordinary work the allowable error of closure might then well be

$$E = 0.02\sqrt{N} \tag{5-11}$$

where E is the error, in feet, and N is the number of times the instrument is set up. Other values of k may be specified to correspond to the precision required and the average length of sight. On first-order leveling the length of sight is varied during the day to conform to atmospheric conditions.

5–34. Sources of error in leveling. All leveling measurements are subject to three sources of error: (1) instrumental, (2) natural, and (3) personal.

INSTRUMENTAL ERRORS

Instrument not in adjustment. The most important adjustment of the level makes the line of sight parallel to the axis of the level vial so that a horizontal plane, rather than a conical surface, is generated as the telescope is revolved. Serious errors in rod readings result if the instrument is not so adjusted, unless plus and minus sights are kept equal in horizontal length. The error is likely to be cumulative, particularly in going up or down a steep hill where all plus sights are longer or shorter than all minus sights unless care is taken to run a zigzag line.

Rod not correct length. Incorrect lengths of the divisions on a rod cause errors similar to those resulting from incorrect markings on a tape. Uniform wearing of the shoe at the bottom of the rod makes H.I. values incorrect, but the effect is cancelled when included in both plus and minus sights. Rod graduations should be checked by comparing them with those on a standardized tape.

NATURAL ERRORS

Curvature of the earth. As noted in section 5–3, a level surface deflects from a horizontal plane at the rate of $0.667M^2$, or about 8 in. per mile. The effect of curvature of the earth is to increase the rod reading. Equalizing the lengths of plus and minus sights cancels the errors due to this cause.

Refraction. Light rays coming from an object to the telescope are bent, making the line of sight a curve concave to the surface of the earth and thereby decreasing the rod reading. Balancing the lengths of plus and minus sights usually eliminates the errors due to refraction, which are negligible in ordinary leveling. Large and sudden changes in atmospheric refraction may be important in precise work. Errors due to refraction tend to be compensating over a long period of time but may be cumulative on a full day's run.

Temperature variations. Heat causes leveling rods to expand, but the effect is not important in ordinary leveling.

If a level vial is heated, the liquid expands and the bubble shortens. This does not produce an error (although it may be inconvenient), unless one end of the tube is warmed more than the other and the bubble therefore moves toward the heated end. Other parts of the instrument warp because of uneven heating, and this distortion affects the adjustments. Shading the level by means of a cover when carrying it, and by an umbrella when it is set up, will reduce or eliminate heat effects. These precautions are followed in precise leveling.

Air boiling or heat waves, near the ground surface or adjacent to heated objects, make the rod appear to wave, and prevent accurate sighting. Raising the line of sight by high-tripod setups, and avoiding sights which pass close to heat sources, such as buildings and stacks, reduces the effect.

Wind. Strong wind causes the instrument to vibrate and makes the rod unsteady. Precise leveling is not attempted on windy days.

Settlement of the instrument. Settlement of the instrument after the plus sight has been taken makes the minus sight too small and therefore makes the recorded elevation of the next T.P. too great. The error is cumulative in a series of setups on soft ground. Unusual care is required in setting up the level on spongy ground, and readings must be taken in quick order, perhaps using two rods, and without walking around the instrument. Alternating the order of taking plus and minus sights helps somewhat.

Settlement of the rod. This condition causes an error similar to that resulting from settlement of the instrument. It can be avoided by selecting firm, solid turning points or, if none are available, by using a steel *turning pin*.

PERSONAL ERRORS

Bubble not centered. Errors due to the bubble not being centered at the time of sighting are the most important of any, particularly on long sights. Experienced levelmen develop the habit of checking the bubble before and after each sight.

Parallax. Parallax caused by improper focusing of the objective and/or eyepiece lens results in incorrect rod readings. Careful focusing eliminates this condition.

Faulty rod readings. These occur because of parallax, weather conditions, long sights, poor target setting and rodding, careless interpolation, transposition of figures, and other causes. Short sights selected to fit weather and instrument conditions reduce the number of reading errors. If a target is used, the rodman should read the rod for the plus sight and have the instrumentman check it independently as the rodman passes on the way to the next T.P. The observer stops to read the minus-sight setting as he moves ahead for the next setup.

Rod handling. Serious errors caused by improper plumbing of the rod are eliminated by using a rod level that is in adjustment.

Target setting. The target may not be clamped at the exact place signaled by the instrumentman because of slippage. A check sight should always be taken after the target is clamped.

Use of long rod. If the vernier reading on the back of a damaged rod is not exactly 6.500 or 7.000 for the short rod, the target must be set to read the same value before extending the rod.

Recording notes. Errors in recording are a common cause of mistakes. Typical examples are transposition of figures, recording of values in the wrong column, and arithmetic mistakes. These errors can be minimized by having the notekeeper mentally estimate the reading, by repeating the value called out by the observer, and by making the standard field-book checks on rod sums and elevations.

5-35. Mistakes. Some of the personal errors listed in section 5-34, such as faulty rod readings due to transposition of figures, incorrect recording of notes, and improper use of the long rod, are classified as mistakes. Several other mistakes will now be described.

Holding the rod in different places for the plus and minus sights on a T.P. The rodman can avoid such mistakes by using a well-defined point or by outlining the base of the rod with keel.

Reading a foot too high. This error occurs because the incorrect foot-mark is in sight near the cross hair. For example, the observer may read 5.98 instead of 4.98. Noting the foot-marks above and below the vernier zero or cross hair will usually prevent this mistake.

Waving the ordinary flat-bottom rod while holding it on a flat surface. This action produces an error because the rotation is about the rod edges instead of the center or the front face. Plumbing by means of a rod level or other means is preferable to waving.

5-36. Elimination of errors and mistakes. Errors in leveling are eliminated by careful adjustment and manipulation of both instrument and rod, and by making the plus and minus sights equal in length. Standard field procedures or routines can be established which eliminate or quickly disclose most errors.

PROBLEMS

5-1. Determine the combined effect of curvature and refraction on sights of 100, 200, 300, 500, and 1000 ft.

5-2. The sight distances on a line of differential levels are as follows: B.S., 450 ft; F.S., 200 ft; B.S., 600 ft; F.S., 300 ft; B.S., 140 ft; F.S., 300 ft; B.S., 150 ft; F.S., 300 ft. What error in elevation results from the combined effect of curvature and refraction?

5-3. What is the difference in elevation of points A and B in Fig. 5-4 if the slope distance is 174 ft and the vertical angle is $+7° 12'$?

5-4. A person on top of a tower observes the angles of depression of two objects A and B (located in the vertical plane in which the tower stands) to be 30° and 60°. The distance between the two objects, which are in the same horizontal plane, is 800.0 ft. The angle subtended at his eye by the line joining the two objects is 30°. What is the height of the top of the tower above the two objects?

5-5. What is the relationship that should exist between the sensitivity of the level vial and the magnification of the telescope on an engineer's level?

5-6. The bubble in a level vial on an engineer's level is drawn off one-half division by heating of the forward (objective-lens) end of the tube. A plus sight of 7.28 ft is obtained on a shot of 200 ft. If the sensitivity of the vial is 20 sec for a 0.01-ft division, what is the correct rod reading?

5-7. With the bubble on an engineer's dumpy level centered, a reading of 4.382 ft is obtained on a rod held 300 ft away. The bubble is then moved six divisions and a new reading of 4.055 ft obtained. Determine the average angular value (sensitivity) of a 2-mm division on the level vial. What is the radius of curvature of the vial?

5-8. A levelman fails to check the bubble and it is off one division on a sight of 250 ft. What error results for a 20-sec bubble?

5-9. Describe two ways of determining the magnifying power of a telescope.

5-10. What are the advantages and disadvantages of the wye level compared with the dumpy level?

5-11. A slope distance of 175 ft and a slope reading of 25 per cent are read with an Abney level. What is the horizontal distance? What is the difference in elevation?

5-12. A rod is divided into $\frac{1}{4}$-in. spaces. Sketch a vernier which will permit a builder to read the rod to $\frac{1}{16}$ in. Sketch one that will read to 0.05 in.

5-13. Prepare a set of differential-leveling notes from B.M. Stone to B.M. Tower and return, using three T.P.'s on each run. Show the note checks.

5-14. The following level notes for the determination of the elevation of B.M. Y do not check. The elevation of B.M. X and the rod readings are correct. Draw a line through each erroneous figure, place the correct value directly above it, and determine the elevation of B.M. Y.

Sta.	B.S.	H.I.	F.S.	Elev.	Sta.	B.S.	H.I.	F.S.	Elev.
B.M. X	6.72	127.36		120.64	T.P. 3	0.54	132.59	8.04	132.05
T.P. 1	12.43	138.55	1.24	126.12	T.P. 4	4.27	124.55	12.31	120.28
T.P. 2	2.65	140.09	1.11	137.44	B.M. Y			3.02	121.53

5-15. An overhead point on a building has an elevation of 135.632 ft. A backsight on B.M. Plug, whose elevation is 128.500 ft, is 2.365 ft. What should be the reading on a vertical rod held upside down from the overhead point?

5-16. Determine the amount a rod extended for a 10-ft reading must be out of plumb to introduce an error of 0.001 ft.

5-17. What error results on a sight of 200 ft with an engineer's level if the rod reading obtained is 12.00 but the top of the 13-ft rod is 4 in. out of plumb?

5-18. Outline and sketch a method by which an elevation in a tunnel can be determined from a B.M. on the surface of the ground.

5-19. Reciprocal leveling across a canyon gives the following readings from the first setup near A: on A, 2.437; on B, 8.254, 8.259, 8.261. For the setup near B: on B, 10.965; on A, 5.148, 5.152, 5.149. If the elevation of A is 1462.793, what is the elevation of B? Determine the error of closure.

5-20. Leveling between B.M.'s A and B, B and C, and C and A gives differences of elevation of $+27.832$, $+14.653$, and -42.464, and distances of 5000 ft, 8000 ft, and 7000 ft, respectively. The elevation of A is 862.541 ft. Determine the correct elevations of B.M.'s B and C. What order of leveling does this represent?

5-21. A rectangular lot running N–S and E–W is 50 ft by 75 ft. To determine earthwork quantities, it is divided into blocks 25 ft square and the following readings in feet are taken successively along N–S lines at the corners: 6.4, 5.8, 4.1; 6.0, 6.7, 5.2; 7.9, 6.8, 6.2; and 9.5, 8.2, 6.7. If the H.I. is 180.3 ft, what is the grade elevation which will make the volume of earth excavation equal to the volume of fill, and thereby avoid the hauling of any dirt to or away from the lot?

5-22. List some errors and mistakes, not given in the text, which might occur in leveling.

Chapter 6

ANGLES, BEARINGS, AND AZIMUTHS

6–1. General. The location of points and the orientation of lines frequently depend upon the measurement of angles and directions. In surveying, directions are given by bearings and azimuths.

6–2. Units of angle measurement. An angle is the difference in direction of two intersecting lines. A purely arbitrary unit is used to define the value of an angle. The standard units in the United States are the degree, minute, and second. Seconds are divided decimally. Radians may be used in computations.

6–3. Measurement of angles. Angles are measured directly in the field by using some device such as a compass, transit, theodolite, or sextant. The compass, transit, and theodolite will be discussed in succeeding chapters.

An angle may be measured indirectly by the tape method, which has already been discussed, and by computing it from the relation to known quantities in a triangle or other simple geometric figure.

6–4. Measurement of direction. The direction of a line is its angle from an established line of reference, called a *meridian*. The compass and transit are used in plane surveying to measure directions of lines.

The reference line generally adopted is either the *true* (geographic) *meridian* or the *magnetic meridian*. If neither of these can be determined readily, any actual or assumed line can be selected and its relation to the true meridian ascertained later. The disadvantage of an assumed meridian is the difficulty, or perhaps impossibility, of reestablishing it if the original points are lost.

The true meridian for any one place upon the surface of the earth is the great circle, projected on the earth's surface, which passes through the observer's position and the north and south *geographic poles*.

SEE '550-D
NOT EXACTLY TRUE
ABOUT print circle

The direction of a magnetic meridian is defined by a freely suspended, magnetized needle which is influenced by the magnetic poles only. A *magnetic pole* is the center of convergence of the magnetic meridians; also a place at which the magnetic dip is 90°.

6–5. Bearings.   Bearings represent one system of designating directions.   The bearing of a line is the acute horizontal angle between the meridian and the line.   The angle is measured from either the north or south, toward the east or west, as may be necessary to give a reading less than 90°.   The proper quadrant is shown by the letter N or S, preceding the angle, and the letter E or W, following it. An example is N 80° E.

True bearings are measured from the local geographic meridian; *magnetic bearings*, from the local magnetic meridian.   Magnetic bearings are obtained in the field by means of a magnetic needle in a compass box.   These bearings may be used along with measured angles to obtain *computed bearings*.

In Fig. 6–1 all bearings in quadrant *NOE* are measured clockwise from the meridian.   Thus the bearing of line *OA* is N 70° E.

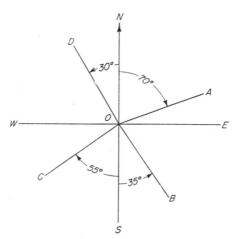

Fig. 6–1.   Bearings.

All bearings in quadrant *SOE* are measured counterclockwise from the meridian.   The bearing of *OB* is S 35° E.

Similarly, the bearing of *OC* is S 55° W and that of *OD* is N 30° W.

In Fig. 6–2 assume that a compass is set up successively at points *A*, *B*, *C*, and *D* and that the bearings are read on lines *AB*, *BA*, *BC*,

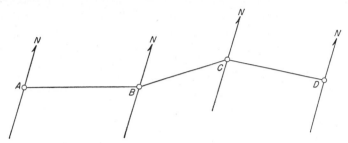

FIG. 6-2. Forward and back bearings.

CB, and *CD*. The bearings of *AB*, *BC*, and *CD* are called *forward bearings*, and the bearings of *BA* and *CB* are then *back bearings*. Forward bearings have the same numerical value as back bearings but opposite letters. If the bearing of *AB* is N 72° E, the bearing of *BA* is S 72° W.

6-6. Azimuths. Azimuths are angles measured clockwise from any meridian. In plane surveying, azimuths are generally measured from north, but astronomers and the United States Coast and Geodetic Survey use south as the reference point.

As shown in Fig. 6-3, azimuths range from 0° to 360° and do not require letters to identify the quadrant. Thus the azimuth of *OA* is 70°; of *OB*, 145°; of *OC*, 235°; and of *OD*, 330°. It is necessary to state in the field notes, at the beginning of the work, whether azimuths are measured from north or south.

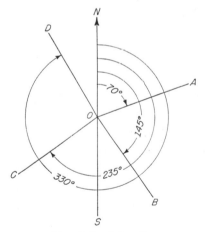

FIG. 6-3. Azimuths.

Azimuths may be *true*, *magnetic*, or *assumed*, depending upon the meridian used. They may also be *computed*, *forward*, or *back* azimuths. Forward azimuths are converted to back azimuths, and vice versa, by adding or subtracting 180°. For example, if the azimuth of *OA* is 73°, the azimuth of *AO* is 253°. If the azimuth of *OC* is 227°, the azimuth of *CO* is 227° − 180° = 47°.

Azimuths are read on the graduated circle of a transit after the instrument has been oriented properly. This can be done by sighting along a line with its known azimuth on the plates and then turning to the desired line.

6–7. Comparison of bearings and azimuths. Because bearings and azimuths are encountered in so many surveying operations, the comparative summary of their properties given in Table 6–1 may be helpful.

6–8. Calculation of bearings. The calculation of bearings from azimuths consists of finding the quadrant in which the azimuth falls and then converting as shown in Table 6–1.

TABLE 6–1

COMPARISON OF BEARINGS AND AZIMUTHS

Bearings	Azimuths
Vary from 0° to 90°	Vary from 0° to 360°
Require two letters and a numerical value	Require only a numerical value
May be true, magnetic, calculated, forward, or back	Same
Measured clockwise and counterclockwise	Measured clockwise only
Measured from north and south	Measured from north only, or from south only

Directions for lines in the four quadrants (azimuths from north):

$$N\ 54°\ E\ \ldots\ldots\ldots\ldots\ldots\ldots 54°$$
$$S\ 68°\ E\ \ldots\ldots\ldots\ldots\ldots\ldots 112°\quad (180° - 68°)$$
$$S\ 51°\ W\ \ldots\ldots\ldots\ldots\ldots\ldots 231°\quad (180° + 51°)$$
$$N\ 15°\ W\ \ldots\ldots\ldots\ldots\ldots\ldots 345°\quad (360° - 15°)$$

Many types of surveys require the calculation of bearings for a *traverse*. A traverse is a series of distances and angles, or distances and bearings, or distances and azimuths, connecting successive instrument points. The boundary lines of a piece of property form a closed traverse. The survey of a highway from one city to another usually is an open traverse, but should be tied to known points if possible.

Figure 6–4 shows a closed traverse for which the bearing of one line, AB, and the angles between the lines are known. Computation of the bearing of a single line is simplified by drawing a sketch similar to Fig. 6–5 and showing all the data. Assume that the bearing of a line AB is N 41° 35′ E, and the angle at B turned to the left (counterclockwise) is 129° 11′. Then the numerical value of the bearing of BC is $129° 11' - 41° 35' = 87° 36'$. By inspection of a sketch, the bearing of BC is S $87° 36'$ E.

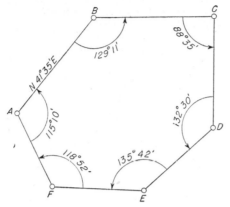

FIG. 6–4.   Closed traverse.

If the bearings of a traverse having more than a few sides are to be computed, a tabular form of the type shown in illustration 6–1 is preferable.   In this shorthand arrangement, northeast bearings, south-

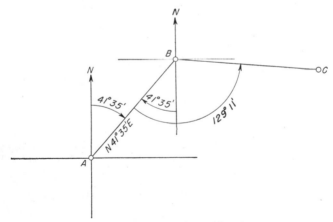

FIG. 6–5.   Computation of bearings.

west bearings, and other angles measured clockwise are called plus; southeast bearings, northwest bearings, and other angles measured counterclockwise are considered minus.   Bearing letters are repeated and shown reversed in parentheses, to call attention to the fact that

Illustration 6–1

COMPUTATION OF BEARINGS

Angles to the Left					Angles to the Right			
AB	N	41° 35' E	+	(SW)	AB	N	41° 35' E	+	(SW)
		129° 11'	–				129° 11'	+
BC	S	87° 36' E	–	(NW)		S	170° 46'	+
		88° 35'	–		BC	N	9° 14' W	–	(SE)
	N	176° 11'	–				88° 35'	+
CD	S	3° 49' W	+	(NE)	CD	S	79° 21' W	+	(NE)
		132° 30'	–				132° 30'	+
	N	128° 41'	–			N	211° 51'	+
DE	S	51° 19' W	+	(NE)	DE	S	31° 51' W	+	(NE)
		135° 42'	–				135° 42'	+
EF	N	84° 23' W	–	(SE)		N	167° 33'	+
		118° 52'	–		EF	S	12° 27' E	–	(NW)
	S	203° 15'	–				118° 52'	+
FA	N	23° 15' W	–	(SE)		N	106° 25'	+
		115° 10'	–		FA	S	73° 35' E	–	(NW)
	S	138° 25'	–				115° 10'	+
AB	N	41° 35' E			AB	N	41° 35' E	

the angles are turned from the back bearings. For example the bearing of AB is N 41° 35' E, but at B the angle 129° 11' is measured from the line BA, whose bearing is S 41° 35' W. Since BA is 41° 35' from south in a plus direction (Fig. 6–5) and angle ABC is turned 129° 11' in a minus direction from BA, then the *angular distance* representing the algebraic summation of these two angular values is −87° 36' measured from the south. Such an angular distance locates a line by giving the reference meridian, direction, and numerical value —in this case, from the south, in a minus direction (counterclockwise), 87° 36'.

Since the angular distance is less than 90°, the line BC must fall in the southeast quadrant, and the bearing is therefore S 87° 36' E.

When the algebraic summation gives an angular distance greater than 90°, the quadrant in which the line falls is determined and the bearing is found from its known relation to the north or south direction. Several examples of angular distances over 90° are shown in illustration 6–1.

The shorthand method is partially self-checking. If the back-bearing letters shown in parentheses are forgotten, the bearings of BC, DE, and FA would be wrong but those of CD, EF, and AB would be correct.

Traverse angles should be adjusted to the proper geometric total before bearings are computed. If the angles total exactly $(n - 2)180°$, where n is the number of sides in the traverse, the original and computed bearings of AB should be the same. If the traverse angles fail to close by say 2 min and are not adjusted prior to the computation of bearings, the original and computed bearings of AB should differ by the same 2 min.

Angles are normally measured to the right (clockwise) in surveying, but their direction should be recorded in the field notes to remove any doubt. The first column in illustration 6–1 shows a computation for angles to the left. The second column gives the bearings for angles measured to the right. A sketch of the two sets of bearings forms a pattern like that of the right and left hands.

6–9. Sources of error. Some of the sources of error in working with angles, bearings, and azimuths are:

a. Using an assumed reference line which is difficult to reproduce.

b. Forgetting to adjust the traverse angles before computing bearings.

c. Orienting an instrument by resighting on magnetic north.

6–10. Mistakes. A few of the mistakes made in work involving bearings and azimuths are:

a. Confusing magnetic and true bearings.

b. Mixing bearings and azimuths.

c. Failing to change the bearing letters when applying the angle at the forward end of a line.

d. Using the angle at the opposite end of a line in computing bearings.

PROBLEMS

6–1. Convert an angular reading of 82° 15′ to radians.

6–2. Convert a reading of 92.65 grads (appearing on a European instrument) to degrees, minutes, and seconds.

6-3. Convert a reading of 400 mils (from the north) to an angular bearing.

6-4. If the bearing of AB is N 72° 10′ E, and if at point A an angle of 62° 47′ is turned clockwise to C, what is the bearing of the line AC?

6-5. If the bearing of AB is N 72° 10′ E, and if at point B an angle of 62° 47′ is turned counterclockwise to D, what is the bearing of line BD? What is the azimuth of BD from the north?

6-6. Convert azimuths of 38°, 96°, 228°, and 310° from the south to bearings.

6-7. A rectangular city lot, 60 ft by 130 ft, fronts on a street whose bearing is N 1° 08′ E. Compute the bearings of the lot boundaries.

6-8. The west side AB of a five-sided field runs due north. The interior angles of the field are as follows: $A = 75°$, $B = 135°$, $C = 70°$, $D = 60°$, and $E = 200°$. Compute the bearing and azimuth of each side.

6-9. The bearing of side AB of a regular hexagon is N 10° 16′ W. What are the azimuths and bearings of the other sides if the interior angles are measured clockwise?

6-10. This is the same as problem 6-9 except that the interior angles are measured counterclockwise.

6-11. The north side, AB, of a six-sided field runs due east. The interior angles of the field are as follows: $A = 75°$, $B = 135°$, $C = 70°$, $D = 60°$, $E = 210°$, and $F = 170°$. Compute the bearing and azimuth of each side.

6-12. The bearings of a traverse that is run on the property lines of a farm are as follows: AB, N 23° 30′ E; BC, S 86° 00′ E; CD, S 42° 30′ E; and DA, S 84° 30′. W. Determine the interior angles at the corners of the property.

6-13. An azimuth-stadia traverse around the boundaries of a mining claim gave the following results: AB, 176° 43′, 374 ft; BA, 356° 43′, 375 ft; BC, 248° 59′, 341 ft; CB, 68° 59′, 340 ft; CD, 280° 10′, 423 ft; DC, 100° 10′, 422 ft; DE, 13° 24′, 398 ft; ED, 193° 24′, 398 ft; EA, 87° 02′, 628 ft; AE, 267° 02′, 626 ft; AB, 176° 44′, 374 ft. Compute the bearings of each line, and the interior angles at the corners of the mining claim.

6-14. The true azimuth of a long line AB is 32° 50′ 42″. The true azimuth of BA is 212° 52′ 36″. Explain the discrepancy.

Chapter 7

THE COMPASS

7-1. General. The compass has been used by navigators and others for many centuries to determine directions. Prior to the invention of the transit and the sextant, the compass furnished surveyors with the only practical means of measuring directions and angles.

The surveyor's compass, like the Gunter's chain, has now become little more than a museum piece. Nevertheless, an understanding of the compass and its vagaries is necessary to check work already done. Also, the compass is still used on rough engineering surveys and is a valuable tool for geologists, foresters, and others.

The engineer's transit is equipped with a compass. In fact, the design of American transits is based upon the requirements of a long compass needle over the center of the instrument, and an erecting telescope. The small size of European transits and theodolites is obtained by means of an inverting telescope and omission of the compass. The compass is available for mounting as an accessory.

7-2. Theory of the compass. A compass consists of a magnetized iron needle mounted on a pivot at the center of a graduated circle. The needle, if not affected by certain forces to be discussed, points toward *magnetic north.*

The *magnetic poles* are located approximately 500 miles from the true *geographic poles* but shift constantly and thus change the direction of the *magnetic meridian.* The magnetic lines of force of the earth, which align the needle, follow the north–south curvature of the earth and thus tend to pull or dip one end of the needle below a horizontal position. The angle of *dip* varies from 0° at the equator to 90° at the magnetic poles.

To balance the effect of dip in the northern hemisphere, the south end of the needle is weighted with a very small coil of wire. The position of the coil may be adjusted to conform to the latitude in which the compass is used. Weights on transit compasses are set

107

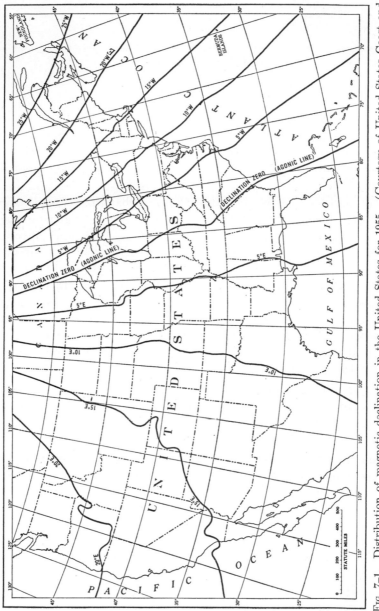

FIG. 7-1. Distribution of magnetic declination in the United States for 1955. (Courtesy of United States Coast and Geodetic Survey.)

for an average latitude of 40° N and usually do not have to be changed for any location in the United States.

As the compass box is turned, the needle continues to point toward magnetic north and gives a reading which is dependent upon the position of the graduated circle.

7–3. Magnetic declination. *Declination* is the horizontal angle between the axis of the magnetic needle and the true or geographic meridian. Navigators call this angle the *variation* of the compass.

An east declination is obtained if the magnetic needle points to the east of north, and a west declination if it points to the west of north. The declination at any particular location can be obtained by establishing a true meridian from astronomical observations and then reading the compass while sighting along the true meridian.

A line drawn through points having the same declination is called an *isogonic line*. The line made up of points having a zero declination is termed the *agonic line*. On the agonic line the magnetic needle defines true north as well as magnetic north.

Figure 7–1 is an isogonic chart covering the United States, for the year 1955. The agonic line cuts diagonally across the country through Michigan, Kentucky, and South Carolina. Points to the west of the agonic line have an east declination, and points to the east of the line have a west declination. As a memory aid, the needle might be thought of as pointing toward the agonic line.

The annual change in declination shown on larger and more detailed charts aids in computing the declination for some years before and after the chart date. The best way to determine the declination at a given location on any date is to make an observation. If this is not possible, the approximate declination can be obtained from the United States Coast and Geodetic Survey.

7–4. Variations in magnetic declination. Variations are periodic or irregular changes in the declination of the magnetic needle. These include secular, daily, annual, and irregular changes.

Secular variation. This is the most important of the changes because of its magnitude. Secular variations follow a roller-coaster (sine-curve) pattern. Records which have been kept at Paris for four centuries show a range from 11° E in 1680 to 22° W in 1820. Secular variation changed the magnetic declination at Baltimore, Maryland, from 5° 11′ W in 1640 to 5° 41′ W in 1700, 0° 35′ W in 1800, 5° 19′ W in 1900, and 7° 25′ W in 1950.

In retracing old property lines run by compass or based upon the magnetic meridian, it is necessary to allow for the difference in magnetic declination at the time of the original survey and at the present date. The difference, due mostly to secular variation, is generally ascribed merely to variation.

Daily variation. The daily variation of the declination of the magnetic needle causes it to swing through an arc averaging approximately 8 min for the United States. The needle reaches its extreme easterly position about 8 A.M., and its most westerly reading about 1:30 P.M. The mean declination occurs about 10:30 A.M. and 8 P.M. These hours and the amount of the daily swing vary with the latitude and the season of the year, but complete neglect of the daily variation is well within the range of error expected in compass readings. The term *diurnal variation* is often used in place of "daily variation."

Annual variation. This periodic swing amounts to less than 1 min of arc and can be neglected. It must not be confused with the annual change (the amount of the secular-variation change in one year), shown on some isogonic charts.

Irregular variations. Unpredictable magnetic disturbances and storms may cause irregular variations of a degree or more.

7-5. Local attraction. The magnetic field is affected by metallic objects and direct-current electricity, both of which cause a local attraction. If the source of the artificial disturbances is fixed, all bearings from a given station will be in error by the same amount. Angles calculated from the bearings taken at the station will be correct, however.

Local attraction is present if the forward and back bearings of a line differ by more than the normal observational errors. Consider the following compass bearings read on a series of lines. The forward and back bearings agree reasonably well at points *B* and *C*. At *D* they differ from those taken at *C* and *E* by roughly 1° 15'. Local attraction therefore exists at point *D* and draws the needle 1° 15' to the west of north.

AB	N 24° 15' W	CD	N 60° 00' E
BA	S 24° 10' E	DC	S 61° 15' W
BC	N 76° 40' W	DE	N 88° 35' E
CB	S 76° 40' E	ED	S 87° 25' W

It is evident that successive stations on a compass traverse should be occupied, and forward and back bearings read, even though the

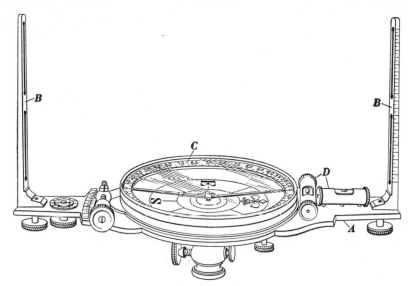

FIG. 7–2. Surveyor's compass.

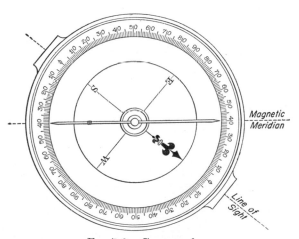

FIG. 7–3. Compass box.

directions of all lines could be determined by setting up the instrument
only on alternate stations.

7–6. The surveyor's compass. The surveyor's compass is shown
in Figs. 7–2, 7–3, and 7–4. George Washington, and thousands of
surveyors who followed him, used this type of instrument to run

land lines—land lines which still determine property holdings and therefore must be retraced. The circle is graduated in degrees or half-degrees, but can be read to perhaps 5 or 10 minutes by estimation.

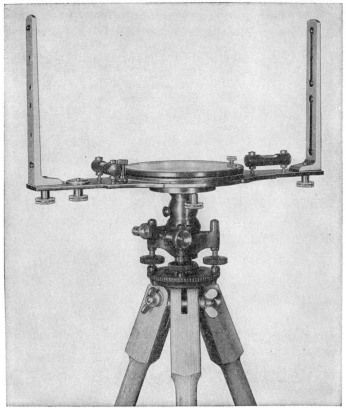

FIG. 7–4. Surveyor's compass. (Courtesy of W. & L. E. Gurley.)

The instrument consists of a metal base plate A, Fig. 7–2, with two vertical sight vanes B placed at the ends and a round compass box C at the center. Two small level vials D are mounted on the plate. The sight vanes are strips of metal with vertical slits to define the line of sight.

The compass box, Fig. 7–3, has a conical point at its center to support the needle, and a glass cover to protect it. A circular scale at the outer rim of the box is graduated in degrees or half-degrees. The zero marks are at the north and south points and in

line with the sight-vane slits. Graduations are lettered in multiples
of 10°, clockwise and counterclockwise from north and south, to 90°
at the east and west. As the sight vanes and compass box are
revolved, the needle shows the bearing of the line observed.

The letters E and W on the compass box are reversed from their
normal positions, to give direct readings. Thus in Fig. 7–3 the
bearing of the line through the vanes is N 40° E.

Accuracy of a compass depends upon the sensitivity of the needle.
A sensitive needle is one which is readily attracted toward a small
piece of iron held nearby, but which settles in the original position
each time the stimulus is removed. Sensitivity itself results from the
needle having (a) proper shape and balance, (b) strong magnetism,
(c) a sharp conical point, and (d) a smooth cup that bears on the pivot.
Tapping the glass cover releases a needle which does not swing freely.
Touching the cover with a moistened finger removes static electricity
which may affect the needle.

Remagnetizing the needle is relatively easy, but resharpening the
pivot is difficult. To retain the conical shape of the pivot and prevent
blunting to a spherical or flat form, which produces sluggishness, the
needle should be lifted from the pivot when not in use. A lever arm
is provided to raise the needle off the pivot and press it against the
glass cover when not needed.

Early compasses were supported by a single leg called a Jacob staff.
A ball-and-socket joint and a clamp were used to level the instrument
and set the plate in a horizontal position. Modern compasses are
mounted on a base with a four-screw leveling head, as shown in Fig.
7–4.

The compass box of a transit is similar in construction to the
surveyor's compass. The zero marks at the north and south points
are on a line parallel with and beneath the telescope. A special
adjustment on some instruments swings the graduated circle through
an arc to compensate for a given declination, thus permitting true
bearings to be read from the needle.

7–7. The forester's and geologist's compass. Figure 7–5 shows a
type of compass employed by geologists and the United States Forest
Service. It can be used as a hand-held instrument or can be supported on a staff or tripod.

The compass is made of aluminum and has brass sights. A declina-

FIG. 7–5.   Compass.   (Courtesy of Keuffel and Esser Company.)

FIG. 7–6.   Brunton pocket transit.   (Courtesy of Keuffel and Esser Company.)

tion adjustment is provided for the raised (upper) compass ring. The beveled (lower) ring is used to turn right angles, or to measure vertical angles by placing an edge of the base on a level surface.

7–8. Brunton compass. Figure 7–6 shows a Brunton pocket transit, which combines the main features of a sighting compass, a prismatic compass, a hand level, and a clinometer. It is an accurate and convenient device for topographic and preliminary surveys of all kinds. It can be used as a hand-held instrument, or mounted on a Jacob staff or tripod.

The Brunton compass consists of a brass case hinged on two sides. The cover at the left has a fine mirror and a center line on the inside face. The hinged sighting point at the extreme left, and the sighting vane at the extreme right, are folded outward when the instrument is in use. The bearing of a line is determined from the compass-needle reading while the point sighted is reflected through the sight vane on the mirror.

The declination adjustment is made by revolving the raised compass ring. The clinometer (vertical-angle) arc inside the compass ring is graduated to degrees and can be read to the nearest 5 min by a vernier on the clinometer arm. Another arc gives grade percentages for both elevation and depression. The compass is held vertically, instead of horizontally, to read vertical angles or grade percentages. The instrument measures $2\frac{3}{4}$ in. by $2\frac{3}{4}$ in. by 1 in. and weighs approximately 8 oz.

The Brunton compass is widely used by geologists on field surveys.

7–9. Typical problems. Typical problems in compass surveys require the conversion of true bearings to magnetic bearings, and vice versa. Declinations for different dates may be involved.

As an example, assume that the magnetic bearing of a property line was recorded as S 43° 30′ E in 1862. The magnetic declination at the place of the survey was 3° 15′ W. The true bearing is needed for inclusion in the subdivision plan of the property.

A sketch similar to Fig. 7–7 makes the relationships clear and should be used by beginners to avoid errors. True north is designated by a full-headed arrow, and magnetic north by a half-headed arrow. The true bearing is seen to be S 46° 45′ E.

Another common problem entails the conversion of a magnetic bearing for one date to that for a different date, the declination hav-

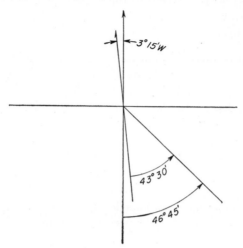

FIG. 7–7.   Bearings.

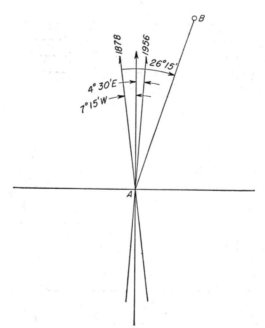

FIG. 7–8.   Magnetic declinations.

ing changed.   For example, the magnetic bearing of a line AB read
in 1878 was N 26° 15′ E.   At that time the declination was 7° 15′ W.
In 1956 the declination at the same place was 4° 30′ E.   The magnetic bearing at the later date is to be determined.

The declination angles are shown in Fig. 7–8.   The magnetic
bearing of the line AB in 1956 is equal to the bearing at the earlier
date minus the sum of the declination angles, or N 14° 30′ E.

7–10. Sources of error in compass work.   Some of the sources of
error in using the compass are:

a. Compass badly out of level.
b. Pivot, needle, or sight vanes bent.
c. Magnetism of needle weak.
d. Magnetic variations.
e. Local attraction.
f. Chaining pins, metal range poles, or a penknife placed near the
   compass.

7–11. Mistakes.   Some mistakes that are of fairly common
occurrence in compass work are:

a. Reading the wrong end of the needle.
b. Declination set off on wrong side of north.
c. Declination set off when reading magnetic bearings.
d. Parallax (sighting at an angle to the needle instead of along it).
e. Failing to check the forward and back bearings when possible.

PROBLEMS

7–1. Change the following true bearings to magnetic bearings if the declination
is 8° 30′ E: N 5° 12′ W,   N 3° 13′ E,   S 83° 09′ W.

7–2. The magnetic bearing of a line forming part of a property survey in 1870
was recorded as N 46° 28′ E.   At that time the magnetic declination was
2° 30′ E.   The magnetic declination in 1955 is 1° 15′ W.   Determine the
true bearing in 1955.

7–3. In 1875 the magnetic bearing of a line was recorded as S 83° 15′ W.   At
that time the magnetic needle pointed 1° 22′ east of the true meridian.   In
1953 the needle pointed 0° 52′ west of the true meridian.   What was
the magnetic bearing at the later date?

7–4. In the process of running a traverse, an instrumentman determines the true
bearing of a line CD and records it as S 81° 58′ W.   After moving to D he
reads the magnetic bearing of DC and finds it to be N 82° 58′ E.   If the
magnetic declination at D is 2° 45′ E, what is the local attraction existing
at D?

7-5. The observed forward bearing of line AB is S 2° 00′ W. The observed bearing of BA is N 1° 15′ W. What is the value of the local attraction at point B, assuming there is none at point A?

7-6. The observed forward bearing of line AB is S 89° 30′ W; the observed back bearing from B to A is S 89° 30′ E; and the observed forward bearing of BC is S 1° 00′ E. There is no local attraction at point A. What is the correct magnetic bearing of line BC?

7-7. What direction of a railroad track will produce the greatest magnetic effect on a compass survey running along it?

7-8. A property description is recorded as follows: Beginning at point A in the westerly line of Park Avenue distant 600.00 ft southerly from the intersection of the same and the southerly line of 57th Street; thence running at right angles with Park Avenue in a course N 42° 07′ W 100.00 ft to point B; thence running in a course N 87° 07′ W 56.56 ft to point C; thence running in a course S 42° 07′ E 140.00 ft to point D at the westerly line of Park Avenue; thence X ft to point A. If Park Avenue and 57th Street intersect at right angles, what is the direction of 57th Street?

7-9. The bearings of the sides of a closed compass traverse are listed. Correct the bearings for observational error and local attraction. Apply the observational error at angle C, which is adjacent to the two short sides of the traverse. Compute the interior angles.

Sta.	Forward Bearing	Back Bearing	Sta.	Forward Bearing	Back Bearing
A	N 29° 30′ W	N 53° 45′ E	D	S 39° 45′ E	S 60° 00′ W
B	N 12° 00′ E	S 28° 00′ E	E	S 6° 15′ W	N 39° 45′ W
C	N 59° 30′ E	S 10° 30′ W	F	S 53° 45′ W	N 6° 15′ E

7-10. In observing for declination of the compass at a given location, the following readings were taken from the compass circle of a transit when the line of sight was in the astronomical meridian (the line of sight being displaced from the meridian between readings):

N 24° 15′ E	N 24° 20′ E	N 24° 15′ E
N 24° 10′ E	N 24° 15′ E	N 24° 20′ E

(a) What is the most probable value of the declination? (b) What is its probable error?

Chapter 8

THE TRANSIT

8-1. General. The instrument used by surveyors and engineers for accurate measurement of angles is the engineer's transit. Practically all transits now are equipped with a vertical arc, thus permitting measurement of vertical as well as horizontal angles.

The standard transit is designed to give readings to the nearest minute of arc, but finer graduations are available at slightly greater cost and permit readings to 30, 20, 15, or 10 sec. Theodolites reading to the nearest second of arc are used on precise triangulation. Some European theodolites read directly to the nearest 0.1 sec and readings can be interpolated to the nearest 0.01 sec.

In making measurements, it is helpful to keep in mind the relationship between angles and distances. Commonly used field conversions are as follows:

$$1 \text{ min of arc} = 0.03 \text{ ft at } 100 \text{ ft} \quad \text{(approx)}$$
$$1 \text{ min of arc} = 1 \text{ in. at } 300 \text{ ft} \quad \text{(approx)}$$
$$1 \text{ sec of arc} = 1 \text{ ft at } 40 \text{ miles} \quad \text{(approx)}$$
$$\sin 1 \text{ min} = 0.00029$$
$$\sin 1° = \tan 1° = 0.01\tfrac{3}{4}$$

Figure 8-1 shows these relationships.

A theodolite reading to the nearest 0.1 sec is theoretically capable of measuring the angle between two points 1 in. apart and 40 miles away.

8-2. The American transit. Transits are manufactured for general and special uses but all have three main parts: (1) upper plate, (2) lower plate, and (3) leveling head. These are shown in their relative positions in Fig. 8-2, and assembled in Fig. 8-3.

The various parts of a transit and its operation can best be learned by actually examining and handling an instrument. Once a transit has been taken apart and assembled, even though it be an old or damaged instrument retired from service, the precise machining and

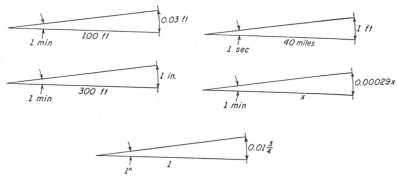

FIG. 8–1. Angle and distance relationships.

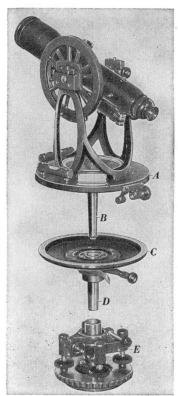

FIG. 8–2. Transit parts. *A*, upper plate; *B*, inner spindle; *C*, lower plate; *D*, outer spindle; *E*, leveling head. (Courtesy of W. & L. E. Gurley.)

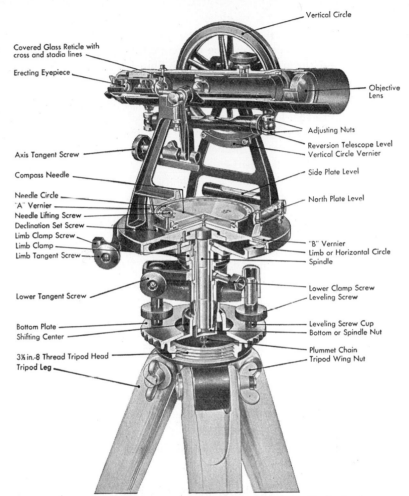

Vertical Circle

Covered Glass Reticle with cross and stadia lines

Erecting Eyepiece

Objective Lens

Adjusting Nuts

Reversion Telescope Level

Axis Tangent Screw

Vertical Circle Vernier

Compass Needle

Side Plate Level

Needle Circle

"A" Vernier

Needle Lifting Screw

North Plate Level

Declination Set Screw

Limb Clamp Screw

Limb Clamp

"B" Vernier

Limb Tangent Screw

Limb or Horizontal Circle

Spindle

Lower Tangent Screw

Lower Clamp Screw

Leveling Screw

Bottom Plate

Shifting Center

Leveling Screw Cup

Bottom or Spindle Nut

3¾ in.-8 Thread Tripod Head

Plummet Chain

Tripod Wing Nut

Tripod Leg

Fig. 8–3. Engineer's transit. (Courtesy W. & L. E. Gurley.)

construction are certain to increase respect for this fine piece of equipment.

8–3. Upper plate. The upper plate, Figs. 8–2 and 8–3, is a horizontal circular plate combined with a vertical *spindle* upon which it revolves about a true vertical axis. Attached to the plate are two level vials, one parallel with the telescope and the other at right angles to it, and two *verniers* set 180° apart. Provisions are made for adjusting the verniers and level vials.

Two vertical *standards*, of either the A or U type, are cast as an integral part of the upper plate, to support the horizontal *cross arms* of the telescope in bearings. The telescope revolves vertically about the center line through the arms. This line is called the *horizontal* (or *transverse*) *axis* of the telescope.

The telescope is similar to that of the engineer's level and contains an eyepiece, a cross-hair ring with one vertical and three horizontal wires, and an objective-lens system. The magnification range of transit telescopes is 18 to 28 diameters. A sensitive vial is attached to the telescope tube so the transit can be used in place of an engineer's level on work where the lower magnification and lesser sensitivity of the telescope vial are satisfactory.

A *clamp screw* for the horizontal axis is tightened to hold the telescope level, or at any desired inclination to the horizontal. After the clamp screw is set, a limited range of vertical movement can be obtained by manipulating the horizontal-axis *tangent screw*.

A *vertical circle* or *arc* is supported by a cross arm and turns with the telescope as it is revolved. The arc normally is divided into half-degree spaces. Readings to the nearest minute are obtained from a vernier having thirty divisions. The vernier is mounted on one of the standards, with provisions for adjustment. If the vernier is set properly, it should read zero when the telescope bubble is centered. If it is out of adjustment, a constant error called the *index error* is found by reading the arc when the bubble is centered. The index error must be applied to all vertical angles, with appropriate sign, in order to obtain correct angles.

The upper plate also contains the *compass box*, and holds the *upper tangent screw*.

8–4. Lower plate. The lower plate, *a* in Fig. 8–4, is a horizontal circular plate graduated on its upper face, *b*. Its underside forms a vertical, hollow, tapered spindle *q* into which the upper plate fits precisely. The upper plate completely covers the lower plate, except for two openings where the verniers exactly meet the graduated circle.

The upper clamp screw *r* fastens the upper and lower plates together. A small range of movement is possible after clamping, by using the upper tangent screw *s*.

8–5. Leveling head. The leveling head consists of two horizontal plates *x* and *y*, Fig. 8–4, with four leveling screws between them. The leveling screws d, set in cups to prevent scoring the brass plate y, are partly or completely enclosed for protection against dirt and injury. Plate y has a collar threaded to fit upon the tripod head.

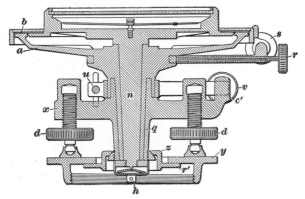

FIG. 8–4. Section through base of transit.

The socket of the leveling head includes a lower clamp u to fasten the lower plate. Lower tangent-screw v is used to make precise settings after clamp u is tightened. The base of the socket is fitted into a ball-and-socket joint z resting on the bottom plate of the leveling head, on which it slides horizontally. A hook h attached to the center of the spindle holds the plumb-bob string.

A recapitulation of the use of the various clamps and tangent screws may be helpful to the beginner. The clamp and tangent screw on one of the standards control the movement of the telescope in a vertical plane. The upper clamp fastens the upper and lower plates together. The upper tangent screw permits a small differential movement between them. The lower clamp fastens the lower plate to the socket. The lower tangent screw turns the plate through a small angle. If the upper and lower plates are clamped together, they will of course move freely as a unit until the lower clamp is tightened. Tangent screws are also called *slow-motion screws*.

Tripods for transits are used interchangeably for levels. Either fixed- or adjustable-leg tripods are suitable.

8–6. Scales. The horizontal limb of the lower plate may be divided in various ways but generally the horizontal circle is graduated into 30-min or 20-min spaces. For convenience in measuring angles

to the right and to the left, the graduations are numbered from 0°
to 360° clockwise, and from 0° to 360° counterclockwise. Figure 8–5
shows these arrangements. On newer transits, the numbers are
slanted to show the direction in which the circle should be read.

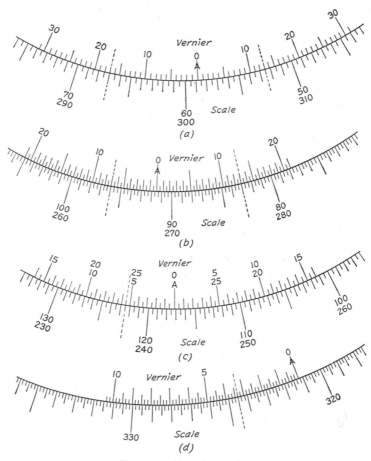

FIG. 8–5. Transit verniers.

The circles of more-precise instruments are graduated in divisions
of 10 or 15 min. The outer set of numbers on some old transits
runs from 0° to 180° and back to 0°. Obsolete instruments had the
circle divided into quadrants like a compass box. Graduations from
0° to 360° facilitate the reading of azimuths and direct angles, and

are therefore more advantageous than the quadrant system of numbering, which was used for bearings.

Transit circles are divided automatically by means of a precise dividing machine operating in an air-conditioned room.   After each line is cut by a sharp tool, a precision gear moves the tool ahead for the next cut.   Under a microscope the division slashes look somewhat rough, but to the naked eye they are smooth.   The marks are painted to make them stand out clearly.

Any small error in the 3- or 4-ft diameter dividing machine is proportionately reduced on the small transit circles.   Graduations on transit scales are correct to within a few seconds of arc.

8–7. Verniers.   The principle of the vernier was demonstrated in section 5–19, and the least count given by the following relation:

$$\text{Least count} = \frac{\text{value of the smallest division on the scale}}{\text{number of divisions on the vernier}}$$

The combinations of scale graduations and vernier divisions generally used on transits are shown in Table 8–1.

TABLE 8–1

TRANSIT SCALES AND VERNIERS

Scale Graduations	Vernier Divisions	Least Count	Fig. No.
30 min	30	1 min	8–5a
20 min	40	30 sec	8–5b, c
15 min	45	20 sec	. . .
10 min	60	10 sec	8–5d

The three types of verniers shown in Fig. 8–5 are used on transits.

Direct, or *single-vernier* (Fig. 8–5d).   This is read in only one direction and must therefore be set with the graduations ahead of the zero (index) mark in the direction to be turned.

Double vernier (Fig. 8–5a, b, and c).   This vernier can be read either clockwise or counterclockwise, only one half being used at a time. Once the index mark has been set coincident with 0° 00′ on the circle, the observer is not limited to turning angles in one direction only.

Folded vernier (Fig. 8–5c). This type avoids the long vernier plate required by the normal double vernier. Its length is that of a direct vernier with half of the graduations placed on each side of the index mark. Except possibly for vertical arcs, the use of folded verniers is not justified by space or cost savings.

8–8. Method of reading verniers. A vernier is read by finding the graduation on the vernier scale which coincides with any graduation on the circle. The vernier index shows the number of degrees passed over on the scale, and the coincident vernier graduation gives directly the fractional part of a degree. The second divisions on each side of the apparently coincident lines should be checked for symmetry of pattern.

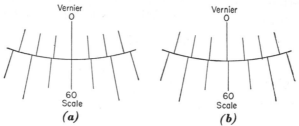

Fig. 8–6. Vernier reading.

In Fig. 8–6a, the zero mark on the vernier is set exactly opposite a graduation on the scale, since the distances between the second vernier and scale graduations on both sides of zero are equal. If two lines appear to be almost coincident and a symmetrical pattern is formed, as in Fig. 8–6b, a reading halfway between them can be interpolated.

Figure 8–5a shows two sets of numbers on the circle and a double vernier. The reading for the inner set is $58° 30' + 17' = 58° 47'$. For the outer circle it is $301° 00' + 13' = 301° 13'$. Note that the vernier is always read in the same direction from zero as the numbering of the circle, that is, on the side of the double vernier in the direction of the increasing angle.

The reading of the inner set of numbers from the double vernier in Fig. 8–5b is $91° 20' + 07' = 91° 27'$; that of the outer circle is $268° 20' + 13' = 268° 33'$.

The folded vernier of Fig. 8–5c reads $117° 05' 30''$ on the inner circle and $242° 54' 30''$ on the outer circle.

The direct vernier of Fig. 8–5d is the type used on a repeating transit or theodolite and reads 321° 13′ 20″ for a clockwise angle.

An understanding of verniers is best obtained by practice in reading various types; by calculating the least count of different combinations of scale and vernier divisions; and by actually constructing several verniers. Typical mistakes in reading verniers include:

a. Not using a magnifying glass.
b. Reading in the wrong direction from zero, or on the wrong side of a double vernier.
c. Failing to determine the least count correctly.
d. Omitting 30 min when the angle is beyond the half-degree mark.

8–9. Properties of an American-type engineer's transit. Transits are designed to have a proper balance between magnification of the telescope, least count of the vernier, and sensitivity of the plate and telescope bubbles. Thus the standard 1-min instrument has the following properties:

Magnification, 18 to 28 diameters.
Field of view, 1° to 2°.
Resolution, 4 to 5 sec.
Minimum focus, 5 to 7 ft (for newer models, 20 in.).
Sensitivity of plate levels per 2-mm division, 60 to 100 sec.
Sensitivity of telescope vial per 2-mm division, 30 to 50 sec.
Weight of instrument head without tripod, 11 to $16\frac{1}{2}$ lb.

Cross hairs usually include vertical and horizontal center hairs and two stadia hairs, as shown in Fig. 8–7b and c. Short stadia lines, used on glass reticules (Fig. 8–7c), avoid confusion between the center and stadia hairs.

A quarter hair, located halfway between the upper and middle hairs (Fig. 8–7d), is sometimes used to increase the range of stadia readings.

The X pattern (Fig. 8–7e) is incorporated in precise instruments to prevent a rod or object seen at a long distance from being completely hidden behind the vertical hair. It also permits the observer to balance distances between the rod and hairs on both sides of the upper and lower sections to insure centering, a task the human eye does in a highly efficient manner. The arrangement shown in Fig. 8–7f, or the variation in Fig. 8–7g, likewise avoids covering the object sighted and aids in centering.

The external-focusing telescope is in balance for an average sight

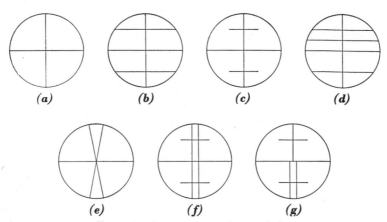

FIG. 8–7.   Arrangement of cross hairs.

FIG. 8–8.   Builder's transit-level.   (Courtesy of Keuffel and Esser Company.)

of approximately 300 ft.   This means the objective lens is far enough out to balance the telescope over the center of the instrument.

The design of the American transit assures that as the spindles wear, unless they are damaged by dirt or an accident, they will still seat and center properly.

The transit can be used to measure angles by repetition—that is, an angle may be repeated any number of times and the total angular distance added on the plates.   A better value is thereby obtained for averaging, and errors are disclosed by comparing the values of the single and multiple readings.

8–10. Other American instruments.   The *builder's transit-level* is a low-priced instrument for use on work requiring only short sights and moderate precision.   The model shown in Fig. 8–8 has a telescope with a magnification of 20 diameters and a resolution of 4.7 sec of arc, a telescope level vial with a sensitivity of 90 sec per 2-mm division, and a horizontal circle and vertical arc reading to 5 min. The cost is approximately one-third that of a standard engineer's transit.

Farm levels, actually transit-levels, have a telescope with a magnification of 12 to 14 diameters, a compass, a telescope level vial with a sensitivity of 4 to 5 min, and a horizontal circle and vertical arc reading to 5 min.

Collimators are sighting devices used (a) in making adjustments of surveying instruments; (b) in establishing lines for fabrication of large objects in a shop; and (c) as optical plummets to center an instrument on a tower over a mark on the ground, or to set a point directly beneath the center of the instrument.

Theodolites have been built by American manufacturers in limited quantity.   A theodolite is a precision surveying instrument for measuring angles.   There are two general classes of theodolites: repeating theodolites and direction theodolites (direction-instrument theodolites).

Repeating theodolites are precise transits which can be read to 10 sec or less.

A direction theodolite is a nonrepeating type of instrument which has no lower motion.   Directions rather than angles are read.   After a sight has been taken on a point, the direction of the line to the point is read on the circle.   An observation on the next mark gives a new direction. The angle between the lines can be found by subtracting the first direction from the second. In some work, such as triangulation, directions are employed in the computations and adjustments in place of angles. Two or more sets of angles may be taken with a direction instrument, for averaging.

A modern theodolite is compact, simple in design, and light in weight, yet rugged enough to withstand severe usage. The telescope, circles, clamps, micrometers, microscope, and leveling screws are fully enclosed and virtually dust- and moisture-proof. An optical-micrometer system is used instead of a vernier. The telescope is short, inverting, internal-focusing, and equipped with a glass reticule. The horizontal and vertical circles are relatively small and are made of glass.

European theodolites are described in more detail in section 8–27.

8–11. Setting up the transit. A transit is taken from its box by holding the leveling head, the underside of the lower plate, or the standards (*not* by lifting the telescope), and is screwed securely on the tripod. A plumb-bob string is hung on the hook at the bottom of the spindle. A slipknot is used to permit the raising or lowering of the bob without retying the string.

A transit carried indoors should be balanced in a horizontal position under one arm, with the instrument-head forward. The same method is suitable in areas covered with brush. In open terrain the instrument may be balanced on a shoulder. The transit telescope should be clamped lightly in a position perpendicular to the plates. The plate clamps should be set lightly to prevent swinging while still permitting ready movement if the instrument is bumped.

The wing nuts on the triopd must be tight, to prevent slippage and rotation of the head. They are correctly adjusted if each tripod leg falls slowly of its own weight when placed in a horizontal position. If the wing nuts are overly tight, or if pressure is applied to the legs crosswise instead of lengthwise to fix them in the ground, the tripod is in a strained position. The result may be an unnoticed movement of the instrument head after observations have begun. Tripod legs should be well-spread, to furnish stability and to place the telescope at a height convenient for the observer.

The plumb bob must be brought directly over a definite point, such as a tack in a wooden stake, and the plates leveled. The tripod legs can be moved in, out, or sideways, to approximately level the plates before the leveling screws are used. Shifting the legs effects the position of the plumb bob and makes setting up a transit more difficult than setting up the level.

Two methods are used to bring the plumb bob within about $\frac{1}{4}$ in. of the proper point. In the first method, the transit is set over the mark and one or more legs are moved to bring the plumb bob into position. One leg may be moved sideways, to level the plates without greatly disturbing the plummet. Beginners sometimes have difficulty with this system because at the start the center of the transit is too far off the point, or the plates are badly out of level. Several movements of the tripod legs may then fail to both level the plates and center the plumb bob.

In the second method, which is particularly suited to level or uniformly sloping ground, the transit is set up near the point and the plates are leveled by moving the tripod legs as necessary. Then, with one tripod leg held in the left hand, another held under the left armpit, and the third held in the right hand, the transit is lifted and placed over the mark. A slight shifting of one leg should bring the plumb bob within $\frac{1}{4}$ in. of the proper position and leave the plates practically level.

The plummet is centered exactly by loosening the four leveling screws and sliding them on the bottom plate by means of the ball-and-socket shifting-head device, which permits a limited movement. To assure mobility in any direction, the leveling screws should be approximately centered on the bottom plate before setting up the instrument.

The transit is accurately leveled by means of the four leveling screws in the same manner as described for the engineer's level. If the plumb bob is still over the mark after leveling, the instrument is ready for use. But if the plates were badly out of level, or the leveling screws were not uniformly set, the plummet moves off the mark. The leveling screws must be loosened and shifted again, and the transit releveled. It is evident that time can be saved by starting with the plates reasonably level, to eliminate excessive manipulation and possible binding.

8–12. Operation of the transit. Horizontal angles are measured with a transit by operating the upper clamp, lower clamp, and tangent screws.   The telescope clamp and tangent screw are utilized to bring the object sighted to the center of the field of view.

Beginners may find it helpful to remember the following rules covering the use of the upper and lower clamps:

  a. The lower clamp is used for backsighting only.
  b. The upper clamp is used for setting the plates to zero, for setting the plates to a given angle, and for foresighting.

Expressed in a different way, it can be said that the lower clamp and tangent screw are used to bring the line of sight along the reference line from which an angle is to be measured.   The upper clamp and tangent screw are used to set zero degrees on the plates before sighting along the reference line, and to obtain a differential movement between the plates when foresighting.   The step-by-step procedure,

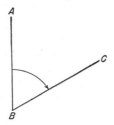

FIG. 8–9.   Measuring an angle.

for measuring a *direct* (interior) angle *ABC* in Fig. 8–9, will be outlined to illustrate the use of the upper and lower motions:

1) Set up the instrument over point *B* and level the plates.   Loosen both motions.   Estimate the size of the angle as a check on the value to be obtained.

2) Set the plates to read approximately zero by holding the upper plate while turning the lower by tangential pressure on its underside. Tighten the upper clamp (snug but not wrench-tight).   The upper and lower plates are now locked together.

3) Bring the vernier zero exactly opposite the plate zero by means of the upper tangent screw.   Use a positive (clockwise) motion.   If the zero is run beyond the point, back off and always finish with a positive motion.   This prevents *backlash* (release of the spring tension, which can change the plate position).

4) Sight point *A* through the telescope.   Set the vertical cross hair on, or almost on, the center line of the range pole or other object marking *A*, by turning the instrument with both hands on the plate edge or on the standards (*not* on the telescope).

5) Tighten the lower clamp.   The plates, which were clamped together before, are now also fastened to the spindle.

6) Set the cross hair exactly on the mark by means of the lower tangent screw, finishing with a positive motion.   Both motions are

now clamped, the plates read zero, and the telescope is pointing to A. The transit is therefore *oriented*, since the line of sight is in a known direction with the proper angle (zero degrees) on the plates. Read the compass bearing for line BA.

7) Loosen the upper clamp and turn the plate until the vertical hair is on, or almost on, point C. The lower plate containing the graduated circle is still clamped to the spindle, and the zero graduation continues to point toward A. Tighten the upper clamp.

8) Set the vertical hair exactly on the mark by means of the upper tangent screw.

9) Read the angle on the plates, using the vernier ahead of the zero mark—in the same clockwise direction as the angle was turned. Read the compass bearing for line BC. Check the angle by comparing the measured value with the angle computed from the bearings.

8–13. Measuring angles by repetition. If an angle is to be measured by repetition (turned two, three, four, or six times), the method just described is followed for the first reading. Then, with the reading for the first angle left on the plates, a backsight is taken on A, as before, by using the lower clamp and tangent screw to retain the angle setting. The transit is now oriented in the starting position, but the single angle is set on the plates, instead of zero degrees.

The upper clamp is loosened and point C sighted again. Next, the upper clamp is tightened and the cross hair brought exactly on the mark with the upper tangent screw. The sum of the first two turnings of the angle is now on the plates. This process can be continued for the number of repetitions desired. The transit should be releveled if necessary after turning the angle, but the leveling screws must not be used between the backsight and the foresight. If an even number of repetitions is taken, half of them should be obtained with the telescope normal, and half with the telescope plunged.

The total angle accumulated on the plates, divided by the number of repetitions, gives the average value. The total angle may be greater than 360°, making it requisite to add a multiple of 360° to the reading before dividing. It is always desirable, therefore, to determine the approximate (single) angle after the first foresight.

It might be assumed that turning an angle ten, fifty, or a hundred times would give an increasingly better answer, but this assumption would not be true. Experience shows that with a 1-min transit having the usual properties, an average observer can point the instrument (align the vertical wire) within about 5 sec of arc.

A 1-min vernier can be read to within 30 sec. An angle on the plates of (say) 42° 11′ 29″ would theoretically be called 42° 11′ by an experienced observer using a magnifying glass. If the angle on the plates is 42° 11′ 31″, presumably a reading to the nearest minute of 42° 12′ would be obtained. In either case, the recorded value would be within 30 sec of the correct angle.

If the transit is in adjustment, is level, and is being used by an experienced observer under suitable conditions, there are only two sources of error in measuring an angle—pointing the telescope and reading the plates. For a 5-sec average pointing error, and a maximum discrepancy of 30 sec in reading a 1-min vernier, the number of repetitions needed to strike a balance is six.

Direct angles, measured singly or by repetition, are commonly used in boundary surveys, hydrographic work, and building construction. *Angles to the right* are direct angles measured clockwise from a backsight on the previous traverse point.

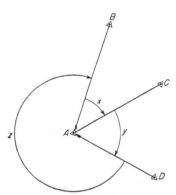

8-14. Closing the horizon. Closing the horizon is the process of measuring the angles around a point to obtain a check on their sum, which should equal 360°. For example, if in Fig. 8–10 only the angles x and y are needed, it is desirable to also turn angle z to close the horizon at A. The method provides an easy way for the beginner to test his readings and pointings. Figure 8–11 shows the

FIG. 8–10.   Closing the horizon.

left page of notes covering the measurement of the angles in Fig. 8–10. The plate readings are changed for each backsight to provide practice in reading the instrument, and for checking purposes.

The difference between 360° and the sum of angles x, y, and z is termed the *horizon closure*. Permissible values of this closure will determine whether the work must be repeated.

Figure 8–12 shows a sample set of notes illustrating the measurement of angles by repetition to close the horizon. In this particular

Point Sighted	Plate Reading	Angle	Mag Bearing		
	CLOSING THE HORIZON				
	🔭 at point A				
B	3°26'		N22°15'E		
C	45°38'	42°12'			
C	~~47°08'~~ ~~42°08'~~		N64°30'E		
D	107°04	59°56'			
D	110°35'		S55°30'E		
B	8°29'	257°54'			
		360°02'			
	Closure	0°02'			

FIG. 8–11. Closing the horizon.

arrangement, the A vernier is set to read zero at the beginning of the work and is not touched again during the entire operation. Both a *vernier closure* (difference between the initial and final vernier readings) and a horizon closure are obtained.

8–15. Laying off an angle. To lay off an angle BAC equal to 25° 30' with the transit at point A (Fig. 8–13) the plates are set to read zero degrees and point B is sighted by using the lower motion. The upper clamp is loosened, the telescope is turned until the vernier reads 25° 30', and the plates are again clamped. The line of sight establishes AC at the proper angle with AB.

To lay off an angle BAC equal to 25° 30' 40'' by repetition with a 1-min transit, an angle BAC' of 25° 30' is laid out as previously described and point C' marked.

Object	Vern. A.	Vern. B	Mean	Unadj Angle	Sta. Adj. Angle
	CLOSING THE HORIZON				
	𝜋 at ∆ A				
	All angles read clockwise				
	Reading ∆B to ∆C				
∆B	0°00'00"	180°00'00"	0°00'00"		
3 Rep N	126°36'20"	306°36'20"			
3 Rep P	253°13'00"	73°13'00"	253°13'00"	42°12'10"	42°12'09"
	Reading ∆C to ∆D				
3 Rep N	(Reading not required)				
3 Rep P	(612°) 252°53'40"	72°54'00"	252°53'50"	59°56'48	59°56'47"
	Reading ∆D to ∆B				
3 Rep N	(Reading not required)				
3 Rep P	(2160°) 0°00'20"	180°00'20"	0°00'20"	257°51'05"	257°51'04"
				360°00'03"	360°00'00"
	Vernier Closure		0°00'20"		
	Horizon Closure		0°00'03"		
	Sta. Adjustment		0°00'01"		

FIG. 8–12. Measuring angles by repetition to close the horizon.

The angle BAC' is then measured by repetition as many times as the desired precision requires. The difference between the angle BAC' and $25° 30' 40''$ can be laid off by measuring the distance AC' and locating C by the following relation: Distance $C'C = AC' \tan C'AC$. The angle BAC can then be turned by repetition as a check.

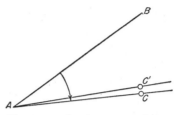

In Fig. 8–13, if the angle BAC' is found by repetition to be $25° 30' 20''$, then $C'AC = 20''$. If distance AC' is 300 ft, then $C'C = 300 \tan 20'' = 0.029$ ft.

Fig. 8–13. Laying out angle by repetition.

8–16. Deflection angles. A deflection angle is a horizontal angle measured from the prolongation of the preceding line, right or left, to the following line. In Fig. 8–14a, the deflection angle at F is $12° 15'$ to the right, written as $12° 15'$ R. At G the deflection angle is $16° 20'$ L.

(a)   (b)

Fig. 8–14. Deflection angles.

A straight line between terminal points is theoretically the most economical route to build and maintain for highways, railroads, pipelines, canals, and transmission lines. Practically, obstacles and conditions of terrain require bends in the route, but deviations from a straight line are kept as small as possible. The use of deflection angles is therefore appropriate for easier visualization, sketching, and computation. Note that in the shorthand method of computing bearings from direct angles in illustration 6–2, the letters for back bearings shown in parentheses are not needed for deflection angles, since these angles are turned from the extended line.

The deflection angle at F (Fig. 8–14a) is measured by setting the plates to zero and backsighting on point E with the telescope plunged (level vial above the telescope). The telescope is then plunged (transited) by turning it $180°$ about its horizontal axis, which puts the level vial beneath the telescope. The line of sight is now on EF extended, and directed toward X. The upper clamp is loosened, point G sighted, the upper clamp tightened, and the vertical wire brought exactly on the mark by means of the upper tangent screw. The A vernier will be under the eyepiece end of the telescope, so the observer can read the deflection angle without moving around the transit.

Deflection angles are subject to serious error if the transit is not in adjustment, as will be shown in Chapter 16. The deflection angle may be too large or too small, the nature of the error depending upon whether the line of sight after plunging is to the right or to the left of the true prolongation (Fig. 8–14b).

To eliminate the error caused by defects in adjustment of the transit, angles are usually doubled or quadrupled by the following procedure: The first backsight is taken with the telescope in the normal position. After plunging, the angle is measured and left on the plates. A second backsight is taken with the telescope plunged, the telescope is again transited back to the normal position for the foresight, and the angle is remeasured. Dividing the total angle by 2 gives an average angle from which the adjustment errors have been eliminated by cancellation. In outline fashion the method is as follows:

Backsight with telescope normal. Plunge and measure angle.
Backsight with telescope plunged. Plunge again and measure angle.
Read total angle and divide by 2 for an average.

8–17. Azimuths. Since azimuths are measured from a reference line, the direction of the initial line must be determined from a previous survey; from the magnetic needle; by a solar, or star observation; or must be assumed. Suppose that in Fig. 8–15 the azimuth of line AB connecting two triangulation stations is known to be 132° 17′ from true north. To find the azimuth of any other line from A, such as AC, first set 132° 17′ on the scale numbered in a clockwise direction and backsight on point B. The transit is now oriented, since the line of sight is in a known direction with the appropriate angle on the plates. Loosen the upper motion and turn the telescope either clockwise or counterclockwise to C, but read the clockwise circle. In this case the reading would be, say, 83° 38′.

Note that after the lower clamp and tangent screw are used to backsight on point B, they are not disturbed regardless of the number of angles read from point A. When the plates read zero, the telescope is pointing true north. Figure 8–16 shows the left page of a sample set of notes for a traverse run by azimuths.

In Fig. 8–15, if the transit is set up at point B instead of at A, the back azimuth of AB (312° 17′) is put on the plates and point A sighted. The upper plate is loosened and sights are taken on points whose azimuths from B are desired. Again, if the plates are turned to zero, the telescope points true north.

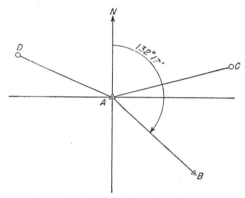

FIG. 8–15. Orientation by azimuths.

An alternative method of orienting the transit at point B is to leave the azimuth of AB (132° 17′) on the plates while backsighting on point A with the telescope plunged. The telescope is then transited to the normal position to bring the line of sight along line AB extended with its proper azimuth on the plates. This method eliminates resetting the plates, but introduces an error if the instrument does not plunge perfectly.

8–18. Sights and marks. Objects commonly used for sights on plane surveys include range poles, chaining pins, pencils, and plumb-bob string. For short sights, string is preferred to a range pole because the small diameter permits more-accurate centering. Small red-and-white targets of thin-gauge metal or cardboard placed on the string extend the length of observation possible.

An error is introduced if the range pole sighted is not plumb. The observer must sight as low as possible on the pole if the mark itself is not visible, and the rodman is obliged to take special precautions in plumbing the rod, perhaps employing a rod level.

		AZIMUTH-TAPE TRAVERSE			
Point Occupied	Point Sighted	Distance	Azimuth	Mag.Bear.	
A	Mag. N		0°00'	Due N	
	B	126.²⁴	23°32'	N23°30'E	
B	A		203°32'	S23°30'W	
	C	82.⁵⁰	93°51'	S86°15'E	
C	B		273°51'	N87°00'W	
	D	122.⁵⁸	137°39'	S42°30'E	
D	C		317°39'	N43°00'W	
	A	216.³⁵	264°46'	S84°45'W	
A	D		84°46'	N84°45'E	
	B		23°34'	N23°30'E	
		Closure	0°02'		

FIG. 8–16. Azimuth traverse (initial orientation on magnetic north).

In layout work on construction, and in topographic mapping, *permanent* backsights and foresights may be established.   These can be marks on structures such as walls, steeples, water tanks, and bridges or can be fixed, artificial targets.   They provide definite points on which the instrumentman can check his orientation without the help of a rodman.

8–19. Prolonging a straight line.   On route surveys, straight lines may be continued from one transit hub through several others.   To prolong a straight line from a backsight, the vertical wire is aligned on the back point by means of the lower motion.   The telescope is plunged, and a point, or points, set on line.

To eliminate the effects of defective adjustment of the transit, a process called *double centering* is used.   After the first point, as C' in Fig. 8–17, has been located with the telescope plunged, the lower motion is released and a second backsight taken on point A, this time with the telescope still plunged.   The telescope is transited again to its normal position and point C'' is marked.   The distance $C'C''$ is bisected to get point C, which is on the line AB prolonged.

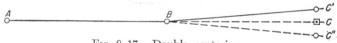

FIG. 8–17.   Double centering.

In outline form the procedure is as follows:

Backsight on point A with telescope normal.   Plunge, and set point C'.

Backsight on point A with telescope plunged.   Transit to normal position, and set point C''.

Split the distance $C'C''$ to locate point C.   Note that $C'C''$ represents twice the plunging error.

8–20. Prolonging a line past an obstacle.   Buildings, trees, telephone poles, and other objects may block survey lines.   Two of the various methods used for extending lines past an obstacle are: (a) the equilateral-triangle method and (b) the right-angle-offset method.

Equilateral-triangle method.   At point B, Fig. 8–18a, a 120° angle is turned off from a backsight on A, and a distance BC of 80.00 ft (or any distance necessary, but preferably less than one tape length) is measured to locate point C.   The transit is then moved to C; a backsight is taken on B; an angle of 60° 00' is put on the plates; and a distance $CD = BC = 80.00$ ft is laid off to mark point D. The transit is moved to D and backsighted on C, and an angle of 120° 00′ is set on the plates. The line of sight DE is now along AB prolonged, if no errors have been made.

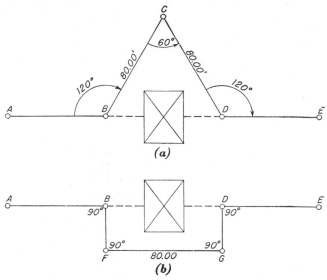

FIG. 8–18. Prolonging line past an obstacle.

Right-angle-offset method. The transit is set up at points B, F, G, and D (Fig. 8–18b) and 90° 00′ angles are turned off at each hub. Distances FG and BF (equal to GD) need only be large enough to clear the obstruction, but longer lengths permit more accurate sights.

The lengths shown in Fig. 8–18 permit students to check their taping and manipulation of the transit by combining the two methods.

8–21. Balancing in. Occasionally it is necessary to set up the transit on a line between two points already established, for example points A and B (Fig. 8–19). This process is called "balancing in," or "wiggling in."

The location of a point C on line is estimated and the transit is set up over it. A sight is taken on point A from the trial point C', and the telescope is plunged. If the line of sight does not pass through B, the transit is moved laterally a distance CC', which is estimated from the proportion $CC' = BB' \times AC/AB$, and the process is repeated. Several trials may be required to locate point C exactly, or close

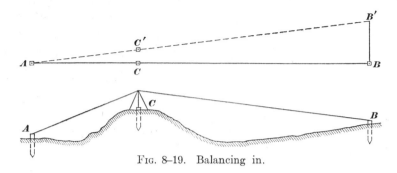

FIG. 8–19. Balancing in.

enough for the purpose at hand. The shifting head of the transit is used to make the final small adjustment.

8–22. Random line. On many surveys it is necessary to run a random line from a point X to a nonvisible point Y, which is a known or indeterminate distance away. This problem arises repeatedly in surveys of the public lands.

On the basis of compass bearings or information from maps and other sources, a random line, such as XY' (Fig. 8–20) is run as close as possible by estimation to the true line XY. The distance XY', and the distance YY' by which the random line misses point Y, are measured and the angle YXY' is found from its calculated sine or tangent. The correct line is then run by turning off the computed angle $Y'XY$.

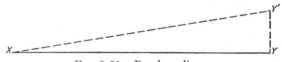

FIG. 8–20. Random line.

8–23. Measurement of a vertical angle. A vertical angle is the difference of direction between two intersecting lines measured in a vertical plane. As commonly used in surveying, it is the angle above or below a horizontal plane through the point of observation. Angles above the horizontal plane are called *plus angles*, or *angles of elevation*. Those below it are *minus angles*, or *angles of depression*. Vertical angles are measured in trigonometric leveling and in stadia work as an important part of the field procedure.

To measure a vertical angle, the transit is set up over a point and the plates are carefully leveled. The bubble in the telescope level vial should remain centered when the telescope is clamped in a horizontal position and rotated 360° about its vertical axis. If the vernier on the vertical arc does not read zero degrees when the bubble is centered, there is an index error which must be added to, or subtracted from, all readings. Confusion of signs is eliminated by placing in the field notes a statement such as "Index error is minus 2 min, to be subtracted from angles of depression and added to angles of elevation."

The horizontal cross hair is set approximately on the point to which a vertical angle is being measured, and the telescope is clamped. Exact elevation or depression is obtained by using the telescope tangent screw. The vernier of the vertical circle is read and any index error applied, to obtain the true angle above or below the horizon. The observer and the recorder must agree in advance which reading will be called out—the uncorrected reading of the angle or the adjusted value, the observed (uncorrected) quantity being preferable.

To eliminate the index error resulting from displacement of the vernier on the vertical arc, and from the lack of parallelism of the line of sight and the telescope level vial, an average of two readings may be taken. One is secured with the telescope normal, the second with the telescope inverted. This method requires the transit to be equipped with a complete vertical circle and reversible level vial.

8–24. European theodolites. European instruments differ from American transits in design, appearance, reading system, and other characteristics. Some of the important features are as follows:

a) The vertical and horizontal circles are read through an eyepiece beside the main telescope by means of an optical system.

b) Glass circles pass or reflect light through the optical system. Fine, smooth lines and close tolerances in the graduations are obtained by an etching process. Lines cut on metal circles by a graduating machine have jagged edges. This defect would be magnified in an optical reading system.

c) Minutes, seconds, and decimal subdivisions are read by means of an optical micrometer instead of a vernier. A choice of graduations is available, 360 deg (sexagesimal) or 400 grades (centesimal). Special tables permit ready conversion from one system to the other.

d) The optical system supplies the arithmetic mean of two diametrically opposite points on the circle in each reading. This is equivalent to the average of the readings of the A and B verniers on a transit.

e) Some theodolites have self-reducing stadia diaphragms which automatically correct the stadia reading for inclination of the line of sight.

f) Most but not all theodolites are without provision for reading angles by repetition.

g) The telescopes are short, internal-focusing, and inverting.

h) Rifle sights help the observer find his target without requiring him to search for it over the top of the short telescope.

i) A three-screw leveling head is standard.

j) The level bubbles, visible without moving away from the eyepiece, are of the coincidence type.

k) An optical plumbing device built into the vertical axis of the instrument eliminates the need for a plumb bob.

l) The compass is an accessory rather than an integral part of the theodolite.

m) Packaging in all-metal containers which are light and compact, and can be made air-tight and water-tight, provides maximum protection and convenience in handling.

n) Tripods are of the wide, double-leg type (a feature now being used on some American instruments also). Light, metallic tripods are now available.

Figure 8–21 shows a direction theodolite which reads directly to 1 sec of arc and can be interpolated to $\frac{1}{10}$ sec. It includes the foregoing features plus others which increase the speed of operation and make possible more-accurate readings. Some practice is required to quickly center an instrument over a point with the optical plummet, but use of this device eliminates the error inherent in a swinging plumb bob on a windy day.

Figure 8–22 shows the arrangement of the horizontal and vertical circles, and the scale of the optical micrometer which is used with both circles. A knob is turned to shift the prism bringing the image to the eyepiece so that only one circle is visible at a time. The circles are divided into 20-min spaces and the whole-degree marks are numbered.

A reading is obtained by turning the micrometer head to make the division lines (which move in opposite directions) coincident. Since an average reading of the two sides of the circle is secured, each graduation is counted as 10 min to save a later division by 2. Movement of the micrometer is limited to 10 min. The set of numbers seen upside down is on the opposite side of the circle.

Fig. 8–21. Theodolite which reads to one second. (Courtesy of Wild Heerbrugg Instruments, Inc.)

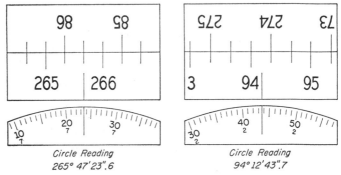

Circle Reading
265° 47' 23".6

Circle Reading
94° 12' 43".7

Fig. 8–22. Coincidence reading of horizontal circle.

In Fig. 8–22 a direction of 265° 40′ is read by counting the number of divisions between 265° and its diametrically opposite graduation, 85°. The micrometer scale gives the additional minutes and seconds, in this example 7′ 23.6″. The vertical circle, read in the same manner, furnishes the zenith distance (the complement of the vertical angle) to avoid the need for signs.

FIG. 8–23. Theodolite. (Courtesy of Kern Instruments, Inc.)

If the horizontal circle is set to zero initially, an angle can be read directly. Usually, however, any value that happens to be on the circle when the telescope is sighted along the reference line is accepted as the first direction. An angle is then determined by subtracting this value from the direction read with the telescope pointed at the next target. To check an angle, or to average readings, the telescope is plunged and the sights are repeated.

Initial positions may be taken at different locations on the circle to reduce errors caused by eccentricity of the circle and slightly imperfect graduations.

The double-circle theodolite shown in Fig. 8–23 incorporates the following important new features, among others:

a) The traditional foot-screws for leveling have been eliminated. Tripod stands are fitted with a ball-and-socket device to speed the rough leveling. A single turn of the three leveling knobs completes the fine leveling process. These knobs are in fact eccentric cams with a horizontal axis. Their design permits a more compact arrangement and prevents lateral play and slippage which may occur because of worn threads in the standard three-screw leveling system.

b) The coincidence method of reading is replaced by a different system in which a double-line graduation can be seen in the field of view of the microscope (Fig. 8–24). One of these lines actually comes from a diametrically opposite point on a second concentric scale. Readings are taken by means of a micrometer pointer which is centered between the lines. This setting gives an average value for the two sides of the circle. The instrument shown is read directly to 10 sec and readings can be interpolated to 1 sec of arc.

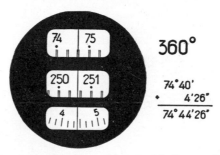

FIG. 8–24. Reading with a double line graduation. (Courtesy of Kern Instruments, Inc.)

c) A special ball-bearing axis is used to insure positioning of the upper part of the instrument within a few seconds. Obviously this is necessary in instruments reading to seconds.

d) A simplified method of clamping the theodolite on a tripod and in the carrying case is embodied.

The optical instruments described have many advantages. They also have disadvantages for some types of work, such as route surveys in which deflection angles are turned. On many surveys, readings to 1 min are sufficiently precise. A circle graduated in a counterclockwise direction is desirable in various kinds of surveying. American engineers consider the inverting telescope awkward in giving line and grade.

8–25. Sources of error in transit work. Errors in transit surveys result from instrumental, natural, and personal sources. Normally it is impossible to determine the exact value of an angle. Precise results can be obtained, however, by (a) following specified procedures in the field, (b) manipulating the instrument carefully, and (c) checking measurements. Probable values of accidental errors and the degree of precision secured can be calculated from the formulas given in Chapter 2.

SOURCES OF INSTRUMENTAL ERRORS

Improper adjustment of level vials, cross hairs, or standards. The adjustments described in Chapter 16 should be checked daily, or more often. Proper field procedures can be devised to counteract the effects of improper adjustments, but may be time-consuming.

Damaged instruments. Transits should be repaired by experienced craftsmen; otherwise the equipment should be retired from use.

Eccentricity of circles or verniers. If the A and B vernier readings differ by exactly 180° for all positions, the circles are concentric and the verniers correctly set. If the readings disagree by a constant amount other than 180°, the verniers are offset and it is best to use only the A vernier. If the difference is not constant, eccentricity of the plates exists. Readings should be taken at several positions on the circle and the results of the A and B verniers averaged.

SOURCES OF NATURAL ERRORS

Wind. Wind vibrates a transit and deflects the plumb bob. Shielding the instrument, or even suspending observations on precise work, may be necessary on windy days.

Temperature changes. Temperature differentials cause unequal expansion of various parts of the transit. A level bubble is drawn toward the heated end of the vial. This effect can be investigated by blowing on one end of the vial and noting the movement of the bubble, and then releveling and checking the position of the cross hairs on a target. Temperature effects are eliminated by shielding the transit from sources of heat or cold.

Refraction. Unequal refraction bends the line of sight and may cause an apparent shimmering of the object sighted. It is desirable to keep the line of sight well above the ground and to avoid sights close to buildings, stacks, and even large individual bushes in generally open spaces. In some cases, observations may have to be postponed until atmospheric conditions have improved.

Settling of the tripod. The weight of the transit may cause it to settle in soft ground. If unfavorable terrain must be crossed, stakes can be driven to support the tripod legs. Work at a given station should be completed as quickly as possible. Stepping near one of the legs, or touching it while looking through the telescope, will demonstrate the effect of settlement upon the position of the bubble and cross hairs.

PERSONAL ERRORS

Instrument not set up exactly over the point. The position of the plumb bob should be checked at intervals during the time a station is occupied, to be certain it is still centered.

Level bubbles not centered perfectly. The bubbles must be checked frequently, and must be releveled if necessary, before backsighting. Note that in leveling, or in measuring vertical angles, the level vial under the telescope is the critical one. For horizontal angles, the telescope can be elevated or depressed in the vertical plane without affecting measurements if the standards are properly adjusted. Hence the bubble at right angles to the telescope is the important one.

Vernier misread. The number of minutes on the scale passed over by the vernier index can be estimated to check a reading.

Improper use of clamps and tangent screws. An observer must form good operational habits and be able to identify the various clamps and tangent screws by their shape without looking at them. Final setting of tangent screws is always made with a positive motion to avoid backlash. Clamps should be tightened just once and not checked again and again to be certain they are secure.

Poor focusing. Correct focusing of the eyepiece on the cross hairs, and of the objective lens on the target, is necessary to prevent parallax. Objects sighted should be placed as near the center of the field of view as possible.

Overly careful sights. Checking and double-checking the position of the cross-hair setting on a target is wasteful of time and actually produces poorer results than one fast observation. The cross hair should be aligned quickly and the next operation begun promptly.

Unsteady tripod. The tripod legs must be tightened so that there is neither play nor strain, and the tripod shoes must be set solidly in the ground. The tripod legs can be tapped lightly to relieve any strain before the first sight is taken.

8–26. Mistakes. Some of the common mistakes to guard against are (a) sighting on, or setting up over, the wrong point; (b) calling out or recording an incorrect value; (c) reading the wrong circle; and (d) using haphazard field procedures.

PROBLEMS

8–1. What is the approximate error in the measured value of an angle if a backsight 900 ft long is taken on a range pole set 8 in. off line?

8–2. When a plumb bob of a transit is $\frac{1}{4}$ in. off center (measured perpendicular to the foresight line), what angular error does this displacement represent if the length of sight is 700 ft?

8–3. A transit equipped with a 1-min telescope bubble per 2 mm is sighted on a rod 500 ft away. If the bubble is off $\frac{1}{2}$ division at the time of sighting, what linear error results from using the transit as a level?

8–4. A transit circle is graduated in 20-min divisions. Sixty spaces on the vernier cover 59 spaces on the scale. What is the least count of the vernier?

8–5. A circle is divided into fifths of a degree. Sketch a vernier which will permit readings to 30 sec.

8–6. Sketch a scale divided into degrees, and a vernier which can be used to read it to the nearest 5 min.

8–7. Draw a portion of the scale of a vertical circle to show a 1-min folded vernier set to read 7° 42′.

8–8. Six repetitions of an angle are measured with a 20-sec transit. The initial reading on the first point is 8° 32′ 20″. The first turning of the angle is 60° 51′ 00″, and the final reading is 13° 38′ 40″. What is the value of the angle?

8–9. For precise layout of a building 300.00 ft square, a base of 300.00 ft is measured along one side and a perpendicular is erected at one end of this base with a 1-min engineer's transit. When this angle is measured by repetition, it is found to be 89° 59′ 45″. How much should the end of the line be offset to give an angle of exactly 90° 00′?

8–10. An angle BAC equal to 35° 05′ 36″ is to be laid off with a 1-min transit. A backsight is taken on B and a point C is set 350.00 ft away with the plates reading 35° 06′. The angle is measured by repetition six times and a value of 210° 34' is obtained.   What offset is required at C to provide the desired angle?

8-11. Deflection angles are read without double sighting at points B and C in the following survey: AB—N 43° 10' E, 725 ft; BC—S 78° 15' E, 960 ft; CD—S 67° 20' E, 850 ft.   A test for plunging error by double centering shows a divergence of 0.22 ft in a distance of 600 ft. What errors are produced in (a) the angles at points B and C, and (b) the location of point C?

8-12. A line XY is prolonged 843.26 ft to point Z by double centering.   The two points set to locate Z are 0.48 ft apart.   What is the angular error introduced in a single plunging?

8-13. The following interior angles to the right are on record for the boundaries of a triangular-shaped piece of property: $CAB = 62° 17'$, $ABC = 85° 31'$, $BCA = 32° 12'$.   Describe two methods of orienting the transit at A, and measuring the azimuths of the lines AB, BC, CA, and AB.

8-14. An instrumentman balancing in at a point C between points A and B, which are approximately 400 ft and 600 ft away respectively, sights point A, plunges, and misses B by an estimated 0.2 ft.   Outline the procedure he should follow to get on line.

8-15. It is necessary to retrace a line between two section corners, A and B, which are not intervisible.   A random line AX is run in the general direction of B, and perpendicular XB is erected.   Lines AX and XB are taped and found to be 2637.4 ft and 7.46 ft, respectively.   Compute the distance AB and the angle XAB which must be turned from the line AX to define AB.   Determine the offset required from AX to set a point C exactly 1320 ft from A on line AB.

8-16. When the line of sight makes an angle of 89° 55' with the horizontal axis of a transit because of inadequate adjustment of the instrument, what error (in decimals of a foot) exists in dropping a point 400 ft (slope distance) from the transit through a vertical angle from $+60°$ to 0° without reversing?

8-17. The vertical angle to a point X is $+6° 19'$ with the telescope normal, and $+6° 15'$ with the telescope inverted.   What is the index error and how is the correction applied?

8-18. With the telescope in the inverted position and the bubble centered, the vertical arc reads $+0° 02'$.   A vertical angle that is read with the telescope in the normal position is $-12° 38'$.   What is the true vertical angle?

8-19. A direction instrument at station A is pointed to stations B, C, and D, and the observed directions are 5° 10' 42", 46° 26' 09", and 78° 53' 24", respectively.   The telescope is plunged and a second set of readings taken on B, C, and D as follows: 185° 10' 45", 226° 26' 11", and 258° 53' 25". Determine the values of the angles BAC, CAD, and DAB.

8-20. How closely should horizontal angles be measured on a survey in order to obtain consistent precision of angles and linear distances if the ratios of linear precision are (a) 1/1000, (b) 1/5000, and (c) 1/10,000?

Chapter 9

TRAVERSING

9–1. Definition and uses. The relative locations of points in a horizontal plane are determined by measurements from control points and control lines, collectively called *horizontal control*. In plane surveying, horizontal control usually consists of a traverse. A *traverse* is a series of consecutive lines whose lengths and directions are known.

An *open traverse*, Fig. 9–1, consists of a series of lines which are continuous but do not return to the starting point. This type is used in most route surveys.

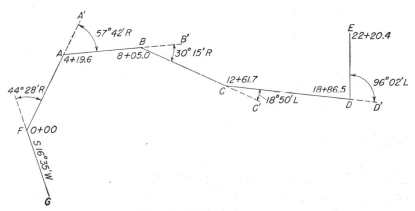

Fig. 9–1. Open traverse.

In a *closed traverse*, such as *ABCDEA*, Fig. 9–2, the lines return to the point of beginning. This type is run for property surveys, topographic maps, and construction projects.

A *hub* is set at each point, such as *A, B,* and *C,* Figs. 9–1 and 9–2, where a change of direction occurs. The hubs are termed *angle points* since an angle is measured at each one.

153

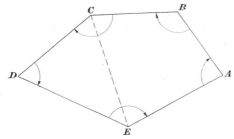

FIG. 9–2. Closed traverse.

9–2. Methods of running a traverse. Traverses are run by (a) compass bearings, (b) direct (interior) angles measured singly or by repetition, (c) deflection angles, and (d) azimuths.

Distances are obtained by pacing, taping, stadia, or computation.

9–3. Traversing by compass bearings. The surveyor's compass was designed for use as a traversing instrument. Bearings are read directly on the compass as sights are taken along the lines (*courses*) of the traverse.

Calculated bearings, rather than observed bearings, are normally used in compass traverses run with a transit. The instrument is oriented at each hub by backsighting on the previous point with the back bearing set on the plates. The angle to the foresight is then read and applied to the back bearing to get the succeeding bearing. Some older transit circles were subdivided into quadrants to permit direct reading of bearings. Calculated bearings are valuable in retracing old surveys but are more important in office computations and mapping.

9–4. Traversing by direct angles. Direct angles, such as *ABC*, *BCD*, *CDE*, *DEA*, and *EAB*, Fig. 9–2, are used almost exclusively on property-survey traverses. They may be read either clockwise or counterclockwise, the survey party progressing around the traverse either to the right or to the left. It is good practice to measure all angles clockwise. Consistently following one method prevents errors in reading, recording, and plotting. The exterior angles should be measured to close the horizon.

9–5. Traversing by deflection angles. Route surveys are commonly run by deflection angles measured to the right or left from the lines extended, as indicated in Fig. 9–1. A deflection angle is not complete without a designation R or L, and of course it cannot exceed 180°. Each angle should be doubled or quadrupled and an average value determined.

9-6. Traversing by azimuths. Topographic surveys are run by azimuths so that only one reference line, usually the true or magnetic north–south line, need be considered. In Fig. 9-3, azimuths are measured clockwise from the north end of the meridian through the angle points. The transit is oriented at each setup by sighting on the previous hub, one of the methods described in section 8–17 being used.

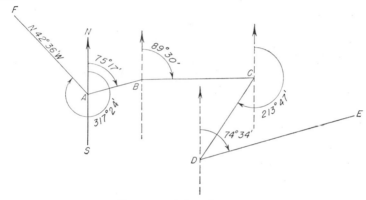

Fig. 9–3. Azimuth traverse.

9-7. Measurement of lengths. The length of each line is obtained by the simplest method capable of satisfying the required precision on a given project. For some geological and agricultural work, pacing is accurate enough. The precision specified for a traverse to locate boundaries is based upon the value of the land and the cost of the survey. On construction work, the allowable limits of closure depend upon the use and extent of the traverse, and the type of project. Bridge location, for example, demands a high degree of precision.

The 100-ft steel tape, read to hundredths on railroad and other surveys, and normally to tenths on highway work, is commonly used. It is good practice to measure lines in both directions as a check, and for open traverses, to close upon a point of known coordinates or location.

Distances measured in both directions by stadia are accurate enough for control on some types of work, such as low-precision topographic mapping.

In closed traverses each line is measured and recorded as a separate distance. On long open traverses for highways and railroads, distances are carried along continuously from the starting point. In Fig. 9–1, beginning with station 0 + 00 at point F, 100-ft stations are marked until hub A at station 4 + 19.6 is reached. Stations 5, 6, 7, 8, and 8 + 05.0 are set on the new course. The length of an open-traverse line is the difference between the stations of its ends.

9–8. Selection of traverse hubs. On property surveys, hubs are set at each corner if the actual boundary lines are not obstructed and can be occupied. If offset lines are necessary, a stake is set near each corner to simplify the measurements and computations. Long lines and rolling terrain may necessitate extra hubs to prolong the courses.

On route surveys, hubs are set at each angle point and at other locations at which they may be necessary to obtain topographic data or to extend the survey. Usually the center line is run before construction begins, and again after it is completed. An offset traverse may be necessary during the earth-moving and roadway-surfacing stages on a highway job.

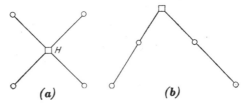

FIG. 9–4. Straddle hubs and ties.

A traverse run for control of topographic mapping serves as a skeleton upon which are hung such details as roads, buildings, streams, and hills. Locations of hubs must be selected to permit complete coverage of the area to be mapped. *Spurs* consisting of one or more lines may branch off as open (*stub*) traverses to reach vantage points.

Traverse hubs, like bench marks, may be lost if not properly described and preserved. Ties are used to aid in finding a survey point, or to relocate one if it is destroyed. Figure 9–4a shows an arrangement of *straddle hubs* well suited to tying-in a point on a highway or elsewhere. The traverse hub H is found by intersecting strings stretched between diagonally opposite ties. Hubs in the position illustrated by Fig. 9–4b are sometimes used but are not as convenient for stringing.

Figure 9–5 and Plate A–1 in Appendix A illustrate typical traverse ties. Short lengths (less than 50 ft) permit use of the metallic tape, but of course the distance to definite and unique points is a controlling factor. Two ties, preferably about at right angles to each other, are sufficient, but three allow for the possibility that one reference mark may be destroyed.

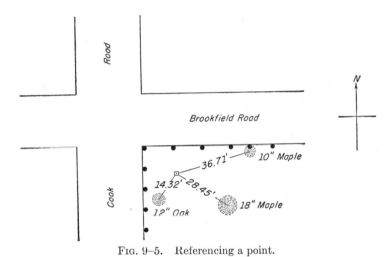

FIG. 9–5. Referencing a point.

Wooden stakes, steel pins, pipes, and metal plates set in concrete are commonly used for hubs. Spikes, bottle caps, tops of tin cans ("shiners"), and chiseled marks are used on paved surfaces.

9–9. Organization of field party. The type of survey and terrain determine the size of party needed. One man pacing distances can run a compass traverse alone. A transitman-notekeeper with one rodman can lay out a stadia traverse. Three men—an instrument-man and two tapemen who also do the rodding—are enough for a transit-tape survey. Additional personnel for notekeeping and rodding always speed the work, but the increased production must be balanced against the greater cost of operating the party. A head chainman with energy and drive is more valuable than a fast instrumentman in keeping an engineering survey party moving.

On some surveys it is desirable to have a party chief who is free
to move around and collect information on lines, hubs, reference
marks, property-owners' names, and other items. The transitman
or the head chainman may serve as party chief, but his range of
movement as chief is then limited.

In brush or wooded country, one or two axemen may be needed
to open lines.

9-10. Traverse notes. The importance of notekeeping was discussed in Chapter 3. Since a traverse is the end itself on a property
survey, and the basis for all other data in mapping, a single error or
omission in recording is one too many. All possible field and office
checks must therefore be made. Examples of field notes for interior-
angle and azimuth traverses are shown in Plate A-7 and Fig. 8-16,
respectively.

9-11. Angle closure. The closure in angle for an interior-angle
traverse is the difference between the sum of the measured angles
and the geometrically correct total for the polygon. The sum of the
interior angles of a closed polygon is equal to

$$(n - 2)180°$$

where n is the number of sides.

This formula is easily derived from known facts. The sum of
the angles in a triangle is 180°; in a rectangle it is 360°; and in a
pentagon it is 540°. Thus each side added to the three required for
a triangle increases the sum of the angles by 180°.

Figure 9-2 shows a five-sided figure in which the sum of the measured interior angles equals 540° 02', giving a closure of 2 min. The
permissible closure is based upon the occurrence of accidental errors
which may increase or decrease the measured angles. It can be computed by the formula

$$c = k\sqrt{n}$$

where $n =$ the number of angles;
     $k =$ a fraction of the least count of the transit vernier used.

For ordinary work, a reasonable value of k is $\frac{1}{2}$ to 1, and the permissible closure for a pentagon is 1 to 2 min.

The algebraic sum of the deflection angles in a closed traverse equals
360°, clockwise deflections being considered plus and counterclock-

wise deflections minus (lines not crossing). A check is available on the bearings computed from deflection angles for an open traverse. The bearing of the last line is equal to the bearing of the first line plus the algebraic sum of the deflection angles.

An azimuth traverse is checked by setting up on the starting point a second time after occupying the successive hubs around the traverse and orienting by back azimuths. The azimuth of the first side should be the same as the original value. Any difference is the closure. If the first point is not reoccupied, the interior angles can be computed from the azimuths and the summation check applied.

In running a traverse by any method, it is advisable to record the magnetic bearings of all lines. Although these cannot be read closer than perhaps 15 min, they will disclose a serious error in an angle.

A *cutoff line*, such as *CE*, Fig. 9–2, can often be run between two stations on a traverse, to produce a smaller closed figure to aid in checking and isolating errors.

Open traverses cannot be checked by a summation of angles. It is particularly important, therefore, to read the magnetic bearings of lines as a rough check. On long traverses, frequent observations on the sun or Polaris may be necessary to determine true bearings.

One way to check an open traverse is to run a separate series of lines with the same or a lesser degree of precision to close the traverse. Long sights and stadia distances may be used, for example, to get a rough check.

Another method is to obtain the coordinates of the starting and closing points by tying in to marks of known position, and comparing the computed difference in coordinates with the actual values. State-wide coordinate systems have been devised by the United States Coast and Geodetic Survey for every state, and permanent monuments have been set for the use of all surveyors. Computation of coordinates for traverse courses is discussed in Chapter 10.

A graphical analysis to determine the location of a mistake can save a lot of field time.[1] For example, if the sum of the interior angles of a five-sided traverse gives a bad closure, say $10° 03'$, it is likely that one mistake of $10°$ and several small errors of 1 min have been made. A method of locating the station at which the mistake occurred so that only one point need be reoccupied will be illustrated.

[1] See Dana E. Low, "Finding Angle-reading Errors in Long Traverses," *Civil Engineering*, Vol. 24 (1954), p. 738.

The procedure shown for a five-sided traverse can be used for traverses having any number of sides.

In Fig. 9–6 the traverse has been plotted roughly by using the measured lengths and angles but has a linear closing error AA'. The perpendicular bisector of line AA' points to the angle in error—in this case, C. A correction applied to this angle will swing the traverse through an arc to eliminate the linear error AA'.

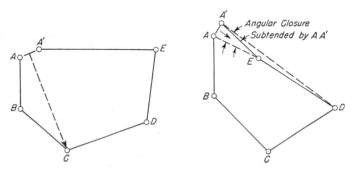

FIG. 9–6. Locating angular error.   FIG. 9–7. Locating angular error.

If, as in Fig. 9–7, a second angle point lies near the perpendicular bisector of AA', then the station at which the error has been made is the one for which the angular closure, when plotted at that station, is subtended by AA'.

9–12. Sources of error.   Some of the sources of error in running a traverse include:

  a. Errors in measurement of angles and distances.
  b. Poor selection of hubs, resulting in bad sighting conditions due to (1) alternate sun and shadow, (2) visibility of only the top of the rod, (3) line of sight passing too close to the ground, (4) lines that are too long or too short, and (5) sighting into the sun.
  c. Failing to double-center, or to double deflection angles.

9–13. Mistakes.   Some of the mistakes to be guarded against in traversing include:

  a. Occupying or sighting on the wrong hub.
  b. Incorrect orientation.
  c. Confusing the angles to the right and left.

PROBLEMS

9–1. The following bearings were obtained in a closed compass survey: AB, S 14° 30′ W; BC, N 27° 45′ W; CD, N 41° 30′ E; DA, S 72° 15′ E. Compute the interior angles of the polygon formed.

9–2. Prepare a typical set of field notes for a closed deflection-angle traverse having five courses. Show the angle check and closure.

9–3. The boundary lines of a farm have the following azimuths from north: AB. 32° 18′; BC, 102° 41′; CD, 210° 34′; DE, 161° 22′; EF, 240° 56′; FG, 5° 47′; GA, 345° 27′. Determine the traverse closure in angle and the calculated bearings of all the lines. Tabulate results.

9–4. List five pertinent points to consider in selecting hubs. In selecting ties,

9–5. What is the angular check on a closed interior-angle traverse of five sides? On a closed deflection-angle traverse of seven sides? On a closed azimuth traverse of nine sides?

9–6. The true azimuth of a line AB, as obtained from the coordinates of monuments at A and B, is 267° 54′ from north. The transit is oriented by occupying A and sighting to B with 267° 54′ set on the plates. Point C is then sighted and its azimuth is found to be 142° 18′. An open deflection-angle traverse $ACDEFGH$ is then run and the following angles are read: C, 6° 17′ L; D, 5° 22′ L; E, 3° 46′ R; F, 8° 39′ L; G, 12° 55′ L. The true bearing of line GH obtained from an observation on Polaris is S 67° 12′ E. Are the traverse angles acceptable?

9–7. In problem 9–6, if hub A is at station 0 + 00 and hub H is at station 42 + 60.5, what precision of linear measurements will be consistent with that of the angles?

9–8. List the duties of each member of a four-man party making a transit-tape boundary survey of a 10-acre farm in rolling terrain partly covered with brush. Some of the boundary lines are fenced and have large trees and brush on them.

9–9. The recorded lengths and interior angles to the right for a six-sided traverse are as follows: AB, azimuth 47° 28′, 438.5 ft; $B = 39° 01′$, $BC = 392.3$ ft; $C = 137° 00′$, $CD = 886.0$ ft; $D = 30° 11′$, $DE = 452.7$ ft; $E = 245° 35′$, $EF = 279.3$ ft; $F = 41° 02′$, $FA = 422.0$ ft; and $A = 232° 14′$. Assuming that the lengths are correct, determine which angle contains a mistake.

9–10. List additional typical sources of errors and mistakes which occur in running direct angle traverses, deflection angle traverses, and azimuth traverses.

Chapter 10

TRAVERSE COMPUTATIONS

10–1. Purpose. Angles and directions for a traverse are readily investigated before leaving the field. Linear measurements, even though repeated, are a more likely source of error and must be checked by office computations to determine whether the traverse closes. The area inside the traverse can be computed by an extension of these calculations. Boundary lines of a piece of property are adjusted to form a closed figure for use in deed descriptions.

The first step in traverse computations is to balance (adjust) the angles.

10–2. Balancing angles. Angles of a closed traverse can be adjusted to the correct geometric total by applying one of the three following types of correction:

1. Arbitrary corrections to one or more angles.
2. Larger corrections to angles where poor signals or observing conditions were present.
3. An average correction which is found by dividing the closure in angle by the number of angles.

These methods are demonstrated in illustration 10–1. For work of ordinary precision, it is reasonable to adopt corrections which are even multiples of the least count of the transit vernier.

If method 1 is used, corrections of 30 sec are subtracted arbitrarily from any three angles to give the proper geometric total for a five-sided traverse. Selection of the angles at A, C, and E rounds off all values to the nearest minute.

If only the top of the rod was visible at C from the setup at B, method 2 might be used and the entire correction of 1 min 30 sec subtracted from the angle at B. Or 1 min might be subtracted from the angle at B and 30 sec subtracted from another angle suspected of being slightly off.

Illustration 10–1

ADJUSTMENT OF ANGLES

Point	Measured Angle	Method 1 Adjustment	Adjusted Angle by Method 1	Multiples of Avg. Corr.	Corr. Rounded to 30″	Successive Difference	Adjusted Angle by Method 3
A	100° 44′ 30″	30″	100° 44′	18″	30″	30″	100° 44′
B	101° 35′	0	101° 35′	36″	30″	0	101° 35′
C	89° 05′ 30″	30″	89° 05′	54″	60″	30″	89° 05′
D	17° 12′	0	17° 12′	72″	60″	0	17° 12′
E	231° 24′ 30″	30″	231° 24′	90″	90″	30″	231° 24′
Total	540° 01′ 30″	90″	540° 00′			90″	540° 00′

Method 3 consists in subtracting $1′ 30″/5 = 18$ sec from each of the five angles. Since the angles were read in multiples of $\frac{1}{2}$ min, applying corrections of 18 sec gives a false impression of their precision. It is desirable, therefore, to establish a pattern of corrections, as shown on the right side of the table.

First a column consisting of multiples of the average correction of 18 sec is tabulated beside the angles. In the next column, each of these multiples is rounded off to the nearest 30 sec. Successive differences (adjustments) are then found by subtracting each value in the rounded-off column of corrections from the previous one. The adjusted angles obtained by using these adjustments must total to exactly the true geometric value. The adjustments fall into a pattern form and thus distort the shape of the traverse less than when all of the closure is put into one angle. This is particularly important in traverses of say twenty, fifty, or a hundred sides.

It should be noted that although the adjusted angles satisfy the geometric condition of a closed figure, they may be no nearer the true values than before adjustment. Unlike corrections for linear measurements, the adjustments applied to angles are independent of the size of an angle.

10–3. Computation of bearings. Computation of bearings was discussed in section 6–8. Angles adjusted to the proper geometric total must be used, otherwise the bearing of the first line will differ from its computed bearing as found by applying the successive angles around a closed traverse, by the amount of the angle closure.

10–4. Latitudes and departures. Closure of a traverse is checked by computing the latitude and departure of each line (course). The latitude of a course is equal to the length of the course multiplied by the cosine of its bearing. Expressed in a different way, it is the length of the projection of a traverse course on a meridian. Latitude is also called *latitude difference* or *northing* or *southing*.

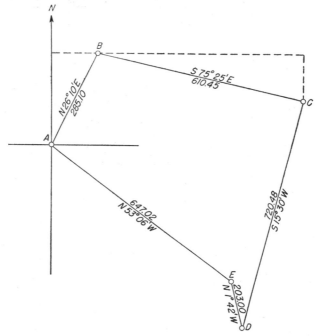

FIG. 10–1. Traverse.

The departure of a course is equal to the length of the course multiplied by the sine of its bearing. It is the length of the projection of a traverse course on a line perpendicular to the meridian. Sketching bearings in all four quadrants will show that the sine and cosine rules for latitudes and departures are independent of the bearing quadrant.

Departures and latitudes are merely the *X*- and *Y*-components used in algebra and mechanics.

North latitudes and east departures are considered plus; south latitudes and west departures are minus. The conditions of closure for a traverse are that (a) the algebraic sum of all latitudes must

Illustration 10–2

COMPUTATION OF LATITUDES AND DEPARTURES

Course	Bearing Distance	Departure	Log Sine	Log Cosine	Latitude
AB	N 26° 10′ E		9.644423	9.953042	
	285.10		2.454997	2.454997	
		+125.72	2.099420	2.408039	+255.88
BC	S 75° 25′ E		9.985778	9.401035	
	610.45		2.785650	2.785650	
		+590.78	2.771428	2.186685	−153.71
CD	S 15° 30′ W		9.426899	9.983910	
	720.48		2.857622	2.857622	
		−192.54	2.284521	2.841532	−694.28
DE	N 1° 42′ W		8.472263	9.999809	
	203.00		2.307496	2.307496	
		− 6.02	0.779759	2.307305	+202.91
EA	N 53° 06′W		9.902919	9.778455	
	647.02		2.810918	2.810918	
		−517.41	2.713837	2.589373	+388.49

equal zero and (b) the algebraic sum of all departures must equal zero.

The computation of latitudes and departures, error of closure, and ratio of error will be illustrated by an example.

The interior angles of illustration 10–1 have been used to compute the bearings shown in Fig. 10–1. Note that all bearings are lettered on the outside of the traverse, and all lengths on the interior. This arrangement can be reversed, but a consistent policy should be followed.

Latitudes and departures are computed by logarithms, the data and results being inserted in a standard prepared form, arranged as shown in illustration 10–2. In practice the forms are printed with column headings and rulings to save time and to simplify checking.

The computed latitudes and departures are then inserted in another prepared form similar to that shown in illustration 10–3. A combined table is preferred by some computers.

Summing the north and south latitudes and subtracting the smaller total from the larger gives the closure in latitude, 0.71 ft and the closure in departure is 0.53 ft. The *linear error of closure* is the hypotenuse of a small triangle with sides of 0.71 ft and 0.53 ft, and repre-

Illustration 10-3

BALANCING LATITUDES AND DEPARTURES

Pt.	Length	Bearing	Latitude North	Latitude South	Departure East	Departure West	Balanced Lat.	Balanced Dep.	Total Lat.	Total Dep.
A									0.00	0.00
	285.10	N 26° 10' E	*+0.08* 255.88		*−0.06* 125.72		N 255.96	E 125.66		
B									N 255.96	E 125.66
	610.45	S 75° 25' E		*−0.18* 153.71	*−0.13* 590.78		S 153.53	E 590.65		
C									N 102.43	E 716.31
	720.48	S 15° 30' W		*−0.21* 694.28		*+0.15* 192.54	S 694.07	W 192.69		
D									S 591.64	E 523.62
	203.00	N 1° 42' W	*−0.06* 202.91			*+0.05* 6.02	N 202.97	W 6.07		
E									S 388.67	E 517.55
	647.02	N 53° 06' W	*+0.18* 388.49			*+0.14* 517.41	N 388.67	W 517.55		
A									0.00	0.00
	2466.05		847.28	847.99 847.28	716.50 715.97	715.97	0.00	0.00		
				0.71	0.53					

Error of closure $= \sqrt{0.71^2 + 0.53^2} = 0.89$ ft

Ratio of error $= \dfrac{0.89}{2466} = \dfrac{1}{2800}$

sents the distance from the starting point A to the computed point A on the basis of the lengths and bearings used. In illustration 10–3 the error of closure is 0.89 ft. The term "error of closure" may be shortened to *closure*, but it should not be called the error since the actual error is never known.

The ratio of error for a traverse is expressed as a reciprocal. Its value is determined from the fraction having the error of closure as the numerator, and the perimeter of the traverse as the denominator. It is similar to the ratio of error in taping. In illustration 10–3 the ratio of error is $0.89/2466 = 1/2800$. The denominator of the reciprocal is not carried beyond multiples of 100, or possibly 10.

The ratio of error is used as the measure of precision. On some surveys it must meet rigid specifications if the work is to be accepted and paid for. The following values of the ratio of error are reasonable for property surveys in the kind of area noted:

Waste land......... 1/500	Small city......... 1/5000
Ordinary farm land.. 1/1000	Metropolitan area.. 1/10,000
Small community.... 1/2000	

A ratio of error of 1/2000 can be obtained with a 1-min transit and an ordinary 100-ft steel tape. If the tape is too long or too short, all lengths of lines would be incorrect but the ratio of error might still fall within acceptable limits. To attain a true ratio of error of 1/10,000, a standardized tape must be used and corrections made for temperature, slope, and tension.

The closure must be distributed throughout the traverse to close the figure on property and other surveys, even though the amount is negligible in map plotting. Two methods of distribution are used: (a) the transit rule and (b) the compass rule.

10–5. The transit rule. The transit rule is used on surveys where the angles are measured with greater accuracy than the distances. Stadia surveys fit in this category. Corrections are made by the following rules:

$$\frac{\text{Correction in latitude for } AB}{\text{Closure in latitude}} = \frac{\text{latitude of } AB}{\text{arithmetical sum of all latitudes}}$$

$$(10\text{--}1)$$

$$\frac{\text{Correction in departure for } AB}{\text{Closure in departure}} = \frac{\text{departure of } AB}{\text{arithmetical sum of all departures}}$$

$$(10\text{--}2)$$

10–6. The compass rule. The compass rule is applied on surveys where the angles and distances are measured with equal precision. It is appropriate for a transit-tape survey on which angles are measured to the nearest minute or half-minute and distances are taped to hundredths of a foot. Corrections are made by the following rules:

$$\frac{\text{Correction in latitude for } AB}{\text{Closure in latitude}} = \frac{\text{length of } AB}{\text{perimeter of traverse}} \qquad (10\text{--}3)$$

$$\frac{\text{Correction in departure for } AB}{\text{Closure in departure}} = \frac{\text{length of } AB}{\text{perimeter of traverse}} \qquad (10\text{--}4)$$

10–7. Application of the rules. Application of either pair of rules is predicated on the assumption that all lines, and all angles, were measured with equal care. If they were not, suitable weights must be given to individual measurements. Small errors of closure can be apportioned by inspection.

The compass rule will be used to distribute the closures in latitude and departure for the traverse of Fig. 10–1. The equations were given in a form easy to remember. In applying them, however, it is simpler to use the following arrangement:

$$\text{Correction in latitude for } AB = \frac{\text{closure in latitude}}{\text{perimeter}} \times \text{length of } AB$$

The other corrections are likewise found by multiplying a constant—ratio of the closure in latitude (or departure) to the perimeter—by the successive course lengths. The computations can be done mentally if the total error is small, or by slide rule. Since the adjustments are made by an arbitrary rule, it is a waste of time to split hairs or carry values beyond the number of decimal places in the original measurements.

In illustration 10–3 the correction in latitude for AB is

$$\frac{0.71}{2466} \times 285 = 0.08 \text{ ft}$$

and that for BC is $\qquad \dfrac{1}{3500} \times 610 = 0.18 \text{ ft}$

Each correction is generally lettered in different-colored ink or pencil above the latitude or departure to which it will be applied. In illustration 10–3, the corrections are shown in small italic numbers. In this example the adjustments are added to the north latitudes and subtracted from the south latitudes, to bring the totals of the north and south latitudes to the same value.

The corrections applied to the tabular values should produce a perfect closure. In rounding off, an excess or deficiency of 0.01 ft may result, but this is eliminated by revising one of the corrections.

10–8. Other methods of computing latitudes and departures. In the example given, logarithms were used to compute the latitudes and departures. Modern offices now use calculating machines and natural functions of the bearing angles for this work. The limited number of significant figures which can be read on a slide rule makes it suitable only for computing corrections and for rough checking.

Traverse tables provide a rapid method of finding latitudes and departures in the field or office by using only addition (the arithmetic process in which the fewest mistakes are made). Sample pages of a traverse table are shown in Table I.

A traverse table is a compilation of the natural sines and cosines of angles multiplied by the integers 1 to 10, or perhaps by 1 to 100. The most complete tables give values for each minute of arc. Others, like Table I, show only the multiples of 15 min.

To find the latitude or departure of a line of given length and bearing, the answer for each digit is taken from the table and the decimal point is moved to the proper place. The quantities for all digits are added to obtain the result.

As an example, the latitude and departure for a course CD having a bearing of S 15° 30′ W and a length of 720.48 ft will be found by tabulation from a traverse table:

Length	Latitude	Departure	
720.	693.8	192.4	(from 72 with decimal
0.48	0.46	0.13	point shifted)
720.48	694.26	192.53	

Differences from the values shown in illustration 10–2 result from using a table carried only to hundredths, and then moving the decimal point. Since two of the values from the table are in tenths only, the answers cannot logically be carried out to hundredths.

10–9. Coordinates. In Fig. 10–1, if the coordinates of point A are 0,0, the departure and latitude of course AB are the X- and Y-

coordinates of point B. The columns of total departures and latitudes in illustration 10–3 therefore give the coordinates of each hub with respect to the starting point A. In practice, one of the traverse hubs is arbitrarily taken as the origin of coordinates, or a tie line is run to some monument whose coordinates are known. To avoid negative values of X and Y, an origin may be assumed south and west of the traverse such that one of the hubs has the coordinates $X = 1000$, $Y = 1000$, or any other suitable values. In a closed traverse, assigning $Y = 0$ to the most southerly point, and $X = 0$ to the most westerly point, saves time.

In nationwide surveys spherical coordinates based on latitude and longitude must be used. Plane coordinates are satisfactory for ordinary surveys of limited extent.

Plane coordinates, and latitudes and departures, are employed in many ways. Examples are (a) map plotting, (b) location of inaccessible points, and (c) computation of areas, omitted measurements, and lengths and directions of property lines.

10–10. Lengths and bearings from latitudes and departures, or coordinates. The length and bearing of a line are readily obtained from the following relationships if the latitude and departure are known:

$$\text{tan bearing} = \frac{\text{departure}}{\text{latitude}} \tag{10-5}$$

$$\text{Length of line} = \frac{\text{departure}}{\text{sin bearing}} = \frac{\text{latitude}}{\text{cos bearing}} \tag{10-6}$$

$$= \sqrt{(\text{departure})^2 + (\text{latitude})^2} \tag{10-7}$$

These formulas also can be applied to any line connecting two points whose coordinates are known. Thus the tangent of the bearing of AB equals the difference of the X-coordinates divided by the difference of the Y-coordinates:

$$\text{tan bearing } AB = \frac{X_B - X_A}{Y_B - Y_A} \tag{10-8}$$

where X_A, Y_A and X_B, Y_B are the coordinates of A and B, respectively.
Likewise,

$$\text{Length } AB = \frac{X_B - X_A}{\text{sin bearing } AB} = \frac{Y_B - Y_A}{\text{cos bearing } AB} \tag{10-9}$$

$$= \sqrt{(X_B - X_A)^2 + (Y_B - Y_A)^2} \tag{10-10}$$

Illustration 10–4

COMPUTATIONS FOR A CLOSING LINE

POINT	LENGTH	BEARING	LATITUDE North	LATITUDE South	DEPARTURE East	DEPARTURE West	COORDINATES Y	COORDINATES X
A							0.0	0.0
	500.5	N 35° 30′ E	407.5		290.6			
B							N 407.5	E 290.6
	251.6	S 70° 10′ E		85.3	236.7			
C							N 322.2	E 527.3
	310.4	S 10° 50′ E		304.9	58.4			
D							N 17.3	E 585.7
	350.7	S 20° 18′ W		328.9		121.7		
E							S 311.6	E 464.0
						B	N 407.5	E 290.6
						Diff.	S 719.1	E 173.4

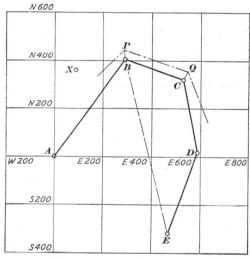

FIG. 10–2. Plot of traverse.

Figure 10–2 and illustration 10–4 will be used to explain these relationships. For example, suppose the length and bearing of a cutoff (or closing) line BE are required. The differences between the X- and Y-coordinates of hubs B and E are E 173.4 and S 719.1 respectively. Then

$$\text{tan bearing} = \frac{173.4}{719.1} \text{ and bearing } BE = \text{S } 13° 33′ 30″ \text{ E}$$

$$\text{Length } BE = \frac{719.1}{\cos 13° 33' 30''} = \sqrt{173.4^2 + 719.1^2} = 739.6 \text{ ft}$$

10–11. Coordinate computations in boundary measurements.
Computation of a bearing from the known coordinates of two points
on a line is a common problem in boundary measurements. If the
lengths and directions of lines from traverse points to the corners of a
field are known, the coordinates of the corners can be determined and
the lengths and bearings of all the sides can be calculated.

In Fig. 10–2, BC is a traverse line and PQ is the property line which
cannot be run directly because of obstructions. The measured
lengths and azimuths are: for BP, 42.5 ft and 354° 50'; for CQ, 34.6 ft
and 26° 40'. From the latitudes and departures of these lines the
coordinates of P and Q are found as follows:

		Y		X
B	N	407.5	E	290.6
BP		+ 42.3		− 3.8
P	N	449.8	E	286.8
C	N	322.2	E	527.3
CQ		+ 30.9		+ 15.5
Q	N	353.1	E	542.8

From the coordinates of P and Q, the length and bearing of the line
PQ are found in the following manner:

		Y		X
Q		+353.1		+542.8
P		+449.8		+286.8
PQ	S	96.7	E	256.0

$$\text{tan bearing } PQ = \frac{256.0}{96.7} \text{ and } PQ = \text{S } 69° 18' \text{ E}$$

$$\text{Length } PQ = \frac{256.0}{\sin 69° 18'} = 273.7$$

By continuing this method around the field, the coordinates of all
the corners and the lengths and bearings of all the lines may be
obtained.

10–12. Traverse orientation by coordinates. If the coordinates of
one traverse hub, as A in Fig. 10–2, and a visible point X, are known,

the direction of the line AX can be computed and used to orient the transit at A. In this way, azimuths and bearings of traverse lines are obtained without the necessity of making astronomical observations.

This procedure is followed in various cities which have control monuments and coordinate systems.

State and Federal mapping agencies will ultimately provide closely-spaced permanent monuments whose coordinates are based upon precise triangulation. Such marks will permit the accurate location of the corners of any piece of property, either by coordinates or by lengths and true bearings.

10–13. Statewide coordinate systems. Plane rectangular coordinates are commonly used in surveys covering the limited areas of plane surveying. In 1913 the United States Coast and Geodetic Survey established the North Carolina coordinate system, by means of which geodetic positions (latitude and longitude) of triangulation stations within the state could be transformed into plane rectangular coordinates (X and Y) on a single grid. By selecting an appropriate common origin and computing the coordinates of the precise-triangulation control marks, these points can be used as reference points for local surveys. All coordinates are made north and east by using an origin to the south and west of the state lines.

As additional points are set and their coordinates determined, they too become usable reference points. Finally, then, local surveys and the accurate restoration of obliterated or destroyed marks having known coordinates are simplified.

Grid systems for every state in the Union have now been devised and tables prepared. The systems use either the Transverse Mercator projection or the Lambert Conformal Conic projection. In large states more than one grid system may be necessary, to avoid excessive errors in reconciling coordinates by latitude and longitude with plane coordinates.

Some cities and counties have their own coordinate systems for use in locating street, sewer, property, and other lines. Because of their limited extent and the resultant discontinuity at city or county lines, such local systems are less desirable than a state-wide grid.

Military grids are used to pinpoint the locations of objects by coordinates, for fire-control and other purposes.

10-14. Sources of error in traverse computations. Some of the sources of error in traverse computations include:

a. Failing to adjust the angles before computing bearings.

b. Improper adjustments of angles, latitudes, and departures.

c. Carrying out corrections beyond the number of decimal places in the original measurements.

d. Poor selection of coordinate axes.

10-15. Mistakes. Some of the more common mistakes in traverse computations are:

a. Applying angle adjustments in the wrong direction and failing to check the angle sum for proper geometric total.

b. Interchanging latitudes and departures, or their signs.

c. Confusing the signs of coordinates.

PROBLEMS

10- 1. Balance the following interior angles (measured to the right) by methods 1 and 3 of section 10-2: A, 68° 34′; B, 108° 53′; C, 65° 29′; D, 116° 57′. What are the bearings of the traverse sides if the bearing of AB is N 81° 04′ E?

10- 2. Balance the following interior angles (measured to the left) by methods 1 and 3 of section 10-2: A, 123° 38′; B, 119° 22′; C, 146° 51′; D, 70° 46′; E, 79° 29′. What are the bearings of the traverse sides if the bearing of AB is N 83° 14′ W?

10- 3. Balance the following deflection angles by method 3 of section 10-2 and compute the bearings of the courses: The bearing of AB is S 36° 45′ W; B, 95° 23′ L; C, 84° 37′ L; D, 62° 10′ L; E, 33° 22′ L; F, 43° 27° R; A, 127° 50′ L.

10- 4. Balance the angles in the following azimuth traverse by any method and compute the bearings of the sides, assuming the first azimuth is correct: AB, 12° 10′; BC, 54° 01′; CD, 200° 12′; DA, 245° 54′; AB, 12° 12′.

10- 5. A tangent (straight line) of a proposed highway location extends from sta. 76 + 38.91 to sta. 92 + 46.78 and has a bearing of N 63° 47′ E. At sta. 91 + 47.32 the tangent intersects the center line of an existing highway whose bearing is N 43° 28′ E. Compute the distance from the existing highway to sta. 92 + 46.78 along a line perpendicular to the proposed highway.

10- 6. For the traverse of problem 10-1, which has sides AB = 194.07, BC = 148.72, CD = 195.19, and DA = 130.92 ft, compute (a) latitudes and departures, (b) linear error of closure, and (c) ratio of error. Balance the latitudes and departures by both the compass rule and the transit rule and compare the results.

10- 7. For the traverse of problem 10-2, which has sides AB = 219.70, BC = 92.21, CD = 277.94, DE = 410.35, and EA = 236.18 ft, compute (a) latitudes and departures, (b) linear error of closure, and (c) ratio of error. Balance the latitudes and departures by both the compass rule and the transit rule and compare the results. For what type of survey is the precision obtained satisfactory? What field errors are not eliminated by balancing the latitudes and departures to produce a closed geometric figure?

10– 8. The lengths of the sides and the unbalanced latitudes and departures of a traverse are as follows:

Course	Length	Latitudes	Departures
AB	357.65	N 326.41	W 146.18
BC	329.22	N 58.27	E 324.02
CA	423.60	S 384.52	W 177.70

Compute the linear closure, the ratio of error, and the new bearings of the sides after the latitudes and departures are balanced.

10– 9. Using a traverse table, compute the latitudes and departures for an open traverse having the following courses: AB, N 15° 00′ E, 276.2 ft; BC, S 74° 30′ E, 435.8 ft; CD, S 15° 45′ W, 654.9 ft.

10–10. Compute the total coordinates of the traverse hubs in problem 10–6.

10–11. The following field notes were taken on a series of lines run around a wooded area: AB, N 89° 40′ E, 368.2 ft; BC, S 89° 10′ E, 387.7 ft; CD, N 88° 44′ E, 416.9 ft. A point E is to be set on a continuation of line AB and 420.0 ft from point D. Calculate the bearing of DE and the angle which must be turned from DE at point E to prolong AB.

10–12. The bearing along the east line of a farm is S 2° 57′ W. A traverse to locate a spring is run from the northeast corner of the farm on the following courses: S 12° 07′ E, 396.5 ft; S 12° 40′ W, 136.7 ft; S 40° 45′ W, 151.3 ft; S 65° 57′ W, 95.7 ft; S 62° 12′ W, 27.2 ft. Compute the right-angle distance from the east property line to the spring.

10–13. Determine the length and bearing of the missing line to close a traverse around a hill having the following courses: AB, North, 60 ft; BC, N 30° E, 300 ft; CD, East, 200 ft; DE, S 60° E, 150 ft; EF, S 45° W, 400 ft.

10–14. Determine the lengths and bearings of the sides of a farm whose corners have the following coordinates: A (+ 200, + 300); B (+ 300, − 400); C (+ 200, − 500); D (− 200, + 200); E (0, + 100).

10–15. Why should the ratio of error *not* be carried out to a reciprocal such as 1/7264.8?

Chapter 11

AREA

11-1. General. One of the reasons for making a property survey is to determine the area of land included within the boundaries. Most deeds give the area of a tract of land as well as a description of the property lines.

The unit of area for lots is the square foot, but for large tracts it is the acre. One acre equals 43,560 sq ft. This figure is derived from the Gunter's chain length of 66 ft. Ten square chains equal one acre. An acre lot, if square, would thus be 208.71 ft on a side.

11-2. Methods of measuring area. The methods of measuring area may be classified under two headings: (1) field measurements and (2) map measurements.

Field measurements may be carried out by means of one of the following methods:

a. Division of the area into triangles.
b. Offsets from straight lines.
c. Double meridian distances.
d. Coordinates.

Map measurements may be made by means of one of the following methods:

a. Division of the area into triangles.
b. Coordinate squares.
c. Use of a planimeter.

Each of these methods will be described and illustrated in the topics which follow.

11-3. Area by division into triangles. A field may be divided into simple geometric figures such as the triangles shown in Fig. 11-1. The area of a triangle whose sides are known may be computed by the formula

$$\text{Area} = \sqrt{s(s-a)(s-b)(s-c)} \qquad (11\text{-}1)$$

176

where a, b, and c are the sides of the triangle and

$$s = \tfrac{1}{2}(a + b + c)$$

Another formula for the area of a triangle is

$$\text{Area} = \tfrac{1}{2}ab \sin C \qquad (11\text{--}2)$$

where C is the angle included between sides a and b.

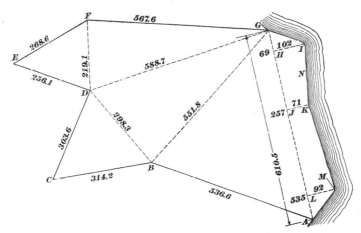

FIG. 11–1. Measurement by triangles.

The area of the field is the sum of the areas of all the triangles. Each side and division line must be measured.

11–4. Area by offsets from straight lines. Irregular fields can be reduced to a series of trapezoids by right-angle offsets from points at regular intervals along a measured line, as indicated in Fig. 11–2. This method is used for cross sections and profiles.

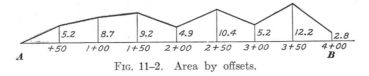

FIG. 11–2. Area by offsets.

The area is found by the formula

$$\text{Area} = b\left(\frac{h_0}{2} + h_1 + h_2 + \ldots + \frac{h_n}{2}\right) \qquad (11\text{--}3)$$

where b is the length of a common interval between the offsets and $h_0, h_1, \ldots h_n$ are the offsets.

Offsets to an irregular boundary from a reference line AB are shown in Fig. 11–2. The enclosed area is

$$50\Big(0 + 5.2 + 8.7 + 9.2 + 4.9 + 10.4 + 5.2$$
$$+ 12.2 + \frac{2.8}{2}\Big) = 2860 \text{ sq ft}$$

11–5. Area by double-meridian-distance method. It is convenient to compute the area of a closed figure by the double-meridian-distance method when the latitudes and departures of the boundary lines are known. The meridian distance of a traverse course is the right-angle distance from the center point of the course to the reference meridian. In order to ease the problem of signs, the reference meridian usually is passed through the most-westerly station of the traverse (the point where the bearings change from east to west).

In Fig. 11–3 the meridian distances of courses AB, BC, CD, DE, and EA are MM', PP', QQ', RR', and TT' respectively.

For the purpose of expressing PP' in terms of convenient distances, draw MF and BG perpendicular to PP'. Then

$$PP' = P'F + FG + GP = \text{meridian distance of } AB$$
$$+ \tfrac{1}{2} \text{ departure of } AB + \tfrac{1}{2} \text{ departure of } BC$$

Thus the meridian distance of any course of a traverse equals the meridian distance of the preceding course, plus one-half the departure of the preceding course, plus one-half the departure of the course itself. It is simpler to use full departures of courses. Therefore *double meridian distances* (D.M.D.'s), which are equal to twice the meridian distances, are employed. A single division by two is made at the end of the computation.

The D.M.D. for any traverse course is equal to the D.M.D. of the preceding course, plus the departure of the preceding course, plus the departure of the course itself.

For the traverse in Fig. 11–3, for example,

D.M.D. of AB = dep. of AB

D.M.D. of BC = D.M.D. of AB + dep. of AB + dep. of BC

Signs of the departures, east plus and west minus, must be considered. When the reference meridian is taken through the most-

westerly station of a closed traverse and calculations of the D.M.D.'s
are started with a course through that station, the D.M.D. of the
first course is its departure.   A check on all computations is obtained
if the D.M.D. of the last course after computing around the traverse
is also equal to its departure but opposite in sign.   If there is a difference, the departures were not correctly adjusted before starting,
or an error has been made in the computations.

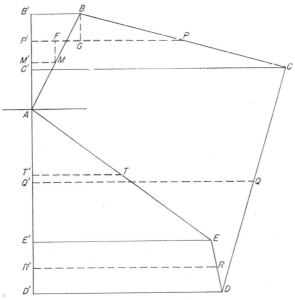

FIG. 11–3.   Meridian distances.

The area enclosed by the traverse $ABCDEA$ in Fig. 11–3 is

$$B'BCC' + C'CDD' - (AB'B + DD'E'E + AEE')$$

The area of each of these figures equals the meridian distance of a
course times its balanced latitude.   The D.M.D. of a course multiplied by its latitude equals the double area.   Summation of all the
double areas gives twice the area inside the entire traverse.

Signs of the products of D.M.D.'s and latitudes must be considered.
If the reference line is passed through the most-westerly station, all
D.M.D.'s are positive.   The products of D.M.D.'s and north latitudes are therefore plus, and the products of D.M.D.'s and south latitudes are minus.

Illustration 11–1

COMPUTATION OF D.M.D.'s

Departure of AB = + 125.66 = D.M.D. of AB
Departure of AB = + 125.66
Departure of BC = + 590.65

+ 841.97 = D.M.D. of BC
Departure of BC = + 590.65
Departure of CD = − 192.69

+1239.93 = D.M.D. of CD
Departure of CD = − 192.69
Departure of DE = − 6.97

+1041.17 = D.M.D. of DE
Departure of DE = − 6.07
Departure of EA = − 517.55

+ 517.55 = D.M.D. of EA Check

To illustrate the procedure, the traverse of Fig. 11–3 and the departures taken from illustration 11–2 will be used. The calculations of D.M.D.'s are shown in illustration 11–1.

The computations for area are generally arranged as in illustration 11–2, although a combined form may be used. The smaller of the two double-area totals is subtracted from the larger, and the result is dived by 2 to get the area in square feet. This area (272,610 sq ft), is divided by 43,560 sq ft to obtain the number (6.258) of acres.

The fact that the total minus double area is larger than the plus double area signifies only that the D.M.D.'s were computed by going around the traverse in a clockwise direction. If the route had been from A through E, D, C, and B and back to A, the total plus double area would have been the greater. Areas carried out beyond the nearest square foot or 0.001 acre cannot be justified for a traverse on which distances were measured to the nearest 0.01 ft and angles were read to 1 min or $\frac{1}{2}$ min.

As a check, the area can be computed by *double parallel distances* (D.P.D.'s).

The D.P.D. for any traverse course is equal to the D.P.D. of the preceding course, plus the latitude of the preceding course, plus the latitude of the course itself.

Illustration 11–2

COMPUTATION OF AREA BY D.M.D.'s AND D.P.D.'s

Course	Balanced Latitude	Balanced Departure	D.M.D.	Double Areas +	Double Areas −	D.P.D.	Double Areas +	Double Areas −
AB	N 255.96	E 125.66	+ 125.66	32,164		+255.96	32,164	
BC	S 153.53	E 590.65	+ 841.97		129,268	+358.39	211,683	
CD	S 694.07	W 192.69	+1239.93		860,598	−489.21	94,266	
DE	N 202.97	W 6.07	+1041.17	211,326		−980.31	5,951	
EA	N 388.67	W 517.55	+ 517.55	201,156		−388.67	201,156	
Total	0.00	0.00		444,646	989,866		545,220	00

444,646

2)545,220

272,610 sq ft = 6.258 acres

The last three columns in illustration 11–2 show the computation of the area of the traverse in Fig. 11–3 by D.P.D.'s. Signs of the latitudes, north plus and south minus, must be used in calculating the D.P.D.'s.

All important engineering computations should be checked by using different methods, or by two persons who could employ the same method. As an example of good practice: An individual working alone in an office might use a calculating machine to compute latitudes and departures and check them by means of a traverse table. He might then calculate areas by D.M.D.'s and check his results by D.P.D.'s. Experienced surveyors and engineers have learned that a half-hour spent in checking computations may save a frustrating day of unsatisfactory closures in the field.

The area of a tract having a circular curve for one boundary, such as that in Fig. 11–4, can be found by dividing the figure into two parts:

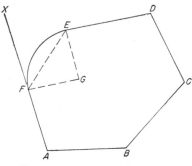

the polygon $ABCDEGF$ and the sector EGF. The radius $R = EG = FG$, and either the central angle EGF or the length EF, must be known or computed, to permit calculation of the area of sector EGF. This area can then be added to the area of $ABCDEGFA$, which is found by the D.M.D. or coordinate method.

Fig. 11–4. Area with curved boundary.

As a variation, the length and direction of EF can be calculated and the area of segment EF added to that of $ABCDEFA$. Note that angle XFE equals one-half of angle EGF.

11–6. Area by coordinates. Determination of area from coordinates is a simple process for a closed traverse with known coordinates for each corner. The area is equal to one-half the sum of the products obtained by multiplying each Y-coordinate by the difference between the adjacent X-coordinates. The X-coordinates must always be taken in the same order around the traverse. The rule can also be stated in another form: The area is equal to one-half the sum of the products obtained by multiplying each X-coordinate by the difference between the adjacent Y-coordinates, taken in the same order around the figure. Using both rules provides a check on the answer.

For the traverse in Fig. 11–5, the rule is applied in the following relation:

$$\text{Area} = \tfrac{1}{2}[X_A(Y_E - Y_B) + X_B(Y_A - Y_C) + X_C(Y_B - Y_D)$$
$$+ X_D(Y_C - Y_E) + X_E(Y_D - Y_A)]$$

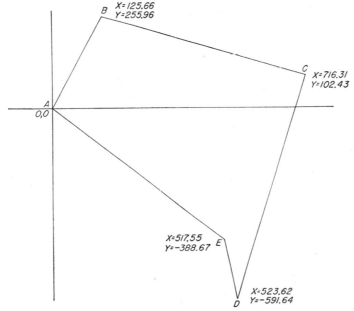

FIG. 11–5. Area by coordinates.

This formula is based on the summation of the areas of a series of trapezoids and can be derived readily or found in any book on coordinate geometry. The coordinates used are the total latitudes and total departures for the points. North and east coordinates are plus; south and west coordinates are minus. It is necessary to take account of these signs in using the formula. To avoid negative signs for coordinates, an origin may be selected to make all signs positive. Some surveyors let X equal zero for the most-westerly point, and let Y equal zero for the most-southerly station. The magnitudes of the coordinates and products are thereby reduced.

The total latitudes and total departures of illustration 11–2 will be used to demonstrate the computation of area by coodinates, with point

Illustration 11–3

COMPUTATION OF AREA BY COORDINATES

Point	Y	X	Difference of X's	Double Area +	−
A	0.00	0.00	517.55 − 125.66 = +391.89		0
B	+255.96	+125.66	0.00 − 716.31 = −716.31	183,347	
C	+102.43	+716.31	125.66 − 523.62 = −397.96	40,763	
D	−591.64	+523.62	716.31 − 517.55 = +198.76	117,594	
E	−388.67	+517.55	523.62 − 0.00 = +523.62	203,515	
A	0.00	0.00			

$$2)\overline{545,219}$$

$$272,610$$
$$\text{sq ft}$$

A as the origin. The procedure and results are shown in illustration 11–3.

11–7. Area from a map by triangles. A plotted traverse can be divided into triangles, the sides of each triangle scaled, and the areas of the triangles found by formula 11–1.

11–8. Area by coordinate squares. To determine the area of a plotted traverse by coordinate squares, the map is marked off in squares of unit area. The number of complete unit squares included in the traverse is counted and the sum of the areas of the partial units is estimated. Areas of partial units can be computed by treating them as trapezoids, but generally this refinement is not necessary.

A simpler method results from the use of transparent paper marked in squares to some scale. The paper is placed over the traverse and the number of squares and partial units counted.

A third method consists in plotting the traverse on coordinate paper and determining the number of units in the manner just described.

11–9. Measurement of area by planimeter. The planimeter mechanically integrates area and records the answer on a drum and disk as a tracing point is moved over the outline of the figure to be measured.

Its major parts are a scale bar, graduated drum and disk, vernier, tracing point and guard, and anchor arm, weight, and point. The scale bar may be fixed, or adjustable as in Fig. 11–6.   The adjustable type can be set to read units of area directly for any particular map scale.   The instrument touches the map at only three places—the anchor point, the drum, and the tracing-point guard.

As an example of the use of the planimeter, suppose the area within the traverse of Fig. 11–3 is to be measured.   The anchor point beneath the weight is set in a position outside the traverse (if inside, a polar constant must be added), and the tracing point is brought over corner A.   An initial reading, say 7231, is taken, the 7 coming from the disk, the 23 from the drum, and the 1 from the vernier.   The tracing point is moved along the traverse lines from A to $B, C, D,$ and E and back to A.   The point may be guided by a triangle or a straightedge, but normally it is steered freehand.   A final reading, perhaps 8756, is made.   The difference between the initial and final readings, or 1525, represents the area if the bar was set exactly to the scale of the map.   Since the bar setting may not be perfect, it is best to check the planimeter constant by running over the perimeter of a carefully-laid-out square 5 in. on a side, with diagonals of 7.07 in.

Assume that the difference between the initial and final readings for the square is 1250.   Then

$$5'' \times 5'' = 25 \text{ sq in.} = 1250 \text{ units}$$
or
$$1 \text{ unit} = \tfrac{25}{1250} = 0.02 \text{ sq in.}$$
and
$$1525 \text{ units} = 30.50 \text{ sq in.}$$

For a map scale of 1 in. = 100 ft, 1 sq in. = 10,000 sq ft and the area measured is 305,000 sq ft.

As a check on the planimeter operation, the outline may be traced in the opposite direction.   The initial and final readings at point A should agree within a limit of perhaps 2 to 5 units.

The precision obtained in using the planimeter depends upon the skill of the operator, the accuracy of the plotted map, the type of paper, and other factors.   Results correct within $\frac{1}{2}$ to 1 per cent can be obtained by careful work.

The planimeter is most useful for irregular areas, such as that in Fig. 11–2, and has applications in many branches of engineering. Steam cutoff diagrams in mechanical engineering are readily investigated by planimetering.   The planimeter is widely used in highway offices for determining areas of cross sections and is helpful in checking computed areas in property surveys.

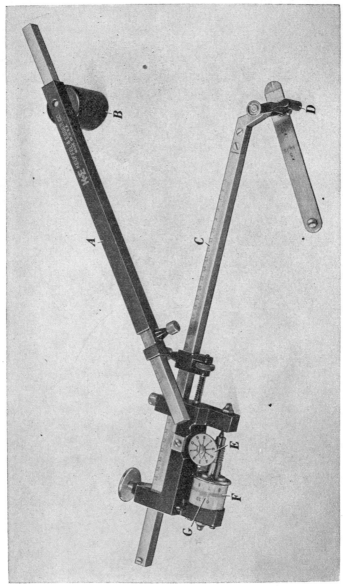

Fig. 11–6. Polar planimeter. A, anchor arm; B, anchor point; C, scale bar; D, tracing point; E, disk; F, drum; G, vernier. (Courtesy of Keuffel and Esser Company.)

11–10. Sources of error. Some of the sources of error in area computations include:

a. Poor selection of intervals and offsets to fit a given irregular boundary properly.

b. Failure to check an area computation by a different method.

c. Poor setting of the planimeter scale bar, and failure to check for the scale constant by tracing a known area.

d. Running off the edge of a map sheet with the planimeter drum.

e. Using different types of paper for the map and the planimeter-calibration sheet.

f. Poor selection of the origin, resulting in minus values for co-ordinates or D.M.D.'s.

g. Failure to draw a sketch to scale or general proportions for checking visually.

h. Adjustments of latitudes and departures not made in accordance with true conditions.

i. Using coordinate squares which are too large and which therefore make estimation of the partial blocks difficult.

11–11. Mistakes. In computing areas, common mistakes by students include:

a. Forgetting the division by 2 in any of the formulas or methods.

b. Confusing the signs of D.M.D.'s, coordinates, latitudes, departures, or areas.

PROBLEMS

11– 1. Determine the area in a housing subdivision which is a perfect hexagon having 800.00-ft sides.

11– 2. Compute the area enclosed by the traverse *ABCDEFGA* in Fig. 11–1.

11– 3. A series of perpendicular offsets were taken at intervals of 25 ft from a transit line to a curved boundary line. Successive measurements, in feet, were as follows: 0.0, 4.6, 8.9, 15.3, 10.4, 13.2, 18.5, 23.4, 17.6, 9.3, 3.2, and 0.0. Compute the area included between the transit line and the boundary line.

11– 4. Offsets to the edges of an irregular field were taken at 100-ft intervals on both sides of a base line. Compute the area of the field by the offset method, from the following data tabulated in the field notes:

Offset L	Sta.	Offset R	Offset L	Sta.	Offset R
0	0 + 00	0	62.5	5 + 00	52.9
25.2	1 + 00	15.4	51.8	6 + 00	40.0
38.1	2 + 00	28.7	35.6	7 + 00	31.2
42.7	3 + 00	39.1	24.8	8 + 00	27.3
56.9	4 + 00	48.7	10.4	9 + 00	8.1

11– 5. The balanced latitudes and departures, in feet, of the courses of part of a closed traverse are as follows: Course AB, N 146.18, E 326.41; BC, N 324.01, E 58.26; CD, S 115.20, W 380.20. Compute the D.M.D. of course CD with respect to a meridian through A.

11– 6. Compute by D.M.D's the area within a closed traverse whose balanced latitudes and departures, in feet, are as follows: AB, S 350, E 160; BC N 310, E 120; CA, N 40, W 280. Check by D.P.D.'s.

11– 7. Compute the area inside the following traverse, the departures and latitudes being given in feet: AB, $(-70, +80)$; BC, $(-50, +20)$; CD, $(+100, 0)$; DE, $(+80, +60)$; EF, $(0, -160)$; FA, $(-60, 0)$.

11– 8. Compute the area in acres of the following traverse by the D.M.D. method and check by D.P.D.'s: AB, N 82° 15' W, 320.5 ft; BC, N 4° 18' E, 417.6; CD, N 77° 31' E, 289.4; DE, S 38° 24' E, 515.6; EA, S 69° 32' W, 337.9.

11– 9. The area of a field as determined with a Gunter's chain is 20 acres. Later, the chain is standardized and found to be the equivalent of 1 link too long. Compute the true area of the field. Assume that the error in the chain is uniformly distributed.

11–10. What is the area of a triangular plot of land which has vertices with coordinates of $(+20, +30)$, $(+30, 0)$, and $(0, 0)$?

11–11. Outline the procedure for adjusting a traverse $ABCDEFA$ in which the coordinates of A and B are fixed by a previous survey.

11–12. Calculate the area of a three-sided field in which AB has a bearing of N 24° 00' W and is 400.00 ft long, AC is 450.00 ft long and bears N 52° 00' W, and BC is an arc of a circle having a radius of 500.00 ft. The center of the arc is southwest of point A.

11–13. A triangular lot is bounded by the following lines: AB, due west, 200.00 ft; BC, N 30° 00' E, 146.42 ft; CA, S 45° 00' E, 179.33 ft. The property is to be divided equally between two people by a line parallel to the east boundary. Compute the areas of the two parts and the lengths of the sides.

11–14. A trapezoidal piece of property is described as follows: Commencing at a $1''$ ϕ pipe on the northwest corner of Oak Drive and State Route 127; thence due west 1700.0 ft along the north right-of-way line of Oak Drive to a $1''$ ϕ pipe; thence due north 1000.0 ft to a $1''$ ϕ pipe; thence due east 1200.0 ft to a $4''$ concrete post; thence along a straight line to the point of beginning. Divide the property into two equal areas by a line originating at the midpoint of the west boundary.

11–15. A planimeter with an initial setting of 1273 is run around a square 5 in. on a side and reads 1398 when returned to the starting point. It is then set on hub A of a plotted traverse with an initial reading of 1619, and is run around the traverse to A again, where it reads 1994. The map scale is 1 in. = 40 ft. What is the area enclosed by the traverse, in square feet?

Chapter 12

STADIA

12–1. General. The stadia method is a rapid and efficient way to measure distances accurately enough for trigonometric leveling, some traverses, and the location of topographic details. Furthermore, a two- or three-man party can replace the three- or four-man party required in transit-tape surveys.

The term *stadia* comes from the Greek word for a unit of length originally applied in measuring distances for athletic contests. The word denoted 600 Greek feet, or 606 ft 9 in. by present-day American standards.

The term "stadia" is now applied to the cross wires and rod used in making measurements, as well as to the stadia method itself. Stadia readings can be taken with modern transits, theodolites, and levels.

12–2. Measurement by stadia for horizontal sights. A transit equipped for stadia work has two additional horizontal cross wires spaced equidistant from the center of the telescope. The interval between stadia wires in most surveying instruments gives a vertical intercept of 1 ft on a rod held 100 ft away. Thus the distance to a rod decimally divided in feet, tenths, and hundredths can be read

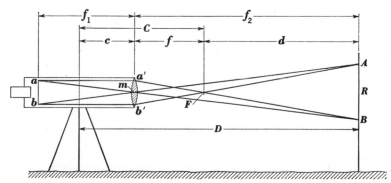

Fig. 12–1. Principle of stadia, external-focusing telescope.

189

directly to the nearest foot. This is sufficiently precise for locating topographic details (such as rivers, bridges, buildings, and roads) which are to be plotted on a map having a scale smaller than 1 in. = 200 ft.

The stadia method is based upon the principle that in similar triangles homologous sides are proportional. Thus in Fig. 12–1, which shows an external-focusing telescope, light rays from points A and B passing through the center of the lens form a pair of similar triangles AmB and amb. Here $AB = R$ is the rod intercept and ab is the interval between the stadia wires.

Standard symbols used in stadia measurements, and their definitions, are as follows:

$f = $ *focal length* of the lens (a constant for any particular compound objective lens). It can be determined by focusing upon a distant object and measuring the distance between the center (actually the *nodal point*) of the objective lens and the cross-hair ring.

$f_1 = $ distance from the center (actually the nodal point) of the objective lens to the plane of the cross hairs when the telescope is focused on some definite point.

$f_2 = $ distance from the center (actually the nodal point) of the objective lens to a definite point when the telescope is focused on that point. When f_2 is infinite, or very large, $f_1 = f$.

$i = $ interval between the stadia wires (ab in Fig. 12–1).

$f/i = $ stadia interval factor, usually 100.

$c = $ distance from the center of the instrument (spindle) to the center of the objective lens. It varies as the objective lens moves in and out for different sight lengths but is generally considered to be a constant.

$C = c + f.$ C is called the stadia constant although it varies slightly with c.

$d = $ distance from the focal point in front of the telescope to the face of the rod.

$D = C + d = $ distance from the center of the instrument to the face of the rod.

Then from similar triangles,

$$\frac{d}{f} = \frac{R}{i}$$

or
$$d = R\frac{f}{i}$$

and
$$D = R\frac{f}{i} + C \tag{12-1}$$

Fixed stadia wires in engineer's transits, levels, and alidades are carefully spaced by instrument manufacturers to make the stadia interval factor f/i equal to 100. The stadia constant C ranges from about 0.75 to 1.25 ft for different telescopes but is usually assumed to be equal to 1 ft. The only variable in the equation, then, is R, the rod intercept between the stadia wires. In Fig. 12–1, if the intercept R is 4.27 ft, the distance from the instrument to the rod is $427 + 1 = 428$ ft.

The stadia interval factor should be determined the first time an instrument is used, and periodically tested thereafter. Plate A–8 in Appendix A shows the notes for such a test.

The external-focusing telescope has been described, since a simple drawing correctly shows the relationships. Most modern telescopes are of the internal-focusing type, in which the objective lens remains fixed in position. A movable negative focusing lens between the objective lens and the plane of the cross wires changes the direction of the light rays. As a result, the stadia constant is so small (perhaps a few tenths of a foot) that it can generally be assumed equal to zero.

Disappearing stadia hairs were used in some older instruments to prevent confusion with the center horizontal hair. Modern glass reticules with short stadia lines and a full-width center line accomplish the same result more efficiently.

12–3. Measurement by stadia for inclined sights. It is impractical to hold a rod at right angles to an inclined line of sight. The intercept on a plumbed rod is therefore read and corrected in order to get true horizontal and vertical distances.

In Fig. 12–2 the transit is set at M and the rod is held at O. With the middle cross hair set on point D to make DO equal to the height of instrument EM, the vertical angle (angle of inclination) is a. Note that in stadia work the height of instrument is defined as the height of the line of sight above the point occupied (*not* above the datum plane as in leveling).

Let S represent the slope distance ED; H, the horizontal distance $EG = MN$; and V, the vertical distance $DG = ON$.

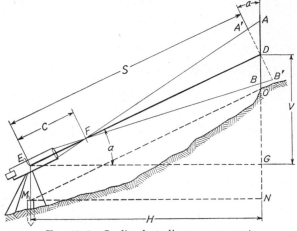

FIG. 12–2. Inclined stadia measurement.

Then $\qquad\qquad H = S \cos a$

and $\qquad\qquad V = S \sin a$

If the rod could be held normal to the line of sight at point O, a reading $A'B'$, or R', would be obtained, making

$$S = R' \frac{f}{i} + C$$

Since the rod is vertical, the reading is AB, or R. For the small angle at D on most practical sights, it is sufficiently accurate to consider that angle $AA'D$ is a right angle. Therefore

$$R' = R \cos a$$

and $\qquad\qquad S = R \frac{f}{i} \cos a + C$

or $\qquad\qquad H = R \frac{f}{i} \cos^2 a + C \cos a \qquad\qquad (12\text{–}2)$

For small angles, $C = 1$ ft approximately, and

$$H = R \frac{f}{i} \cos^2 a + 1 \qquad\qquad (12\text{–}3)$$

If $f/i = K$,

$$H = KR \cos^2 a + 1 \qquad\qquad (12\text{–}4)$$

To avoid multiplying R by $\cos^2 a$, which is a large decimal number, the formula for H is usually rewritten for use in computation as

$$H = KR - KR \sin^2 a + C \qquad (12\text{--}5)$$

The vertical distance is found by the formula

$$S = R\frac{f}{i} \cos a + C$$

or $\qquad\qquad V = R\dfrac{f}{i} \sin a \cos a + C \sin a \qquad (12\text{--}6)$

For small angles, $\sin a$ is very small and the quantity $C \sin a$ can be neglected. Substituting for $\sin a \cos a$ its equal $\frac{1}{2} \sin 2a$, the formula becomes

$$V = KR(\tfrac{1}{2} \sin 2a) \qquad (12\text{--}7)$$

In the final form generally used, K is taken as 100 and the formulas for reduction of inclined sights to horizontal and vertical distances are

$$H = 100\ R - 100\ R \sin^2 a + 1 \qquad (12\text{--}8)$$

and $\qquad\qquad V = 100\ R(\tfrac{1}{2} \sin 2a) \qquad (12\text{--}9)$

Tables, diagrams, and special slide rules (see Fig. 12–3) enable the surveyor to obtain a quick solution to these formulas. Table II lists horizontal and vertical distances for a slope length of 100 ft and various vertical angles.

An unfamiliar table should always be investigated by substituting values in it which will give known answers. For example, angles of 0°, 30°, and 45° can be used to check tabular results. Assuming a vertical angle of +30° 00′, a rod intercept of 1.00 ft, and a stadia constant C of 1 ft, the following results are secured: By Table II,

$$H = 75.00 \times 1.00 + 1 = 76 \text{ ft}$$

By formula 12–8,

$$H = 100 \times 1.00 - 100 \times 1.00 \times 0.50^2 + 1 = 76 \text{ ft}$$

An example of a typical computation required in practice will be given. Assume that in Fig. 12–2 the elevation of M is 268.2 ft, the H.I. is $EM = 5.6$ ft, the rod intercept is $AB = R = 5.28$ ft, the vertical angle a to point D at 5.6 ft on the rod is +4° 16′, and $C = 1$ ft.

From Table II, for an angle of +4° 16′ and a slope length of 100 ft,

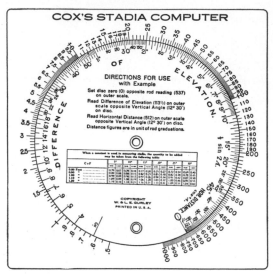

FIG. 12–3.   Cox stadia computer.

the horizontal distance is 99.45 ft and the vertical distance is 7.42 ft.
Then

$$H = (99.45 \times 5.28) + 1 = 525.1 + 1 = 526 \text{ ft}$$

and $V = (7.42 \times 5.28) + 0.08 = 39.18 + 0.08 = 39.3 \text{ ft}$

The elevation of point O, then, is

$$268.2 + 5.6 + 39.3 - 5.6 = 307.5 \text{ ft}$$

The advantage of sighting on the H.I. is evident.   Since the rod
reading and the H.I. are opposite in sign and cancel each other, they
can be omitted from the elevation computation.   If the H.I. cannot
be sighted because of obstructions, setting the middle cross hair on
the full foot mark just above or below the H.I. simplifies the arithmetic.

Determination of elevation differences by stadia can be compared
with differential leveling.   The H.I. corresponds to a plus sight, and
the rod reading to a minus sight.   On these is superimposed a vertical
distance which may be either plus or minus, its sign depending upon
the angle of inclination.

12–4. Stadia rods.   Various types of markings are used on
stadia rods but all have bold geometric figures designed for legibility

at long distances. Stadia rods are graduated in feet and tenths. Hundredths must be interpolated. Different colors aid in distinguishing the numbers and the graduations.

One-piece, folding, and sectional rods having lengths of 10 or 12 ft are common. Longer rods increase the sight-distance limit but are heavy and awkward to handle. A quarter-hair between the middle cross hair and the upper stadia hair is a better solution for shots over 2000 ft. On short sights the ordinary leveling rod is satisfactory.

12–5. Beaman arc. The Beaman arc, Fig. 12–4, is a device placed on some transits and alidades to facilitate stadia computations. It may be part of the vertical circle or may be a separate plate. The H and V scales of the arc are graduated in per cent.

FIG. 12–4. Beaman arc.

The V scale shows the difference of elevation per 100 ft of slope distance, whereas the H scale gives the correction per 100 ft to be subtracted from the stadia distance. Since V is proportional to $\frac{1}{2}\sin 2a$, and the correction for H depends upon $\sin^2 a$, spacing of the graduations decreases as the vertical angle increases.

The indicator of the V scale is set to read 50 (or perhaps 30 on some instruments) when the telescope is horizontal. Minus values are thereby eliminated. Readings greater than 50 are obtained on sights above the horizon; readings less than 50, on sights below the horizon. In Fig. 12–4 the V scale reads 80. The arithmetic required in using the Beaman arc is simplified by setting the V scale on a whole number and letting the middle cross hair fall somewhere near the H.I.

The elevation of a point B sighted with the transit set up over point A is found by the following formula:

Elev. B = Elev. A + H.I. + (arc reading − 50) (rod
          intercept) − rod reading of center cross hair   (12–10)

Careful attention must be given to signs.

To illustrate the computation, assume that in Fig. 12–2 the V-scale reading is 56, the rod intercept is 6.28 ft, the H.I. is 4.2 ft, the rod reading of the center wire is 7.3 ft, and the elevation of point M is 101.5 ft. Then

Elev. O = $101.5 + 4.2 + (56 − 50)(6.28) − 7.3 = 136.1$

12–6. Instruments with movable stadia lines. European theodolites and alidades have been developed in which *curved* stadia lines appear to move apart, or move closer together, as the telescope is elevated or depressed. Actually, the lines are engraved on a glass

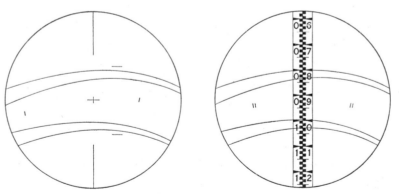

FIG. 12–5. Curved stadia lines. Left: field of telescope without rod. Right: field of telescope with rod (horizontal distance = 100 × 22.7 = 22.7 m; difference of height = 20 × 16.7 = 3.30 m). (Courtesy of Kern Instruments, Inc.)

plate which turns around a center (situated outside the telescope) as the telescope is transited.

In Fig. 12–5 the upper and lower lines (the two outer lines) are curved to correspond to the variation in the trigonometric function $\cos^2 a$ and are used for distance measurements. The two inner lines are employed to determine differences in elevation and are curved to represent the function $\sin a \cos a$. A vertical line, a center cross, and short stadia lines are marked on a second, but fixed, glass plate which is in focus simultaneously with the curved lines.

A constant stadia-interval factor of 100 is used for measurement of horizontal distances. A factor of 20, 50, or 100 is applied to measurements of elevation differences, its value depending upon the angle of slope. The factor to be used is indicated by short lines placed between the elevation curves.

12–7. Other methods of measuring distances. Several methods of measuring distances indirectly have been developed, in which angles are read accurately on a rod held horizontally. One of these methods utilizes the optical theodolite and a *subtense bar*.

FIG. 12–6. Subtense bar. (Courtesy of Kern Instruments, Inc.)

The invar subtense bar shown in Fig. 12–6 is set on a tripod and aligned perpendicular to the traverse line by means of a sighting device on top of the bar. Fixed targets near the ends of the bar are exactly 2 meters apart. The angle between the targets is measured with a theodolite reading to 1 sec of arc or less, and the horizontal distance is taken from a table, such as Table III. An advantage of the subtense-bar method is that horizontal distances are always obtained directly, even though inclined sights are taken.

For sights of 500 ft or less, the accuracy should be equal to that of an ordinary tape traverse. Precision of 1/10,000 is attainable by taking several readings of the angle for averaging.

An accessory available for some theodolites is the double-image range-finder, or *stadiometric prism*.[1]

A prism placed horizontally across the central section of the telescope objective creates a second image of a horizontal stadia rod, laterally displaced with respect to the first image formed by the telescope objective. The rod is seen directly through the section of the objective not covered by the prism. Through the central area (objective *and* prism) the rod appears to be displaced to one side. Since the angle of lateral displacement between the two images is constant, only the apparent displacement between the two rod images has to be measured in order to be able to calculate the distance from instrument to rod. This principle was first applied by an American (Richards) in 1894.

The rod must be set up horizontally, and at right angles to the line of sight of the instrument. A vernier or index (deflected image) painted on one end of the stadia rod is lined up against the rod graduation (direct image) at a point which indicates the distance from instrument to rod.

For simplicity and greater accuracy, an *optical micrometer* can be mounted in front of the prism to replace a vernier. A more precise reading of fractional units is then made directly on a micrometer drum.

An accessory consisting of a *Boskowitz prism* (wedge-shaped glass disk) connected with a bubble accomplishes slope compensation. Centering the bubble causes a rotation of the Boskowitz prism across the field of view, resulting in a rod reading which indicates horizontal distance. Other stadiometric prism accessories give slope distances.

12–8. Field notes. An example of stadia field notes is shown in Plate A–9. The transit is usually oriented by a meridional azimuth, and clockwise angles are taken to desired points.

In stadia work, many shots may be taken from one hub. Orienta-

---

[1] Descriptive material courtesy of Kern Instruments, Inc.

tion should therefore be checked by sighting on the control line after every ten or twenty topographic points and before leaving the hub.

Since horizontal sights save time by eliminating reduction computations, they should be used in place of inclined sights whenever possible. Rod readings then become minus sights, as in profile leveling.

Columns in the notes are arranged in the order of readings—point sighted, rod intercept, azimuth, and vertical angle. A sketch and pertinent data are placed on the right-hand page as usual. Reduction of the notes is done in the office, unless the information is needed immediately for control or is to be plotted on a plane-table sheet.

12–9. Field procedure. Proper field procedures save time and reduce the number of mistakes in all surveying operations. The order of taking readings best suited for stadia work involving vertical angles is as follows:

a. Bisect the rod with the vertical wire.

b. With the middle wire approximately on the H.I., set the lower wire at a foot mark.

c. Read the upper wire, and subtract the reading of the lower wire from it to get the rod intercept. Record (or call out to the notekeeper) only the answer—the intercept.

d. Move the middle wire to the H.I. by using the tangent screw.

e. Release the rodman for movement to the next point by giving the proper signal.

f. Read and record the horizontal angle.

g. Read and record the vertical angle.

This procedure will enable an instrumentman to keep two or three rodmen busy in open terrain where points to be located are widely separated. The same order can be followed when the Beaman arc is used, but in step d the V scale is set to a whole number, and in step g the H- and V-scale readings are recorded.

12–10. Stadia traverses. In a transit-stadia traverse, distances, horizontal angles, and vertical angles are measured with the same instrument. Reduction of stadia notes as the survey progresses provides elevations to be carried from hub to hub. Average values of stadia distances and differences in elevation are obtained from a foresight and a backsight on each line.

12–11. Topography. The stadia method is most useful in locating numerous topographic details, both horizontally and vertically, by transit or plane table. In urban areas, angle and distance readings can be taken faster than a notekeeper is able to record the measurements and prepare a sketch.

The use of stadia in topographic work will be covered in more detail in the chapters on topography and the plane table.

12–12. Stadia leveling. The stadia method is adaptable to trigonometric leveling. The H.I. (above a datum plane) is determined by sighting on a point of known elevation, or by setting the instrument over such a point and measuring the height of the horizontal axis above it with a stadia rod. The elevation of any point can then be found by computation from the rod intercept and the vertical angle. If desirable, a leveling circuit can be run to establish and check the elevations of two or more points.

12–13. Precision. A ratio of error of 1/500 can be obtained for a transit-stadia traverse run with ordinary care. Short sights, a long traverse, and careful work may give ratios up to 1/1000. Errors in stadia work are usually the result of poor rod readings rather than

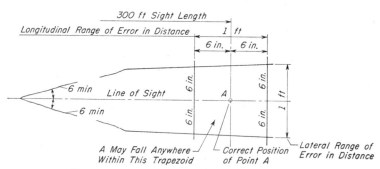

Fig. 12–7. Comparable precision of angles and stadia distances.

incorrect angles. An error of 1 min in reading a vertical angle does not appreciably affect the horizontal distance. The same error produces a difference in elevation of about 0.1 ft on a 300-ft sight.

Figure 12–7 shows that if stadia distances are read to the nearest foot (the usual case), horizontal angles to topographic points need be read only to the nearest 5 or 6 min for comparable precision on 300-ft sights. A distance to the nearest one foot is assumed to be correct to within about $\frac{1}{2}$ ft. Allowing the same $\frac{1}{2}$-ft error laterally, the line of sight can be off about 5 min. Angles therefore can be read without using the vernier, merely by estimating the position of the vernier index.

The precision of trigonometric leveling by stadia depends upon the lengths of sights and the size of the vertical angles required.

12–14. Sources of error in stadia work. The errors which occur in transit operations are inherent in stadia work too. Additional sources of error include the following:

Instrumental errors

    a. Improper spacing of the stadia wires.

    b. Index error.

    c. Incorrect length of rod graduations.

Personal errors

    a. Rod not held plumb.

    b. Incorrect rod readings resulting from long sights.

    c. Careless leveling for vertical-arc readings.

Most errors in stadia work can be eliminated by (a) careful manipulation of the instrument, (b) limiting the length of sights, (c) using a good rod and a rod level, and (d) averaging readings in the forward and backward directions.

12–15. Mistakes. Some typical mistakes in stadia work are the following:

    a. Index error applied with wrong sign.

    b. Confusion of plus and minus vertical angles.

    c. Arithmetic mistakes in computing the rod intercept.

    d. Use of incorrect stadia interval factor.

PROBLEMS

12– 1. An external-focusing telescope has a focal length of 10 in. What error in the spacing of the stadia wires will reduce the stadia interval factor from 100 to 99.00?

12– 2. In making stadia measurements, why is it advisable to keep the sight line on the lower cross hair at least 3 ft above all intervening ground?

12– 3. Determine the stadia interval factor for an external-focusing telescope whose average $(f + c) = 0.98$ ft. Stadia distances (constant not included) to points A, B, C, D, and E were 107, 181, 231, 310, and 368 ft, respectively. Corresponding taped distances were 107.12, 181.49, 231.47, 310.96, and 368.04.

12- 4. A transit has a stadia interval factor of 104 and a stadia constant of 1.0 ft. If for a horizontal sight the intercept read on a rod equals 3.50 ft, what is the distance from the center of the instrument to the rod?

12- 5. A transit has an interval factor of 101.0. What is the length intercepted on a rod for a horizontal distance of 100 ft, if the line of sight is inclined downward at an angle of 12° 00′?

12- 6. If transit-stadia shots averaging about 500 ft are taken to the nearest foot with an external-focusing telescope and the computed distances are not corrected for the stadia constant, how close should the angles be read to give corresponding precision?

12- 7. The specifications for a stadia traverse being run over the site of a proposed reservoir require a precision not lower than 1/750. What is the lower limit of vertical angles for which it is necessary to reduce inclined sights to horizontal distances?

12- 8. A rod intercept of 5.00 ft at a vertical angle of +6° 00′ to the H.I. on the rod is read with an instrument having $f/i = 100$ and $C = 1.0$ ft. What is the horizontal distance?

12- 9. Compute the ground elevations for the following stadia readings made with a transit set over station A at elevation 657.4 ft, sights being taken on the H.I. of 5.2 ft. Stadia constant = 0. Check by means of Table II.

Point	Intercept	Vert. Angle	Point	Intercept	Vert. Angle
1	4.76	+4° 20′	4	5.44	+3° 00′
2	2.84	+6° 30′	5	8.84	−1° 45′
3	6.52	−3° 15′	6	2.26	+8° 30′

12-10. A transit is set over station A with an H.I. of 4.8 ft. An intercept of 6.51 ft is read on a rod held on B.M. Fox at elevation 310.82 ft. What is the elevation of station A if the vertical angle to 7.5 ft on the rod is −8° 52′ and $C = 1.2$ ft?

12-11. A field 640 ft wide in an east-west direction and 1350 ft long in a north-south direction is to be mapped by stadia. The transit is set up over the northeast corner of the field (elev. 775.0 ft) with an H.I. of 5.0 ft. Compute the rod intercept and the vertical angle to the 5.0-ft mark on the rod for a point located 45 ft east of the west line of the field and 250 ft north of the south line, and having an elevation of 660.0 ft.

12-12. A transit is set over a hub A with an H.I. of 4.8 ft, and a vertical angle of +1° 30′ is read to 7.0 ft on the rod held at hub B. The stadia distance read is 400 ft. If the elevation of hub A is 175.0 ft, what is the elevation of B? Natural sine of 1° is 0.0175, and natural cosine of 1° is 0.9998. Assume that values of sines are proportional for other small angles.

12-13. On a traverse line between two hubs A and B, obstructions prevented sighting on the H.I. In the forward pointing from A to B with an H.I. of 5.0 ft, the distance read was 200 ft and the vertical angle read to 7.0 ft on the rod was +2° 00′. On the backsight from B to A with an H.I. of 4.9 ft, the distance read was 200 ft and the vertical angle was −0° 30′

to 8.2 on the rod. What is the elevation of B if the elevation of A is 660.0?

12-14. A transit is set up over a point X, elevation 214.5 ft, with an H.I. of 4.9. A Beaman-arc reading of 72 on the V scale and 5 on the H scale is obtained by sighting to 5.8 ft on a rod held at point Y. The rod intercept is 3.20 ft. Determine the horizontal distance XY and the elevation of point Y.

12-15. A transit at point A, elevation 862.4, has an H.I. of 4.8 ft. A V-scale reading of 33 and an H-scale reading of 3 are taken from the Beaman arc with the telescope sighting 5.6 ft on a rod held at point B. The rod intercept is 5.48 ft. Compute the horizontal distance AB and the elevation of point B.

12-16. Compute the error of closure and adjust the elevations of the following azimuth-stadia traverse by distributing the error of closure in proportion to the differences in elevation between adjacent hubs:

COURSE	AZIMUTH	FORESIGHT		BACKSIGHT	
		Stadia	Vert. Angle	Stadia	Vert. Angle
AB	90° 00′	3.98	+2° 09′	3.97	−2° 11′
BC	97° 51′	4.45	−1° 19′	4.45	+1° 17′
CD	18° 02′	7.34	+2° 36′	7.31	−2° 38′
DE	271° 47′	4.12	−3° 44′	4.11	+3° 43′
EF	281° 28′	2.49	+1° 47′	2.50	−1° 49′
FG	212° 45′	5.15	−4° 28′	5.13	+4° 27′
GA	205° 47′	2.97	+3° 56′	2.98	−3° 58′

12-17. Prepare a complete set of transit-stadia field notes for a three-sided closed traverse having a length of approximately 1500 ft, and differences in elevation of about 40 ft.

12-18. Readings are taken on a 2-meter subtense bar with an optical theodolite, and the following angles are obtained: 31′ 07″, 31′ 08″, 31′ 09″, 31′ 08″. What is the horizontal distance from the theodolite to the subtense bar? Check the computation by means of Table III.

Chapter 13

TOPOGRAPHIC SURVEYS

13–1. General. Topographic surveys are made to determine the configuration (relief) of the surface of the earth and to locate the natural and artificial features thereon. A topographic map is a large-scale representation, by means of conventional symbols, of a portion of the earth's surface, showing the *culture, relief, hydrography,* and perhaps the *vegetation.* Products of man, such as roads, trails, buildings, bridges, canals, and boundary lines, are termed artificial features (culture). Names and legends on maps are included in this classification.

Topographic surveys are made and used by engineers to determine the most desirable and economical location of highways, railroads, bridges, buildings, canals, pipelines, transmission lines, and other facilities; by geologists to investigate mineral, oil, water, and other resources; by foresters in locating fire-control roads and towers; by architects in housing and landscape design; by agriculturists in soil conservation; and by geographers and scientists in numerous fields.

A *planimetric map,* or *line map,* shows the natural and/or cultural features in plan only. A *hypsometric map* presents relief by conventions such as *contours, hachures, shading,* and *tinting.* Several methods of locating topographic details in both horizontal and vertical position will be discussed. The preparation of maps from topographic surveys is covered in Chapter 14.

13–2. Control for topographic surveys. The first requirement of any topographic survey is good control.

Horizontal control is provided by two or more points on the ground accurately fixed in position horizontally by distance and direction. These points provide data to orient and check traverses, plane-table surveys, and terrestrial and aerial photographs. A system of horizontal-control points is established by triangulation or traversing.

Horizontal control for ordinary work is generally a traverse, although one line may suffice for a small area. Triangulation is the most economical basic control for surveys extending over a state or the entire United States. Monuments of the state-wide coordinate systems are excellent for all types of work but unfortunately there are not enough of them available in most areas.

Vertical control is provided by two or more bench marks which are in or near the area to be surveyed. A vertical-control net is established by lines of levels starting from, and closing on, bench marks. Elevations may be determined for the traverse hubs, with provision in some cases for marks set nearby and out of the way of construction. A lake surface is a continuous bench mark and should be utilized when possible. Even a gently flowing stream may serve as supplementary control. Barometric leveling is now employed to extend the vertical-control net in rugged terrain.

Topographic details are usually built upon a framework of traverse hubs whose positions and elevations have been established. Any errors in the hub positions or their elevations are reflected in the location of topography. It is advisable, therefore, to run, check, and adjust the traverse and level circuits before topography is taken, rather than to carry on both processes simultaneously. This is particularly true in plane-table work where an error in the elevation or position of an occupied station will displace the plotted locations of cultural features and contours.

The kind of control (triangulation or traverse), and the method selected to obtain topography, govern the speed, cost, and efficiency of a topographic survey.

13–3. Topographic details. Objects to be located in a survey may range from single points to meandering streams and complicated geological formations. The process of tying topographic details to the control net is called *detailing*.

13–4. Methods of locating points in the field. Seven methods used to locate a point P in the field are illustrated in Fig. 13–1. One line (distance) must be known in each of the first four methods. The positions of three points must be known or identifiable on a chart to apply the seventh method, which is called the three-point problem. Known or measured distances are shown in the figure as full lines. The quantities to be measured in the respective diagrams are:

1. Two distances.
2. Two angles.
3. One angle and the adjacent distance.

4. One angle and the opposite distance.
5. One distance and a right-angle offset.
6. The intersection of string lines from straddle hubs.
7. Two angles at the point to be located.

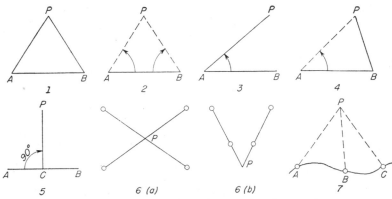

FIG. 13–1.　Locating a point P.

Straddle hubs are generally used as references for important points which might be disturbed or lost, rather than to locate topography. An experienced party chief employs whichever method is appropriate in a given situation; he must consider both field and office (computation and map) requirements.

13–5. Location of lines.　Most objects can be located by considering them to be composed of straight lines, each line being determined by two points.　Irregular or curved lines may be assumed straight between points sufficiently close together.　Thus detailing becomes a process of locating points.　Two examples will illustrate the measurements made to locate straight and curved lines.

In Fig. 13–2, the house *abcdea* is to be tied to traverse line *AB*. The building is so shaped that only two main corners, such as *a* and *e*, need be found.　Corner *a* could be located by any of the first five methods of Fig. 13–1 but an angle and a distance are used as shown. It is good practice to locate a third corner, if possible, to provide a check.　All sides of the house are measured by tape and the lengths are recorded on a sketch.

Since a transit is used to measure the angle, the distances to *a* and *e* could be measured by tape or stadia.　All the measurements may be

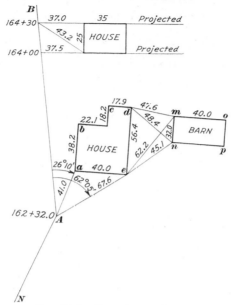

Fig. 13–2. Location of details.

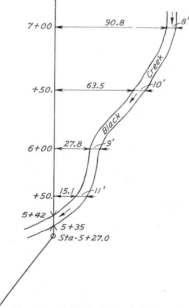

Fig. 13–3. Location of creek
by offset method.

shown on the sketch, but generally the angles and the distances from the traverse points are tabulated on the left page of the field book to avoid crowding the sketch. The topographic points are then identified by consecutive numbers, rather than letters.

The location of a crooked stream by using the offset method is shown in Fig. 13–3. At intervals along the traverse line, offsets to the edges of the creek are measured. The offsets can be taken at regular intervals or spaced at distances which will permit the line to be considered straight between the successive offsets.

13–6. Location of lines from a single point. The single-point method may be used to locate lines of a closed figure, such as the boundaries of a field. A point O is chosen from which all corners can be seen, as in Fig. 13–4a. The direction to each corner is found by measuring all the central angles, or by azimuths from point O. The lengths of all radiating lines, such as OA and OB, are taped or read by stadia, and the sides of the field are computed by trigonometry since two sides and the included angle in each triangle are known. As a check, the coordinates of each corner can be calculated from the lengths and directions of the radiating lines and used to determine the boundary lengths.

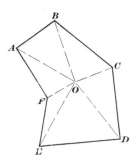

FIG. 13–4a. Location of lines.

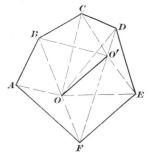

FIG. 13–4b. Location of lines.

A more-rigid solution of the boundary measurements can be obtained by using the method shown in Fig. 13–4b. A line OO' is chosen as the base and its length is carefully measured. Angles are taken from each end of the base to all corners, and the lengths of the radiating lines are taped or read by stadia as in the single-point method.

13–7. Contours. The best method of representing hills, mountains, depressions, and ground-surface undulations on a two-dimensional sheet of paper is by contours. A contour is a line connecting points of equal elevation. Contours may be visible on the ground, as in the case of a lake shore-line, but usually the elevations of only a few points are found and the contours are sketched between these controls.

Contours are shown on maps as the traces of level surfaces of different elevations, as in Fig. 13–5. Thus level surfaces cutting a vertical cone would form circular contours. They would intersect a sloping cone to produce elliptical contours. On uniformly sloping surfaces, such as those in highway cuts, contours are straight lines.

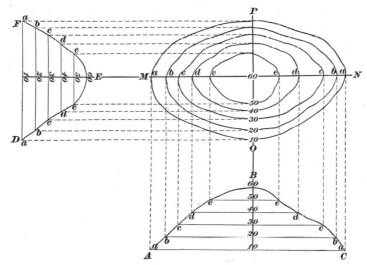

FIG. 13–5. Contour lines.

Most contours are irregular lines like the closed loops for the hill in Fig. 13–5. The vertical distance between the level surfaces forming the contours is called the *contour interval*. Intervals of 1, 2, 5, 10, 20, 25, 40, 50, 80, and 100 ft are used. The proper one for any area is determined by the type of terrain, the purpose of the survey, and the map scale. The United States Geological Survey uses 5-, 10-, and 20-ft intervals for some of its topographic sheets drawn to scales of 1:24,000 and 1:31,680. Intervals of 50, 80, and 100 ft are common on maps of mountainous regions having scales of 1:62,500 and 1:63,360.

Figure 13–6 is a contour map showing 25-ft contours. *Spot elevations* are given for critical points such as peaks, sags, streams, and highway crossings.

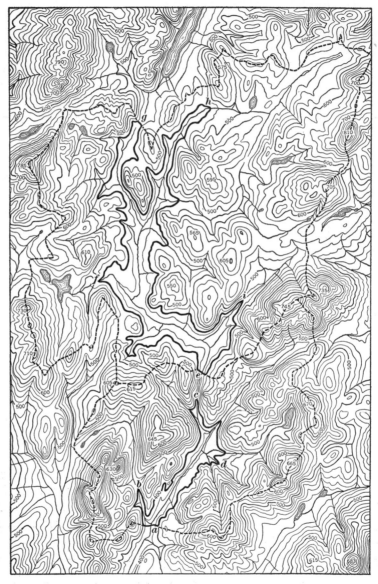

Fig. 13–6. Contour map.

13–8. Characteristics of contours. Certain characteristics of contours are fundamental in their location and plotting.

a. Evenly spaced contours show a uniform slope.

b. The distance between contours indicates the steepness of the slope. Wide spacing denotes flat slopes; close spacing, steep slopes.

c. Contours which increase in elevation represent hills. Those which decrease in elevation portray valleys. A contour forming a closed loop around lower ground is termed a *depression contour*. Contour elevations are shown on the uphill side of the lines, or in breaks, to avoid confusion.

d. Irregular contours signify rough, rugged country. Smooth lines designate gradual slopes and changes.

e. Contour lines tend to parallel each other on uniform slopes.

f. Contours never meet except on a vertical surface such as a wall or cliff. They cannot cross except in the unusual case of a cave or an overhanging shelf. Knife-edge conditions are seldom found in natural formations.

g. Valleys are usually characterized by V-shaped contours, and ridges by U-shaped contours.

h. The *V*'s formed by contours crossing a stream point upstream.

i. The *U*'s made by contours crossing a ridge line point down the ridge.

j. Contours tend to parallel streams and have an M shape just above stream junctions.

k. Contours cross curbs and a crowned sloping street in typical U-shaped curves.

Keeping these principles in mind will make it easy to visualize contours when looking at an area, and will prevent serious mistakes in sketching. Numerous points may be necessary to locate a contour in certain types of terrain. For example, in the unusual case of a level field which is at the contour elevation, exact location of a single contour would be time-consuming, or perhaps impossible.

On map sheets having a contour interval of 10 or 20 ft, *half-interval supplementary contours* may be used to better depict topographic details in the flatter areas of otherwise rugged terrain. Half-interval and other supplementary contours are differentiated by showing them as dashed lines.

13–9. Methods of obtaining topography. Location of topography is usually accomplished by one of the following methods:

a. Transit-tape.

b. Transit-stadia.

c. Plane table.

d. Coordinate squares.

e. Offsets from a center line.

f. Photogrammetry.

A brief explanation of the use, advantages, and disadvantages of each will be given.

13–10. Transit-tape method. The transit-tape method is the most accurate, but it is also the slowest and is therefore too costly for ordinary work covering a large area. Angles are measured with a transit, and distances are taped from the traverse hubs to the required points. After corners of buildings, bridges, and other objects have been located, their lengths, widths, and projections may be taped and sketched in the field book.

Transit-tape surveys are made in cities where distances must be accurately known and recorded, even though a normal-scale map cannot show this precision. In topographic mapping the transit-tape method is usually reserved for traverse lines, and the details are taken by some other system.

13–11. Transit-stadia method. The transit-stadia method is rapid, and sufficiently accurate for most topographic surveys. Stadia distances, azimuths, and vertical angles are read for lines radiating from the transit to the required points.

Contours may be found by either the *direct method* or the *indirect method*. In the direct method, the rod reading (foresight) which must be subtracted from the H.I. to give the contour elevation is determined. The rodman then selects trial points which he believes will give this minus sight, and is directed uphill or downhill by the instrumentman until the required rod reading is actually secured (within 0.1 to 0.5 ft, the allowable discrepancy depending upon the terrain and the required accuracy).

For example, in Fig. 13–7 if the transit is set up at point A, whose elevation is 674.3 ft, and if the H.I. is 4.9 ft, the elevation of the line of sight is 679.2 ft. If 5-ft contours are being located, a reading of 4.2 or 9.2 with the telescope level will place the rod on a contour point. After one of these points has been located by trial, the distance and azimuth are read and the process is repeated. The work is speeded by using a piece of red cloth which can be moved up and down on the stadia rod to cover the required reading.

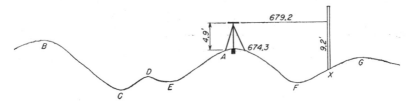

FIG. 13-7. Direct method of locating contours.

The maximum distance between contour points is determined by the terrain and the accuracy required. The tendency for beginners is to take more sights than necessary in ordinary terrain. Contours are sketched between the located points as a part of the drafting-room work, but they may also be drawn in the field book to clarify unusual conditions.

Unless the rod can be read by using the transit as a level, the direct method of locating contours is impractical. Too much time is wasted if the combination of a vertical angle and a stadia distance must be juggled to get a required difference in elevation.

For the indirect method, the stadia rod is set on critical points where there are changes in ground slope, such as B, C, D, E, F, and G in Fig. 13-7. Elevations are obtained with the telescope level whenever possible, to save time in reducing notes and to increase the accuracy. Points are selected at random, or along desired azimuth lines. The rodman moves clockwise to facilitate notekeeping and plotting. Contours are interpolated between the high and low points whose elevations are found.

The direct method is advantageous in gently-rolling country. The indirect method is better in rough, rugged terrain. Plate A-9 in Appendix A shows sample notes for a transit-stadia survey.

13-12. Plane-table method. In the plane-table method an alidade is sighted on a rod held at the point to be located, and the stadia distance and the vertical angle (or Beaman arc) are read. The direction of the line is drawn along the alidade ruler, thus eliminating the need for measuring or recording any horizontal angles. Vertical angles too are avoided, if possible, by using the alidade as a level.

The instrumentman sketches contours by either the direct or indirect method while looking at the area. Since the map is plotted in the field, coverage can be checked by observation. Plane-table usage is discussed in Chapter 15.

13–13. Coordinate squares. The method of coordinate squares (grid method) is better adapted to locating contours than culture, but can be used for both. The area to be surveyed is staked in squares 10, 20, 50, or 100 ft on a side, the size depending upon the terrain and the accuracy required. A transit may be used to lay out two lines at right angles to each other, such as AD and $D3$ in Fig. 13–8. Grid lengths are marked on these two lines and the other corners are staked by intersections of taped lines. Corners are identified by the number and letter of the intersecting lines. If a transit is not available, all layout work can be done with a tape.

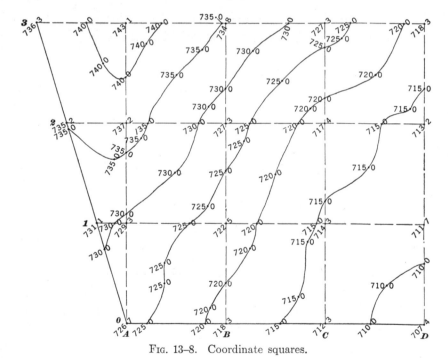

Fig. 13–8. Coordinate squares.

To obtain elevations of the corners, the engineer's level is set up in the middle of the area, or in a position from which level sights can be taken on each point. Contours are interpolated between the corner elevations by estimation, or by calculated proportional distances.   Except for plotting the contours, this is the same procedure as that used in the borrow-pit problem.

13–14. Offsets from the center line.   After the center line for a route survey has been run by transit and tape, a profile is taken to get elevations at the regular stations and at critical points.   Details such as fences and buildings are then located by right-angle offsets. The right angle can be measured by a *pentagonal prism* of the type shown in Fig. 13–9, or estimated by bringing the palms of the hands together with arms outstretched in front of the body.

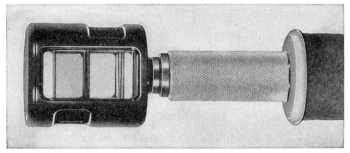

Fig. 13–9.   Double pentagonal prism.   (Courtesy of Kern Instruments, Inc.)

Cross-sectioning consists in taking a vertical section of the surface of the ground at right angles to the center line of a route survey. In effect, it is profiling normal to the center line.   Rod readings are secured at all breaks in the ground surface and are recorded with their respective distances out.   Plate A–10 in Appendix A is a sample set of cross-section notes.

Cross sections are usually plotted on special paper.   This paper is most commonly ruled in 1-in. squares divided decimally with lighter lines 0.1 in. apart horizontally and vertically.   The cross-section notes—when plotted with the base width and side slopes for a proposed highway or canal—outline the areas of cuts and fills, which are readily measured by planimetering.   Excavation quantities can be calculated from the areas of the cross sections and their known distances apart.

On some surveys, contour points are located along with any decided changes in slope of the ground.   For example, if 5-ft contours

are being delineated, a typical set of notes on the right-hand page of a
field book would be in the following form:

L				C.L.	R			
$\dfrac{85}{63}$	$\dfrac{80}{45}$	$\dfrac{75}{28}$	$\dfrac{70}{9}$	72.4	$\dfrac{75}{12}$	$\dfrac{80}{27}$	$\dfrac{85}{38}$	$\dfrac{90}{56}$

The numerator of a fraction represents the contour elevation, and
the denominator is the distance out from the center line.

The contour points can be plotted on cross-section paper to obtain
the equivalent of a set of cross-section notes, or the contours might be
drawn on the plan view of a proposed highway.

Readings are taken with an engineer's level or with a hand level.

13–15. Photogrammetry. Plotting topography from measurements on aerial photographs is one phase of photogrammetry. Topographic maps of the United States Geological Survey prepared by
this method now outnumber those compiled by plane-table and other
surveys. The method is particularly advantageous for large and
rugged areas.

A separate chapter (Chapter 18) is devoted to the fundamental
principles of photogrammetry.

13–16. Selection of field method. Selection of the field method to
be employed on any topographic survey depends upon the following
considerations:

a. Purpose of the survey.   e. Size and type of area involved.
b. Map use.   f. Cost.
c. Map scale.   g. Equipment available.
d. Contour interval.   h. Experience of the personnel.

Items a, b, c, d, and e are interdependent. The cost will be a
minimum if the most suitable method is chosen for a project. On
large-scale work, personnel cost rather than equipment investment
will govern (except perhaps in photogrammetric offices). A private
surveyor making a topographic survey of 50 or 100 acres, however,
may be governed in his choice of method by the equipment he owns.

Special training is necessary before the average surveyor can do
photogrammetric work. Relatively few men have had enough plane-
table experience to become efficient in its operation.

13–17. Specifications for topographic surveys. Specifications for topographic surveys and maps of large areas generally state the maximum errors permitted in horizontal positions and vertical elevations. Typical specification clauses might be as follows:

Horizontal accuracy: For maps to scales larger than 1:20,000, not more than 10 per cent of the points tested shall be in error by more than $\frac{1}{30}$ in. For maps to scales smaller than 1:20,000, the limit of error is $\frac{1}{50}$ in., which represents 40 ft. These limits of accuracy shall apply in all cases to positions of well-defined points only, such as monuments, bench marks, highway intersections, and corners of large buildings.

Vertical accuracy: Not more than 10 per cent of the elevations tested shall be in error by more than one-half the contour interval.

The accuracy of any map may be tested by comparing the positions of points whose locations or elevations are shown upon it with corresponding positions as determined by surveys of a higher accuracy.

Published maps meeting certain accuracy requirements may have noted in their legends that "This map complies with the national standard map-accuracy requirements."

The plotted horizontal positions of objects are checked by an independent traverse (or triangulation) run to points selected by the person or organization for whom the survey is made. A profile run from any point, in any arbitrary direction, is compared with one made from the plotted contours. Thus both field work and map drafting are checked.

13–18. Sources of error in topographic surveys. Sources of error in topographic surveys include the following:

a. Control not established, checked, and adjusted before topography is taken.
b. Control points too far apart.
c. Control points poorly selected for proper coverage of area.
d. Poor selection of points for contour delineation.

13–19. Mistakes. Typical mistakes in topographic surveys include the following:

a. Improper selection of contour interval.
b. Unsatisfactory equipment or field method for the particular survey and for the terrain conditions.
c. Insufficient horizontal and vertical control of suitable precision.

d. Too few contour points taken.

e. Omission of some topographic details.

PROBLEMS

13– 1. Define contour interval.

13– 2. A contour map has an interval of 25 ft and a scale of 1 in. = 100 ft. If adjacent contours are 80 ft apart on one portion of the map, what is the actual (shortest) distance on the ground between points on the adjacent contours?

13– 3. On a map drawn to a scale of 1 in. = 200 ft the contour lines are $\frac{3}{8}$ in. apart at a certain place. The contour interval is 20 ft. What is the ground slope in per cent between points on adjacent contours?

13– 4. If a model is to be constructed at a scale of 1:2400 and the thickness of cardboard to be used is $\frac{1}{4}$ in., what is the contour interval in feet, for each thickness of the material?

13– 5. In the following diagram, the numbers represent the ground elevations at points in a tract of land:

57		56	W	55		56		58
60	V	63		58	Z	60		63	X
58		59		55		58		59

About which letter can a closed 5-ft contour be drawn—V, W, X, or Z?

13– 6. What is the best method of determining the water-surface elevation of a lake disturbed by light winds?

13– 7. Prepare a set of field notes for locating all the topographic details shown in Fig. 13–2. Scale the distances and angles. Use different methods from those shown, including each of the first five methods of section 13–4 at least once.

13– 8. Show how the map in Fig. 13–6 could be tested for accuracy by means of an overlay sketch.

13– 9. What are the pertinent factors to be taken into account in selecting the proper scale for a specific transit-stadia topographic-mapping project?

13–10. What is the purpose of preparing a topographic map for a new portion of a city? For a city park? For the site of a new industrial plant?

13–11. Outline a method for making a topographic survey of a lot 150 ft by 200 ft having a maximum difference of elevation of 10 ft. Assume that only a tape is available, and improvise your own equipment.

13–12. Outline in detail how you would make a topographic survey and map of a farm consisting of 200 acres in gently-rolling open country. The contour interval is to be 5 ft and the scale of the final map is 1 in. = 200 ft. The survey must include all horizontal and vertical control, buildings, and other physical features. List the equipment needed. The time limit for the field work is fifteen days. Estimate the cost of the survey per acre.

13–13. Give examples and sketch the terrain conditions for which the most desirable method of locating contours would be (a) the coordinate-square method, (b) the direct method, and (c) the indirect method.

Chapter 14

MAPPING

14–1. General. There is an increasing use of maps by engineers and the general public. All engineering construction projects require maps or site plans. Industries searching for suitable locations for new plants must have maps showing terrain conditions. If maps are not available, the best location may be passed over or time lost while a survey is run.

The military services have always depended upon a steady flow of up-to-date maps. The Army Map Service alone published 500,000,000 copies of over 30,000 different maps during World War II.

An engineer must know how to make maps, to be better able to interpret them. Maps for laymen must be clear and easily understood if they are to give maximum service.

Most maps are made for some definite reason; for example, to show topography, boundaries of property, precise location of traverse points, routes of highways or railroads, soil-erosion control areas, forested and reforestation areas, mineral lands, and other special features.

14–2. Mapping agencies. Maps are prepared by private surveyors, industries, cities, counties, states, and several agencies of the Federal government. Unfortunately, the results of many surveys have been squandered by failure to coordinate them with earlier or later work. Valuable maps are gathering dust, unknown and unavailable to prospective users. A start has been made to improve this deplorable situation by setting up depositories in some cities and states. There every obtainable map of the area will be filed for the use of interested persons.

Some of the agencies producing maps on a national scale are the United States Geological Survey, the Hydrographic Office of the United States Coast and Geodetic Survey, and the Army Map Service.

The U.S.G.S. makes topographic maps covering most of the United States. Standard sheets cover $7\frac{1}{2}$- or 15-min quadrangles and show the works of man in black, contours in brown, water features in blue, and woodland areas in green.

An index map presenting the status of topographic mapping in the United States and its territories and possessions is available free of charge from the Geological Survey. Other index maps giving the status of aerial photography, aerial mosaics, geologic mapping, horizontal control, and vertical control in the United States are published by the same agency.

The Hydrographic Office prepares charts of the coast line and coastal waters for the United States and other areas throughout the world.

The Army Map Service devotes a substantial measure of its peacetime efforts to the development of mapping techniques, the improvement of mapping specifications, and the accumulation, evaluation, and maintenance of existing maps.

14–3. Map drafting. Map drafting may be divided into four parts: (a) plotting the traverse; (b) plotting the details; (c) drawing the topography and special data; and (d) finishing the map.

The discussion in this chapter will be confined to large-scale maps primarily.

14–4. Plotting the traverse. Measurements of lengths and angles are used to plot a traverse.

Distances are plotted from the field data to a selected scale, such as 1 in. equals 10, 20, 40, 50, or 100 ft. An engineer's scale is used but is supplemented by steel scales and dividers for plotting control points accurately.

The choice of a scale depends upon the purpose, size, and required precision of the finished map. The dimensions of a standard sheet, the type and number of topographic symbols, and the need for scaling distances are some of the considerations involved.

Map scales are given in three ways: (a) by a *ratio* or *representative fraction*, such as 1/2000; (b) by an *equality*, such as 1 in. = 200 ft; and (c) *graphically*. Two graphical scales at right angles to each other and in diagonally opposite corners of a map sheet permit accurate measurements to be made even though the paper changes dimensions.

A map drawn to any scale can be enlarged or reduced by means of a *pantograph*.

Angles for a traverse are plotted by (a) coordinates, (b) tangents, (c) chords, and (d) protractors.

a) *Coordinate method.* The most accurate method of plotting a traverse is by coordinates. If the latitudes and departures of traverse lines are available from area computations, the total X-coordinate and the total Y-coordinate for each angle point are readily determined and plotted from an origin through one corner of the traverse. For extensive surveys, the map sheet is first laid out in a grid pattern with unit squares of convenient size such as 100, 400, 500, or 1000 ft. The unit squares are checked by measuring the diagonals.

Any errors in plotting the coordinate points are detected by comparing the scaled distance and bearing of each line with the length and direction measured in the field or computed.

Small circles, $\frac{1}{8}$ in. or less in diameter, are used to mark the traverse hubs. Lines should extend only to the circumference of these circles to preserve the exact center point. On most topographic maps the hub locations and traverse lines are omitted from the finished drawing. If shown, they may be drawn in red ink to make them less prominent on a print.

Bearings and lengths of traverse lines are always given unless the coordinates are tabulated. They are placed on the lines so that they can be read easily when the user looks at the sheet from the bottom or from the right-hand side. The bearings should be forward bearings and continuous around the traverse. When these rules conflict, the direction of the bearing is noted by an arrow, as in Fig. 14–7.

b) *Tangent method.* To lay off an angle by the tangent method, a convenient distance is measured along the reference line to serve as a base. Thus, in Fig. 14–1, to plot a 12° 14′ deflection angle at point A, a length AB equal to 10 in. is first marked on the prolongation of the back line. A perpendicular with a length equal to the distance AB times the natural tangent of 12° 14′ (equal to 2.17 in.) is erected at B to locate point C. The line connecting A and C makes the desired angle with AB. Any length of base can be used, but a distance of 10 or 100 units requires only the movement of the decimal place in the natural tangent taken from a set of tables.

The tangent method is employed extensively for plotting deflection angles. It is not so advantageous for large direct angles.

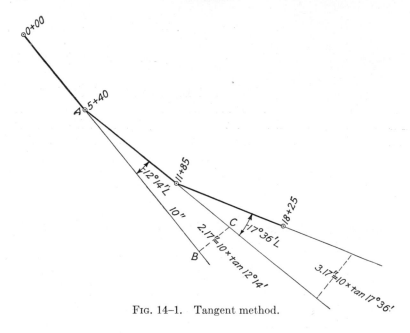

FIG. 14–1.　Tangent method.

c) *Chord method.* To lay off an angle by the chord method, as indicated in Fig. 14–2 a convenient base length of 10 units is first marked on one side, *BA*, giving point *D*. With the vertex *B* as the center and a radius of 10 units, an arc is swung. Then with point *D* as

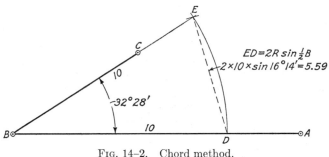

FIG. 14–2.　Chord method.

the center, and a radius equal to the chord for the desired angle, another arc is swung. The intersection of the two arcs locates *E*. The line connecting points *B* and *E* forms the other side of the angle.

The chord for a desired angle may be found by multiplying twice the distance *BD* by the sine of half the angle. Thus in Fig. 14–2 the chord is $2 \times 10 \times \sin 16° 14'$. By making the base length 10, 50, or 100 units to some scale, the chord is readily calculated by using natural sines taken from a trigonometric table.

d) *Protractor method.* A protractor is a device made of paper, plastic, or metal, cut in a full circle or a semicircle, with angle graduations along the circumference. A fine point identifies the center of the circle. The protractor is centered at the vertex of the angle, with the zero line along one side, and the proper angle point is marked along the edge.

Protractors are available in sizes having radii from 2 to 8 in. A metal circle with a movable arm extending beyond the edge, as illustrated in Fig. 14–3, is often used. The arm a rotates about the center b and has a vernier c reading to minutes. A similar arrangement on drafting machines makes plotting fast and accurate.

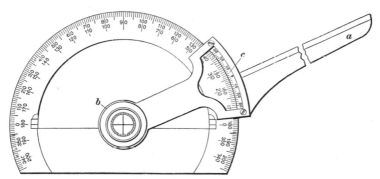

FIG. 14–3. Protractor.

Protractors are universally used for the plotting of details but are not suitable for high-precision work on traverses or control.

14–5. Advantages and disadvantages of the different methods. The computations of coordinates for hubs in closed traverses are readily checked. Any large errors in plotting are found by scaling. Correction usually involves replotting only one point. For example, if the scaled lengths of lines CD and DE of a plotted traverse are not equal to their field measurements, point D is off. The independence of each point in the plotting procedure is a definite advantage.

The tangent method is accurate and probably the best way to lay out a single angle precisely. In plotting a traverse, however, an error in any angle or distance is carried through the remainder of the traverse. If a traverse fails to close, each angle and line must be checked. If the closure is due to drafting rather than the field work, it may be necessary to rotate each line, except the first, slightly and progressively.

The chord method has the disadvantage that errors in any traverse line are passed along to succeeding courses. Erection of a perpendicular is eliminated but determination of the chord lengths is somewhat more laborious than finding perpendicular offsets.

Layout of angles by protractor is the fastest but least accurate of the four methods.

14–6. Plotting details. Boundary corners and important points upon which construction work may depend are plotted by coordinates or the tangent method, but the protractor is used for most details. Orientation of the protractor zero line is by meridian for details located by azimuths or bearings, and by the backsight line if direct angles were measured. Angles are marked along the edge of the protractor, and distances are scaled from the vertex to plot the detail. To avoid obliterating the vertex, and to reduce the erasures, the engineer's scale can be laid along the line through the plotted point and the distance marked. An alternative method consists of drawing a short line through the point at the approximate distance by estimation, and then marking along it.

For accuracy, the distance to the detail should be less than the radius of the protractor unless the type with an extended arm is used.

14–7. Plotting contours. Points to be used in plotting contours are located in the same manner as those for details. Contours found by the direct method are sketched through the points. Interpolation between the plotted points is necessary for the indirect method.

Interpolation to find contour points between points of known elevation can be done in several ways:

a. Estimating.

b. Scaling the distance between points of known elevation and locating the contour points by proportion.

c. Using a rubber band graduated to some scale and stretching it to make convenient marks fall on the known elevations.

d. Using a triangle and scale, as indicated in Fig. 14–4. To interpolate for the 420-ft contour between point A at elevation 415.2 and point B at elevation 423.6, first the 152 mark on one of the

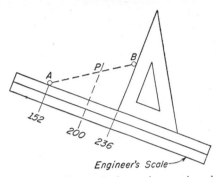

Fig. 14–4. Interpolation using engineer's scale and triangle.

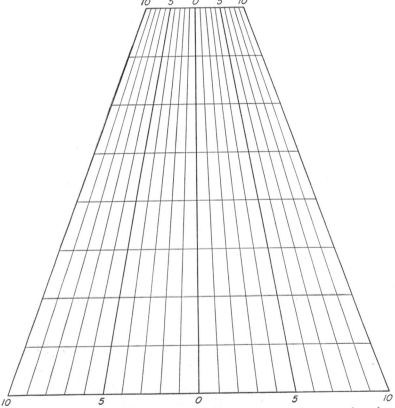

Fig. 14–5. Contour finder for interpolating contours between plotted elevations, assuming uniform slope. (Courtesy of Keuffel and Esser Company.)

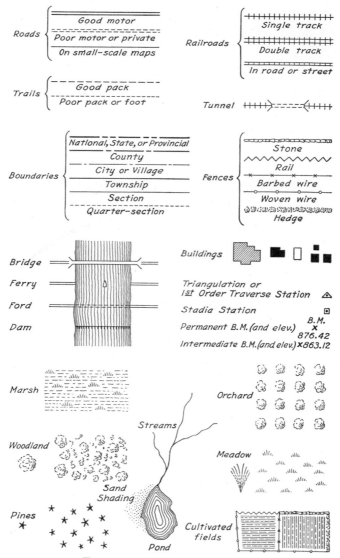

FIG. 14–6.　Topographic symbols.

engineer's scales is set opposite A. Then with one side of the triangle against the scale and the 90° corner at 236, the scale and the triangle are pivoted together around A until the perpendicular edge of the triangle passes through point B. The triangle is then slid to the 200 mark and a dash drawn to intersect the line from A to B. This is the interpolated contour point P.

e. Using a converging-line device, such as that in Fig. 14–5, which can be pivoted and adjusted to fit the difference in elevation between any two points. The procedure is illustrated by the following example: Assume two plotted points have elevations of 17.6 and 25.9. Draw a straight line between these points. Determine the difference between the given elevations to the nearest whole number. Since $25.9 - 17.6 = 8.3$, use 8. Place the contour finder over the map so that its horizontal lines are parallel to the line drawn and so that 8 intervals nearly fill the space between the plotted points. Adjust the finder until the 17.6 point lies 0.6 into the first interval and the 25.9 point lies 0.9 beyond the eighth interval. With a needle point, punch through the contour finder at the contour points desired.

The standard color for inked contour lines is sepia. Every fifth or tenth line is heavier. The contour interval depends upon the terrain, the scale, and the purpose of the map.

Hills, mountains, depressions, and ground-surface undulations can also be represented by hachures and other forms of hill-shading. Hachures are short lines drawn in the direction of the slope. They are heavy and closely spaced for steep slopes, and fine and widely separated for gentle slopes. They show the general shape of the ground rather than actual elevations and thus are not suitable for most engineering work.

14–8. Topographic symbols. Standard symbols are used to represent special topographic features, thereby making it possible to show many details on a single sheet. Figure 14–6 gives a few of the hundreds of symbols employed on topographic maps. Considerable practice is required to draw these symbols well at a suitable scale. A fully detailed map with coloring and shading is a work of art.

14–9. Locating the traverse on a map sheet. The appearance of a finished map has considerable bearing on its acceptability and value.

A map which is poorly arranged, carelessly lettered, and unfinished-looking does not inspire confidence in its accuracy.

The first step in map arrangement is to determine the position of the traverse and topography which will properly balance the sheet. Figure 14–7 shows a traverse (no topography outside the traverse) suitably placed. Before any plotting is done, the proper scale for a sheet of given size must be determined.

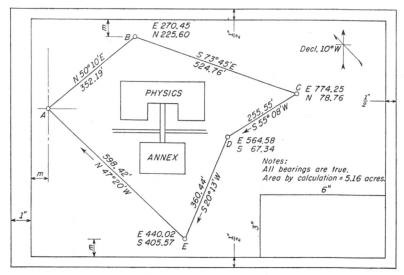

Fig. 14–7. Map layout.

Assume that an 18-in. by 24-in. sheet with a 1-in. border on the left (for possible binding), and a $\frac{1}{2}$-in. border on the other three sides, is to be used.   If the most-westerly station A has been selected as the origin of coordinates, then divide the total departure to the most-easterly point C by the number of inches available for plotting in the east-west direction.   The maximum scale possible in Fig. 14–7 is 774.25 divided by 22.5, or 1 in. = 34 ft.   The nearest standard scale which will fit is 1 in. = 40 ft.

This scale must be checked in the Y-direction by dividing the total Y-coordinate of 225.60 + 405.57 = 631.17 ft by 40 ft, giving 15.8 in. required in the north-south direction.   Since $16\frac{1}{2}$ in. is available, the scale of 1 in. = 40 ft is satisfactory, although 1 in. = 50 ft provides a better border margin.

In Fig. 14–7 the traverse is centered on the sheet in the Y-direction by making each distance m equal to $\frac{1}{2}[17 - (631.17/40)]$, or 0.61 in. The weights of the title, notes, and arrow compensate for the traverse being to the left of the center of the sheet.

If topography is to be plotted outside the traverse, the maximum north-south and east-west distances to topographic features must be added to the traverse coordinates before computations are made for the scale and centering distances.

On some types of maps it is permissible to skew the meridian with respect to the borders of the sheet in order to better accommodate a traverse relatively long in the NE–SW or NW–SE direction. When a traverse with topography is to be plotted by any means other than coordinates, it is advisable to first make a sketch showing controlling features. If this is done on tracing paper, orientation for the best fit and appearance is readily determined by rotating and shifting the tracing.

14–10. Meridian arrow. All maps should show a meridian arrow for orientation purposes. It should preferably be near the top of the sheet, although it may be shifted elsewhere for balance. An arrow should not be so large, elaborate, or heavily blacked in that it becomes the focal point of the sheet, as was true on maps of fifty years ago.

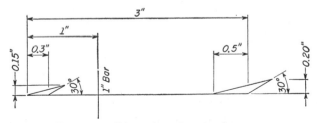

Fɪɢ. 14–8. Dimensions for simple arrow.

Either the magnetic or true meridian, or both, may be shown. A true-meridian arrow is identified by a full head and full feather, and a magnetic arrow by a half-head and half-feather. Figure 14–8 shows dimensions of an arrow that is suitable for routine maps. In practice, an arrow is traced from a sheet of standards, or cut out for pasting on the map.

14–11. Title. The title may be placed wherever it will better balance the sheet, but it is always kept outside the property lines on a boundary-survey sheet.   Usually the title occupies the lower right-hand corner, with any pertinent notes just above or to the left of it. A search for a particular map in a bound set or in a loose pile of drawings is facilitated if all titles are in the same location.   Since sheets are filed flat, bound on the left border, or hung from the top, the lower right-hand corner is the most convenient position.

The title should contain the name of the property or project, its owner or user, the location, the date, the scale, and the name of the surveyor.   Additional data may be required on special-purpose maps. Lettering should be simple in style rather than ornate, and should conform in size with the individual map sheet.   Emphasis is placed on the most important parts of the title by increasing the height of letters and using upper-case letters.

Perfect symmetry about a vertical center line is necessary, since the eye tends to exaggerate any defection.   Also, an appearance of stability is obtained by having a full-width bottom line.

An example of a title and its arrangement for the 18-in. by 24-in. sheet of Fig. 14–7 is shown in Fig. 14–9.   The letters in lines 1 and 2 could be $\frac{1}{4}$ in. high; those in line 3, $\frac{5}{16}$ in. high; and those in the last two lines, $\frac{1}{8}$ in. high.

University of Hawaii
Civil Engineering Department
TRANSIT-STADIA SURVEY OF ENGINEERING CAMPUS
Scale 1 inch = 20 feet   Date 8 Nov. 1955
Survey by L. Gill, T. Hall, A. Aker   Map by   J. Jones

Fig. 14–9.   Title arrangement.

No part of a map better portrays the artistic ability of a draftsman than a neat, well-arranged title.

14–12. Notes.   Notes cover special features pertaining to the individual map, such as the following:

All bearings are true bearings [or calculated, or magnetic].
Area by calculation is X acres.
Area by planimeter is Y acres.
Legend [explanation of unusual symbols; for example, * represents cooling towers].

Notes must be in a prominent place where they are certain to be seen upon even a cursory examination of the map.

14–13. Paper.   Drawing paper for surveying maps should be of excellent quality, take ink without spreading, stand erasures, and not deteriorate with age. Good brown detail paper and high-grade white drawing paper are commonly used. Cloth-backed white paper and aluminum-backed paper are desirable for important work. They are expensive but more resistant to dimensional changes and rough handling.

Many maps are drawn or traced on transparent paper or fine linen so that blueprints can be made from them. An original paper drawing may be finished in pencil for printing, but maps of a permanent nature should be inked.

Blueprinted maps have the disadvantage of changing dimensions because of variations in temperature and humidity, and the printing process itself. Surveys of city lots are normally drawn on small sheets and reproduced by the ozalid method, which does not entail wetting and drying the printing paper.

14–14. Sources of error in mapping. Sources of error in mapping include the following:

a. Not checking (scaling) distances when plotting by coordinates.

b. Plotting by protractor.

c. Using a soft pencil for plotting.

d. Variations in dimensions of map sheet.

14–15. Mistakes. Some of the more common mistakes in mapping include the following:

a. Improper orientation of topographic notes in field and office.

b. Using wrong edge of engineer's scale.

c. Making arrow too large, complex, or black.

d. Omitting the scale or necessary notes.

e. Failing to balance the sheet by making a preliminary sketch.

PROBLEMS

14– 1. If it is desired to keep plotting errors within 20 ft, what is the smallest scale that should be used?

14– 2. On a plane-table sheet having a scale of 1/96,000, what is the smallest distance that can be plotted?

14– 3. List examples of large-scale maps, intermediate-scale maps, and small-scale maps.

14– 4. Approximately how much can an 18-in. by 24-in. blueprinted map change in size in a single day because of temperature and moisture variations of the atmosphere?

14– 5. Sketch the conventional symbols for streams, woodland, marsh, meadows, and cultivated fields.

14– 6. Is there any difference between a map and a chart?   Between a map and an aerial photograph?

14– 7. Plot the topography in the notes of Plate A–9 in Appendix A.

14– 8. Plot the following traverse by coordinates to a scale of 1 in = 50 ft: *AB*, N 75° 10′ E, 262.7 ft; *BC*, S 67° 04′ E, 324.6 ft; *CD*, S 15° 42′ W, 287.5 ft; *DE*, S 87° 00′ W, 396.5 ft; *EA*, N 12° 30′ W, 365.4 ft.

14– 9. In problem 14–8, azimuths and distances to the corners of boundary fences were taken from the traverse points as follows: *A′*, 300° 15′, 45.0 ft; *B′*, 5° 10′, 57.5 ft; *C′*, 89° 47′, 125.5 ft; *D′*, 170° 48′, 92.6 ft; *E′*, 238° 05′, 87.6 ft.   Draw the fence lines.

14–10. In problem 14–8, azimuths and distances to a lake shore were taken from the traverse points as follows: *A*, 100° 40′, 56.5 ft; *A*, 121° 15′, 126.5 ft; *B*, 132° 19′, 121.7 ft; *B*, 237° 10′, 82.5 ft; *C*, 268° 51′, 26.0 ft; *D*, 302° 31′, 14.0 ft; *D*, 341° 56′, 102.5 ft; *E*, 70° 25′, 151.0 ft; *E*, 10° 19′, 15.8 ft.   Plot these points and join them with lines to represent a lake shore.   Finish the map, giving proper symbols, lengths and bearings of the fence lines, an arrow, and a title.   Show the land on one side of the lake wooded and that on the other side cultivated.

14–11. Why do the features shown on a topographic map of a large area differ from those on a map of a small area?

14–12. What are the advantages and disadvantages of cellulose acetate for plotting maps as compared with tracing paper or linen?

14–13. List the items which you think should be in the explanatory notes on a map of the site of a proposed factory building.

14–14. List the important items usually lettered in upper-case letters, and those in lower-case letters, (a) on a topographic map and (b) on a subdvision map of property bordering a river or lake.   What is meant by a "stick-up" on a map?

14–15. Describe the lithographic process of preparing a map sheet.

Chapter 15

THE PLANE TABLE

15–1. General. The plane table is one of the oldest types of surveying instruments. In its modern form a plane-table outfit consists of a tripod; drawing board; an alidade equipped with stadia wires; a stadia rod; and a tape. In the field a sheet of drawing paper is fastened to the board and a map is made by plotting directions and distances obtained by sighting with the alidade.

Mapping topographic features while they are in full view is advantageous in many types of surveys in civil and mining engineering, forestry, geology, agriculture, and military operations. Geologists use the Brunton compass and plane table almost exclusively in their surveys. A small board, a light tripod, and a peep-sight alidade, collectively known as a *traverse table*, are standard equipment in military mapping.

Although the plane table is considered obsolete by some people, and relatively few private surveyors own or have used this equipment, more plane tables are in use now than ever before.

15–2. Description of the plane table. The drawing board of a plane table (usually 24 in. × 31 in.) is carefully made in such a way that it resists warping and other damage from weathering. The upper side is smooth but has some means, such as brass screws, for attaching the paper to the board. At the center of the underside of the board is a socket with threads which fit a head fastened to the top of the tripod.

Two radically different tripod heads, the *Coast and Geodetic Survey type* and the *Johnson head*, are available for leveling and orienting the board. The Coast and Geodetic Survey type, Fig. 15–1, has four leveling screws, and a clamp and a tangent screw like those of a transit. Leveling and orientation are accomplished easily.

The Johnson head has a ball-and-socket arrangement to hold the board in position after leveling, and to prevent its turning in a hori-

FIG. 15–1. Plane table outfit with U. S. Coast and Geodetic
Survey type of head, and old-type alidade.

zontal direction.   Clamp *A*, Fig. 15–2, regulates the motion of the
table as it moves on the larger ball joint.   It is tightened, after the
board has been leveled by pressing or lifting on one side.   The lower
clamp *B* controls the movement of the board about the vertical axis
and is clamped after orientation.

FIG. 15–2. Johnson-type head.

Keeping the table level is the most difficult part of plane-table work
for beginners.   Even light pressure on an edge of the board applies
an effective turning moment on the relatively small supporting area of
the leveling head.

The alidade, Fig. 15–1, consists of a telescope supported by a pedestal rigidly attached to a wide ruler. The telescope is similar to that of a transit and is equipped with one vertical and three horizontal cross hairs. A sensitive level vial, a vertical arc, and perhaps a Beaman arc are provided. The telescope may be centered over the blade, or be offset to place the line of sight along the edge.

Two types of alidades are in use. The *fixed-tube alidade* has its telescope rigidly attached to the transverse axis like that of a transit. The telescope on the *tube-in-sleeve alidade* can be rotated about its longitudinal axis like the telescope of a wye level.

FIG. 15–3.   Modern alidade with self-reducing stadia lines.
(Courtesy of Kern Instruments, Inc.)

The base, or blade, of the alidade is a steel plate several inches wide and up to 18 in. long on some instruments. A bull's-eye level, a compass needle, and lifting knobs may be mounted on the blade.

Accessories used with the plane table include a scale, triangles, a compass, a magnifying glass, a French curve, a slide rule, erasers, a protractor, a declinator, and Scotch drafting tape. A *declinator* is a brass plate on which a compass box and two level vials are mounted. Two edges of the plate are parallel with the north-south line of the compass circle. The declinator is used, in the absence of a compass on the blade, to determine bearings and to orient the alidade by placing an edge against the base.

An alidade of European design is shown in Fig. 15–3. It is a self-reducing stadia instrument and has a parallel-ruler plotting device.

15–3. Use of the plane table. The plane table is best suited for traversing and taking topography. It is seldom used to run boundary lines or route surveys, although some details may be added by plane table after transit-tape surveys have been made.

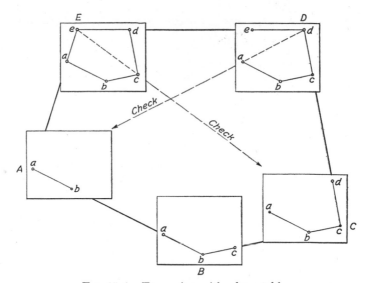

FIG. 15–4. Traversing with plane table.

With a sheet of drawing paper firmly fastened on the board, the table is set up over any point such as A, Fig. 15–4, and leveled. The beveled edge of the alidade blade is then placed over the corresponding point a on the paper. This point may be selected in a convenient position on the board if not previously plotted. The direction to a point B is obtained by sighting through the telescope to align it and then drawing a line along the beveled edge. The stadia distance and vertical angle are read and reduced immediately, and b is located by scaling the horizontal distance on line ab. The difference in elevation computed from the stadia reading is applied to the elevation of A (assuming a reading on the H.I.) to obtain the elevation of B. This value is noted beside the plotted point for ready reference.

On precise work, horizontal control in the form of triangulation or traverse stations, and vertical control represented by bench marks scattered over the area to be mapped, must be plotted carefully on the sheet in advance of any field work. Stadia readings are reduced and plotted as soon as taken, since notes are not recorded. Sketching and interpolation for contours should be kept abreast of the plotting while the ground location of all mapped points is still fresh in the observer's mind.

Obviously the drawing paper must be resistant to moisture and temperature changes, because the same sheet may be used in the field for extended periods. A hard pencil, 6H or 8H, is necessary to avoid smudges. The board may be covered with a waterproof material to protect the drawing. A small "window" is left open over the working area. Plastic sheets which can be marked with a stylus are employed in modern practice.

15–4. Setting up and orienting the plane table. After the board is screwed on the tripod head and the paper is fastened, the tripod is set up so that the plotted point is over the corresponding hub on the ground. Generally this relationship is estimated by eye for small-scale maps. If greater accuracy is required, a plumb bob is used, or a pebble is dropped from the underside of the board to check the position. The table must be carefully leveled by means of the leveling screws (or by the ball-and-socket movement of the Johnson head).

For convenience in drafting and to avoid pressure on the table which will disturb its level, the board should be placed at a height about 1 in. lower than the observer's elbows.

The table may be oriented by (a) compass, (b) backsighting, or (c) resection.

a) To orient by compass, the alidade is laid in the direction deemed most desirable for the north-south line, and the board is turned until the compass on the blade, or the declinator against the ruler, reads north. The board is then clamped and a line is drawn along the blade edge for future reference.

If a line AB of known bearing, say S 28° 30′ E, has already been plotted, the alidade is placed along AB and the table turned until the compass reads S 28° 30' E. The table is then clamped. Orientation by needle is not recommended if the backsighting or resection method can be employed readily.

b) The backsighting method is most commonly used in traversing, although the table may initially be oriented by compass to get north at the top or left side of the sheet. After a line AB has been drawn by sighting from a setup at A to point B, the table is moved to B, set up, and leveled. With the alidade along BA, the table is turned until point A is lined in, and the board is then clamped. The directions of other sights taken with the table in this position will automatically be referred to the same reference line or meridian as AB.

c) Resection will be discussed in section 15–8.

After the table has been oriented by any of the three methods, prominent distant points should be sighted and short lines drawn near the edge of the sheet in their direction. At intervals the alidade can be laid on these lines and the occupied station point to recheck the orientation. By observing on the *permanent backsights* the services of a rodman are not required.

15–5. Traversing. To run a traverse, the table is set up over the initial point A of the survey, leveled, and clamped. Point a on the plane-table sheet, Fig. 15–4, is marked to represent this hub. With the edge of the ruler on a and the alidade sighted at B, line ab is drawn. The distance AB may be determined by tape or stadia and its length marked off according to the scale of the map to locate b. It is essential that this first course be plotted accurately because it serves as the base line for all other measurements.

The table can now be moved to hub B, set up, and leveled. It is oriented by placing the edge of the blade on line ba and turning the board on its vertical axis until the alidade sights point A. The distance BA is measured and the average of AB and BA is used in laying out ab. The next hub C is observed with the blade touching b, the distance BC is determined, and the length bc is plotted. In similar fashion, succeeding points can be occupied and the traverse lines plotted on a map. Whenever possible, check sights should be taken on previously occupied hubs. Small discrepancies are adjusted, but if a plotted point is missed by an appreciable distance, some or all of the measurements should be repeated.

Details can be located while the traverse is being run, or later. It is desirable to close and adjust the traverse before taking topography, inasmuch as all plotting done at an incorrectly located station will be offset.   Two methods are used to obtain details—radiation and intersection.

15–6. Radiation method. With the table oriented at any station of the traverse, radiating lines may be drawn to points whose locations are desired, as indicated in Fig. 15–5.   Generally distances are measured by stadia, but a cloth tape is suitable for short sights.   The radiating lines, or *rays*, are drawn along the edge of the blade and the distances are scaled.

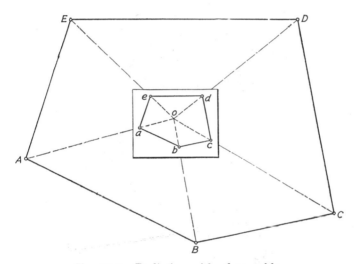

FIG. 15–5.   Radiation with plane table.

15–7. Intersection, or graphical-triangulation, method.   In the intersection method, shown in Fig. 15–6, rays of indefinite length are drawn toward the same point from at least two setups of the plane table.   The intersection of the rays is the location of the point desired. One measured line serves as a base.   No other distances are required.

The term graphical triangulation is sometimes applied to this method, which corresponds to triangulation by transit intersections. The method is particularly important in locating inaccessible and distant points.   In actual field practice, both radiation and intersection may be used on the same setup.   Most shots are taken by radiation.

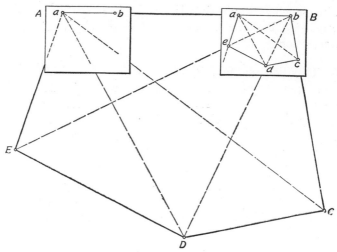

FIG. 15–6. Intersection with plane table.

15–8. Resection. Resection is a method of orientation employed when the table occupies a position not yet located on the map. Solutions for two field conditions will be described. In the first, called the *two-point problem*, the length of one line is known. In the second, the *three-point problem*, the locations of three fixed points are known.

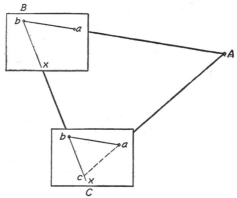

FIG. 15–7. Two-point problem.

15–9. The two-point problem. In Fig. 15–7 line *ab* represents the known length *AB* on the ground. With the table oriented at *B* and the alidade aligned on *C*, a line *bx* of indefinite length is drawn. The distance *bc* is not measured since the observer may wish to reserve judgment on the most advantageous position for his next instrument station, or he may wish the rodman to remain at point A. The table is moved to hub C (any point on line bx), oriented by backsighting along xb, and clamped. The alidade blade is set on a and pivoted around this point until the corresponding station A is sighted. A line drawn along the ruler from point a to intersect line bx gives the location c of the occupied point. Line ac is called a resection line.

15–10. The three-point problem. The three-point method of location has many varied uses. It permits the topographer to set up the plane table at any favorable position for taking topography and then to determine its location on a map by sighting three plotted points. These points might be church steeples, water towers, flagpoles, lone trees, radio masts, jutting cliff formations, and other prominent signals. The three-point method is employed in navigation to ascertain the position of a ship by observing on three shore features recognizable on a coastal chart.

The three-point problem is discussed frequently in technical literature. Trigonometric, mechanical, and graphical solutions have been devised. The tracing-paper, three-arm-protractor, and trial solutions will be described.

If the plane table is on a great circle through the three known points, its location is indeterminate. A strong solution results (a) when the table is well inside the great triangle formed by the three points, or (b) when the table is not near the great circle passing through the three points.

Tracing-paper method. A piece of transparent paper is fastened to the table as shown in Fig. 15–8. From any point p' on the paper, three radiating lines $p'a'$, $p'b'$, and $p'c'$ are drawn toward hubs A, B, and C, which can be observed through the alidade. The tracing paper is then moved until the three radiating lines pass through the corresponding points a, b, and c previously plotted on the map. The vertex of these lines, p'', is the correct location of the table. This point is marked and the board turned to make the lines radiate to the hubs A, B, and C on the ground. The board is then clamped.

Three-arm-protractor method. A similar solution can be obtained mechanically by means of a device called a three-arm protractor. This instrument has a center (somewhat like that of a drafting machine) around which two of the arms can be rotated. The desired

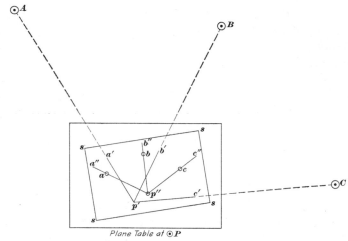

FIG. 15–8.   Tracing-paper method.

angle between each rotating arm and the fixed arm is set by a vernier on a 360° graduated circle.

Angles $Ap'B$ and $Bp'C$ in Fig. 15–8 are read with a sextant or a transit.   The protractor arms are clamped to these angles and then made to pass through the plotted points a, b, and c by trial.   The three-arm protractor is not used on plane-table work but is a valuable tool in hydrographic surveying and coastal navigation.

Lehmann's method.   If tracing paper is not available, a *trial solution* by Lehmann's method can be used.   In this method the table is oriented by estimation, and resection lines are drawn through the plotted positions a, b, and c of the three reference points.   The three lines will form a *triangle of error* if the orientation is not perfect.   An experienced observer can reduce the triangle to a point by two or three trials.

Three rules which facilitate the procedure will be stated.   In these rules the *point sought* is the point on the plane-table sheet representing the station occupied.   The point sought may be inside the triangle of error, or in one of the six areas formed by extending the resection lines beyond the triangle of error, as shown in Fig. 15–9.   The three rules successively eliminate the impossible locations of the point sought, and define its true position.   The surveyor is assumed to be facing the signals, and the directions right and left are given accordingly.

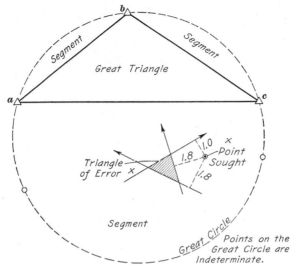

FIG. 15–9.   Lehmann method.

RULE 1.   The point sought is inside the triangle of error if the station occupied is within the *great triangle* (the triangle formed by the three signals), as shown in Fig. 15–10.   This is the simplest case. The exact location of the point sought is determined by rule 3.

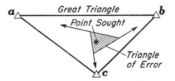

FIG. 15–10.   Triangle of error.

RULE 2.   The point sought is either to the right of all three resection lines drawn from the fixed points, or to the left of all three resection lines.   In Figs. 15–9 and 15–11 the point sought must be in one of the two areas marked with an *x*.   Elimination of one of these possible areas, and the exact location of the point sought, are determined by rule 3.

RULE 3.   The point sought is always distant from each of the three resection lines in proportion to the distances from the respective signals to the plane-table station. As an example of the use of this rule, assume that in Fig. 15–9 the estimated distances (or possibly the distances read by stadia) from the plane table to the three signals A, B, and C are 1800 ft, 1800 ft, and 1000 ft respectively. The distances are therefore in the proportion of 1.8 to 1.8 to 1.0.

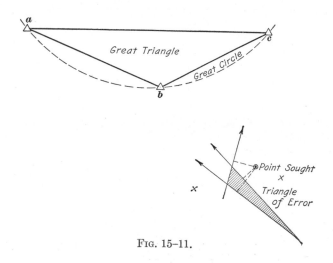

FIG. 15–11.

Using trial sketches, perpendiculars are erected on each of the three resection lines until the unique arrangement is obtained which will give perpendiculars having lengths in the required proportion. Their intersection is the point sought.

After the trial location, T, of the table has been found, the blade of the alidade is laid along point T and the plotted position of the most distant station, a in Fig. 15–9. The table is then reoriented by sighting on the signal at A, and the board is clamped. New resection lines are drawn through points b and c. If the position of the table found by trial is not perfect, a small triangle of error is formed again and the process may have to be repeated once more.

Although the three rules given are sufficient for all cases (actually only the last two are needed, since rule 1 is a special case), two additional rules are helpful:

a) When the point sought is outside the great circle, as in Fig. 15–11, it is always on the same side of the resection line from the most distant point as the intersection of the other two lines.

b) When the point that is sought falls within one of the three segments of the great circle, as in Fig. 15–9, the line drawn from the middle point lies between the point sought and the intersection of the other two lines.

15–11. Leveling. Elevations are obtained by using the alidade as a level, or by reading vertical angles and slope distances. After the alidade has been leveled carefully, a sight may be taken upon a rod set on a bench mark to obtain the H.I. Often the H.I. is simply found by measuring the height of the telescope above the point occupied, by standing the rod alongside the table. The H.I. being known, the rod readings are taken as in ordinary leveling to determine the elevations of points.

Trigonometric leveling is commonly used where considerable difference of elevation exists. This method requires the use of vertical angles and stadia distances, from which differences of elevation are obtained by calculation. A Beaman arc on the alidade facilitates computations, but a stadia-reduction chart, slide rule, or stadia table may be used.

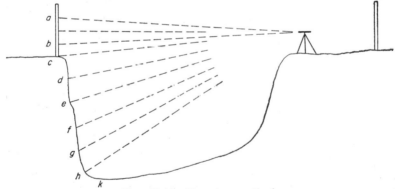

Fig. 15–12. Stepping method.

The *stepping method* of obtaining elevations is sufficiently accurate for some purposes, and in rough terrain it saves time and effort on the part of the rodman. In Fig. 15–12, assume that the elevation of point k at the bottom of a gorge is needed on a survey employing two rodmen, one on each side of the canyon. After the intercept on the rod between stadia hairs, ab, is found to be say 5.2 ft, the upper hair is set on the base of the rod at c. The position d where the lower cross hair strikes the ground is noted, and the upper cross hair is depressed to sight this point.   The process is continued until point h is found, and the remaining drop to the lowest spot k is estimated at perhaps 2 ft.   The difference in elevation between c and k is therefore 28 ft.

Differences of elevation are generally computed in the field and plotted on the plane-table map.   The topographer may compute as well as plot, or he may have one member of the party make the stadia reductions.   Contours are drawn through points established by the direct method, or are interpolated if breaks in slope have been taken. Spot elevations are shown for grade crossings, for peaks and depressions which do not fall at contour levels, and for all other critical points.

The number of points taken need be only 50 to 60 per cent of the number on a comparable transit-stadia survey to locate contours with the same degree of precision.   Furthermore, features shown on the map can be compared with the terrain as work progresses, and any discrepancies readily discovered.

One of the greatest difficulties arising in the use of the plane table is keeping it level.   Pressing on one corner of the board is a practical way to center the bubble and complete a few sights with the Johnson head.   This procedure eliminates the necessity of loosening the ball-and-socket joint, which operation usually disturbs the orientation.

15–12. Advantages and disadvantages of the plane table.   Some of the advantages of the plane table over the transit-stadia method follow:

   a. The map is made while looking at the area.
   b. Irregular lines, such as stream banks and contours, can be sketched.
   c. Notes are not taken.
   d. Fewer points are required for the same precision in locating contours.
   e. A map is produced in less over-all time (field plus office).

Some disadvantages of the plane table in comparison with the transit-stadia method are as follows:

   a. More field time is necessary.
   b. Bad weather halts field work.
   c. Control must be plotted in advance for precise work.
   d. More time is required to become proficient with the plane table than with the transit.

e. Distances must be scaled if areas are to be computed and lengths taken from the map.

f. Many awkward items must be carried.

g. The plane table is unsuitable for wooded country.

15–13. Plane-table pointers. One of the troublesome problems in operating a plane table is to keep the alidade blade on the plotted position of the occupied point, such as P in Fig. 15–13. As the alidade is moved to sight a detail, the edge moves off point P. A solution sometimes tried is to use a pin at P and pivot around it, but a progressively larger hole is gouged in the paper with each sight.

Some alidades, such as that in Fig. 15–3, have a parallel ruler attached to the blade, and this provides the best answer. The next best is to place the alidade within an inch or two of the point P, pivot as necessary for a sight, and then transfer the line through P by using two triangles as shown in Fig. 15–13. The small error produced by the ec-

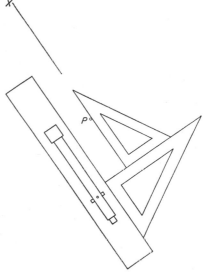

FIG. 15–13.   Transfer of pivot point.

centric sight is no greater than that resulting from not being exactly over the ground point P, or even that caused by the telescope axis not being over the edge of the blade.

Other pointers on the use of the plane table that may be helpful are as follows:

1. Use buff or green detail paper to lessen the glare.
2. Plot and ink the traverse in advance of the detailing, showing lengths of traverse lines, coordinates of triangulation stations, and useful signals available.
3. Have at least one vertical control point for each three hubs of a traverse, and show all known elevations.
4. Have all of the accessories.
5. Cover the portion of the map not being used.

6. Set up the table slightly below elbow height.
7. Check the orientation on two or more lines if possible.
8. Check the distance and elevation difference in both directions when setting a new hub. Use the average value in plotting.
9. Read the distance first, then the vertical angle; or with a Beaman arc, read the H scale and then the V arc.
10. Lift the forward end of the alidade blade to pivot, instead of sliding the blade.
11. Clean the blade frequently to remove graphite.
12. Reduce stadia readings in the following preferred order: Beaman arc, slide rule, charts, tables, formulas.
13. Check the location of hubs by resection and by *cutting in* (sighting and plotting) prominent objects.
14. Draw short lines at the estimated distance on the map to plot points. Do not start the lines at the hub occupied.
15. Keep in mind the comparable limits of accuracy for direction (angle) and distance.
16. Identify points by consecutive numbers or names as they are plotted. Number the contours.
17. Have the rodman make independent sketches on long shots, for later transference to the plane-table map.
18. Use walkie-talkie sets to help the rodmen describe topographic features for the observer when he cannot identify them because of distance and obstacles.
19. Use the same points to locate details and contours whenever possible.
20. Locate contours by the direct method in gently sloping and rolling terrain. Use the indirect method in rugged country and areas having uniform slopes.
21. Sketch contours after three points have been plotted. Points on the map lose their value if they cannot be identified on the ground.
22. Show spot elevations for summits, sags, bridges, road crossings, and all other critical points.
23. Tie a piece of colored cloth on the stadia rod at the required rod reading to speed work in locating contours by the direct method.
24. Use cotton rope $\frac{3}{8}$ in. in diameter soaked in hot paraffin, with knots of different colors at 5- or 10-ft intervals, in making measurements in areas covered by brush and timber.

25. Employ the stepping method in areas where access is difficult.

26. Draw lines at 1-in. intervals on all four margins of the plane-table sheet at the time the first plotting is done. The lines provide a means of determining the expansion and contraction of the paper.

27. Utilize vertical aerial photographs for plane-table sheets. The planimetric details can be checked and contours added.

28. Use a 6H or harder pencil to avoid smudging.

15–14. Sources of error in plane-table work. Sources of error in plane-table operation include the following:

a. Table not level.

b. Orientation disturbed during the detailing.

c. Sights too long for accurate sketching.

d. Poor control.

e. Traversing and detailing simultaneously.

f. Too few points taken for good sketching.

15–15. Mistakes. Some typical mistakes that are made in plane-table work are as follows:

a. Detailing without proper control.

b. Table not level.

c. Orientation incorrect.

PROBLEMS

15– 1. The alidade on a plane table is placed 4 in. off the proper point in sighting at an object 90 ft away. The map scale is 1 in. = 25 ft. Is the error significant? Explain.

15– 2. The telescope of an alidade is centered over a blade 3 in. wide. What error is introduced in plotting a shot 50 ft long if the map scale is 1 in. = 100 ft? If the shot is 200 ft and the map scale is 1 in. = 400 ft? If the sight is 600 ft and the map scale is 1 in. = 1000 ft?

15– 3. Upon what two things does the size of the triangle of error depend in the Lehmann solution of the three-point problem?

15– 4. A plane table is set inside the triangle formed by the three known points. Show how the position of the table is located.

15– 5. In three-point location of the plane table by the Lehmann method, what is the strongest location?

15– 6. Upon what factors does the accurate orientation of a plane table depend?

15– 7. Locate your position in the classroom by the three-point method. Mark three points, one in a corner and two on the blackboards. Measure the horizontal distances from the corner to the two points on the blackboard. Plot the points to scale on a sheet 8½ in. by 11 in. Sight over an edge of the engineer's scale to obtain the resection lines. Change positions so that you are first inside the great triangle, then outside the great triangle but inside the great circle, and finally outside the great circle.

15– 8. On a traverse 4 miles long, an experienced plane-table man uses an alidade with a 22-power telescope and a self-reading rod graduated to permit readings to 0.01 ft. He balances his sights and limits them to 600 ft. What maximum errors in distance and elevation are reasonable?

15– 9. A plane-table traverse for a soil-conservation project is run after orienting on a line whose direction is known. A sight is taken on B.M. Steeple, at elevation 860.12 ft and near the starting point. Another sight is taken on B.M. Lafayette, at elevation 885.49 ft and adjacent to the closing hub. Determine the closure in elevation and adjust the elevations of the traverse hubs. The readings are taken on the H.I. unless noted. H.I. 5.2 ft at A, and 5.5 ft at D.

Hub	Point Sighted	Stadia Distance (ft)	Vertical Angle, or Rod Reading with Telescope Level
A	B.M. Steeple		4.20 ft
	B	242	$+3° 16'$
B	A	242	$-3° 18'$
	C	470	$+2° 30'$
C	B	472	$-2° 32'$
	D	388	$-1° 25'$
D	C	387	$+1° 24'$
	B.M. Lafayette		3.69 ft

Chapter 16

ADJUSTMENT OF INSTRUMENTS

16-1. General. Surveying instruments are designed and constructed to give correct horizontal and vertical measurements. A good instrument, properly handled, may stay in adjustment for months or longer, and last a lifetime. Nevertheless, equipment should be tested periodically, and adjusted to maintain its accuracy. A level, for example, should be checked each day it is used on important work.

It is not feasible to rigidly set the level vials and cross hairs in perfect position on most levels and transits, since replacement or adjustment of parts would then necessarily become a factory operation. Temperature changes, jarring, and undue tension on adjusting screws may cause an instrument to go out of adjustment.

Proper field procedures, such as double centering, keeping backsights and foresights equal, and releveling when the bubble goes off as the telescope is rotated about a vertical axis, permit accurate work to be done with an instrument out of adjustment. Frequently, however, a few minutes spent in making adjustments will reduce the time and effort required to operate an instrument efficiently. Furthermore, some errors may be introduced that can be eliminated only by adjusting the instrument.

Precise adjustment of transits, levels, and alidades in the field is made easier if the following conditions exist:

a. Terrain permitting solid setups, level sights of at least 300 ft, and measurement of a vertical angle of 45° or more.

b. Good atmospheric conditions—no heat waves, and no sight lines passing through alternate sun and shadow or directed into the sun.

c. Instrument in the shade or shielded from the direct rays of the sun.

Three permanent points set approximately 300 ft apart on a straight line on level or nearly level ground, and preferably at the same elevation, expedite adjustments. Organizations having a number of instruments in use, and surveyors working in one area over a long period of time, find it profitable to set such permanent points.

Standard methods and a prescribed order must be followed in making adjustments. Correct positioning of parts is attained by loosening or tightening the proper adjusting nuts and screws with special pins. Time is wasted if each adjustment is perfected on the first trial, since some adjustments affect others. The complete series of tests may have to be repeated several times if the instrument is badly off. A final check of all the adjustments should be made to insure that none has been disturbed.

Straight, strong adjusting pins that fit the capstans should be used, and the capstans should be handled with care to avoid damaging the soft metal. Adjustment screws have been properly set when an instrument is shipped from the factory. Tightening the capstan screws too much (or not enough) nullifies otherwise correct adjustment procedures and may leave the instrument in worse condition than it was before testing.

16–2. Tapes. Tapes are tested by comparing them with a standard. Many surveyors and surveying organizations have a standardized tape which is used only to check other tapes, or they have fixed marks set a known distance apart for the same purpose. The National Bureau of Standards will test any steel tape for a nominal fee and will furnish a certificate giving its correct characteristics for the tension and method of support desired.

Hard usage, kinks, and repairs change the length of a tape. Comparison with a standardized tape at frequent intervals permits even an old tape to be used with assurance.

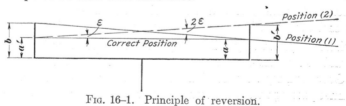

Fig. 16–1. Principle of reversion.

16–3. Principle of reversion. Most adjustments of surveying instruments are checked by the method of reversion. The method consists in reversing the instrument in position to double the error and make it more apparent. Assume that in Fig. 16–1 the angular error between the correct and unadjusted lines is ϵ. This error is caused by the difference in length of a and b as shown in position *1*. After the telescope is turned 180° in azimuth, the unadjusted line occupies position *2* because a and b have changed places.

Since the angle between positions *1* and *2* is 2ϵ, it follows that single reversion doubles the error. The correct adjustment is secured by making a equal to b.

16–4. Adjustment of the wye level. The purpose of an engineer's level is to establish a horizontal plane of sight when the telescope is revolved about a vertical axis. The principal lines of a wye level (Fig. 16–2) which must be adjusted to maintain this condition are the following:

a. Axis of sight. The line from the optical center of the objective lens to the intersection of the cross hairs.

b. Axis of the collars. The line joining the centers of the collars.

c. Axis of the level bubble. The line tangent to the circular arc of the level vial at its midpoint.

d. Axis of the bottom of the wyes. The line tangent to the inner surfaces of both wyes at the supporting (lowest) points for the telescope.

e. Axis of the level bar. The lengthwise reference line or axis of the level bar which is perpendicular to the vertical axis.

f. Vertical axis. The line through the spindle about which rotation takes place.

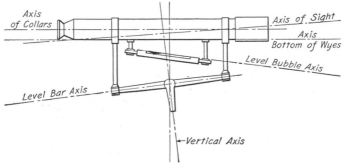

FIG. 16–2. Wye level.

For perfect adjustment, the axis of sight and the axis of the collars must coincide. Lines a, b, c, d, and e must be parallel to each other and at right angles to the vertical axis. To provide this relationship in a wye level, it is necessary that the cross hairs, level vial, and wyes be adjustable. The three adjustments required will be described.

ADJUSTMENT OF CROSS HAIRS

Purpose. To make the axis of sight coincide with the axis of the collars.

Test. Level the instrument and sight the intersection of the cross hairs upon some sharply defined point. Clamp the vertical axis. Unfasten the wye clips. Revolve the telescope in the wyes and note whether the intersection of the cross hairs remains on this point. If a displacement occurs with the telescope inverted, mark a second point beside the first one.

Correction. Bring the intersection of the cross hairs halfway back to the original point by means of the capstan screws which hold the cross-hair ring in the telescope tube. Repeat the operation until the intersection remains on the original point during a complete revolution of the telescope.

ADJUSTMENT OF LEVEL VIAL

Purpose. To make the axis of the level bubble parallel to the axis of sight.

Test. Level the instrument over two opposite leveling screws. Clamp the vertical axis. Open the wyes, lift the telescope, turn it end for end, and replace it in the wyes. The distance the bubble moves off center represents double the error.

Correction. Turn the capstan nut at one end of the level vial to move it up or down until the bubble is brought halfway back to the central position. Level the instrument and retest.

ADJUSTMENT OF WYES

Purpose. To make the axis of the level bubble perpendicular to the vertical axis. The axis of sight, the axis of the level vial, and the axis of the collars are in correct relation following the previous adjustments. The axis of the level bar and the vertical axis are fixed by the manufacturer and are not adjustable. To bring the axis of sight parallel to the level bar it is necessary to make the axis of the wyes parallel to the level bar. The wyes must be of equal height.

Test. Level the instrument with the telescope directly over two opposite leveling screws. Then revolve it 180° about its vertical axis.

The distance the bubble has moved off center represents double the error.

Correction. Change the height of the wye by means of the adjusting screws on it to bring the bubble halfway back toward the centered position. Level the instrument with the leveling screws and repeat the test until the level bubble remains centered as the telescope is revolved about the vertical axis.

PEG ADJUSTMENT

The foregoing three adjustments are called indirect adjustments. It is good practice to test their accuracy by the peg adjustment described in section 16–5 for the dumpy level. The process is the same for both types of levels. However, the error is corrected by moving the level vial of the wye level, and by moving the cross hairs for the dumpy level. If the wyes or the collars are not properly turned or have become worn, the peg adjustment must be used instead of reversing the telescope in the wyes. The chief advantage of the wye level—ease of adjustment by removing and turning the telescope —is thereby lost.

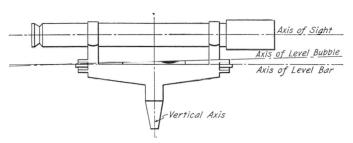

Fig. 16–3. Dumpy level.

16–5. Adjustment of the dumpy level. In the dumpy level, Fig. 16–3, the standards are not adjustable and the telescope tube cannot be revolved or reversed in them. Accordingly there are fewer adjustable parts. The principal lines, defined as for the wye level, are the following:

    a. Axis of sight.
    b. Axis of the level bubble.
    c. Axis of the level bar.
    d. Vertical axis.

For perfect adjustment, it is necessary that the axis of sight, the axis of the level bubble, and the axis of the level bar be parallel to each other and perpendicular to the vertical axis. There are two adjustable parts: the cross hairs and the level vial.

ADJUSTMENT OF LEVEL VIAL

Purpose. To make the axis of the level bubble perpendicular to the vertical axis.

Test. Set up the level, center the bubble, and revolve the telescope about the vertical axis. The distance the bubble moves off the central position is double the error.

Correction. Turn the capstan nuts at one end of the level vial to move the bubble halfway back to the centered position. Level the instrument by means of the leveling screws. Repeat the test until the bubble remains centered during a complete revolution of the telescope.

PRELIMINARY ADJUSTMENT OF HORIZONTAL CROSS HAIR

Purpose. To make the horizontal cross hair truly horizontal when the instrument is leveled.

Test. Set up the level and sight a sharply defined point with one end of the horizontal cross hair. Turn the telescope slowly on its vertical axis so that the cross hair moves across the point. If it does not remain on the point for the full length of the cross hair, the instrument is out of adjustment.

Correction. Loosen the four capstan screws holding the cross-hair ring. Rotate the ring in the telescope tube until the horizontal hair is in a position where it will remain on the point as the telescope is turned. The screws should be carefully tightened in their final position.

PEG ADJUSTMENT

Purpose. To make the axis of sight parallel to the axis of the level bubble. This adjustment is also called the *two-peg method* and the *direct adjustment.*

Test. Level the instrument over a point C halfway between two stakes A and B about 300 ft apart. See Fig. 16–4. Determine the difference in rod readings a_1 and b_1 on A and B, respectively. Since the distance to the two points is the same, the true difference in elevation is obtained even though the axis of sight is not exactly horizontal.

Then set up the instrument at D on line with the stakes and close to one of them—A in this case—and level. If the eyepiece is only a few inches from the rod, the reading on A must be taken by sighting through the objective-lens end of the telescope. Usually a pencil is centered in the small field of view. A rod reading b_2 is taken on B.

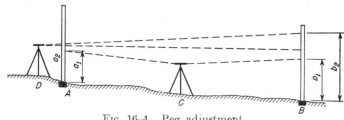

FIG. 16–4. Peg adjustment.

If the axis of sight is parallel to the axis of the level bubble (that is, horizontal), the rod reading b_2 should equal the rod reading at A plus the difference in elevation between A and B, or $(b_1 - a_1) + a_2$. The difference, if any, between the computed and actual readings is the error to be corrected by adjustment.

Correction. Loosen the top (or bottom) capstan screw holding the cross-hair ring, and tighten the bottom (or top) screw to move the horizontal hair up or down and give the required reading on the rod at B. Several trials may be necessary to get an exact setting.

An alternative method of testing the adjustment is by reciprocal leveling. A setup is made close to A and readings are taken on A and B. The level is moved to a position near B and similar sights are taken. The difference in elevation is computed and the cross-hair ring shifted to give a reading on the distant rod equal to the reading on the near point plus the difference in elevation of the hubs.

If the difference in elevation of A and B is known, only one setup is required near either point for the adjustment.

16–6. Adjustment of the transit. The transit is designed to measure the vertical and horizontal projections of angles, and to serve as a level. To these ends, certain lines and axes must be precisely positioned. The principal lines of a transit, Fig. 16–5, are:

a. Axis of the plates. Any line through the top surface of the upper and lower plates and the center of rotation.

b. Axis of the plate bubble. The line tangent to the circular arc of the level vial at its midpoint.

  c. Vertical axis.   Same as for the level.
  d. Axis of the standards.   The line through the center of rotation
    of the telescope axle and the bearings in the standards.
  e. Axis of sight.   Same as for the level.
  f. Axis of the telescope-level bubble.   Same as for the level.

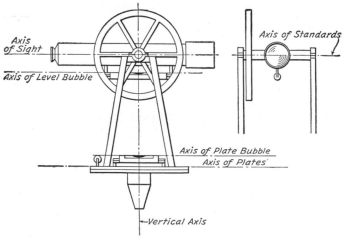

FIG. 16–5.   Transit.

For correct adjustment, a must be parallel to b and perpendicular
to c; d must be parallel to a; e perpendicular to d; and f parallel to e.
To maintain these relationships, the plate-level vials, cross hairs,
standards, telescope-level vial, and vertical-circle vernier must be
adjustable.

ADJUSTMENT OF PLATE-LEVEL VIALS

Purpose.   To make the axis of each plate-level bubble perpendicular to the vertical axis.

Test.   Set up the instrument, bring one of the plate-level vials
over two opposite leveling screws, and center it.   Revolve the instrument 180° about the vertical axis to place the same level vial, turned
end for end, over the same leveling screws.   The distance the bubble
moves from its central position is double the error.

Correction.   Turn the capstan screws at one end of the level vial
to move the bubble halfway back to the centered position.   Level the
instrument by means of the leveling screws.   Repeat the test until the

bubble remains centered during a complete revolution of the instrument.

Adjust the other bubble in the same manner.

PRELIMINARY ADJUSTMENT OF VERTICAL CROSS HAIR

Purpose. To place the vertical cross hair in a plane perpendicular to the horizontal axis of the instrument.

Test. Set up the transit and sight on a well-defined point with one end of the vertical cross hair. Turn the telescope on its horizontal axis so that the cross hair moves along the point. If it departs, the cross hair is not perpendicular to the horizontal axis.

Correction. Loosen all four capstan screws holding the cross-hair ring and turn the ring slightly until the vertical hair remains on the fixed point during the rotation of the telescope. Tighten the capstan screws and recheck the adjustment.

ADJUSTMENT OF VERTICAL CROSS HAIR

Purpose. To make the axis of sight perpendicular to the horizontal axis.

Test. This test applies the double-centering procedure for prolonging a straight line. Level the transit and backsight carefully on a well-defined distant point A, Fig. 16–6, clamping the plates. Plunge

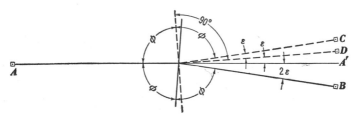

FIG. 16–6. Double reversion.

the telescope and set a foresight point B at approximately the same elevation as A, and at least 600 ft away if possible. With the telescope still in the inverted position, unclamp either plate, turn the instrument on the vertical axis, backsight on the first point A again, and clamp the plate. Plunge the telescope back to its normal position and set a point C beside the first foresight point B. The distance between B and C is four times the error of adjustment because of the double reversion.

Correction.   Loosen one of the side capstan screws which hold the cross-hair ring to the telescope tube and tighten the opposite screw to move the vertical hair one-fourth of the distance CB to point D. Repeat the test until the telescope sights the same point A' after double reversing from a permanent backsight.

ADJUSTMENT OF HORIZONTAL CROSS HAIR

Purpose.   To bring the horizontal cross hair into the optical axis of the telescope.   This is necessary if the transit is to be used for leveling or for measuring vertical angles.

Test.   Set up and level the transit over point A, Fig. 16–7.   Line in two stakes B and C at approximately the same elevation.   Stake B should be at minimum focusing distance from A, perhaps 5 or 10 ft, and stake C at least 300 ft away.

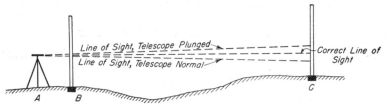

FIG. 16–7.   Adjustment of horizontal cross hair.

Take readings of the horizontal cross hair upon a rod held first on B and then on C.   Plunge the telescope, turn the instrument about its vertical axis, and sight on B again, setting the horizontal hair on the first rod reading.   Then with the vertical and horizontal axes clamped, read the rod held on the far stake C.   Any discrepancy between the two readings on the rod at C is approximately double the error.

Correction.   By means of the top and bottom capstan screws holding the cross-hair ring, move the horizontal hair until it intercepts the rod halfway between the two readings on C.   Repeat the test and adjustment until the horizontal-hair reading does not change for the normal and plunged sights on the far point.

ADJUSTMENT OF STANDARDS

Purpose.   To make the horizontal axis of the telescope perpendicular to the vertical axis of the transit.

Test. With the transit carefully leveled parallel to the transverse axis, sight a well-defined high point A, Fig. 16–8, at a vertical angle of at least 30°, and clamp the plates. Depress the telescope and mark a point B near the ground. Plunge the telescope, unclamp either plate, turn the instrument about the vertical axis, sight point A again, and then clamp the plate. Now depress the telescope and set another point, C, near B. Any discrepancy between B and C is the result of unequal height of the standards and represents approximately twice the error.

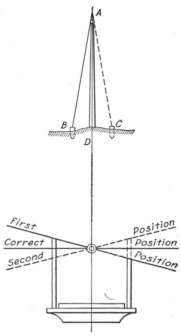

FIG. 16–8. Adjustment of standards.

Correction. Set a point D approximately halfway between B and C, and sight on it. With the plates clamped, elevate the telescope and bring the line of sight on point A by raising or lowering the movable block in one of the standards. To raise the transverse axis, first loosen the friction screws holding the trunnion cap on the standard and then tighten the capstan screw below the block. To lower the axis, reverse the procedure. The friction screws holding the trunion cap must be set carefully to prevent the telescope from being too loose, or from binding.

Repeat the test and adjustment until the high and low points remain in the line of sight with the telescope in both the normal and inverted positions.

ADJUSTMENT OF TELESCOPE-LEVEL VIAL

Purpose. To make the axis of the level bubble parallel to the axis of sight of the telescope.

Test. Same as for the peg adjustment of the dumpy level.

Correction. The level vial is moved, by means of the capstan nut holding it to the telescope tube, to correct any error found.

ADJUSTMENT OF VERTICAL-CIRCLE VERNIER

Purpose. To make the vernier of the vertical circle read zero when the telescope-level bubble is centered (that is, to make the index error zero).

Test. Level the instrument with both plate-level bubbles. Revolve the telescope about the horizontal axis until the telescope bubble is centered. Then read the vertical-circle vernier. The angle that is read is the index error.

Correction. Loosen the capstan screws holding the vernier plate and move it to make the zero marks of the vernier and vertical circle coincide. Then tighten the capstan screws.

16–7. Adjustment of the plane-table alidade. The adjustments of an alidade are similar to those for the transit and level, but they need not be as refined since the plane table is used for less-precise work. The importance of any slight defect of adjustment can be judged by its effect upon the map to be drawn. Adjustments for the fixed-tube and tube-in-sleeve types of alidades are similar. The most critical adjustment is that of the vertical arc, which must be used constantly to determine elevations.

Adjustment of level vials on blade to make their axes parallel to blade. Level the board, draw guide lines along the blade ends, and lift the alidade and turn it end for end, placing it between the guide lines to avoid the effect of any warping in the board. If the bubble goes off center, bring it halfway back by means of the adjusting screws. Then relevel and test again.

Adjustment of vertical cross hair to make it perpendicular to transverse axis. The procedure is the same as for the transit.

Adjustment of telescope-level vial to make its axis parallel to axis of sight. For a rigidly attached vial, the procedure is the same as the peg method for the level vial on a transit telescope. For a striding level (tube-in-sleeve telescope), attach the striding level to the telescope tube, center the bubble, and pick up and turn the striding level end for end. If the bubble moves off center, bring it halfway back by means of the adjusting screws.

Adjustment of cross-hair ring to make axis of sight coincide with axis of telescope sleeve. The procedure is the same as for the adjustment of the cross-hair ring in the wye level, the telescope being rotated in the sleeve.

Adjustment of vertical-arc vernier.   The procedure is the same as for the transit vertical-arc vernier.

Adjustment of vernier-control level bubble.   Level the telescope and set the vernier to read zero.   Center the vernier-control bubble by means of the adjusting screws.

16–8. Adjustment of the Beaman stadia arc.   The index mark for the V scale of a Beaman arc can be adjusted to avoid the need for an index correction.

Purpose.   To make the index read 50 when the axis of sight is horizontal.

Test.   Clamp the telescope with the axis of sight horizontal.   The reading of the V scale should be exactly 50.

Correction.   If the V scale is not perfectly set, loosen the screws holding the arc plate, move it to a position giving a reading of 50, and tighten the screws.   Proper clearance must be allowed between the arc and the circle.

16–9. Adjustment of the hand level.   The horizontal cross hair is the only part of a Locke hand level which can be adjusted.

Purpose.   To make the axis of sight horizontal when the bubble is centered.

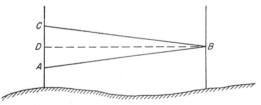

FIG. 16–9.   Adjustment of hand level.

Test.   With the hand level on a solid support at elevation A, and with the bubble centered, mark a point B on a post or building corner. See Fig. 16–9.   The distance AB should not be greater than 100 ft. Support the level at B, center the bubble, and note whether the line of sight strikes point A.   If it does not, mark another point, C.

Correction.   Bisect the distance AC and set point D.   With the level at B and the bubble centered, move the cross hair to D by means of the adjusting screws.

16–10. Sources of error in adjustment of instruments. Some of the sources of error in adjustment of surveying instruments are as follows:

  a. Shifting of the instrument—caused by settlement, pressure by the observer, or wind.
  b. Adjusting screws worn or not properly set.
  c. Threads of adjusting screws not fine enough for a precise setting.
  d. Air boiling, instrument in direct sunlight, and sights taken through alternate sunlight and shadow.
  e. Poor sights resulting from parallax.
  f. Uneven wear on different parts of the instrument.

16–11. Mistakes. Typical mistakes in adjustment of surveying instruments include:

  a. Arithmetical errors.
  b. Adjustments not made in the proper order.
  c. Failure to recheck all adjustments as the final step.

PROBLEMS

16– 1. What are the three most important rules to follow in making adjustments of surveying instruments?

16– 2. After leveling a wye level the instrumentman finds that the bubble moves off center when the telescope is rotated 180° about the vertical axis. What is wrong, and what must be done to correct the defect in adjustment?

16– 3. The telescope of a wye level is rotated 180° about its longitudinal axis. What adjustment is investigated thereby? What correction is made, if needed?

16– 4. What defect in adjustment of the level is nullified by balancing backsights and foresights in differential-leveling operations?

16– 5. What three precautions should be taken if work must be done with a level which is known to be out of adjustment?

16– 6. Which is the more exact method of adjusting a level, the peg method or the reversal method? Why?

16– 7. Describe the proper method of adjusting for parallax when using a level.

16– 8. Compare the adjustments of the wye level with those of the dumpy level.

16– 9. What is the purpose of the peg adjustment of the dumpy level?

16–10. Can the horizontal cross hair of a dumpy level be correctly adjusted by the peg method before the axis of the level bubble is made perpendicular to the vertical axis? Explain.

16–11. Explain fully the method of use of an engineer's transit which will eliminate errors caused by lack of adjustment from measurements of both horizontal and vertical angles.

16–12. A transit does not have a level vial attached to the telescope tube. List the steps required to test and adjust the vernier on the vertical circle.

16–13. List the errors, due to defects of adjustment of a transit, which are eliminated by the following procedures: (a) always sighting with the intersection of the vertical and horizontal cross hairs; (b) reading vertical angles with the telescope in both the direct and reversed positions and taking the average; (c) reading horizontal angles to a high point with the telescope in both the direct and reversed positions and taking the average.

16–14. List three instrument adjustments which may be inaccurate without affecting the correct projection of a line if it is produced by the double-centering method.

16–15. What is the effect of the optical axis of the objective lens not coinciding with the axis of the telescope tube?

16–16. If the line of sight of a transit when revolved about the horizontal axis describes a plane which is inclined to the vertical, what does the adjustment involve?

16–17. What is the purpose of the adjustment of the vertical hair to make the axis of sight perpendicular to the horizontal axis of a transit telescope?

16–18. In the two-peg test with the level at point B, Fig. 16–4, the instrument is found to be 4.10 ft above B. The reading on a rod held on point A is 7.12 ft. With the instrument near A, the reading on the rod at A is 4.73 ft, and that on the rod at B is 1.60 ft. What is the true difference in elevation between A and B? Explain how the instrument would be adjusted.

16–19. A transit is set up over a point A and sighted on point B 300 ft away. The telescope is then plunged and point C set on line 600 ft distant. With the telescope in the plunged position, the instrument is pointed on A again. The telescope is then plunged back to normal, and point C' is set. Distance CC' measures 0.20 ft. What adjustment is needed? What is the angular error introduced by a single plunging? How is the adjustment made?

16–20. A wye level was set up midway between two stakes A and B 300 ft apart. The stakes were then driven so that the rod reading on each stake was 5.476 ft. The level was set up near A and carefully leveled. The reading on a rod held at A was 5.252 ft and that on the rod at B was 5.260 ft. What should have been the correct reading on B for this setup? How is the level adjusted?

16–21. A horizontal angle to the right is measured between a high point and a low point and found to be $23° 48'$. A sight is then taken on the high point, the telescope is depressed, and a point is set on the ground. The telescope is plunged and a second sight is taken on the high point. When the telescope is depressed, the line of sight misses by 0.25 ft (to the right) the mark previously set. What is the effect of the lack of adjustment of the instrument on the horizontal angle that had been read, if the vertical angle between the high and low points is $60°$?

PART II

Chapter 17

DETERMINATION OF MERIDIAN

17--1. General. To fix property lines and other survey courses, directions as well as lengths must be known. The direction of a line is determined by the horizontal angle between it and some reference line, usually a meridian. This meridian may be an assumed line, a magnetic north-south line, or a true meridian through the celestial poles.

The magnetic needle furnishes one means of ascertaining the north-south line. Since magnetic forces are variable in direction throughout the earth, and the compass needle is sensitive to local attraction, this method is not reliable for accurate surveying. A true north-south line determined by observations on the sun or stars is necessary if the location of points is to be permanently fixed.

This chapter will present the fundamental facts of field astronomy as applied to observations on the sun and Polaris (the North Star) for azimuth. Some additional study will permit the student to make observations by using any of the stars whose positions are given in an ephemeris or the *American Nautical Almanac*. Copies of the ephemeris are made available free of charge by the various companies manufacturing surveying equipment. More-extensive tables are given in *Ephemeris of the Sun and Polaris* (published by the General Land Office), the *Nautical Almanac*, and the *American Ephemeris*.

Possession of an ephemeris will be assumed in the following discussion. (The Keuffel and Esser ephemeris has been used for reference in this chapter.)

17–2. Methods of determining azimuth. The following methods for determining a true north-south line will be examined briefly: (1) *Sun observations* by (a) shadow method, (b) equal-altitudes method, and (c) direct observations; (2) *circumpolar-star observations* at (a) culmination, (b) elongation, and (c) any hour angle.

Students usually find the study of field astronomy somewhat

difficult because it requires many definitions, spherical trigonometry, and visualization in three dimensions. Several examples of simple methods which can be used for rough determinations of azimuth will be given before the more-technical features are discussed.

17-3. Shadow method. It is possible to establish a meridian by the shadow method without any equipment except a piece of string. In Fig. 17-1, points A, B, C, D, E, and F mark the end of the shadow of a plumbed staff or a telephone pole at intervals of perhaps 30 min of time throughout the period from 9 A.M. to 3 P.M. A smooth curve is sketched through the marks. With the staff as a center, and any appropriate radius, a circular arc is swung to obtain two intersections, x and y, with the shadow curve. A line from the staff through m, the midpoint of xy, approximates the meridian.

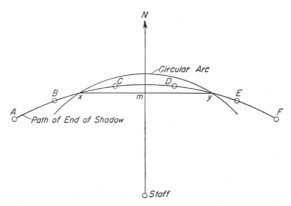

FIG. 17-1. Determination of azimuth by shadow method.

If the pole is plumb, and the ground is level, and if the shadow points are carefully marked, the angle between the line established and the true meridian should not be larger than 30 min of arc. Since the sun moves diagonally across the equator instead of traveling along a perfect east-west path, some error is inherent in the method.

17-4. Meridian by equal altitudes of the sun. Determination of the meridian by equal altitudes of the sun requires a transit, but the method is similar in principle to the shadow method. Assume that the meridian is to be passed through a point P, Fig. 17-2, over which the transit is set up. At some time between 8 A.M. and 10 A.M., say about 9 A.M., with a dark glass over the eyepiece or objective lens, the sun's disk is bisected by both the horizontal and vertical cross hairs. The vertical angle is read, the telescope is depressed, and point x is set at least 500 ft from the instrument. Shortly before 3 P.M., with the vertical angle previously read placed on the arc, the sun is followed until the vertical and horizontal cross hairs again simultaneously bisect the sun. The telescope is depressed and a point y is set at approximately the same distance from P as x. The bisector of angle xPy is the true meridian.

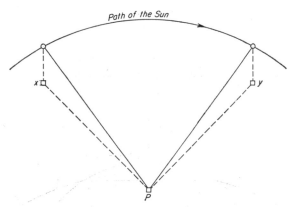

FIG. 17–2. Azimuth by equal altitudes of the sun.

As in the shadow method, perfect results cannot be attained because the changing declination of the sun gives it a diagonal path. The declination of the sun is its distance north or south of the equator.

Other disadvantages of the method are the time required, the possibility of the sun being obscured at the time of the second sight, and the difficulty of setting the vertical angle exactly (since most arcs read only to the nearest minute). The last problem can be eliminated by setting hub x first, then elevating the telescope to observe the sun as it passes over the point, and leaving the vertical angle on the arc until the afternoon sight has been taken.

17–5. Meridian from Polaris at culmination. Figure 17–3 shows the apparent motion of Polaris as seen from the earth. The star moves in a counterclockwise direction around the north-south axis of the earth extended, but twice each day it is on the line of this axis for an observer at any location. The point at the upper limit of its travel is called *Upper Culmination* (U.C.), and the point at the lower extremity, *Lower Culmination* (L.C.). At *Eastern Elongation* (E.E.) and *Western Elongation* (W.E.) the star reaches its most distant position from the meridian.

If an observer at point O sights on Polaris at the exact instant of upper culmination or lower culmination for his longitude, he need only depress the telescope and set a hub X on the ground to obtain a true north-south line, OX. If it is more convenient to do so, the horizontal angle from the star to a mark can be measured to give the azimuth of a desired line.

The exact time of culmination at Greenwich, England, for any date is available in an ephemeris. A few simple calculations are required to translate the time to other locations.

Some basic principles of field astronomy will now be given, along with their use in observations.

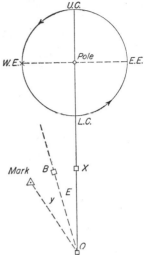

Fig. 17–3. Azimuth at culmination.

17–6. Definitions. In observations upon heavenly bodies, the sun and stars are assumed to lie on the surface of a celestial sphere of infinite radius having the same center as the earth. All stars appear to move around centers which are on the north-south axis of the celestial sphere. Figure 17–4 illustrates some of the terms used in field astronomy. Here S represents a heavenly body, as the sun or a star. Students will find it helpful to sketch the various features on a true sphere or globe.

The *zenith* is the point where the plumb line produced above the horizon meets the celestial sphere. On a diagram it is usually designnated by Z.

The *nadir* is that point on the celestial sphere directly beneath the observer, and directly opposite to the zenith.

A *vertical circle* is any great circle of the celestial sphere passing through the zenith and nadir. As a great circle, a vertical circle is the line of intersection of a vertical plane with the celestial sphere.

An *hour circle* is any great circle on the celestial sphere whose plane is perpendicular to the plane of the celestial equator. Hour circles

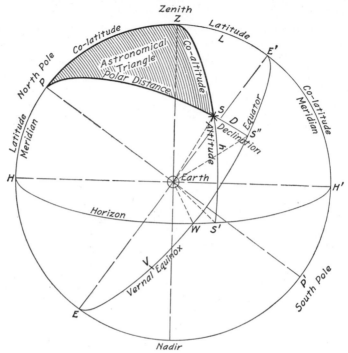

FIG. 17–4.   Celestial sphere.

correspond to meridians and longitudinal lines, and are used to measure hour angles.

The *celestial equator* is the great circle on the celestial sphere whose plane is perpendicular to the axis of rotation of the earth.   It is the earth's equator enlarged in diameter to that of the celestial sphere. Half of the equator is represented by $EWS''E'$.

A *celestial meridian* is the hour circle which contains the zenith. It is also defined as the vertical circle which contains the celestial pole. The intersection of the plane of the celestial meridian with the plane of the horizon is the astronomic meridian line used in plane surveying.

The *horizon* is a great circle on the celestial sphere whose plane is perpendicular to the direction of the plumb line.   In surveying, the plane of the horizon is determined by the use of a spirit level.   Half of the horizon is represented by $HWS'H'$.

An *hour angle* is the angle between the plane of the hour circle passing through a celestial body or point and the plane of the celestial meridian. It may be measured by the angle at the pole between an hour circle and the meridian, or by the arc of the equator which is intercepted by those circles.

The *Greenwich hour angle* of a heavenly body is the angle measured from the meridian of Greenwich westward to the meridian over which the body is passing at any moment. In the ephemeris it is designated by GHA.

The *declination* of a heavenly body is the angular distance measured along the hour circle between the body and the equator; it is plus when the body is north of the equator, and minus when south of it. Declination is usually denoted by D in formulas, and is represented by $S''S$ in Fig. 17–4.

The *position* of a heavenly body with respect to the earth, at any moment, is given by its declination and Greenwich hour angle.

The *polar distance* of a body is the angular distance from the pole. It is equal to 90° minus the declination.

The *altitude* of a heavenly body is the angular distance measured along a vertical circle above the horizon. Altitude is represented by $S'S$ and in formulas is usually denoted by h. It is measured by means of the vertical arc of a transit or theodolite.

The *co-altitude*, or *zenith distance*, equals 90° minus the altitude.

The *azimuth* of a heavenly body is the arc of the horizon measured clockwise from either the north or south point to the vertical circle through the body. The azimuth from the south is represented by $H'S'$. It is measured as a horizontal angle by means of a transit or theodolite.

The *latitude* of an observer is the angular distance on his meridian between the equator and the zenith. It is also the angular distance between the pole and the horizon. Latitude is measured north or south of the equator. In formulas it is denoted by L.

The *vernal equinox* is the point of intersection of the celestial equator and the ecliptic apparently traversed by the sun in passing from south to north. It is the astronomer's zero-zero point of coordinates in the sky. On a diagram it is designated by V.

Refraction is the angular increase in the apparent altitude of a heavenly body due to the bending of light rays passing obliquely through the earth's atmosphere. It varies from zero for an altitude of 90° to a maximum of about 35 min at the horizon. The correction for refraction, in minutes, is roughly equal to the natural cotangent of the observed altitude. Small corrections must also be made for temperature and pressure variations.

Refraction makes observations on heavenly bodies near the horizon less reliable than those taken at high altitudes. The correction is always subtracted.

Parallax results from observations being made from the surface of the earth instead of at its center. It causes a small angular decrease in the apparent altitude, hence the correction is always added.

17–7. Time. Four kinds of time may be used in computing an observation.

Sidereal time. A sidereal day is the interval of time between two successive upper transits of the vernal equinox over the same meridian. Sidereal time is star time. The sidereal time at any instant is equal to the hour angle of the vernal equinox.

Apparent solar time. An apparent solar day is the interval of time between two successive lower transits of the sun. Apparent solar time is sun time, and the length of the day varies somewhat. The average apparent solar day is 3 min 56 sec longer than a sidereal day.

Mean solar, or civil, time. This is the time kept by a fictitious sun which is assumed to move at a uniform rate. It is the basis for watch time and the 24-hr day.

The *equation of time* is the difference between mean solar and apparent solar time. Its value is continually changing as the sun gets ahead of, then falls behind, the mean sun. Values for each day of the year are given in an ephemeris.

Standard time. This is the mean time at meridians 15 deg or 1 hr apart, measured eastward and westward from Greenwich. Eastern standard time (E.S.T.) is the time of the 75th meridian and differs from Greenwich time by 5 hr (later). Standard time was adopted in the United States in 1883.

In working with longitude and time zones, it is helpful to remember the following relations:

$$360° \text{ of longitude } = 24 \text{ hours}$$
$$15° = 1 \text{ hour}$$
$$1° = 4 \text{ minutes (of time)}$$

17–8. Star positions. If the pole could be seen as a definite point in the sky marked by a star, a meridian observation would require only a simple sighting. Since the pole is not so marked, observations must be made on stars—preferably stars close to the pole—whose radii of rotation and positions at given times are listed in a nautical almanac or an ephemeris. Stars appear to move counterclockwise because of the earth's clockwise rotation.

The visible star nearest the north pole is Polaris, a part of the constellation Ursa Minor, which constellation is also called the Little Dipper. The radius of rotation of Polaris, measured by a vertical angle along the meridian through the position of an observer, is its polar distance. The value of this angle changes slightly from year to year but it is approximately 0° 56′.

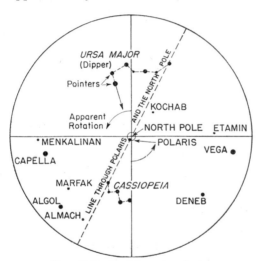

Fig. 17–5. Position at polaris.

Polaris is located in the sky by first finding the Big Dipper, in Ursa Major. The two stars of the dipper farthest from the handle are the Pointers, as shown in Fig. 17–5. Polaris is the nearest bright star along the line through the pointers and is also distinguished by its position at the end of the handle of the Little Dipper.

17–9. Observation on Polaris at culmination. As previously noted, if Polaris can be observed at upper or lower culmination, the meridian is readily laid out on the ground. At culmination, however, the star appears to be moving rapidly in the east-west direction. Accurate time is therefore required to obtain a precise meridian, and only a single sight is possible for each culmination.

Since the sidereal day is 23 hr 56.1 min and the mean solar (civil) day is 24 hr, culmination occurs about 4 min earlier each day of the calendar year. Over a period of many years, however, there is very little difference in the time of culmination for the same date.

Ephemerides list the time of culmination and elongation at Greenwich for every 10th or 15th day throughout the year. It is necessary to convert these tabulations to the standard time of the place of observation.

An observation at culmination is simple to compute. There are two important disadvantages, however: A small error in time causes a relatively large error in azimuth, and both culminations may come at awkward hours—even during daylight in the summer.

17–10. Computations for time of culmination. Three computations or corrections must be made to convert the time of culmination listed in an emphemeris for Greenwich, England, to the standard (watch) time for culmination at any other location. These computations will be illustrated for an observation on 18 December 1954 at latitude 46° 42′ North, longitude 93° 18′ West, by taking pertinent values from an ephemeris.

1) Correction to convert the time of upper culmination tabulated in the ephemeris for Greenwich on certain dates, to the actual date of observation. The result obtained by interpolating in the table is as follows. The interpolated date or value is inset.

15 December	20^h 17.3^m GCT	
18 December	$\frac{3}{10} \times 39.5 = 11.8^m$	20^h 05.5^m
25 December	19^h 37.8^m	

2) Correction for longitude 93° 18′ west of Greenwich. A place at longitude 93° 18′ is approximately $\frac{1}{4}$ the way around the world from Greenwich, and therefore the time difference is $\frac{1}{4}$ day. The average change (decrease) in time of culmination per day (or per 360° of longitude) is 3.93 min over an entire year, but for the 10-day interval being used, the change is 3.95 min per day. The correction for 93° 18′ of west longitude is

$$3.95 \times \frac{93.3}{360} = -1.0 \text{ min}$$

3) Correction for longitude west of 90th meridian. A correction

must be applied for the difference in time of culmination at longitude 90° and that at 93° 18′. This means converting standard (watch) time to local time at the place of observation. Since 1° corresponds to 4 min of time, the correction is

$$3.30 \times 4 = + 13.2 \text{ min}$$

The plus indicates that culmination occurs later at longitude 93° 18′ West than at the time-zone meridian. Note that standard time at the 90th meridian is six hours later than Greenwich time, but it takes Polaris approximately six hours to travel from the meridian of Greenwich to the meridian of the place of observation.

The three computations show that at the moment Polaris culminates over the meridian of the observer at longitude 93° 18′, a watch set for the time zone of the 90th meridian should read

$$20^h 05.5^m - 1.0^m + 13.2^m = 20^h 17.7^m$$

Notice that if the observer had been on the 90th meridian a correction of only 1 min would have been necessary to get the local time of culmination after interpolating in the ephemeris.

Ephemeris tables are based on 40° latitude as an average for the United States. Since the star is on the meridian at culmination, latitude has no effect on the watch time.

17–11. Observation on Polaris at elongation. Observing Polaris at elongation instead of at culmination has several advantages: (a) The star has a negligible east-west movement and appears to travel along the vertical wire for at least 15 min before and after elongation. (b) The watch time need not be precise. (c) Several sights can be taken and averaged to eliminate instrumental and personal errors. A minor disadvantage is the somewhat longer computation procedure.

The observation is made by first sighting on an illuminated mark with the plates set to zero, and then loosening the upper motion and sighting on the star. The angle from mark to star, y in Fig. 17–3, is read. The telescope is plunged, a second sight taken on the star, and the angle read again. The process is repeated for the desired number of readings. As a final step, the original mark should be resighted to be certain the plates read zero.

An alternative method is to sight the star at elongation with zero on the plates, depress the telescope, and set a stake B, Fig. 17–3, several hundred feet from the instrument. The procedure is repeated

Illustration 17–1

COMPUTATION OF THE BEARING OF POLARIS AT ELONGATION

Time of W. E. at Greenwich, 18 Dec. 1954	2^h 05.3^m
Correction for longitude west of Greenwich −	1.0^m
Correction for longitude west of 90th meridian +	13.2^m
Correction for latitude other than 40° +	0.8^m
Time of W. E. at observer's location	2^h 18.3^m

Polar distance of Polaris by interpolation from the ephemeris:

16 December	0° 56.42′		
18 December	$\frac{2}{15} \times 0.05 = 0.01$	0° 56.41′	
31 December	0° 56.37′		

Bearing of Polaris at W. E. by double interpolation:

Polar distances	0° 56.33′	0° 56.41′	0° 56.67′
Latitude 46°	1° 21.1′	1° 21.2′	1° 21.6′
Latitude 46° 42′		**1° 22.2′**	
Latitude 47°	1° 22.6′	1° 22.7′	1° 23.1′

after plunging as a check. The direction to true north can be laid off the next day after computing the angle E.

17–12. Computations for an observation at elongation. A computation for the time of western elongation and the bearing of Polaris at elongation is given in illustration 17–1. The data are the same as in section 17–10, but an additional (fourth) correction must be made for latitude other than 40°.

The star is 1° 22.2′ to the west of north at elongation. This is the value of angle E, Fig. 17–3. Adding the angle y between the mark and the star produces the desired true bearing of the line from O to the mark.

Another means of computing the angle E between Polaris at elongation and the meridian is by the formula

$$\sin E = \frac{\sin \text{polar distance}}{\cos \text{latitude}} \qquad (17\text{–}1)$$

In the example,

$$\sin E = \frac{\sin 0° 56.41′}{\cos 46° 42′} = 0.023928$$

and

$$E = 1° 22.3′$$

The mean polar distances for the years 1955 through 1960 are shown in Table 17–1.

TABLE 17–1

MEAN POLAR DISTANCES FOR THE YEARS 1955–60

Year	Mean Polar Distance	Year	Mean Polar Distance
1955.........0° 56′ 30″		1958.........0° 55′ 43″	
1956.........0° 56′ 14″		1959.........0° 55′ 28″	
1957.........0° 55′ 58″		1960.........0° 55′ 13″	

For observations made less than 30 min before or after elongation, the correction to the bearing at elongation can be computed by the formula

$$C = Kt^2 \qquad (17\text{–}2)$$

where C = a correction to the angle, in seconds of arc;

K = a factor depending upon the bearing at elongation;

t = the time, in minutes, before or after elongation.

The value of K may be found from Table 17–2.

TABLE 17–2

CORRECTION FACTORS FOR BEARINGS AT ELONGATION

Bearing at Elongation	K
1° 10′.....................................0.040	
1° 20′.....................................0.046	
1° 30′.....................................0.051	
1° 40′.....................................0.057	
1° 50′.....................................0.063	

For the values previously found and an observation 30 min after elongation, the correction is

$$C = 0.047(30)^2 = 42 \text{ sec}$$

The small value of the correction demonstrates the advantage of observing Polaris at or near elongation since a large error in watch time causes only a small error in the azimuth.

17–13. Observation on Polaris at any hour angle. Frequently it is more convenient to make an observation on Polaris at any hour angle than at culmination or elongation. The difference between the time of observation and the time of culmination is computed, and the bearing of Polaris at that hour angle taken from the ephemeris.

A sample set of field notes and the computations for the bearing of the reference line are shown in illustration 17–2. A second horizontal

Illustration 17-2

OBSERVATION ON POLARIS AT ANY HOUR ANGLE

Data

⯄ at △ Cass   Lat. 47° 22′ 13″ N   Long. 94° 32′ 18″ W   6 Sept. 1954

Point Sighted	Watch Time	Watch Correction	Horizontal Angle Clockwise	Vertical Angle
△ Snow			0° 00′	
Polaris	5ʰ 44ᵐ 05ˢ	0ᵐ 00ˢ	72° 22′ 40″	48° 08′
△ Snow			0° 00′	

Hour Angle of Polaris

GCT of upper culmination 7 September 1954		2ʰ 50.3ᵐ
Correction for one day at 3.93ᵐ per day	+	3.9ᵐ
GCT of upper culmination 6 September 1954		2ʰ 54.2ᵐ
Correction for longitude 94.54° west of Greenwich	−	1.0ᵐ
Local time of upper culmination		2ʰ 53.2ᵐ
Correction for longitude 4.54° west of 90th meridian	+	18.2ᵐ
CST of upper culmination at longitude 94° 32.3′ W		3ʰ 11.4ᵐ
Actual time of observation		5ʰ 44.1ᵐ
Time difference from culmination		2ʰ 32.7ᵐ
Correction for 3.93ᵐ per day (approx. 10ˢ per hour)	+	0.4ᵐ
Hour angle (west of upper culmination)		2ʰ 33.1ᵐ

Bearing

For latitude 47° 22.2′ and polar distance of 0° 56.99′, and hour angle of 2ʰ 33.1ᵐ, bearing of Polaris (west of north)	0° 52.9′
Clockwise angle △ Snow to Polaris	72° 22.7′
Clockwise angle △ Snow to North	73° 15.6′
Bearing △ Cass to △ Snow	N 73° 15.6′ W

angle should be obtained with the telescope plunged, and the watch time recorded, to permit computation of an average value of the bearing.

17–14. Practical suggestions on Polaris observations. The following suggestions make observations on Polaris easier to perform:

1. It is most convenient to use eastern elongation during the summer season in the United States.
2. Have the noteforms ready in advance of starting field work.
3. Have a watch, flashlight, reflector, and pencils. Note that the accuracy of vernier readings is lowered at night. Lighting from

the side causes parallax if the plates are not at the same level. Hold the flashlight over the compass box behind the ground-glass upright piece and let the light diffuse through it.

4. The mark must be visible at night, and recognizable and definite in the daytime.

5. Set up the transit in daylight if possible. If the altitude of Polaris is known, observations can begin before dark.

6. The altitude of Polaris is equal to the latitude of the place when the star is at elongation. The star may be a degree off and out of the field of view near culmination.

7. Use a paper reflector held on the telescope by a rubber band. The light must not be too bright or the star becomes invisible. It cannot be too dim or the cross hairs fade out. Most theodolites have a special receptacle to accommodate batteries and a bulb for lighting the cross wires, horizontal circle, micrometer scale, and vertical arc.

8. For pointings at high altitudes, the telescope objective lens may slide back and throw the instrument out of focus.

9. Use a sketch to eliminate errors in the relationships between the mark, north, and the star.

10. The value of 1 deg of arc in miles indicates the limit of accuracy obtainable. If the assumed latitude of the observer's position is in error by 1 mile, the maximum error in azimuth at a latitude of 45° is roughly 1.5 sec.

17–15. Comparison of solar and Polaris observations. Compared with Polaris observations, sights on the sun (a) are more convenient, (b) will not give results so precise, (c) can be made while the survey is in progress, and (d) have a limiting accuracy of perhaps 1 or 2 min with methods normally used.

17–16. Methods of observing the sun. Observations on the sun can be made directly by using over the eyepiece a dark glass which is optically plane and parallel. They can be taken indirectly by focusing the sun's image on a piece of paper held behind the eyepiece. Looking at the sun directly through the telescope without a dark glass may result in permanent injury to the eye.

The best hours for observing are between 8 and 10 A.M., and between 2 and 4 P.M.

At least four observations, two normal and two plunged, with a minimum of time between them, should be obtained. The path of the

Illustration 17–3

SOLAR OBSERVATION FOR AZIMUTH

π at $\triangle$ Rover   Latitude 42° 45′ N   Longitude 73° 56′ W   30 June 1954

Point Sighted	Telescope	Watch Time (EDST)	Vertical Angle	Horizontal Angle (Clockwise)
$\triangle$ Ridge				0° 00′
♃ Sun	Direct	3ʰ 33ᵐ 10ˢ	52° 54′	209° 33′
♃ Sun	Direct	3ʰ 34ᵐ 20ˢ	52° 43′	209° 42′
♄ Sun	Plunged	3ʰ 35ᵐ 37ˢ	52° 22′	210° 02′
♄ Sun	Plunged	3ʰ 36ᵐ 49ˢ	52° 10′	210° 11′
$\triangle$ Ridge				0° 00′
Mean		3ʰ 34ᵐ 59ˢ	52° 32.2′	209° 52′

Refraction and Parallax Corr.

$$\text{(for 78° F)} \qquad = - \qquad 0.6' \quad \text{(Index error}$$
$$\text{True altitude} \qquad h = \overline{\quad 52° 31.6'\quad} \quad = 0° 00')$$

Correction   0ʰ GCT to noon $= + \; 12^h$
Correction   To 5th time zone $= + \; 5^h$
Correction   For daylight saving $= - \; 1^h$
EDST of observation $= \quad \overline{3^h \; 34^m \; 59^s}$
Greenwich civil time of observation $= \quad 19^h \; 34^m \; 59^s = 19.58^h$
Declination 30 June 1954 0ʰ GCT $= \quad 23° \; 13.4'$
Corr. for 19.58ʰ = 0.15′ × 19.58 $= - \quad \dfrac{02.9'}{23° \; 10.5'}$
Declination $= \quad$

$$\cos Z_n = \frac{\sin D}{\cos L \cos h} - \tan L \tan h$$

log sin 23° 10.5′ = 9.594989	
colog cos 42° 45′ = 0.134113	log tan 42° 45′ = 9.965855
colog cos 52° 31.6′ = 0.215816	log tan 52° 31.6′ = 0.115438
log 0.88088 = 9.944918	log −1.20585 = 0.081293

$$+0.88088$$
$$\cos Z_n = -0.32497$$
$$Z_n = 108° \; 57.8'$$

Since the observation was made in the afternoon, this angle is counter-clockwise from north.   The minus sign indicates an angle greater than 90°.

Azimuth of sun $= 251° \; 02.2'$
$\triangle$ Ridge to sun $= 209° \; 52'$
Aximuth of $\triangle$ Rover to $\triangle$ Ridge $= \overline{\quad 41° \; 10'}$ (from north)

sun can be considered a straight line over a period of 5 min, and the average value of the readings used in computations. Plotting the vertical and horizontal angles against time for the four readings provides a good check. Note in illustration 17–3 that for approximately equal differences in time between observations, the changes in vertical angles are approximately equal, and the changes in horizontal angles are roughly equal.

The diameter of the sun as viewed from the earth is approximately 32 min of arc. Bisecting such a large object which is moving both horizontally and vertically is difficult, but the average person can do it with an accuracy of perhaps 1 min of arc.

A better method is to observe the border of the sun. In Fig. 17–6a the disk is brought tangent to both cross hairs first in one quadrant and then in the diagonally opposite quadrant. Averaging the two readings eliminates consideration of the semidiameter.

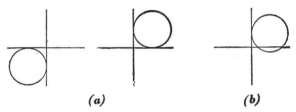

(a)   *(b)*

Fig. 17–6. Observation on the sun.

To avoid coordinating the movement of both tangent screws with the sun, it is simpler to follow the disk by keeping the vertical cross hair tangent to it and letting the sun come tangent to the horizontal hair, as in Fig. 17–6b. Since the altitude changes faster than the azimuth during the observing hours, it is preferable to keep the vertical hair tangent.

The transit is oriented by setting the plates to read zero and sighting along the fixed line from the observer's position to a mark. After recording the times, the vertical angles, and the horizontal angles for four or more observations, the mark is resighted to be certain the plates still read zero.

Before work is begun, the observer should have (a) the noteforms ready, (b) an ephemeris and the correct watch time, (c) the latitude and longitude of the place of observation, and (d) the index error of the instrument.

17–17. Required quantities in determining azimuth by direct solar observation. Five things must be known or determined in a solar observation for azimuth: the latitude, the declination of the sun, the time, the altitude of the sun, and the horizontal angle from some reference line to the sun.

Latitude can be taken from a map or found by a separate observation. North latitudes are considered plus in the standard formulas. An error of 1 mile in the assumed latitude produces an error of less than 0.5 sec in azimuth for locations within the United States.

Declination of the sun is given in an ephemeris for each day of the year, along with the change per hour. The declination of the sun depends on its astronomical position and is independent of the observer's location. It is the same for all observers in any part of the world at the same instant. North declinations are always considered plus, regardless of the latitude of the observer.

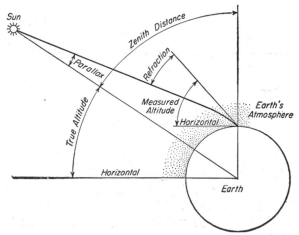

Fig. 17–7. Altitude, refraction, and parallax. True altitude = measured altitude − refraction + parallax. (Courtesy of Keuffel and Esser Company.)

The time of observation must be adjusted for the difference between watch time and Greenwich civil time. A correction is required only for the time zone, not for the exact longitude of the observer. Every manufacturer's ephemeris now lists the declination for Greenwich civil noon rather than for Greenwich apparent noon. Use of this time eliminates the correction for the equation of time. Greenwich noon is 12 hours Greenwich civil time.

The apparent altitude of the sun is its angular distance above the horizon as measured by the engineer's transit. To obtain the true altitude, the observed value must be corrected for index error, for refraction and parallax, as indicated in Fig. 17–7, and for the semidiameter of the sun if the border is sighted in only one quadrant. Errors of adjustment of the standards and cross hairs are eliminated by sighting with the telescope both normal and plunged. Careful leveling is required.

The horizontal angle to the center of the sun is measured from some fixed line. This angle combined with the computed bearing of the sun at any instant gives the bearing of the reference line.

17–18. Notes and computations for a solar observation. Determination of the azimuth of a line by observation on the sun requires the solution of a spherical triangle defined by the zenith, the north pole, and the sun. This is the *PZS* triangle, Fig. 17–4. The angle *PZS*, or Z_n, at the zenith is the bearing of the sun from the meridian through the place of observation.

One form of the equation used in solving the *PZS* triangle is

$$\cos Z_n = \frac{\sin D}{\cos L \cos h} - \tan L \tan h \qquad (17\text{–}3)$$

where Z_n = angle from the meridian to the sun, measured clockwise in the morning and counterclockwise in the afternoon;

D = declination of the sun at the moment of observation;

L = latitude of the place;

h = altitude of the center of the sun at the time of observation.

An example illustrating the field data and calculations for a solar observation is given in illustration 17–3. The conditions are shown in Fig. 17–8.

17–19. Sources of error in meridian observations. Some of the sources of error in meridian observations include:

a. Transit not perfectly leveled.

b. Horizontal axis of the instrument not truly horizontal.

c. Index error not corrected.

d. Sun not bisected by both cross hairs.

e. Time not correct, or not read exactly at the moment of observation.

f. Parallax in readings taken at night.

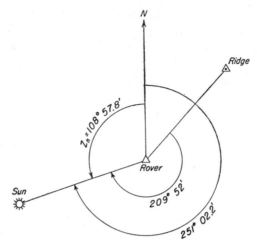

Fig. 17–8.　Relationship of sun, mark, and north.

17–20. Mistakes.　Some of the more common mistakes that occur in observations for meridian are:

a. Sighting on the wrong star.

b. Using a poor signal on the reference line.

c. Computational errors.

PROBLEMS

17– 1.　Why is sun-dial time not accurate?

17– 2.　Why is the moon not commonly used for meridian observations?

17– 3.　Describe and show by means of a sketch a method for determining, without the use of a table or any equipment, whether Polaris is on the meridian of the observer.

17– 4.　A man living at longitude 110° 50′ W has his watch set for 1 hour of daylight-saving time.　What is his watch reading at Greenwich noon?

17– 5.　A clock at longitude 165° E is set for 2 hours of daylight-saving time.　What does this clock read at Greenwich noon?

17– 6.　The coordinates of a point on the earth's surface are latitude and longitude.　What are the coordinates of the sun in the same system?

17– 7.　A flag waving in the morning sun from a 90-ft pole casts a shadow on level ground at a distance of 117 ft from the pole.　What is the altitude of the sun?

17– 8.　A transit in perfect adjustment is carefully set up over a monument. What are the errors which might occur in the determination of azimuth by a sight on Polaris at culmination?　At elongation?　At any hour angle?

17– 9.　Do standard time zones follow exact 15° intervals?　Explain.

17–10. Why does the calendar day start at midnight? Why does the astronomer's day begin at noon?

17–11. Explain the gain or loss of one day in crossing the International Date Line.

17–12. What is the maximum difference between mean solar time and apparent solar time?

17–13. How can accurate time be obtained for an observation on Polaris?

17–14. At the latitude of Los Angeles (approximately 34°), the watch reading was 1 min in error for an observation on Polaris for azimuth. The position of the star was about half way between U.C. and E.E. What is the resulting error in azimuth?

17–15. An observation made on Polaris at U.C. gives an observed altitude angle of 36° 14′. If the declination of Polaris is 88° 57′, what is the latitude of the observer?

17–16. An observation for azimuth is made on Polaris near E.E. at 1:25 A.M. on 19 June 1955. Compute the four corrections required for a location at latitude 43° 00′ N, longitude 83° 30′ W.

17–17. An observation is made on Polaris at E.E. on 18 May at a place in latitude 40° 00′ N and longitude 85° 00′ W. Compute the local time of E.E. for the following ephemeris listings: 16 May, E.E. at 4 hr 17.3 min; 1 June, E.E. at 3 hr 14.7 min. If the angle from a monument to the star is 78° 14′ to the right, what is the true bearing of the line from the observer's position to the monument?

17–18. An observer at point A in latitude 40° N sights on Polaris 3 hr after W.E. and reads the angle from mark B to the star as 15° 24′ R. What is the azimuth of line AB?

17–19. How long will Polaris appear to climb (or descend) the wire without departing more than 20 sec in arc at latitude 35° N?

17–20. A transit was set up on triangulation station Rose and sighted on a light shown from station Mud. A horizontal angle of 34° 10′ 30″ was then turned clockwise to Polaris when the star was at western elongation. The declination of Polaris on the date of observation was +88° 59′ 12″. The position of station Rose is 40° 45′ 35″ N, 74° 10′ 40″ W. Determine the true bearing of the line from Mud to Rose.

17–21. Most ephemeris tables do not cover latitudes from 0° to 10°. What would you do if an observation became necessary at latitude 5° N and only an ephemeris was available?

17–22. What is the approximate error in azimuth for an observational error of 1 min in reading the altitude of the sun in June? The latitude of the station is 40° N.

17–23. Prepare a set of notes and a sketch for four solar observations made during the morning with a transit.

17–24. In making an observation on the sun for azimuth, two readings are taken with the telescope normal and two with the telescope plunged. Show on a sketch the check available within the data themselves before computations are made.

17-25. What are the sides of the *PZS* triangle used in computing a solar observation, and what are the angles opposite them?

17-26. Compute the azimuth of the line from the occupied station *A* to a mark *B* for the following data:

25 Sept. 1956   Lat. 34° 00′ N   Long. 118° 20′ 54″ W   Temp. 68°

Position of Sun	Horizontal Angle	Vertical Angle	Watch Time PST
NE quadrant	79° 13′ 40″	27° 29′	16ʰ 25ᵐ 05ˢ
	79° 20′ 40″	27° 23′	16ʰ 25ᵐ 35ˢ
SW quadrant	80° 04′ 20″	27° 44′	16ʰ 26ᵐ 12ˢ
	80° 08′ 40″	27° 39′	16ʰ 26ᵐ 35ˢ

Chapter 18

PHOTOGRAMMETRY

JOHN O. EICHLER

Professor of Civil Engineering
Georgia Institute of Technology

18-1. General. Photogrammetry is the art and science of making measurements from either *terrestrial photographs* or *aerial photographs*. A phototheodolite, which consists of a camera mounted on a tripod, as shown in Fig. 18-1, is used in terrestrial photogrammetry. Mapping by ground methods is more limited in scope than aerial photogrammetry, but can be employed in plotting vertical cliffs, mountainous terrain, and special features.

Photographs taken with a camera of the type shown in Fig. 18-2 are used in aerial photogrammetry. Both *vertical photographs* and *oblique photographs* are used. Verticals are taken with the camera axis vertical, or as nearly vertical as is possible. Obliques are made with the camera axis inclined intentionally at a comparatively large angle to the vertical. A *high-oblique photograph* is one that includes the horizon; a *low-oblique photograph* does not include the horizon.

The beginning of photogrammetry goes back more than 100 years, but the rapid advance of the science did not occur until after World War I. Both Federal agencies and private companies have improved the cameras, plotting instruments, and plotting techniques, so that maps made from aerial photographs are as good as those made by the plane table or the transit-stadia method. Contour intervals of 1 and 2 ft are now being plotted by using new instruments and techniques.

The advantages of aerial photographs in mapping include (a) speed of coverage of an area, (b) ease of obtaining topographic details in inaccessible areas, (c) freedom from possible omission of data in the field, and (d) the tremendous amount of detail shown. It should be noted, however, that too much detail prevents important features from being emphasized, as they are on a map.

18–2. Aerial photogrammetry.   A photograph taken from an aeroplane is not a true map of the earth's surface.   It is a perspective projection rather than an orthographic projection.   Also, most aerial photographs contain tilt, despite all precautions taken to keep the camera vertical.   Methods have been devised to overcome these limitations so that both planimetric and topographic maps may be constructed from aerial photographs.

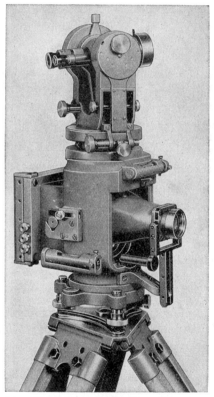

FIG. 18–1. Phototheodolite. (Courtesy of Wild Heerbrugg Instruments, Inc.)

The aeroplane that is used to carry the camera must have special characteristics such as stability in flight, long range, economy in operation, and good visibility for the pilot and for camera operation.

The aerial camera must be precise but can be either the single- or multiple-lens type. For topographic mapping, the single wide-angle lens is common. Nominal focal lengths of the most commonly used single-lens cameras are 6 in., $8\frac{1}{4}$ in., and 12 in. Aerial cameras are built to use either roll film or glass plates, but the use of roll film is more prevalent. The usual size of roll is $9\frac{1}{2}$ in. by 200 ft, which produces 250 exposures 9 in. by 9 in.

FIG. 18–2. Fully automatic aerial camera. (Courtesy of Wild Heerbrugg Instruments, Inc.)

Special mounts hold the camera rigid in the aeroplane and permit the camera to be leveled readily. No device has been perfected to keep the camera axis absolutely vertical. Vertical photographs, therefore, almost always have distortions caused by a small angle between a truly vertical line and the axis of the camera. Specifications on some private contracts state that the maximum tilt in any one photograph must not exceed 3°, and the average for a project must not be greater than 1°. For some Government work, the maximum values are 4° and 2°.

The drive mechanism on the camera can be operated automatically or by hand. This mechanism moves the film for successive exposures and also sets the shutter. An intervalometer may be connected to the camera in order to provide automatic operation at definite intervals ranging from 1 second to 120 seconds.

The frame, across which the film passes, holds the film in the correct focal plane, either by air pressure or a vacuum, and contains *the fiducial marks* which are printed on each photograph. These marks locate on the photograph the geometric axes whose intersection must be on the optical axis of the camera (at the foot of the perpendicular from the emergent nodal point of the lens to the plane of the photograph). This intersection is called the *principal point.*

Vertical photographs used for photogrammetric mapping are made in strips, the line of flight usually running north and south, or lengthwise over the area to be mapped. The strips have a *sidelap* (strip overlap) of 25 per cent, plus or minus 10 per cent. The *forward overlap* (advance) averages 60 per cent, plus or minus 5 per cent. The 60 per cent overlap insures that the images of all points appear in at least two and preferably three photographs.

18–3. Scale of vertical photograph. The scale is the ratio of the length of a line on the map to the length of the corresponding line on the ground. For vertical photographs, however, the value of the scale is not the same for all lines because of the differences in elevation of their terminal points. The scale formula which applies to perfectly flat terrain (Fig. 18–3) is

$$\frac{d}{D} = S = \frac{f}{H - h} \tag{18–1}$$

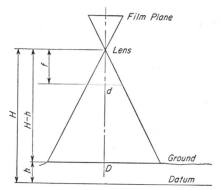

FIG. 18–3.   Photographic scale.

where d = length of line on photograph;

   D = length of line on ground;

   S = scale;

   f = focal length;

H = altitude of aeroplane above datum plane (usually mean sea level);

h = elevation of line (terrain) above datum plane.

For lines at different elevations, the scale varies.   If the terminals of a line are at different elevations, their average elevation is used in the formula.

Although it is difficult to obtain a uniform scale for a vertical photograph, the lengths of lines can be determined from the fundamental relationship between photographic coordinates x and y and ground coordinates X and Y.   This relationship may be stated as follows:

$$\frac{x}{X} = \frac{f}{H - h} \tag{18-2}$$

$$\frac{y}{Y} = \frac{f}{H - h} \tag{18-3}$$

The ground coordinates are referred to the *plumb point* (the point on the ground directly under the exposure station) as the origin, the coordinate axes being parallel to the geometric axes of the photograph. The X-axis is taken in the direction of the line of flight.

To find the length of a line AB, which has unequal terminal elevations, the photographic coordinates of the terminals are measured by using the principal point as the origin.   These coordinates (x_a, y_a, x_b, and y_b), the altitude of the aeroplane, the focal length of the lens, and the elevations (h_A and h_B) of the terminal points of the line, can then be substituted in the following formulas:

$$X_A = \frac{H - h_A}{f} x_A \tag{18-4}$$

$$X_B = \frac{H - h_B}{f} x_B \tag{18-5}$$

$$Y_A = \frac{H - h_A}{f} y_A \tag{18-6}$$

$$Y_B = \frac{H - h_B}{f} y_B \tag{18-7}$$

The true horizontal distance is

$$AB = \sqrt{(X_A - X_B)^2 + (Y_A - Y_B)^2} \tag{18-8}$$

18–4. Image displacement. The distance on a photograph from the image of any ground point to its fictitious image projected to a datum plane is the image displacement caused by topographic relief. On vertical photographs, image displacements caused by topographic relief always radiate from the principal point. Thus in Fig. 18–4,

$$d = r - r_1 \tag{18-9}$$

and
$$\frac{r}{R} = \frac{f}{H - h} \qquad \text{or} \qquad r = \frac{Rf}{H - h}$$

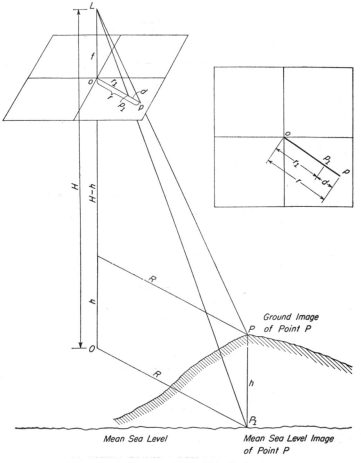

Fig. 18–4. Topographic relief displacement.

Also,
$$\frac{r_1}{R} = \frac{f}{H} \quad \text{or} \quad r_1 = \frac{Rf}{H}$$

then
$$d = \frac{Rf}{H - h} - \frac{Rf}{H} = \frac{Rfh}{H(H - h)}$$

Substituting r and r_1 in the above expression,

$$d = \frac{rh}{H} \tag{18–10}$$

and
$$d = \frac{r_1 h}{H - h} \tag{18–10a}$$

where d = image displacement;

r = radial distance on photograph from principal point to visible (ground) image, P, of a point;

r_1 = radial distance on photograph from principal point to P_1, the position of point P projected to the datum plane, mean sea level;

h = height of point or object above datum plane;

H = height of aeroplane above datum plane.

Formula 18–10 is useful in computing the heights of points and objects when stereoscopic instruments are not available. Frequently, the height of an object above the ground, rather than above a datum plane, is desired. The formula then becomes

$$d = \frac{rh}{H - h_1} \tag{18–10b}$$

where h_1 (not shown in Fig. 18–4) = height of ground above datum plane.

EXAMPLE. It is desired to find the height of an object shown on an aerial photograph by the image-displacement method. The flight altitude of the aeroplane is 4800 ft above mean sea level, and the elevation of the ground is 350 ft. Measurements on a photograph give r = 11.81 mm and r_1 = 11.66 mm.

From formulas 18–9 and 18–10,

$$d = r - r_1 = 11.81 - 11.66 = 0.15 \text{ mm}$$

and
$$h = \frac{d(H - h_1)}{r} = \frac{0.15(4800 - 350)}{11.81} = 56.5 \text{ ft}$$

18–5. Stereoscopic vision.

Stereoscopic vision is that particular application of *binocular vision* (simultaneous vision with both eyes) which enables the observer to view an object, or two different per-

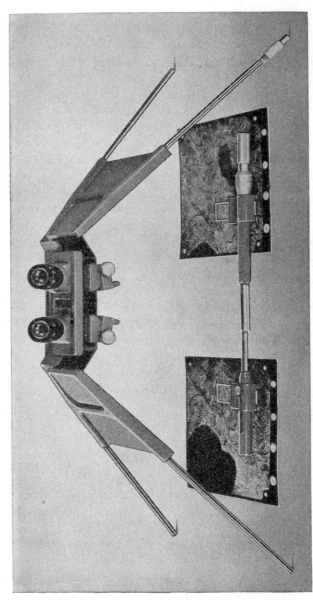

FIG. 18-5. Folding mirror stereoscope with stereometer (parallax bar). (Courtesy of Wild Heerbrugg Instruments, Inc.)

spectives of an object, such as two photographs taken from different camera stations, so as to obtain therefrom the mental impression of a three-dimensional model. Thus when two overlapping photographs are correctly oriented and viewed throught a stereoscope, each photograph is seen with only one eye and a three-dimensional model appears to exist on the table. Stereoscopic vision makes it possible to plot contours as well as planimetric details from photographs. Figure 18–5 shows a *mirror stereoscope*.

18–6. Parallax. Parallax is the apparent displacement of the position of a body with respect to a reference point or system caused by a shift in the point of observation. Parallax is measured along the x-axis of the photograph, there being no parallax in the y-direction for a truly vertical photograph.

Absolute parallax of a point is the algebraic difference between the distances of the two images of the point on two photographs from their corresponding principal points, measured parallel to the *air base* (the x-axis). It is found by measuring the x-coordinates of a point on both photographs of a stereoscopic pair and applying the relation

$$p = x - x_1 \qquad (18\text{–}11)$$

where x is measured on the left photograph and x_1 is measured on the right photograph.

Correct algebraic signs must be used when values are substituted in the formula.

Some of the most important formulas in photogrammetry are these expressions for parallax:

$$X = \frac{B}{p} x \qquad (18\text{–}12)$$

$$Y = \frac{B}{p} y \qquad (18\text{–}13)$$

$$H - h = \frac{B}{p} f \qquad (18\text{–}14)$$

where X and Y = ground coordinates measured from the plumb
   point;
   B = air base = distance between two exposure stations;
   p = absolute parallax;
   x and y = photographic coordinates;
   H = altitude of aeroplane;

h = elevation of object above sea level;
f = focal length of lens.

Figure 18–6 shows the fundamental principles used in deriving the parallax formulas. These formulas enter into many of the problems in photogrammetry such as those requiring the length of a line and the elevation of a point.

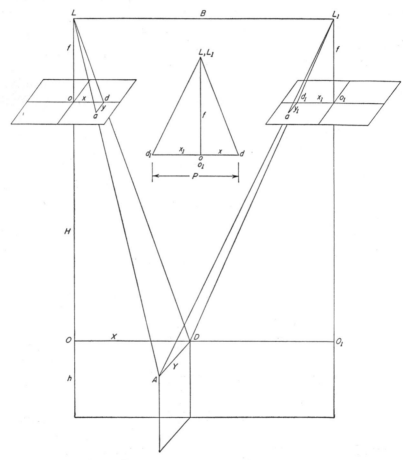

FIG. 18–6. Parallax relationships.

18–7. Measuring-stereoscopes. Measuring-stereoscopes provide a means of measuring parallax and studying stereoscopically a pair of photographs. Examples are the *stereocomparagraph*, Fig. 18–7, and the *contour finder*. These small instruments utilize the same principles as the larger and more precise machines such as the *multiplex projector*, Fig. 18–8, the *Kelsh plotter*, and the *Wild autograph*. Differences in parallax are measured by the aid of a *floating mark*. Two dots superimposed on the photographs are fused mentally by the observer and produce the floating mark.

FIG. 18–7. Stereocomparagraph in use. (Courtesy of Fairchild Camera and Instrument Corporation.)

A micrometer screw is used to move one of the dots (usually the right one) in the x direction. When the dots are fused over a point, they appear to rest upon it. If the instrument is moved to a different point, the dot will appear to float in the air, or bury itself in the ground. The dots can again be made to rest upon the new point by turning the micrometer screw. The micrometer-screw reading is a measure of the difference in parallax between the two points.

To obtain the absolute parallax for use in the formulas, the differences of readings taken from a measuring stereoscope are added to the calibration constant. This constant is found by measuring the absolute parallax of a point on two photographs. The floating mark is then set over this point and the micrometer is read. The difference between the micrometer reading and the measured absolute parallax is the calibration constant.

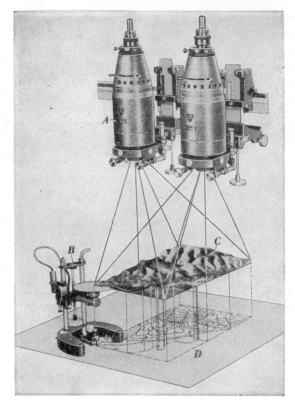

FIG. 18–8.   Formation of stereoscopic model with multiplex.   *A*, multiplex projectors; *B*, tracing table; *C*, model; *D*, manuscript map.   (Courtesy of U. S. Geological Survey.)

EXAMPLE.   It is required to determine the calibration constant of a measuring stereoscope.   The coordinates of a point measured on two photographs are $x = +80$ mm (left photograph) and $x_1 = +10$ mm (right photograph).   Also, with the measuring stereoscope over the point, the micrometer reads 16.3 mm.

The absolute parallax is

$$p = 80 - 10 = 70 \text{ mm}$$

The calibration constant is then

$$C = 70 - 16.3 = 53.7 \text{ mm}$$

This constant is added to all other micrometer readings to get the true parallax of any point.

Measuring stereoscopes also have an attachment for drawing contours.   The absolute parallax for any definite elevation may be obtained by substituting values in formula 18–14 and solving for p. The micrometer reading to be set on the measuring stereoscope is found by subtracting the calibration constant from the absolute parallax.

18–8. Photograph interpretation. Interpretation of photographs is one of the important aspects of aerial photogrammetry. An aerial photograph completely depicts all cultural features. Roads, railroads, rivers, trees, and cultivated lands are easily distinguished. Factors which aid in identifying objects on photographs include shape, size, pattern, shadow, tone, texture, and site location.

Photo interpretation requires study, experience, and an understanding of geology, engineering, and other sciences.

18–9. Mosaics. An aerial-photographic mosaic is an assembly of individual aerial photographs. It contains a vast amount of detail and serves many purposes, although a mosaic is not a map. Mosaics may be (a) controlled, (b) semicontrolled, or (c) uncontrolled.

A *controlled mosaic* is made from photographs that have been corrected for tilt (if known), carefully brought to the same scale, and laid to an accurate horizontal control. Photographs can be corrected for tilt and scale differences by the use of a rectifying camera, Fig. 18 9.

An *uncontrolled mosaic* usually is prepared by matching images of highways, rivers, and other objects on the photographs.

A *semicontrolled mosaic* combines some of the features of each of the other two types.

The procedure in laying photographs is basically the same for all types of mosaics. The photographs should be glossy single-weight prints laid on a hard, nonporous surface which is permanent in nature and relatively stable despite changes in temperature and humidity.

For the temporary layout, the center strip of photographs is laid out first. If a highway or railroad is shown, its direction may be used as an azimuth for orienting the strip. The first photograph is placed at some convenient point on the mounting surface, and the other prints are laid in succession by matching details, or, in the case of a controlled mosaic, by adjusting to fit the control points. The photographs are not cut at this time.

After the first strip is completed, the adjoining rows are oriented

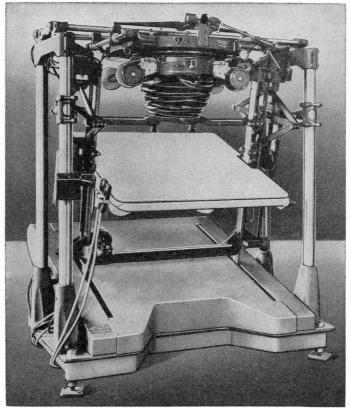

FIG. 18–9.   Rectifying camera.   (Courtesy of Bausch and Lomb.)

and laid.   When all photographs have been placed, the position of each one is marked and the photographs are removed.

The entire first photograph is then pasted to the mounting surface. The other photographs are trimmed with a razor blade or sharp knife by cutting only through the emulsion.   Each photograph is bent along the cut line and torn back.   The feathered edge which results can be smoothed by rubbing with fine sandpaper.   The prints are then matched.

Cutting lines may be chosen along the sides of roads, the edges of woods, or other suitable delineations.   Crossing fence-lines, roads, or other division lines that will show even a slight failure in matching should be avoided.   Only the center portion of each photograph should be used, if possible, because this part is distorted the least by topographic relief.

Adhesive is applied and the other photographs are pasted down. All excess adhesive is forced from under the prints by a movement away from the center and is removed with a wet sponge. Rubber cement is satisfactory for classroom use, but gum arabic or starch glue may also be employed.

After the mosaic has been completed, it is photographed and copy prints are made. The original can be filed and the prints used for study.

18–10. Radial-line plotting. Radial-line plotting is one method of constructing a planimetric map from aerial photographs. The method is based upon two fundamental photogrammetric principles: (a) On a truly vertical photograph, image displacements caused by topographic relief radiate from the principal point. (b) On a truly vertical photograph, the angles between rays passing through the principal point are equal to the horizontal angles formed by the corresponding lines on the ground.

The operations to be performed in radial-line plotting when two control points (one line) are known, may be outlined as follows:

1. Select control points (such as road intersections and corners of buildings) that are well-defined on the photographs.
2. Prick all the control points through the photographs onto the plot, and draw a circle around each one.
3. Locate the principal point on each photograph by the intersection of lines through opposite fiducial marks.
4. Mark the principal points O_1, O_2, . . . O_n.
5. Transfer the principal points by observation, or stereoscopically, to the overlapping photographs and prick them through. These points are called *conjugate principal points*.
6. Select at least two *pass points* along the margins of each photograph and opposite the principal point. In Fig. 18–10 the pass points for the second photograph are x_2 and y_2, and those for the third photograph are x_3 and y_3.
7. Mark the pass points on the three photographs in which they appear.

Theoretically, the length of only one line is required to construct a map from aerial photographs. Additional points, however, aid in preparing a more accurate map. The known line should have well-defined, easily recognizable terminal points, such as a and b in Fig. 18–10, and should appear in the first pair of overlapping photographs. The elevations of the terminal points are not required.

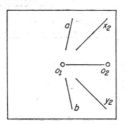 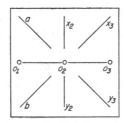 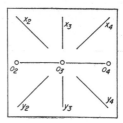

FIG. 18–10.   Radial line plotting.

After the pass points have been selected and marked, rays from the principal point are drawn through them.   The rays should extend beyond the points by perhaps $\frac{3}{4}$ in.   Templates are now prepared by using transparent sheets, heavy paper, or (in the "lazy daisy" method) slotted arms.

A transparent sheet is placed over each photograph and rays are drawn from the principal points through each of the pass points, conjugate points, and control points.   The rays are extended at least $\frac{3}{4}$ in. beyond each point.   The same procedure is followed in using paper templates, but a special slotting and punching machine must be available.   Adjusting strips and studs are employed to orient the rays in the metal-arm system.

After all the rays have been drawn on the photographs, those passing through the terminal points a and b of the known line are marked on the first two templates.   The principal points and conjugate principal points are designated on all other templates.   The average scale of the photographs may be selected for use but normally a larger one is adopted.   The correct scale length of the line AB is then computed.

The first template is taped to a suitable flat surface.   Template II is placed over template I, with the lines joining the principal points and conjugate principal points in coincidence.   Template II is now moved along this line until the intersection of the rays through the control points a and b is separated by the correct map distance previously determined, as shown in Fig. 18–11.   The map positions of x_2 and y_2 are also located by the intersections of the proper rays.

Template II is taped down and template III is placed over it, with the lines joining the principal points and conjugate principal points in coincidence. Template III is slid along this line until the rays through x_2 and y_2 on template III intersect the positions of x_2 and y_2 previously established.

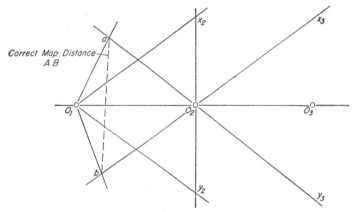

Fig. 18–11. Establishing correct map scale and location of points x_z and y_z.

For truly vertical photographs, the three rays through any point will intersect at a point. If a small triangle of error results because of tilt in the photographs, template III is slid back and forth along the coincident line to reduce this triangle. Template III is now taped down. The map positions of x_3 and y_3 are determined by the intersections of the proper rays.

This procedure is continued until all the templates have been laid. Additional control points may be visible, in which case the templates can be adjusted to conform with them. After all the control points and pass points have been located, they are transferred to a map sheet. A vertical Sketchmaster may be used to draw planimetric details on the map sheet. For a scale quite different from that of the prints, the photographs can be projected on the map sheet by a *Saltzman projector*, or a similar instrument for drawing planimetric details.

18–11. Flight mission. When the area to be mapped has been identified, it is necessary that a plan of the flight or photographic mission be made. The information needed to plan a flight mission consists of:

a. Area to be photographed.

b. Focal length of camera.

c. Scale of photography.

d. Side and forward lap.

e. Ground speed of aeroplane.

This information enables the flight personnel to compute: (1) altitude of aeroplane above mean sea level; (2) area covered by each photograph; (3) time interval between photographs; (4) number of strips; and (5) number of photographs.

1) The altitude of the aeroplane is computed by formula 18–1.

2) The distance on the ground covered by each photograph is readily calculated from the scale formula. If 9-in. by 9-in. photographs are used, the ground distance in feet shown on a print in each direction is $\frac{9}{12}$ times the denominator in the approximate scale.

3) If the overlap is 60 per cent, the ground distance between photographs is 40 per cent of that shown on each photograph. The speed of the aeroplane being known, the time interval in seconds between photographs is equal to the distance between photographs in feet divided by the speed of the aeroplane in feet per second.

4) The number of flight strips needed is now calculated. The lateral coverage for an overlap of 25 per cent is 75 per cent of the ground distance shown on each photograph. To counteract any possible variation in the flight line, a width equal to one-fourth of the lateral coverage of each photograph is added on each side of the area to be flown as a safety factor. The number of flight strips is equal to the width of the area in feet plus two times one-fourth of the lateral ground coverage of one photograph, divided by the effective lateral coverage of one photograph.

5) Flight lines are usually taken lengthwise over an area, to decrease the number of turns required. The number of photographs per strip is equal to the length of the area in feet divided by the distace between photographs. Two photographs are taken at each end of each flight strip as a safety factor.

EXAMPLE. It is desired to compute a flight mission for an area 5 miles wide and 10 miles long. The aeroplane has a speed of 80 miles per hour. A camera with a focal length of $8\frac{1}{4}$ in. is to be used. The approximate scale is 1 : 10,000; the average elevation of the ground is 1200 ft; and the photographs are to be 9 in. by 9 in. The forward overlap is 60 per cent and the lateral overlap 25 per cent.

1) The flight altitude H is found by formula 18–15. Thus

$$H - h_a = \frac{f}{S} = H - 1200 = \frac{8.25/12}{1/10,000}$$

$$H - 1200 = 6875$$

and $$H = 8075 \text{ ft}$$

2) The longitudinal and lateral coverage on the ground for each photograph is

$$\tfrac{9}{12} \times 10,000 = 7500 \text{ ft}$$

The effective longitudinal coverage is

$$7500 \times 0.40 = 3000 \text{ ft}$$

The effective lateral coverage is

$$7500 \times 0.75 = 5625 \text{ ft}$$

3) The time between exposures is therefore

$$\frac{3000}{(80 \times 5280)/(60 \times 60)} = 25.5 \text{ sec}$$

4) The number of strips is

$$\frac{5(5280) + 2(\tfrac{1}{4} \times 7500)}{0.75 \times 7500} = 5.4, \text{ or } 6$$

5) The number of photographs per strip is, theoretically,

$$\frac{10 \times 5280}{3000} = 17.6$$

As a factor of safety add two photographs at each end, making a total of $18 + 2 + 2 = 22$ photographs.

Figure 18–12 shows the flight map and sections of forward and lateral overlap.

18–12. Sources of error in photogrammetry. Some of the sources of error for beginners in photogrammetric work follow:

a. Neglect of displacement due to difference in elevation.
b. Differences in flight height of plane.
c. Inaccuracies in connecting principal points.
d. Failing to set the floating dot correctly on the point.
e. Incorrect orientation of photographs.

18–13. Mistakes. Typical mistakes of students and beginners in photogrammetric mapping are as follows:

a. Reading scales incorrectly.
b. Mixing units.
c. Failing to provide proper control.
d. Disregarding change of scale of photographic prints due to temperature and humidity.
e. Photographs not correctly placed under stereoscope.

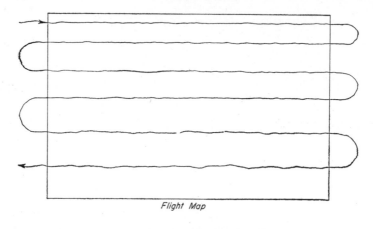

Flight Map

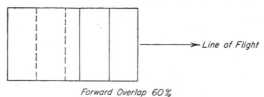

Forward Overlap 60%

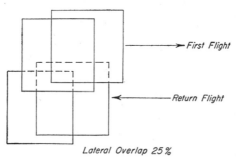

Lateral Overlap 25%

FIG. 18–12.   Flight map and overlaps.

PROBLEMS

18– 1. An area 10 miles wide and 15 miles long is to be photographed with a camera having a focal length of 8 in. and producing 9-in. by 9-in. negatives. The aeroplane has a speed of 100 miles per hour.   The approximate scale is to be 1 : 20,000.   Average elevation of the ground is 1000 ft.   The forward overlap of the photographs is to be 60 per cent and the lateral overlap 25 per cent.   Find: (a) flight altitude of the aeroplane; (b) ground distance covered by each photograph; (c) interval in seconds between photographs; (d) number of strips; and (e) number of photographs for each strip.

18– 2. From a vertical photograph select a tree, building, or other object whose top and bottom are visible. Make the necessary measurements as accurately as possible and find the height of the object by use of the topographic-relief formula. Steel millimeter scales are suggested.

18– 3. Information taken from an aerial photograph includes the following: flight altitude, 10,000 ft; focal length, 6 in.; elevation of A, 300 ft; and elevation of B, 350 ft. The photographic coordinates of the images a and b are:

Point	x	y
a	+ 70.0 mm	− 3.0 mm
b	+ 30.0 mm	− 25.0 mm

Find the horizontal length of the line AB.

18– 4. Two overlapping vertical photographs are taken at an altitude of 10,000 ft with a camera having a focal length of 6 in. The air base is 8000 ft and the photographic coordinates are as follows:

POINT	LEFT PHOTOGRAPH		RIGHT PHOTOGRAPH
	x	y	x
a	+ 50.0 mm	+ 10.0 mm	+ 12.0 mm
b	+ 1.00 mm	− 30.0 mm	

Find the horizontal length of the line AB by use of the parallax formulas.

18– 5. The elevation of point A is 400 ft and the micrometer-screw readings for a and b on two overlapping photographs are:

Point	Micrometer Reading
a	12.0 mm
b	13.3 mm

Find the elevation of point B. Use the camera and flight information given in problem 18–4.

18– 6. Make an uncontrolled mosaic of an area.

18– 7. If the distance between two points on a photograph is $2\frac{1}{2}$ in. and the ground distance is 2500 ft, what is the scale?

18– 8. What advantages does an aerial photographic map have when used for (a) city planning, (b) tax maps, (c) property ownership, and (d) highway-location?

18– 9. An aerial camera with a focal length of $6\frac{1}{4}$ in. is used to take photographs at an altitude of 8000 ft above sea level. What is the scale of the photographs if the average elevation is 1000 ft?

18–10. The mean air base scaled from a stereo pair of air photographs is 85.50 mm. Flying height above datum is 19,000 ft. Mean altitude of principal points is 600 ft. If the parallax bar of a contour finder reads 16.20 mm on a point of altitude 645 ft, what is the bar setting for the 700-ft contour?

18–11. List some of the advantages and disadvantages of mosaics.

18–12. An area is to be mapped from the air at a scale of 1 in. = 2000 ft with a camera having a focal length of 12 in. Calculate the flight altitude.

18–13. What area is covered by a 7-in. by 9-in. negative if a camera with a focal length of 10 in. is used, H = 12,000 ft and h = 1500 ft?

18–14. An aerial camera with a lens having a focal length equal to $6\frac{1}{4}$ in. is used to take photographs at an altitude of 7000 ft above sea level. What is the scale of the photographs if the terrain is level and at an elevation of 1000 ft?

18–15. It is desired to make a series of photographs on a scale of 800 ft to the inch. A K-17 camera with a lens having a focal length equal to 12 in. is to be used. At what height must the plane fly? For 9-in. by 9-in. negatives, a 60 per cent end lap, and an aeroplane ground speed equal to 120 miles per hour, determine the interval of time between pictures.

18–16. A K-3B camera with a lens having a focal length of $8\frac{1}{4}$ in. and producing a 7-in. by 9-in. negative (7-in. dimension in direction of flight) is to be used to map an area 6 by 16 miles. The end lap is to be 60 per cent and the side lap 50 per cent. The scale is to be 800 ft per inch. How many pictures will be required? If a 150-ft roll of film 9 in. wide costs $70, and if contact prints cost 15 cents each, what is the total cost of negatives and prints?

18–17. Given the following data: Flying height above mean elevation of ground = 12,000 ft; f = 8.25 in.; pictures 7 in. by 9 in.; overlap = 60 per cent in 7-in. direction; mean elevation = 1000 ft. If the distance from the principal point to the pictured position of A is 1.5 in., and if the elevation of A is known to be 2020 ft, what is the displacement of A due to relief?

18–18. A stream has an average width of 3.6 mm on a print to the scale of 1/42,000. What is the width of the stream on a map to the scale of 1 in. = 3000 ft?

18–19. On a vertical photograph of flat terrain, the distance between two points is scaled as 3 in. On a map to a scale of 4 in. per mile the distance between the same points is 1 mile. What is the scale of the photograph?

18–20. Select a four- or five-sided traverse from a pair of overlapping photographs. Find the area of the traverse by means of the parallax formulas.

Chapter 19

BOUNDARY SURVEYS

19–1. General. The earliest surveys were made to locate or relocate boundary lines of property. Trees and other natural objects, or stakes placed in the ground, were used to identify the corners. As property increased in value and owners disputed rights to land, the importance of permanent monuments and written records became evident. Property titles now are transferred by *deeds* which contain a description of the boundaries of the property.

Property is described in several ways: (a) by metes and bounds, (b) by block-and-lot system, (c) by coordinate values for each corner, or (d) by township, section, and smaller subdivision. The first three methods will be discussed briefly in this chapter. Subdivision of the public lands into townships and sections will be covered in Chapter 20.

Practically all property surveys today are wholly or partly re-surveys rather than originals. In retracing old lines a surveyor must exercise acute judgment based on practical experience and a knowledge of land laws, and be precise in his measurements. The necessary mathematics and the proper use of the transit, tape, and level can be learned in a relatively short time. This background must be bolstered by tenacity in searching the records of all adjacent property as well as studying the description of the land in question. In the field, a surveyor must be untiring in his efforts to find points called for by the deed. Often it is necessary to obtain testimony from old settlers or others having knowledge of accepted land lines and the location of corners, reference points, fences, and other evidence of the lines.

A land surveyor may be confronted with defective surveys; incompatible descriptions and plats of common lines for adjacent tracts; lost or obliterated corners and reference marks; discordant stories by local residents; questions of riparian rights; and a multitude of legal decisions on cases involving property boundaries. His duty to a client is to sift all available evidence and try to obtain a meeting of minds among persons involved in any property-line dispute. In this task he is doing professional work although he has no legal authority to force a compromise or settlement of any kind. Fixing of title boundaries must be done by agreement of adjacent owners or by court proceedings. To serve legally as an expert witness in proceedings to establish boundaries, a surveyor must be registered.

Many municipalities have rigid laws covering subdivisions. Regulations may specify the minimum size of lot; the allowable closures for surveys; the types of corner marks to be used; the minimum width of streets, and the procedure for dedicating them; the rules for registry of plats; and other matters. The mismatched street and highway layouts of today could have been eliminated by suitable subdivision regulations in past years.

Boundary surveying is learned only by practice in the field and study of the laws pertaining to land. Discussion in an elementary text must of necessity be brief. For more-extensive coverage the reader is referred to several excellent books on the subject in the References, page 535.

19–2. Basis of land titles. In the eastern part of the United States, individuals acquired the first land titles by gift or purchase from the English Crown. Surveys and maps were completely lacking or inadequate, and descriptions could be given only in general terms. The remaining land in the Thirteen Colonies was transferred to the states at the close of the Revolutionary War. Later this land was parceled out to individuals, generally in irregular tracts. The boundary lines were described by metes and bounds (directions by magnetic bearings, and lengths in Gunter's chains, poles, or rods).

Many original transfers, and subsequent ownerships and subdivisions, were not recorded. Those that were legally registered usually had scanty or defective descriptions since land was cheap and abundant. The trees, rocks, and natural landmarks defining the corners were soon disturbed. The intersection of two property lines might be described only as "the place where John killed a bear," or "the bend in a footpath from Jones' cabin to the river."

Numerous problems in land surveying stem from the confusion engendered by early property titles, descriptions, and compass surveys. The locations of thousands of corners have been established by compromise after resurveys, or by court interpretation of all available evidence pertinent to their original or intended positions. Other corners have been fixed by *squatters' rights, adverse possession,* and *riparian changes*. Many boundaries still are in doubt, particularly in areas having marginal land where the cost of a survey exceeds the value of the property.

The fact that the four corners of a field can be found, and that the distances between them agree with the calls in a description, does not necessarily mean they are in the proper place. Title or ownership is complete only when the land covered by a deed is positively identified and located on the ground. A deed is the written document by which ownership of land is transferred from one person to another.

Years of experience in a given area are needed by a land surveyor in order for him to become familiar with local conditions, basic reference points, and legal interpretations of boundary problems. The method used in one state for prorating differences between recorded and measured distances may not be acceptable in another state. Different interpretations are given locally to the superiority or definiteness of one distance over another associated with it; to the position of boundaries shown by occupancy; to the value of corners in place in a tract and its subdivisions; and to many other factors. Registration of land surveyors is therefore required in most states to protect the public interest.

19–3. Property description by metes and bounds. Descriptions by metes and bounds have a *point of beginning,* such as a stake, fence post, road intersection, or some natural feature. In recent years artificial permanent monuments long enough to reach below the frost line have been used. They consist of metal pipes, steel pins, and concrete posts. Lengths and bearings of successive lines from the point of beginning are given. Any lengths in chains, poles, and rods are being replaced by measurements in feet and decimals secured by means of the surveyor's tape. Bearings may be magnetic or true, the latter being preferable of course.

In relocating an old survey, precedence (weight of importance) is commonly assigned as follows: (1) Marks or monuments in place; (2) calls for boundaries of adjoining tracts; (3) courses and distances shown in the original notes or plat.

The importance of permanent monuments is evident—in fact wooden stakes are not acceptable for new property corners in some states. A map attached to the description clarifies it and scaling provides a rough check on the angles and distances.

Property descriptions are written by surveyors and lawyers. A single error in transcribing a numerical value, or one incorrect or misplaced word or punctuation mark, may result in litigation for a generation or more, since the intentions of *grantor* (person selling property) and *grantee* (person buying property) are not fulfilled.

In order to increase the precision of property surveys, large cities and some states have established control monuments to supplement the triangulation stations of the United States Coast and Geodetic Survey. Property corners can then be tied to these control points, and boundary lines can be relocated with assurance.

A description of a piece of property in a deed should always contain the following information:

a) *Point of beginning.* This should be identifiable, permanent, well-referenced, and near the property. If the coordinates are known, they should be given.

b) *Definite corners.* Clearly defined points, with coordinates if possible.

c) *Lengths and directions of the sides of the property.* All lengths in feet and decimals, and directions by angles or true bearings, must be given to permit computation of the error of closure. Omitting the length or bearing of the closing line to the point of beginning and substituting a phrase "and thence to the point of beginning" is no longer permitted in most states. The date of the survey must be included. This is particularly important if the bearings are referred to magnetic north.

d) *Names of adjoining property owners.* These are given to avoid claims for land in case an error in the description leaves a gap.

e) *Area.* The included area is normally given to aid in determining the value of the property, and perhaps its identification. Areas of rural land are given in acres; those of city lots, in square feet.

An example of a metes-and-bounds description of a suburban lot in the eastern section of the United States follows:

> Beginning at the center of a stone monument located on the South property line of Maple Street in the Town of Snowville, New York, about 452 feet from the east line of Adams Road, at the northeast corner of land now owned by James Brown; thence along east line of Brown S 5° 10′ E, two hundred fifty-two and eight tenths (252.8) feet to an iron pipe on the north line of property owned by Henry Cook; thence along a fence on north line of Cook's land S 82° 41′ E one hundred ninety-seven and three tenths (197.3) feet to center of stone wall on the west line of Charles Williams; thence N 46° 10′ E one hundred thirty-four and five tenths (134.5) feet along center line of the stone wall to an

iron pipe set at the end of the wall; thence N 5° 10′ W two hundred ten and no tenths (210.0) feet to a stone monument on the south line of Maple Street; thence S 84° 50′ W three hundred (300.0) feet along south line of Maple Street to place of beginning, containing 1.64 acres more or less. The bearings given are true bearings.

A typical old description of a city lot follows:

Beginning at a point on the west side of Beech Street marked by a brass plug set in a concrete monument located one hundred twelve and five tenths (112.5) feet southerly from the city monument No. 27 at the intersection of Beech Street and West Avenue; thence along the west line of Beech Street S 15° 14′ 30″ E fifty (50) feet to a brass plug in a concrete monument; thence at right angle to Beech Street S 74° 45′ 30″ W one hundred fifty (150) feet to an iron pin; thence at right angles N 15° 14′ 30″ W parallel to Beech Street fifty (50) feet to an iron pin; thence at right angles N 74° 45′ 30″ E one hundred fifty (150) feet to place of beginning; bounded on the north by Norton, on the east by Beech Street, on the south by Stearns, and on the west by Weston.

19–4. Property description by block-and-lot system. In subdivisions and in large cities it is more convenient to identify individual lots by *block and lot number,* by *tract and lot number*, or by *subdivision name and lot number.* Examples are:

Lot 34 of Tract 12314 as per map recorded in book 232 pages 23 and 24 of maps, in the office of the county recorder of Los Angeles County.

Lot 9 except the North 12 feet thereof, and the East 26 feet of Lot 10, Broderick's Addition to Minneapolis. [Note that parts of two lots are included in the parcel described.]

That portion of Lot 306 of Tract 4178 in the City of Los Angeles, as per Map recorded in Book 75 pages 30 to 32 inclusive of maps in the office of the County Recorder of said County, lying Southeasterly of a line extending Southwesterly at right angles from the Northeasterly line of said Lot, from a point in said Northeasterly line distant Southeasterly 23.75 feet from the most Northerly corner of said Lot.

Map books in the city or county recorder's office give the location and dimensions of all the blocks and lots. It is now standard practice to require subdividers to file a map with the proper office showing the type and location of monuments, size of lots, and other pertinent information such as the dedication of streets. It is evident that if the boundary lines of a tract are in doubt, the individual lot lines must be questioned also.

The block-and-lot system is a short and unique means of describing property for tax purposes as well as for transfer. Identification by street and house number is satisfactory only for tax-assessment records.

19–5. Property description by coordinates. The advantages of state-wide coordinate systems in improving the accuracy of local surveys, and in facilitating the relocation of lost and obliterated corners, have led to their legal acceptance in property descriptions. The coordinate description of corners may be used alone, or as an alternative method. Wider use of the coordinate system will be made as more reference points become available to the local surveyor.

An example of a description in which coordinates are used will be given by quoting a complete deed of easement.

DEED OF EASEMENT

This indenture, made this 7th day of February, 1953, between JOHN S. DOE, party of the first part, and CITY OF ALAMEDA, a municipal corporation, party of the second part,

Witnesseth:

That the said party of the first part, for and in consideration of the sum of One ($1.00) Dollar to him in hand paid by the party of the second part, in lawful money of the United States, at or before the execution and delivery of these presents, the receipt whereof is hereby acknowledged, does hereby grant, bargain, sell, transfer and convey unto the said party of the second part a permanent easement and right of way, at any time, or from time to time, to construct, maintain, operate, replace, remove and renew an underground sanitary sewer and storm drain in, through, under and along that certain piece or strip of land in the City of Alameda, State of California, particularly described as follows, to-wit:

BEING a strip of land six feet (6.00') wide,

COMMENCING at United States Coast and Geodetic Survey Monument "Otis Mo" having the coordinates $y = 461,113.18$ feet and $x = 1,496,962.81$ feet as based on the California Coordinate System Zone 3, as are all coordinates, bearings and distances in this description;

THENCE South 75° 38' 32" West 40.21 feet to the intersection of the center lines of Otis Drive (formerly Front Street) and Mound Street as shown on the Map of Alameda, surveyed and drawn by J. T. Stratton and filed in the Alameda County Recorder's Office July 24, 1879, on Page 1 of Book 6 of Maps, whose coordinates are $y = 461,103.21$ feet and $x = 1,496,923.86$ feet and which intersection is shown on Drawing 3667, Case 54, City Engineer's files, Alameda, California, which drawing is hereby made a part of this instrument as Exhibit "A" attached;

THENCE along the center line of Otis Drive South 47° 41' 56" East 295.10 feet to the intersection of the center lines of Court Street and Otis Drive as shown on the aforesaid map by J. T. Stratton, and whose coordinates are $y = 460,904.59$ feet and $x = 1,497,142.12$ feet; .

THENCE along the center line of Court Street South 42° 20′ 33″ West 135.00 feet;

THENCE North 47° 41′ 56″ West 30.00 feet to the east corner of the parcel as deeded to John S. Doe and recorded in Book 6598 of Official Records at Page 353, in the Alameda County Recorder's Office, and which point is the TRUE POINT OF BEGINNING, having the coordinates $y = 460,825.00$ feet and $x = 1,497,029.00$ feet;

THENCE along the northeast line of the said parcel North 47° 41′ 56″ West 58.77 feet to the north corner.

THENCE along the Northwest property line South 42° 20′ 33″ West 6.00 feet;

THENCE South 47° 41′ 56″ East 58.77 feet to the Southeast line of said parcel;

THENCE along the said line North 42° 20′ 33″ East 6.00 feet to the TRUE POINT OF BEGINNING.

TO HAVE AND TO HOLD the above mentioned and described easement, together with the appurtenances, unto the said party of the second part, its successors and assigns forever for the sole object and purpose of at any time, or from time to time, to construct, maintain, operate, replace, remove and renew an underground sanitary sewer and storm drain, as above set out and for no other purpose, and should the said real property herein described be at any time used for any other purpose by said party of the second part than for the easement and right of way for the purposes hereinabove set out, or should the use of said real property for said purposes be permanently terminated or permanently discontinued, then this easement and right of way hereby granted and conveyed shall immediately lapse and become null and void and said easement and right of way shall immediately revert to the grantor.

IN WITNESS WHEREOF, the said party of the first part has hereunto set his hand and seal, the day and year first hereinabove written.

_____
(Signature)

Approved as to form:

_____
City Attorney of the City of Alameda

Description approved:

_____
City Engineer of the City of Alameda

19–6. Field work. The first task in the field is to locate the property corners. Here a most valuable instrument to the land sur-

veyor—the shovel—frequently comes into use.   In many cases one
or more lines may have to be run from control points some distance
away to check or establish the location of a corner.   If two points are
available with known coordinates on a state-wide or local system, a
connecting line or traverse is used to transfer true bearings or coordinates to the property boundaries, as indicated in Fig. 19–1.

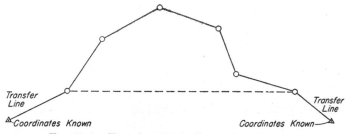

FIG. 19–1.   Transfer of coordinates to a traverse.

Generally a closed traverse is run around the property, all corners
being occupied if possible.   Fences, trees, shrubbery, hedges, party
walls, and other obstacles may necessitate a traverse that is inside or
outside the property.   From measurements to the corners, it is
possible to calculate their coordinates and the lengths and bearings
of the sides.   All measurements should be made with a precision
suited to the value of the land.   If coordinates on a grid system are to
be used in the description, the accuracy of the system itself should
be maintained if possible.

Measurements made with a standardized tape and corrected for
temperature and tension may not agree with distances on record or
those between the marks.   This provides a real test for the surveyor.
Perhaps his tape is different in length from the one used in the
original survey; the marks may have been disturbed, or be the wrong
ones; the monuments may not check with others in the vicinity
believed or known to be correct; and several previous surveys may
not agree with each other.

Bearings, and angles between adjacent sides, may not fit those
called for.   The discrepancy could be due to a faulty original compass
survey, incorrect corner marks, or other causes.

19–7. Registration of title.   To remedy the difficulties arising
from inaccurate descriptions and disputed boundary claims, some
states provide for the registration of title to property under rigid

rules. The usual requirements include marking each corner with standardized monuments referenced to established points, and recording a plat drawn to scale and containing specified items. Titles are then guaranteed by the court under certain conditions.

A number of states have followed Massachusetts' example and maintain separate *land courts* dealing exclusively with land titles. As the practice spreads, precision of property surveys will be increased and the transfer of property simplified.

A comparable service is offered by *title insurance companies* which search, assemble, and interpret official records, laws, and court decisions affecting ownership of land. The title company insures a purchaser against loss by guaranteeing that its findings regarding defects, liens, encumbrances, restrictions, assessments, and easements are correct. Defense against lawsuits is provided by the company against these threats to a clear title if the claims are shown in the public records and are not exempted in the policy. The location of corners and lines is not guaranteed. Hence it is necessary to establish on the ground the exact boundaries called for by the deed and the title policy.

Many technical and legal problems are considered before title insurance is granted. In Florida, for example, title companies refuse to issue a policy covering a lot if the fences in place are not on the property line. Occupation and use of land belonging to a neighbor but outside his apparent boundary line as defined by a fence may lead to a claim of adverse possession.

Adverse rights are obtained against all except the public by occupying a parcel of land for a period of years specified by law and performing certain acts. Possession must be (a) actual, (b) exclusive, (c) open and notorious, (d) hostile, (e) continuous, and (f) under color of title. In some states all taxes must be paid. The time required to establish a claim of adverse possession varies from a minimum of 7 years in Florida to a maximum of 60 years for urban property in New York. The customary period is 20 years.

The continuous use of a street, driveway, or footpath by an individual or the general public for a specified number of years results in establishment of a right-of-way privilege which cannot be withheld by the original owner.

19–8. Sources of error. Some of the sources of error in boundary surveys follow:

a. Corner not defined by a unique point.
b. Unequal precision of angles and distances.
c. Length measurements not made with a standardized tape and corrected for tension, temperature, and slope.
d. Magnetic bearings not corrected to the date of the new survey.

19–9. Mistakes. Typical mistakes in connection with boundary surveys are the following:

a. Use of wrong corner marks.
b. Failure to check deeds of adjacent property as well as the description of the parcel in question.
c. Ambiguous deed descriptions.
d. Omission of the length or bearing of the closing line.
e. Failure to close on known control.

PROBLEMS

19– 1. Determine from one of the publications listed in the References the meaning of eminent domain; riparian rights; adverse possession; deed; and title.

19– 2. What must the surveyor do in interpreting obscure descriptions?

19– 3. List the essential points covering the problem which arises when corners in place do not agree with deed descriptions.

19– 4. What is the first job of a surveyor employed to survey a farm located in an unfamiliar area?

19– 5. List in their order of importance the following items used in legally interpreting deed descriptions: written and measured lengths; written and measured bearings; monuments; witness corners and ties; areas; and testimony of living and dead witnesses. Justify your answer.

19– 6. A survey of a city block starting from proven corner monuments shows that the block is 2.62 ft longer than the plat distance. Lot boundaries were never staked. Show on a sketch how the excess is distributed, and explain.

19– 7. Use the conditions given in problem 19–6, but assume that the lots have been staked for one half of the block.

19– 8. Outline and sketch the procedure for surveying and monumenting the boundary of a piece of land which is to be split into three irregular parts. Using assumed data, write a description for the deed of one part.

19– 9. Two neighbors have a boundary dispute and hire a surveyor to check the line. Outline the authority of the surveyor, (a) assuming that the line he establishes is satisfactory to his clients and (b) assuming that it is unsatisfactory to one or both of them.

19–10. A surveyor, running the metes-and-bounds boundary lines of an area prior to subdividing it, is unable to find one of the original corners, so he sets his own. The subdivision is completed and the lots are sold. Another surveyor, two years later, proves that the new corner is 8 ft east of the original corner. Which is the legal corner? Why? What should be done about the other corner?

19–11. A farmer owning 200 acres of rolling terrain near a city hires a surveyor to subdivide the property for sale as lots. Outline the steps to be taken by the surveyor.

19–12. In establishing or re-establishing property lines or corners, what judicial authority does a licensed surveyor possess if his locations do not agree with those of another licensed surveyor or individual?

19–13. List all types of pertinent information or data which should appear on a completed plan of a property survey.

19–14. An error has been made on a plat of a subdivision and duly recorded. How can this defect be remedied and by whom?

19–15. Write a metes-and-bounds deed description for the house and lot where you live, assuming courses and distances where necessary. Draw a sketch map of the property and buildings, showing all information which should appear on a plan to be filed with the deed description at the registry of deeds.

19–16. In a description of land by metes and bounds, what purpose or purposes may be served by the statement "more or less" added to the acreage?

19–17. Telephone poles are set on two corners of a rectangular lot. Explain how you would make a survey of the lot to locate its boundaries and to determine the area.

19–18. Starting with a house number and street name, obtain a copy of the deed description of the property by searching the records in the County court house. Determine whether the corners described can be located readily on the ground.

Chapter 20

SURVEYS OF THE
PUBLIC LANDS

20–1. General. The term public lands has been applied broadly to the areas which have been subject to administration, survey, and transfer of title under the public-land laws of the United States. These lands include those turned over to the Federal Government by the Colonial States, and those larger areas acquired by purchase from (or treaty with) the native Indians, or foreign powers that had previously exercised sovereignty.

Twenty-nine States and the Territory of Alaska, Fig. 20–1, comprise the public domain which has been, or will be, subdivided into rectangular tracts. The area represents approximately 72 per cent of the United States.

> The title to the vacant lands, therefore the direction over the surveys, within their own boundaries, was retained by the Colonial States, the other New England and Atlantic Coast States (excepting Florida), and later by the states of West Virginia, Kentucky, Tennessee, and Texas, in which areas the United States public land laws have not been applicable.
>
> The beds of navigable bodies of water are not public domain and are not subject to survey and disposal by the United States. The sovereignty is in the individual states.
>
> In 17 of the 29 states . . . the swamp and overflowed lands, though public domain, pass to the States upon identification by public land survey, and approved selection, the title being subject to the disposal by the States.[1]

Survey and disposition of the public lands was governed originally by two factors:

a. A recognition of the value of a grid system of subdivision, based on experience in the Colonies and Europe.

[1] *Manual of Instructions for the Survey of the Public Lands*, 1947 edition, United States Government Printing Office.

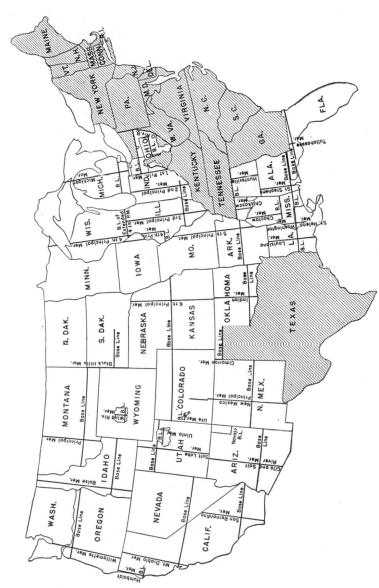

Fig. 20-1. Areas covered by the public lands surveys. Areas not covered are cross-hatched.

b. The need of the Colonies for revenue from the sale of the public lands. Monetary returns from sale of the public lands were disappointing, but the farsighted vision of the planners of the grid system of subdivision deserves commendation.

20–2. Instructions for survey of the public lands. The United States system of public-lands surveys was inaugurated in 1784, with the territory northwest of the Ohio River as a test area. Sets of instructions for the surveys were issued in 1785 and 1796. Manuals of instructions were issued in 1855, 1881, 1890, 1894, 1902, 1930, and 1947.

In 1796 a Surveyor General was appointed and the numbering of sections was changed to the system now in use. Supplementary rules were promulgated by each local Surveyor General "according to the dictates of his own judgment" until 1836, when the General Land Office was reorganized. Copies of changes and instructions for local use were not always preserved and sent to Washington. As a result, no office in the United States has a complete set of instructions under which the original surveys were supposed to have been made. Although the same general method of subdivision was followed, detailed procedures were altered in surveys made at different times in various areas of the country.

Most of the later public-land surveys have been run by the procedures to be described, or variations of them. The job of the present-day surveyor consists in retracing the original lines and perhaps further subdividing sections. To do so, he must be thoroughly familiar with the rules, laws, equipment, and field conditions governing the work of his predecessors in a given area.

Basically, the rules of survey stated in the 1947 *Manual of Instructions* are as follows:

> The public lands shall be divided by north and south lines run according to the true meridian, and by others crossing them at right angles, so as to form townships six miles square. . . .
>
> The corners of the townships must be marked with progressive numbers from the beginning; each distance of a mile between such corners must be also distinctly marked with marks different from those of the corners.
>
> The township shall be subdivided into sections, containing as nearly as may be, six hundred and forty acres each, by running through the same, each way, parallel lines at the end of every two miles; and by marking a corner on each of such lines at the end of every mile. The sections shall be numbered, respectively, beginning with the number one in the

northeast section, and proceeding west and east alternately through the township with progressive numbers till the thirty-six be completed.

Authority to establish section lines at intervals of one mile was given in 1800 and is included in all manuals of instructions since that date.

Additional rules of survey covering field books, subdivision of sections, adjustment for excess and deficiency, and other matters, are given in the manuals. Surveys were made by private surveyors, who were paid $2 per mile of line run until 1796 and $3 per mile run thereafter, on a contract basis. Sometimes the amount was adjusted in accordance with the importance of the line, the terrain, the location, and other factors. From his meager fee the surveyor had to pay and feed his party of at least four men while on the job, and in transit to and from distant points. He had to brush out and blaze the line, set corners and other marks, and provide satisfactory notes and one or more copies of completed plats. The contract system was discarded in 1910. Public-lands surveyors are now appointed.

Since meridians converge, it is evident that the requirement that lines shall conform to the true meridians, and townships shall be six miles square, is mathematically impossible. An elaborate system of subdivision was therefore worked out as a practical solution.

It should be noted that two principles furnish the legal background for stabilizing land lines:

a. Boundaries of public lands established and returned by duly appointed surveyors are unchangeable.

b. Original township and section corners established by surveyors must stand as the true corners which they were intended to represent, whether in the place shown by the field notes or not.

In general, the procedure for the survey of the public lands provides for the following subdivisions:

a. Division into quadrangles, or tracts, approximately 24 miles square.

b. Division of tracts into townships (16), approximately 6 miles on a side.

c. Division of townships into sections (36), approximately 1 mile square.

d. Subdivision of sections (usually by the local surveyor).

It will be helpful to keep in mind that the purpose of the grid system was to obtain sections 1 mile on a side. To this end, all discrepancies were thrown into the sections bordering the north and west township boundaries to get as many regular sections as possible.

20–3. Initial point. Subdivision of the public lands became necessary in any area as settlers moved in and mining or other land claims were filed. The original hope that surveys would precede settlement was not fulfilled.

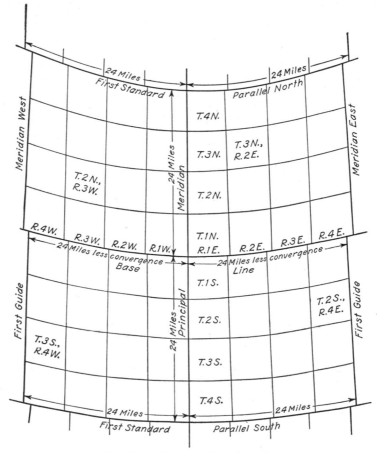

FIG. 20–2. Survey of quadrangles.

In each area an initial point was established and located by astronomical observations. The manual of 1902 was the first to specify an indestructible monument, preferably a copper bolt, firmly set in a rock ledge if possible, and witnessed by rock bearings.

Thirty-two initial points are available in the United States, and three in Alaska. Additional points will be required in Alaska.

A principal meridian and a base line were passed through each initial point, such as the point in the center of Fig. 20-2.

20-4. Principal meridian. From each initial point, a true north-south line called a principal meridian (Prin. Mer. or P.M.) was run north and/or south to the limits of the area to be covered. Generally a solar attachment—a device for solving mechanically the mathematics of the astronomical triangle—was used. Monuments were set for section and quarter-section corners every 40 chains, and at the intersections with all meanderable bodies of water (streams 3 ch. or more in width, and lakes covering 25 acres or more).

The line was supposed to be within 3 min of the cardinal direction. Two independent sets of linear measurements were required to check within 20 lk. (13.2 ft) per 80 ch., which corresponds to a ratio of error of only 1/400. The allowable difference between sets of measurements is now limited to 14 lk.

20-5. Base line. From the initial point, the base line was extended east and/or west as a true parallel of latitude to the limits of the area to be covered. As required for the principal meridian, monuments were set for section and quarter-section corners every 40 ch., and at the intersections with all meanderable bodies of water. Permissible closures were the same as those for the principal meridian.

Base lines were run as circular curves with chords of 40 ch. by (a) the solar method, (b) the tangent method, or (c) the secant method.

Solar method. An observation is made with the solar attachment to determine the direction of true north. A right angle is then turned off and a line extended 40 ch., where the process is repeated. The series of lines so established, with a slight change in direction every half-mile, closely approaches a true parallel. Obviously if the sun is obscured, the method cannot be used.

Tangent method. This method of laying out a true parallel is illustrated in Fig. 20-3. A 90° angle is turned to the east or the west, as may be required, from a true meridian, and corners are set every 40 ch. At the same time, proper offsets are taken from tables and measured north from the tangent to the parallel. In the example shown, the offsets in links are 1, 2, 4, $6\frac{1}{2}$, . . . 37. The error resulting from taking right-angle offsets instead of offsets along the converging lines is negligible.

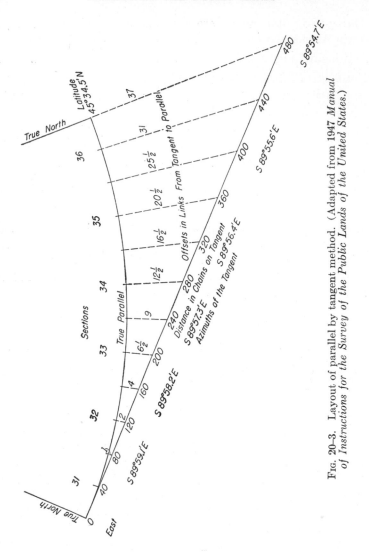

FIG. 20-3. Layout of parallel by tangent method. (Adapted from 1947 Manual of Instructions for the Survey of the Public Lands of the United States.)

The main objection to the tangent method is that the parallel departs considerably from the tangent and therefore two lines must be brushed out.

Secant method.   This method of laying out a true parallel is shown in Fig. 20–4.   It actually is a modification of the tangent method in which a line parallel to the tangent at the 3-mile (center) point is passed through the 1-mile and 5-mile points to obtain minimum offsets, as shown in Tables V and VI in Appendix B.

Field work consists in establishing a point on the true meridian, south of the beginning corner, at a distance taken from a table for the latitude of the desired parallel. The proper bearing angle from the same table is turned to the east or west from the true meridian to define the secant, which is then projected 6 miles. Offsets are measured north or south from the secant to the parallel.

The advantages of the secant method are its simplicity, the fact that the offsets are small and can be measured perpendicular to the secant without error, and the reduced amount of clearing required.

20–6. Standard parallels (correction lines).
After the principal meridian and base line have been run, standard parallels (Stan. Par. or S.P.), also called correction lines, are run as true parallels of latitude 24 miles apart in the same manner as was the base line. All 40-ch. corners are marked. In some of the early surveys, standard parallels were placed at intervals of 30 or 36 miles.

Standard parallels are numbered consecutively north and south of the base line; examples are First Standard Parallel North and Third Standard Parallel South.

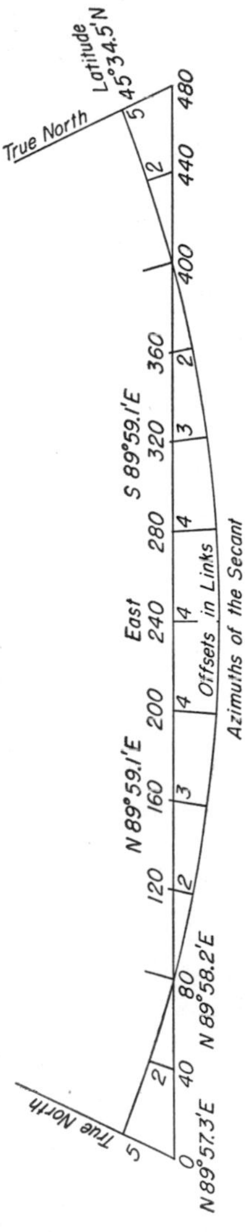

20–7. Guide meridians.
Guide meridians (G.M.) are run due north from the base line and standard parallels at intervals of 24 miles east and west of the principal meridian, in the same manner as was the principal meridian, and with the same limits of error. Before the work is started, the chain or tape must be checked by measuring 1 mile on the base line or standard parallel. All 40-ch. corners are marked.

Because of convergence of the meridians, a *closing corner* (CC) is

FIG. 20–4. Layout of parallel by secant method. (Adapted from 1947 *Manual of Instructions for the Survey of the Public Lands of the United States*.)

set at the intersection of each guide meridian and a standard parallel or base line. The distance from the closing corner to the *standard corner* (SC), which was set when the parallel was run, is measured and recorded in the notes as a check. Any error in the 24-mile length of the guide meridian is put in the northernmost half-mile.

The guide meridians are numbered consecutively east and west of the principal meridian; examples are First Guide Meridian West and Fourth Guide Meridian East.

20–8. Township exteriors. Meridional (range) lines and latitudinal (township) lines. Division of a quadrangle, or tract, into townships is accomplished by running range (R.) lines and township (T. or Tp.) lines.

Range lines are true meridians through the standard township corners previously established at intervals of 6 miles on the base line and standard parallels. They are extended north to intersect the next standard parallel or base line.

The formulas for convergence of meridians (derived in various texts on geodesy, with results given in Table IV) are as follows:

$$\theta = 52.13d \tan \phi \qquad (20\text{--}1)$$

$$c = \tfrac{4}{3} Ld \tan \phi \qquad \text{(slight approximation)} \qquad (20\text{--}2)$$

where θ = angle of convergence, sec;
d = distance between meridians, miles, on a parallel;
ϕ = mean latitude;
c = linear convergence, ft;
L = length of meridians, miles.

Township lines join township corners previously established at intervals of 6 miles on the principal meridian, guide meridians, and range lines.

20–9. Designation of townships. Townships are identified by a unique description based upon the principal meridian which governs them.

A north-and-south row of townships is called a *range*. Ranges are numbered in consecutive order east and west of the principal meridian, as indicated in Fig. 20–2.

An east-and-west row of townships is called a *tier*. Tiers are numbered in order north and south of the base line. By common practice, the term "tier" is usually replaced by "township" in designating the rows.

An individual township is identified by its serial number north or south of the base line, followed by the number east or west of the principal meridian. An example is Township 7 South, Range 19 East, of the Sixth Principal Meridian. Abbreviated, this becomes T 7 S, R 19 E, 6th P.M.

20–10. Subdivision of a quadrangle into townships. The method to be used in subdividing a quadrangle into townships is fixed by regulations in the *Manual of Instructions*. Under the old regulations, township boundaries were required to be within 21 min of the cardinal direction. Later this was reduced to 14 min in order to keep the interior lines within 21 min of the cardinal direction.

The detailed procedure for subdividing a quadrangle into townships can best be described as a series of steps designed to produce the maximum number of regular sections with a minimum amount of unproductive travel by the field party. The order of the work is shown by consecutive numbers in Fig. 20–5. Some of the details are described in the following steps:

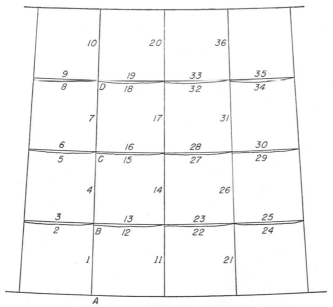

Fig. 20–5. Order of running lines for the subdivision of a quadrangle into townships.

a) Begin at the southeast corner of the southwest township, point *A*, after checking the chain or tape against a 1-mile measurement on the standard parallel.

b) Run north on the true meridian for 6 miles, setting alternate section and quarter-section corners every 40 ch. Set township corner *B*.

c) From *B*, run a random line *2* due west to intersect the principal meridian. Set temporary corners every 40 ch.

d) If the random line has an excess or deficiency of 3 ch. or less (allowing for convergence), and a falling north or south of 3 ch. or less, the line is accepted. It is then corrected back, line *3*, and all corners are set in their proper positions. Any excess or deficiency is thrown into the most-westerly half-mile.

The method of correcting a random line having an excess of 1 ch. and a north falling of 2 ch. is shown in Fig. 20–6.

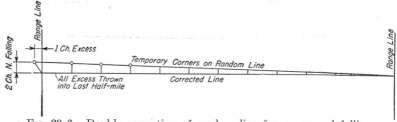

Fig. 20–6. Double correction of random line for excess and falling.

e) If the random line misses the corner by more than the permissible 3 ch., all four sides of the township must be retraced.

f) The same procedure is followed until the southeast corner, *D*, of the most-northerly township is reached. From *D* the range line *10* is continued as a true meridian to intersect the standard parallel or base line, where a closing corner is set. All of the excess or deficiency in the 24 miles is thrown into the most-northerly half-mile.

g) The second and third ranges of townships are run in the same way, beginning at the south line of the quadrangle.

h) While the third range is being run, random lines are also projected to the east and corrected back, and any excess or deficiency is thrown into the most-westerly half-mile.

20–11. Subdivision of a township into sections. The detailed procedure for subdividing a township can be described most readily as a series of steps designed to produce the maximum number of regular sections 1 mile on a side. Sections are numbered from 1 to 36, beginning in the northeast corner of the township and ending in the southeast corner, as shown in Fig. 20–7.

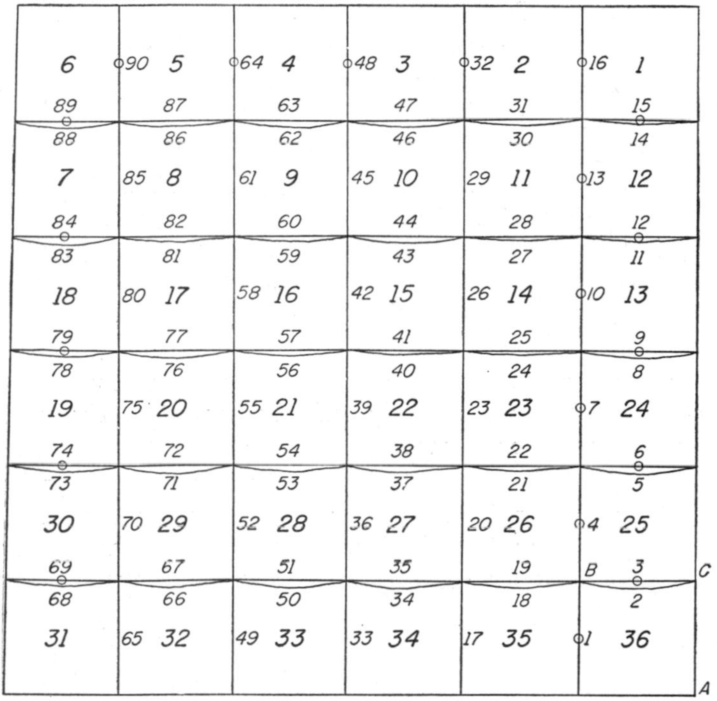

6	⌀90 5	⌀64 4	⌀48 3	⌀32 2	⌀16 1
89	87	63	47	31	15
88	86	62	46	30	14
7	85 8	61 9	45 10	29 11	⌀13 12
84	82	60	44	28	12
83	81	59	43	27	11
18	80 17	58 16	42 15	26 14	⌀10 13
79	77	57	41	25	9
78	76	56	40	24	8
19	75 20	55 21	39 22	23 23	⌀7 24
74	72	54	38	22	6
73	71	53	37	21	5
30	70 29	52 28	36 27	20 26	⌀4 25
69	67	51	35	19	B 3 C
68	66	50	34	18	2
31	65 32	49 33	33 34	17 35	⌀1 36

FIG. 20–7. Order of running lines for the subdivision of a township into sections.

a. Set up at the southeast corner of the township, point *A*, and observe the meridian. Retrace the range line northward, and the township line westward, for 1 mile to compare the meridian, the needle readings, and the tape with those of the previous surveyor.

b. From the southwest corner of Sec. 36, run north *parallel* with the east boundary of the township. Set quarter-section and section corners on line *1*, Fig. 20–7.

c. From the section corner just set, run a random line *parallel* with the south boundary of the township eastward to the range line. Set a temporary quarter-corner at 40 ch.

d. If the 80-ch. distance on the random line is within 50 lk., falling or distance, the line is accepted. The correct line is calculated, and the quarter-corner is located at the *midpoint* of the line *BC* connecting the previously established corner *C* and the new section corner *B*.

e. If the random line misses the corner by more than the permissible 50 lk., the township lines must be rechecked and the cause of the error determined.

f. The east range of sections is run in similar manner until the southwest corner of Sec. 1 is reached. From this point a random line is run northward to connect with the section corner on the north township line. The quarter-corner is set 40 ch. from the south section corner. All discrepancies in the 6 miles are thrown into the last half-mile.

g. Successive ranges of sections across the township are run until four have been completed. All meridional lines are parallel with the east side of the township, and all east-west lines are parallel with the south boundary.

h. When the fifth range is being run, random lines are projected to the west as well as to the east. The quarter-corners in the west range are set 40 ch. from the east side of the section, all excess or deficiency resulting from errors and convergence being thrown into the most-westerly half-mile.

i. If the north side of the township is a standard parallel, instead of running a random line to the north, lines parallel with the east township boundary are projected to the correction line and closing corners are set. The distance to the nearest standard corner is measured and recorded.

j. True bearings of the interior range lines for any latitude can be obtained by applying corrections from tables for the convergence at a given distance from the east boundary.

By throwing the effect of convergence of meridians into the western-most half-mile of the township and all errors to the north and west, twenty-five regular sections 1 mile square are obtained. Also, the south half of Secs. 1, 2, 3, 4, and 5, and the east half of Secs. 7, 18, 19, 30, and 31, are normal size.

20–12. Subdivision of sections. To divide a section into quarter-sections, straight lines are run between opposite quarter-section corners previously established or re-established. This rule holds whether or not the quarter-section corners are equidistant from the adjacent section corners.

To divide a quarter-section into quarter-quarter-sections, straight lines are run between opposite quarter-quarter-section corners established at the midpoints of the four sides. The same procedure is followed to obtain smaller subdivisions.

If the quarter-sections are on the north or west side of the township, the quarter-quarter-section corners are placed 20 ch. from the south or east quarter-section corners—or a proportional distance if the total length on the ground is not equal to that on record.

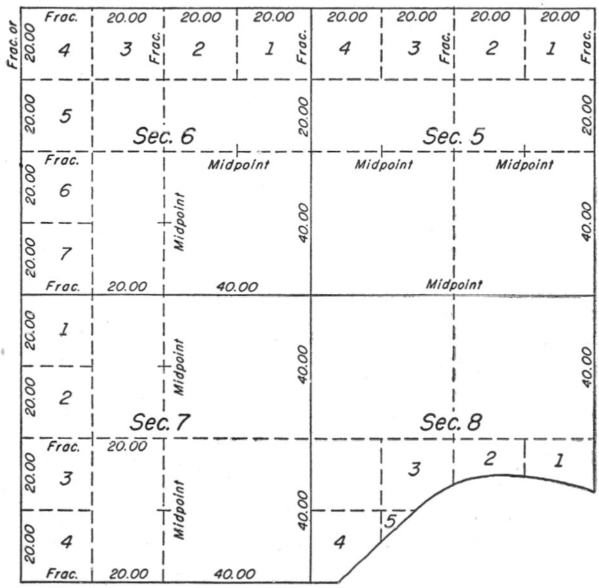

Fig. 20–8. Subdivision of regular and fractional sections.

20–13. Fractional sections. The quarter-sections along the north and west boundaries of a township made irregular by discrepancies of measurements and convergence of the range lines are usually numbered and sold as lots, as indicated in Fig. 20–8. One such quarter-section in a Wisconsin township contains 640 acres!

In sections made fractional by rivers, lakes, or other bodies of water, lots are formed bordering on the body of water and numbered consecutively through the section (see Sec. 8 in Fig. 20–8). The boundaries of the lots usually follow the quarter-section and quarter-quarter-section lines, but extreme lengths and narrow widths are avoided, as are areas of less than 5 acres or more than 45 acres.

Lot lines are not actually run in the field. Like the quarter-section lines, they are merely indicated on the plats by protraction. The areas by which the lots are sold are computed from the plats.

20–14. Notes. Specimen field notes for each of the several kinds of lines to be run are shown in various instruction manuals. Actual field notes had to follow closely the model sets.

The original notes, or copies of them, are maintained in a land office in each state, for the benefit of all interested persons.

TABLE 20–1

SUBDIVISION STEPS

Item	Subdivision of a Tract	Subdivision of a Township
Starting point........	SE corner of SW township	SW corner of SE section (36)
Meridional lines		
Name............	Range line	Section line
Direction.........	True north	North, parallel with east range line
Length...........	Six miles = 480 chains	One mile = 80 chains
Corners set.......	Quarter-section and section corners at 40 and 80 chains alternately	Quarter-section corner at 40 chains. Section corner at 80 chains
Latitudinal lines		
Name............	Township line	Section line
Direction of random	True east–west parallel	East, parallel with south side of section
Length......	Six miles less convergence	One mile
Permissible error...	Three chains, length or falling	Fifty links, length or falling
Distribution of error		
Falling............	Corners moved proportionately from random to true line	Corners moved proportionately from random to true line
Distance..........	All error thrown into west quarter-section	Error divided equally between quarter-sections

[Work repeated until north side of area is reached. Subdivision of last area on the north of the range of townships and sections follows.]

TABLE 20-1—*Continued*

Case I.   When Line on the North Is a Standard Parallel

Item	Subdivision of a Tract	Subdivision of a Township
Direction of line......	True north	North, parallel with east range line
Distribution of error in length........	Placed in north quarter-section	Placed in north quarter-section
Corner placed at end .	Closing corner	Closing corner
Permissible errors....	Specified in Manual of Instructions	Specified in Manual of Instructions

Case II.   When Line on the North Is Not a Standard Parallel

Item	Subdivision of a Tract	Subdivision of a Township
Direction of line......	No case	Random north and correct back to section corner already established
Distribution of error in length........	....	Same as Case I

[Other ranges of townships and sections continued until all but two are laid out.]

Item	Subdivision of a Tract	Subdivision of a Township
Location of last two ranges.............	On east side of tract	On west side of township
Next-to-last range subdivided..........	As before	As before
Last range Direction of random	True east	Westerly, parallel with south side of section
Nominal length....	Six miles less convergence	One mile less convergence
Correction for temporary corners...	Corners moved proportionately from random to true line	Corners moved proportionately from random to true line
Distribution of error of closure........	Corners moved westerly (or easterly) to place error in west quarter-section	Corner is placed on the true line so that error falls in west quarter-section

20–15. Outline of subdivision steps.   Pertinent points in the subdivision of quadrangles into townships, and townships into sections, are summarized in Table 20-1.

20–16. Marking corners.   Various materials were approved and used for monuments in the original surveys.   These included pits and mounds; stones; posts; charcoal; and broken bottles.   A wrought-iron pipe 2 in. in inside diameter and 30 in. long is now standard except in rock outcrop, where a brass tablet $3\frac{1}{4}$ in. in diameter is specified.

Stones and posts were marked with one to six notches on one or two faces.   The arrangements identify a monument as a particular section or township corner.   Each notch represents 1 mile of distance to a township line or corner.   Quarter-sections were marked with the fraction "$\frac{1}{4}$" on a single face.

In the prairie country, where large stones and trees were scarce, a system of pits and mounds was used to mark corners.   Different groupings of pits and mounds, 12 in. deep and 18 in. square, designated corners of the several classes.   Unless perpetuated by some other type of mark, these corners were lost in the first ploughing.

20–17. Witness corners.   Whenever possible, monuments were witnessed by several adjacent objects such as trees and rock outcrops. Bearing trees were blazed on the side facing the corner and marked with scribing tools.

When a regular corner fell in a creek, pond, swamp, or other place where it was impracticable to place a mark, *witness corners* (WC) were set on all lines leading to the corner.   The letters WC were added to all other marks normally placed on the corner, and the corner was in turn witnessed in the usual manner.

20–18. Meander corners.   A meander corner (MC) was established on survey lines intersecting the bank of a stream having a width greater than 3 ch., or a lake, bayou, or other body of water of considerable extent.   The distance to the nearest section corner or quarter-section corner was measured and recorded in the notes.   A monument was set and marked MC on the side facing the water, and the usual witnesses were noted.   If practicable, the line was carried across the stream or other body of water by triangulation to another corner set in line on the farther bank.

A traverse joining successive meander corners along the banks of streams or lakes was begun at a meander corner and followed as closely as practicable the sinuosities of the bank until the next meander corner was reached.   The traverse was checked by calculating the position of the new meander corner and comparing it with its known position on a surveyed line.

Meander lines follow the mean high-water mark and are used for plotting and protraction of area only. They are *not* boundaries defining the limits of property adjacent to the water.

20–19. Lost and obliterated corners. A common problem in re-surveys of the public lands is the replacement of lost or obliterated corners. This difficult task requires a combination of experience, hard work, and ample time to reproduce the location of a wooden stake or post monument incorrectly set 75 years ago on an undependable section line, and with all witness trees long-since cut or burned by apathetic owners.

An *obliterated corner* is one at whose point there are no remaining traces of the monument, or its accessories, but whose location has been perpetuated or may be recovered beyond reasonable doubt. The corner may be restored from the acts or testimony of interested landowners, surveyors, qualified local authorities, or witnesses, or from written evidence. Satisfactory evidence has value in the following order:

a. Evidence of the corner itself.
b. Bearing trees or other witness marks.
c. Fences, walls, or other evidence showing occupation of the property to the lines or corners.
d. Testimony of living persons.

A *lost corner* is one whose position cannot be determined, beyond reasonable doubt, either from traces of the original marks or from acceptable evidence or testimony that bears on the original position. It can be restored only by rerunning lines from one or more independent corners (existing corners that were established at the same time, and with the same care as the lost corner). Usually single- or double-proportionate measurements are necessary.

Proportionate measurements allot the discrepancies between the original and later recordings among the several parts of a line in the proportions in which the original recorded measurements were distributed.

20–20. Precision of public-lands surveys. The precision required in the early surveys was of a very low order. Frequently it fell below that which the notes showed. A small percentage of the surveys were made by men drawing upon their imagination in the comparative comfort of a tent. Obviously no monuments were set and the notes serve only to confuse the situation for present-day surveyors and landowners. Some surveyors threw in an extra chain-length at intervals to assure a full measure!

The poor results obtained in many areas were due primarily to the following reasons:

a. Lack of training of personnel. Some contracts were given to men without any technical background.
b. Poor equipment.
c. Surveys made in unsettled and apparently valueless areas.
d. Marauding Indians, swarms of insects, and dangerous animals.
e. Lack of appreciation for the need of accurate work.
f. Surveys made in piecemeal fashion as the Indian titles and other claims were extinguished.
g. Work done by contract at low prices.
h. Absence of control points.
i. Field inspection not provided until 1850, and not actually carried out until 1880.
j. Magnitude of the problem.

In general, considering the handicaps listed, the work was reasonably well done in most cases.

20–21. Descriptions by township, section, and smaller subdivision. Description by the sectional system offers a means of defining boundaries uniquely, clearly, and concisely. Several examples of acceptable descriptions are listed.

> Sec. 6, T 7 S, R 19 E, 6th P.M.
> Frac. Sec. 34, T 2 N, R 5 W, Ute Prin. Mer.
> The SE ¼, NE ¼, Sec. 14, Tp. 3 S, Range 22 W, S.B.M. [San Bernardino Meridian].
> E ½, NE ¼, Sec. 20, T 15 N, R 10 E, Indian Prin. Mer.
> E 80 acres of the NE ¼ of Sec. 20, T 15 N, R 10 E, Indian Prin. Mer.

Note that the last two descriptions do not necessarily describe the same land.

Sectional land which is privately owned may be partitioned in any manner at the option of the owner. The metes-and-bounds form is preferable for irregular parcels. In fact, metes and bounds are required to establish the boundaries of mineral claims, and various grants and reservations.

Differences between the physical and the legal (or record) ground locations and areas may result because of departures from accepted procedures in description writing; loose and ambiguous statements; or dependence upon the accuracy of early surveys.

20-22. Sources of error. Some of the many sources of error in retracing the public-lands surveys follow:

a. Discrepancy between the length of the chain of the early surveyor and that of the modern tape.

b. Changes in the magnetic declination and/or the local attraction.

c. Lack of agreement between field notes and actual measurements.

d. Changes in watercourses.

e. Nonpermanent objects which were used for corner marks.

f. Loss of witness corners.

20-23. Mistakes. Typical mistakes in the retracement of boundaries in public-land surveys are as follows:

a. Failure to follow the general rules of procedure governing the original survey.

b. Neglecting to check the tape used against distances on record for marks in place.

c. Resetting corners without exhausting every means of relocating the original corners.

PROBLEMS

20- 1. Why are the boundaries of public lands established by duly appointed surveyors unchangeable, even though set incorrectly in the first surveys?

20- 2. Describe the method of running a principal meridian. State the precision required.

20- 3. Determine the offsets from a secant which can be used to lay out a base line at latitude 42° 00′ N.

20- 4. What is the convergence, in feet, of two meridians originally 12 miles apart, after 12 miles, in latitude 36° N?

20- 5. What is the distance, in miles, between a principal meridian and the Second Guide Meridian East?

20- 6. Where are the closing corners located on township boundary lines? What areas do these closing corners govern?

20- 7. Outline the steps for subdividing a typical quadrangle into townships. Show on a large sketch the order of the work by numbering the lines consecutively.

20- 8. Outline the steps for subdividing a typical township into sections. Show on a large sketch the order of the work by numbering the lines consecutively.

20– 9. What are the steps in the subdivision of the public lands which are left to the local surveyor?

20–10. What are the two causes for sections in a normal township being smaller than 640 acres? Which sections usually are not regular?

20–11. Which lines in the public-lands surveys are laid out parallel to other lines?

20–12. Which section line is run as a random line?

20–13. Assuming that the lines in place are straight and correct, what is the airline distance from the southeast corner of Sec. 2, T 6 S, R 5 E of the San Bernardino Meridian, to the northwest corner of Sec. 11, T 6 S, R 3 E?

20–14. Approximately how many acres are in the S $\frac{3}{4}$ of the S $\frac{1}{2}$ of the SE $\frac{1}{4}$ of Sec. 6?

20–15. How many acres are contained in the SE $\frac{1}{4}$ of the SW $\frac{1}{4}$ of the NE $\frac{1}{4}$, of Sec. 17?

20–16. How many rods of fence will be required to enclose the following area: the S $\frac{1}{2}$ of the SW $\frac{1}{4}$ of Sec. 27, T 12 N, R 5 W, and the NE $\frac{1}{4}$ of the SW $\frac{1}{4}$ of the same section?

20–17. A man owns part of lot 4 in Sec. 6. Make up necessary data to give a complete description of any part of this lot. Show its location by a sketch.

20–18. The owner of the NW $\frac{1}{4}$ of the NW $\frac{1}{4}$ of Sec. 8 wishes to have his corners monumented. Assume that all section corners and quarter-section corners originally set by the public-lands surveyors are in place. Outline the procedure, using a sketch to show all lines run and the new corners set.

20–19. Why are meander lines not the boundaries defining the area of ownership of tracts adjacent to the water?

20–20. A meanderable river follows a winding course from southwest to northeast across a section. The position of the regular southwest corner of the section falls in the water. Draw a sketch illustrating this condition, and indicate the position of the meander and witness corners and the meander lines.

20–21. Sketch the protracted subdivisions of Sec. 5 as shown on an official plat, assuming that the north, south, east, and west boundaries are, respectively, 78.24, 80.36, 78.88, and 80.20 ch. Determine the areas.

20–22. The east line of the NE $\frac{1}{4}$ of Sec. 4 has a record distance of 40.12 ch. The length measured in the field is 40.20 ch. At what distance from the northeast corner of Sec. 4 would you set the southeast corner of lot 1? Give the reason for your answer.

20–23. What advantage would a stadia-interval factor of 132 (instead of the usual 100) have in public-lands surveys?

20–24. Explain how metes and bounds can be used in areas covered by the public-lands surveys.

Chapter 21

CONSTRUCTION SURVEYS

21-1. General. In recent years the construction industry has become the largest single industry in the United States. Construction surveying, as the basis for all construction and part of it, has therefore become increasingly important. It is estimated that 60 per cent of all surveying man-hours are spent on location-type surveys giving line and grade. Nevertheless, sufficient attention has not always been given to surveys and maps of underground utilities and some types of construction projects. Surveys for a subdivision usually cost less than 1 per cent of the expenditure for surfacing streets and laying water and sewer lines.

A topographic survey of the area is the first requirement in locating or positioning a structure. Reference points to control the construction stakes and to aid in checking the progress of work are needed.

A few of the most common types of construction surveys, with which every engineer should be familiar, will be described briefly. Construction surveying is best learned on the job by adopting basic principles to the project at hand. Because each project introduces individual problems, textbook coverage of construction surveying is somewhat limited.

21-2. Staking out a pipeline. The flow in water lines is usually under pressure, but most sewers have gravity flow. Alignment and grade must therefore be carefully watched on sewer pipes. Larger water lines also have definite grades because blowoffs are needed at low points and air releases are required at high points.

Construction stakes are normally set on the center line and on a parallel offset line at 50-ft stations when the ground is reasonably uniform. Generally they are closer on horizontal and vertical curves and for pipes of large diameter. On hard surfaces where stakes cannot be driven, points are marked by paint, spikes, drill holes, or other means.

Figure 21-1 shows the arrangement of *batter boards* for a sewer line.

Batter boards are usually 1″ × 6″ boards nailed to 2″ × 4″ posts which have been pointed and driven into the ground. The top of the batter board is placed a full number of feet above the invert (lower inside surface), or above the flow line, of the pipe. Nails are driven into the tops of the boards so that a string stretched between them will define the center of the pipeline. A graduated stick is used to measure the required distance from the string to the pipe invert, or to the flow line. Thus the string gives both line and grade. It can be kept taut by hanging a weight on each end after wrapping it around the nails.

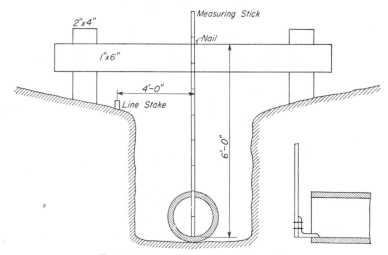

FIG. 21–1. Batter board for sewer line.

In Fig. 21–1, instead of a fixed batter board, a 2″ × 4″ carrying a level vial can be placed on top of the offset-line stake whose elevation is known. Measurement is made from the underside of the leveled 2″ ×4″ with a tape or graduated stick to establish the flow line.

On some jobs the engineer's level is set up in the ditch to give line and grade.

Suitable grades for trenches to avoid excessive cut and fill, and to permit connections with other facilities, are determined from a profile such as that in Fig. 5–25.

21–3. Staking out grades. Staking out grades is the reverse of taking profiles, although in both operations the center line should first be marked and stationed in horizontal location.

Grade elevations are determined by a leveling process. A level is set up and its H.I. found by reading a plus sight on a bench mark. The difference between the H.I. and the grade elevation at any station is the *grade rod*. The *ground rod* at each station is obtained by holding the rod on successive stations. Grade rod minus the ground rod at a station is the cut or fill at that station. The cut or fill is marked on an offset-line stake on the side facing the center line. The station is given on the other side of the stake. If stakes are driven to grade, the tops are marked with blue keel.

As an example, assume that the H.I. of a level is 292.5 ft, the grade elevation of station $0 + 00$ is 280.0 ft, the rod readings on the ground at station $0 + 00$ and $1 + 00$ are 10.4 and 8.3 ft, respectively, and a $+1.00$ per cent grade is to be laid out.

At station $0 + 00$ the grade rod is $292.5 - 280.0 = 12.5$ ft. The cut is $12.5 - 10.4 = 2.1$ ft, and the stake is marked C 2.1.

At station $1 + 00$ the grade elevation is $280.0 + 1.0 = 281.0$ ft and the grade rod is $292.5 - 281.0 = 11.5$ ft. The cut is therefore $11.5 - 8.3 = 3.2$ ft, and this stake is marked C 3.2.

If a target rod is used, the target can be set at the proper elevation to put the base of the rod at grade, or an even number of feet above or below it. Stakes are then driven until the horizontal line of sight of the level coincides with the center line of the target when the rod is held on top of each stake.

21–4. Staking out a building. The first task in staking out a building is to locate it properly on the correct lot by making measurements from the property lines. Most cities have an ordinance establishing setback lines to improve appearance and fire-protection.

Stakes may be set initially at the exact building corners as a visual check on the positioning of the structure, but obviously such stakes are lost when work is begun on the footings. A set of batter boards and reference stakes, located as shown on Plate A–11 in Appendix A, is therefore placed near each corner but out of the way of construction. The boards are nailed a full number of feet above the bottom of the footing, or above the elevation of the first floor. A bench mark (two or more on large projects) beyond the construction area but within easy sight distance is necessary to control elevations.

Nails are driven into the tops of the batter boards so that strings stretched between them will define the outside wall line of the building. Again, the boards give line and grade.

Permanent foresights may be helpful to establish the principal lines of the structure.   Targets or marks on nearby existing buildings are commonly used if movement due to thermal effects and settlement is considered negligible.   On concrete structures, such as retaining walls, offset lines are used because the outside wall line is obstructed by forms.

Plate A–11 shows the location of batter boards and the steps to be followed in setting them for a small building.

21–5. Staking out a highway.   Location stakes for a highway are set on the center line and on an offset line at full 100-ft stations, at the beginning and end of horizontal and vertical curves, and at other critical points.   A profile is run on the center line and the elevation is determined at each of the stakes.

To guide the contractor in making excavations and embankments, *slope stakes* are set at the intersection of the ground and each side slope, as shown in Fig. 21–2.   Slope stakes are located by a trial-and-error method based upon mental calculations involving the H.I., the grade rod, the ground rod, half the width of the roadway, and the side slope.   One or two trials are generally sufficient to fix the position of the stake within an allowable error of 0.3 ft to 0.5 ft.

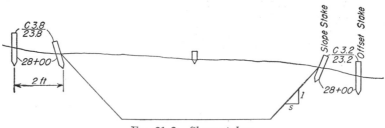

FIG. 21–2.   Slope stakes.

Grade stakes are set at the intersection of grade and ground.   Three transition sections occur in passing from cut to fill, and a grade stake is set in each one, as indicated in Fig. 21–3.   A line connecting the grade stakes defines the change from cut to fill.

Location-staking of railways and canals follows the methods used for highways.

21–6. Sources of error.   Some of the sources of error in construction surveys follow:

a. Movement of stakes and marks.
b. Failing to check the diagonals of a building.
c. Lack of foresight as to where construction will void points.
d. Failing to use tacks for proper line when justified.
e. Notation for cut or station on stake not checked.
f. Wrong datum for cuts, as cut to finish grade instead of cut to subgrade.

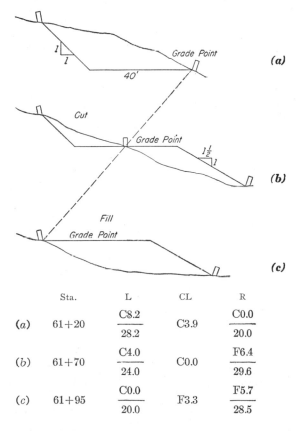

	Sta.	L	CL	R
(a)	61+20	C8.2 / 28.2	C3.9	C0.0 / 20.0
(b)	61+70	C4.0 / 24.0	C0.0	F6.4 / 29.6
(c)	61+95	C0.0 / 20.0	F3.3	F5.7 / 28.5

FIG. 21-3. Grade points at transition sections.

21-7. Mistakes. Typical mistakes that are often made in construction surveys include the following:

a. Arithmetic mistakes, generally due to lack of a check.
b. Use of incorrect elevations, grades, and stations.

c. Carrying out computed values beyond the accuracy possible in the field (a good hundredth is worth all the bad thousandths).

d. Reading the rod on top of the center-line stakes instead of on the ground beside them.

e. Failure to compute midpoint grades by successive increments so that any error will be evident if the last grade elevation does not check.

PROBLEMS

21- 1. How far apart should stakes be set on a sewer job on a flat grade? On a steep grade? On sharp curves?

21- 2. By means of a sketch, show how and where batter boards should be set for an I-shaped building 120 ft by 60 ft, all wings being 20 ft wide.

21- 3. Are batter boards ever placed inside a building? Explain.

21- 4. What is the best method of checking the length of the sides of a building, and the locations of the corner stakes?

21- 5. List two or more ways of stilling the swing of a plumb-bob line extending several stories outside of a building wall.

21- 6. Can the corner of a building be plumbed by running the vertical cross hair of a transit up and down the wall line?

21- 7. What tolerance is reasonable for the plumbing of elevator shafts?

21- 8. What method can be used to check the deviations from the vertical of steel tubes driven to form cast-in-place concrete piles?

21- 9. Arrange in proper order the following sequence of giving construction lines: (a) for foundation, (b) for excavation, (c) for main structure, (d) for subdivisions of the structure.

21-10. Discuss the suitability of a 0.00 per cent grade for a street.

21-11. On a construction contract, is the owner or the contractor responsible for the layout accuracy?

21-12. What are the advantages of the coordinate system for an overpass layout?

21-13. Outline a suitable method for giving grade for (a) a parking lot, (b) a reinforced-concrete culvert, (c) a footing for a bridge pier.

21-14. If a pipeline is parallel to and near the curb, would it be preferable to put the offset line on the curb or on the road surface?

Chapter 22

CIRCULAR CURVES

22-1. General. Straight (tangent) sections of most types of transportation routes, such as highways, railroads, and pipelines, are connected by curves in both the horizontal and vertical planes. An exception is a transmission line, in which a series of straight lines is used with direct angular changes.

Two types of horizontal curves are employed—circular arcs and spirals. A *simple curve*, Fig. 22–1a, is a circular arc connecting two tangents. A *compound curve*, Fig. 22–1b, is composed of two circular arcs of different radii tangent to each other, with their centers on the same side of the common tangent. The combination of a short length of tangent connecting two circular arcs having centers on the same side, as in Fig. 22–1c, is called a *broken-back curve*. A *reverse curve*, Fig. 22–1d, consists of two circular arcs tangent to each other, the centers being on opposite sides of the common tangent. Reverse, compound, and broken-back curves are unsuitable for modern high-speed highway and railroad traffic.

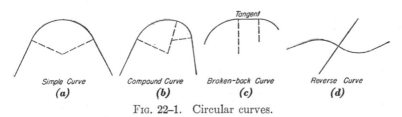

| Simple Curve | Compound Curve | Broken-back Curve | Reverse Curve |
| *(a)* | *(b)* | *(c)* | *(d)* |

Fig. 22–1. Circular curves.

Easement curves are desirable to lessen the sudden change in curvature at the junction of a tangent and a circular curve. A *spiral* makes an excellent easement curve because its radius decreases uniformly from infinity at the tangent to that of the curve it meets. Spirals are used to connect a tangent with a circular curve, a tangent with a tangent (double spiral), and a circular curve with a circular curve. Figure 22–2 illustrates these arrangements.

The effect of centrifugal force on a vehicle passing around a curve can be balanced by *superelevation* of the outer rail of a track and the outer edge of a highway pavement. The correct superelevation on a spiral increases uniformly with the distance from the beginning of the spiral, and is in inverse proportion to the radius at any point. Properly superelevated spirals insure smooth and safe riding qualities with less wear on equipment. For detailed coverage of the spiral and superelevation, the reader is referred to one of the books on route surveying listed in the References.

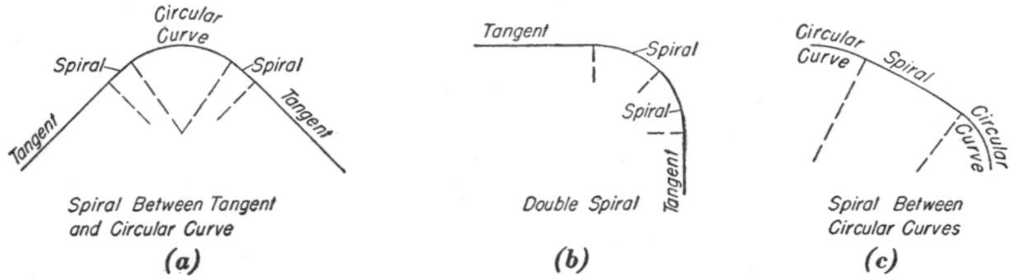

Fig. 22-2. Use of spiral transition curves.

Circular arcs and spirals are used for curves in the horizontal plane because they are readily laid out in the field by transit and tape.

Grade lines are joined in the vertical plane by parabolic curves, discussed in Chapter 23. Elevations on parabolic curves are easily computed and can be established on the ground by leveling.

22-2. Degree of curve. In European practice and some American highway work, circular curves are designated by their radius; for example, "1000-ft curve" and "3200-ft curve." American railroads and various highway departments prefer to identify curves by their *degree,* employing either the chord definition or the arc definition.

In railroad practice, the degree of curve is the angle at the center of a circular arc subtended by a chord of 100 ft. This is the *chord definition* and is indicated in Fig. 22-3a. In some highway work, the degree of curve is the angle at the center of a circular arc subtended by an arc of 100 ft. This is the *arc definition,* as illustrated in Fig. 22-3b. Formulas relating the radius R and the degree D are shown beside the illustrations.

Radii of chord- and arc-definition curves for values of D from 1° to 6° are given in Table VII. Although the differences appear to be small in this range, they have some significance in computations.

The chord-definition curve is consistent in using chords for computation and layout. Its disadvantages are: (a) R is not directly proportional to the reciprocal of D; (b) the formula for length is slightly approximate; (c) corrections are necessary in using the short-cut formulas for tangent distance and external distance; (d) greater difficulty is encountered in checking sharp curves.

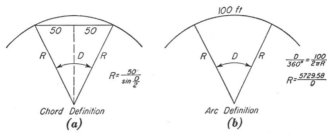

FIG. 22–3. Degree of curve.

The arc-definition curve has the disadvantage that most measurements between stations are less than a full tape length. Computations are facilitated since exact answers for the radius, tangent distance, and external distance are obtained from tabular values for a 1° curve by dividing by the degree D. Also, the formula for length is exact, this being an advantage in preparing right-of-way descriptions.

The arc and chord definitions give practically the same result when applied to the flat curves common on modern highways and railroads.

Circular curves are usually laid out in the field by deflection angles and taped chords.

22–3. Derivation of formulas. Circular-curve elements are shown in Fig. 22–4. The *point of intersection* of the tangents (P.I.) is also called the *vertex* (V). The *beginning of the curve* (B.C.) and the *end of the curve* (E.C.) are also termed the *point of curvature* (P.C.) and the *point of tangency* (P.T.). Other expressions for these points are *tangent to curve* (T.C.) and *curve to tangent* (C.T.).

The distance from the B.C. to the P.I., and from the P.I. to the E.C., is the *tangent distance* (T). The line connecting the B.C. and the E.C. is the *long chord* (L.C.). The *length of curve* (L) is the distance from the B.C. to the E.C. measured along the curve for the arc definition, or along 100-ft chords for the chord definition.

The *external distance* (E) is the distance from the vertex to the curve on a radial line.   The *middle ordinate* (M) is the (radial) distance from the middle point of a chord of a circular curve to the middle point of the corresponding arc.

The change in direction of the two tangents is the deflection angle Δ, which is equal to the central angle.

By definition, and by inspection of Fig. 22–4, relations for the arc definition follow:

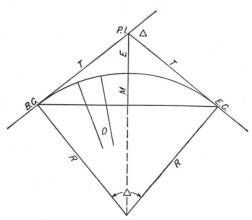

FIG. 22–4.   Circular curve elements.

$$\frac{D°}{360°} = \frac{100}{2\pi R} \quad \text{and} \quad R = \frac{100 \times 360}{2\pi D} = \frac{5729.58}{D} \qquad (22\text{–}1)$$

$$T = R \tan \frac{\Delta}{2} \qquad (22\text{–}2)$$

$$T_a = \frac{T_1°}{D_a} \qquad (22\text{–}3)$$

$$L = 100 \frac{\Delta}{D} \qquad (22\text{–}4)$$

$$\text{L.C.} = 2R \sin \frac{\Delta}{2} \qquad (22\text{–}5)$$

$$\frac{R}{R + E} = \cos \frac{\Delta}{2}; \; E = R\left(\sec \frac{\Delta}{2} - 1\right) = R \, \text{exsec} \, \frac{\Delta}{2} \qquad (22\text{–}6)$$

$$E_a = \frac{E_1°}{D_a} \qquad (22\text{–}7)$$

$$\frac{R - M}{R} = \cos \frac{\Delta}{2}; \; M = R\left(1 - \cos \frac{\Delta}{2}\right) = R \text{ vers } \frac{\Delta}{2} \quad (22\text{–}8)$$

The formulas for T, L, E, and M apply also to a chord-definition curve. Small corrections must be added to the values of T_a and E_a found by formulas 22–3 and 22–7 respectively.

The formula relating R and D for a chord-definition curve is as follows:

$$R = \frac{50}{\sin D/2} \quad (22\text{–}9)$$

22–4. Sample computation. Assume that field measurements show $\Delta = 8° 24'$ and the station of the P.I. is 64 + 27.46, and that terrain conditions require use of the maximum degree of curve permitted by the specifications, which is, say, 2° 00′. Then, for an arc-definition curve,

$$R = \frac{5729.58}{2} \qquad = 2864.79 \text{ ft}$$

$$T = 2864.79 \times 0.073238 = 210.40 \qquad \text{or} \qquad T = \frac{420.8}{2} = 210.40*$$

$$L = 100 \times \frac{8.40}{2} \qquad = 420.00$$

$$E = 2864.79 \times 0.002693 = 7.70 \qquad \text{or} \qquad E = \frac{15.4}{2} = 7.70*$$

$$M = 2864.79 \times 0.002686 = 7.69 \text{ ft}$$

$$
\begin{aligned}
\text{Station P.I.} &= 64 + 27.46 \\
T &= \underline{2 + 10.40} \\
\text{Station B.C.} &= 62 + 17.06 \\
L &= \underline{4 + 20.00} \\
\text{Station E.C.} &= 66 + 37.06
\end{aligned}
$$

The computations for T and E marked with an asterisk are short-cut methods based upon the use of tables which list the tangent and external distances of 1° curves for various values of Δ. Division of these values by D gives R, T, and E directly for the arc-definition curve. Small corrections must be applied for a chord-definition curve.

Computations for the stations of the B.C. and E.C. should be arranged as shown. Note that the station of the E.C. cannot be obtained by adding the tangent distance to the station of the P.I., although the position of the E.C. on the ground is determined by measuring the tangent distance from the P.I.

After the curves have been inserted, the stationing must follow the actual line to be constructed. An *equation of chainage* is therefore applied to correct the original stationing. This equation represents the difference between the sum of the two tangents and the length of the curve. Its numerical value increases after each curve in the route.

22-5. Curve layout. Except for unusual cases, such as street railways, the radii of curves in route surveys are generally too large to permit swinging an arc from the curve center. Circular curves are therefore laid out by (a) deflection angles and chords, (b) tangent offsets, (c) chord offsets, (d) middle ordinates, and (e) other methods. Layout by deflection angles from the tangents is the standard method and the only procedure which will be discussed in this text.

In Fig. 22-5, assume that the transit is set up over the B.C. (station $62 + 17.06$ in the preceding example). The first point to be marked on the curve is station $63 + 00$, since cross sections are normally taken, construction stakes are set, and computations of earthwork are made at full stations and critical points. The distance from the B.C. to the next full station is called the *subchord, c*.

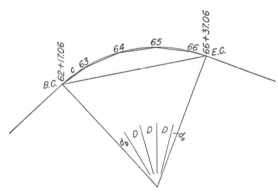

FIG. 22-5.   Deflection angles for a circular curve.

The *deflection angle* from a tangent for a full 100-ft arc is $D/2$, since an angle formed by a tangent and a chord is measured by one-half the intercepted arc. The *subdeflection angle* $d/2$ from the B.C. to station $63 + 00$ is computed by the proportion

$$\frac{d}{2} : \frac{D}{2} = c : 100$$

from which
$$\frac{d}{2} = \frac{cD}{200} \tag{22-10}$$

A small subdeflection angle is expressed in minutes, rather than in degrees, and formula 22–10 then becomes

$$\frac{d}{2} = 0.3cD \tag{22-11}$$

where D is in degrees and the subdeflection angle is in minutes.

In this example,

$$\frac{d}{2} = 0.3 \times 82.94 \times 2 = 49.76 \text{ min}$$

Deflection angles are normally carried out to several decimal places for checking purposes, and to avoid accumulating small errors when D is an odd value, for example 3° 17.24′.

With the transit set up over the B.C., it is oriented by backsighting on the P.I., or on a point along the back tangent, with 0° 00′ on the plates. The subdeflection angle of 49′ 45″ is then turned. Meanwhile the 17-ft mark of the tape is held on the B.C. The 100-ft end of the tape is swung until the line of sight hits the point 0.06 ft back from the 100-ft mark. This is station 63 + 00.

The rear tapeman next holds the zero mark on station 63, and the forward tapeman sets station 64 by direction from the instrumentman, who has placed an angle of 1° 49′ 45″ on the plates.

Deflection angles to stations following 63 are found by adding $D/2 = 1° 00′$ for each full chord. The subdeflection angle $d/2$ for the final subchord equals 22.24 min. As a check, the deflection angle from the B.C. to the E.C. must equal $\Delta/2$. In the field it is essential to read and check the deflection angle to the E.C. (when visible from the B.C.) before starting to run the curve. An error in Δ, T, or L, or in the stationing, will then be discovered without wasting time running an impossible curve.

Field notes for the curve of this example are recorded in Plate A–12 as they would appear in a field book. The notes run up the page to permit sketching in a forward direction.

For a 2° 00′ curve, the lengths of arcs and chords are the same to two decimal places.   On sharper curves the chords would be shorter than the corresponding arc lengths.   For example, the chord measurement to lay out a 100-ft arc for a 6° 00′ curve is 99.95 ft.

In many cases it is desirable to *back in* a curve by setting up over the E.C. instead of the B.C.   One setup is thereby eliminated and the long sights are taken on the first measurements.   In precise work it is better to run in the curve from both ends to the center, where small errors can be adjusted more readily.

22–6. Setups on the curve.   Obstacles and extremely long sight distances sometimes make it necessary to set up on the curve.   The simplest procedure to follow is one which permits use of the same notes computed for running the curve from the B.C.

In this method the transit is backsighted on any station on the curve, with the telescope inverted and the plates set to *the deflection angle for that station from the B.C.*   The telescope is plunged to the normal position, and the deflection angles previously computed for the various stations from the B.C. are used.

In the example of sections 22–4 and 22–5, if a setup is required at station 65, place 0° 00′ on the plates and sight to the B.C. with the telescope inverted.   Plunge, set the plates to read the deflection angle 3° 49′ 45″, and set station 66.   Or, if the B.C. is not visible, set 0° 49′ 45″ on the plates, sight on station 63, plunge, set 3° 49′ 45″ on the instrument, and locate station 66.

A simple sketch will make clear the geometry basic to this procedure.

22–7. Sight distance on horizontal curves.   Highway safety requires certain minimum sight distances in zones where passing is permitted, and in nonpassing areas to assure a reasonable stopping distance if there is an object on the roadway.   Specifications and tables list suitable values based upon vehicular speeds, the perception and reaction times of the average individual, the braking distance for a given coefficient of friction during deceleration, and the type and condition of the pavement.

A minimum sight distance of 600 ft is desirable for speeds as low as 30 miles per hr.

An approximate formula for sight distance can be derived by referring to Fig. 22–6, in which the clear sight distance past an obstruction is the length of the long chord AS, denoted by C; and the required clearance is the middle ordinate PM, denoted by m. Then in triangles SPG and SOH,

$$m : SP = \frac{SP}{2} : R \qquad \text{and} \qquad m = \frac{(SP)^2}{2R}$$

Usually m is small compared with R, and SP may be assumed equal to $C/2$. Then

$$m = \frac{C^2}{8R} \qquad\qquad (22\text{--}12)$$

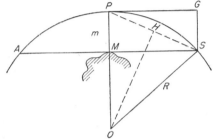

FIG. 22–6. Sight distance.

If the distance m from the center line of the highway to the obstruction is known or can be measured, the available sight distance C is calculated from the formula. Actually the car travels along the curve on either the inside or outside lane; so the sight distance AS is not exactly the true stopping distance. The computed distance is on the safe side and is satisfactory for practical use.

22–8. Compound and reverse curves. Special problems. Compound and reverse curves are combinations of two or more circular curves. They should be used only for low-speed traffic ways, and in terrain where simple curves cannot be fitted to the ground without excessive construction costs.

Special formulas have been derived to facilitate computations for such curves and are demonstrated in texts on route surveying. A compound curve is run by setups at the B.C. and E.C., or perhaps by one setup at the *point of compound curvature* (C.C.). Reverse curves are handled in similar fashion.

Many special problems in connection with curves arise in office design and in field layout. It may be necessary to pass a curve through a given point such as an underpass or bridge crossing; to relocate a new tangent a certain distance inside or outside of the old tangent; or to replace a broken-back curve with a simple curve. These problems are solved by applying a basic understanding of curve fundamentals and referring to a route-surveying text.

22–9. Sources of error.   Some of the sources of error in curve computations and layout are:

a. Inability to set on the plates the required subdivisions of a minute for the deflection angles.
b. Poor intersections between tape line and sight line on flat curves.
c. Use of less than full tape lengths on arc-definition curves.
d. The large numbers which must. be used to obtain answers with six significant figures.

22–10. Mistakes.   Some typical mistakes that occur in laying out a curve in the field are the following:

a. Failure to double or quadruple the deflection angle at the P.I. before computing or laying out the curve.
b. Adding the tangent distance to the station of the P.I. to get the station of the E.C.
c. Using 100.00-ft chords to lay out arc-definition curves having D greater than 2°.
d. Taping subchords of nominal length for chord-definition curves having D greater than 5° (a nominal 50-ft subchord for a 6° curve requires a measurement of 50.02 ft).

PROBLEMS

22– 1. A circular highway curve has a 1500-ft radius. What is its degree of curve?

22– 2. Two tangents to a highway curve form an angle of 14° 30′ R. If the curve has a radius of 2500 ft, what is the tangent distance T?

22– 3. A 6° 00′ circular highway curve has a Δ of 22° 40′. If the station of the B.C. is 42 + 37.5, what is the station of the vertex? Of the E.C.?

22– 4. Compute the middle ordinate and the external distance for the data of problem 22–2.

22–· 5. A simple circular railroad curve (chord definition) has $D = 4° 00′$ and Δ = 15° 30′ L, and the vertex is at station 23 + 78.20. Tabulate all the data required to lay out the curve.

22– 6. The vertex of a simple circular highway curve is at station 42 + 23.9. The intersection angle Δ is 10° 00′ L, and the station of the B.C. is 39 + 73.3. Compute and tabulate all data required to lay out the curve in the field.

22– 7. A highway curve 600.00 ft long and having a radius of 3819.71 ft is to be fitted between tangents which intersect at station 60 + 10.00. Compute and list all data required to lay out the curve in the field.

22– 8. Inspection of field conditions indicates that the external distance for a simple circular curve should be about 48 ft. The vertex angle Δ is equal to 25° 30′ and the P.I. is at station 51 + 47.3. Compute and list all data necessary to lay out and check a suitable highway curve in the field.

22– 9. If a transit is set up on the ¼ point of a circular curve and a backsight is taken on the B.C. with 0° 00′ on the plates, what is the deflection angle to the E.C.?

22–10. If a transit is set up on the midpoint of a circular curve and a backsight is taken on the B.C. with 0° 00′ on the plates, what is the deflection angle to the ¾ point of the curve?

22–11. In problem 22–3, assume that a setup is required at station 43 + 00 on the curve. Outline the method of orienting the instrument at station 43 + 00 to run in the remainder of the curve.

22–12. In problem 22–7, what sight distance is available if there is an obstruction to vision 20 ft inside the curve on a radial line through the vertex?

22–13. List in their order of importance the influence of R, D, L, T, E, M, and C in selecting curves to fit ground conditions. Justify your listing.

22–14. Prepare a set of field notes for running a circular curve of 60-ft radius for a street-car track making a 90° right turn on to a cross street.

22–15. A circular arc having a 200-ft radius joins two tangents which meet at an angle of 60° 00′. The curve is to be divided into six equal parts. (a) Determine the length of each part of the arc; the chord length required to lay off each arc; and the deflection angles at the points of tangency to lay off each chord point. (b) If the curve is run to its center from each end, and if the center point as established from the B.C. is 30.90 ft from the P.I., but as laid out from the E.C. is 32.80 ft, in which half of the curve has a mistake been made? What is the amount of the error in the incorrect position?

Chapter 23

PARABOLIC CURVES

23–1. General. Parabolic curves are used in the vertical plane to provide a smooth transition between grade lines on highways and railroads. They are also employed in the horizontal plane on landscaping work and for other functions which require a curve of pleasing appearance that can be laid out with a tape. The parabolic curves used in route-surveying practice differ only slightly from large radius circular curves.

Parabolic curves can be computed by the *tangent-offset method* and by the *chord-gradient method*. Both systems are based upon the following property of a parabola:

> *Offsets from a tangent to a parabola are proportional to the squares of the distances from the point of tangency.*

In this brief treatment only a single arithmetic method will be demonstrated. It is applicable to curves having either equal tangents or unequal tangents. Another property of the parabola supplements the tangent-offset rule in this method:

> *The center of a parabola is midway between the vertex and the long chord; that is, the external distance always equals the middle ordinate.*

A vertical curve must (a) fit the grade lines it connects, (b) have a length sufficient to meet the specification covering the maximum rate of change of grade per station (0.05 to 0.10 per cent on railroads), and (c) provide the required sight distance. Generally the vertex is placed at a full station in railroad work but it may be at a plus station on a highway layout.

23–2. Computations for an equal-tangent curve. In Fig. 23–1 a −2.00 per cent grade meets a +1.60 per cent grade at station 87 + 00 and at elevation 743.24 ft. Assume that an 800-ft curve fits the ground conditions fairly well and satisfies the specifications.

Grade elevations on the tangents are determined by computing forward and backward from the vertex. The elevation of point A (the center of the long chord), found by averaging the elevations of the B.C. and the E.C., is 750.44 ft. Point B, the midpoint of the curve, is halfway between point A and the vertex at elevation 746.84.

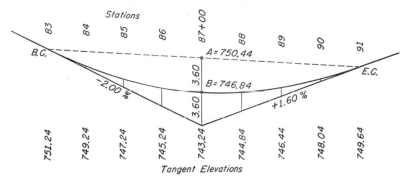

FIG. 23–1. Equal tangent vertical curve.

The tangent offset at the center of the curve is therefore 3.60 ft. Offsets from the tangents at the other full stations are

$$(\tfrac{1}{4})^2 \times 3.60 = 0.22 \text{ ft}$$
$$(\tfrac{1}{2})^2 \times 3.60 = 0.90 \text{ ft}$$
$$(\tfrac{3}{4})^2 \times 3.60 = 2.02 \text{ ft}$$

Final elevations on the curve are shown in the usual form in illustration 23–1. Offsets can be computed from one tangent for the full

Illustration 23–1

EQUAL-TANGENT VERTICAL CURVE

Station	Point	Tangent Elevation	Tangent Offset	Elevation on Curve
92		751.24		
91	E.C.	749.64	0.00	749.64
90		748.04	0.22	748.26
89		746.44	0.90	747.34
88		744 84	2.02	746.86
87	P.I.	743.24	3.60	746.84
86		745.24	2.02	747.26
85		747.24	0.90	748.14
84		749.24	0.22	749.46
83	B.C.	751.24	0.00	751.24
82		753.24		

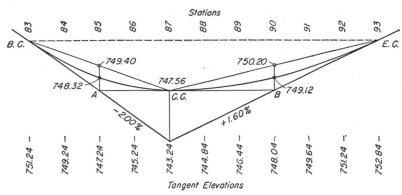

FIG. 23-2. Unequal tangent vertical curve.

length of the curve but it is simpler to use symmetrical offsets on both sides of the vertex.

The grades shown in Figs. 23–1 and 23–2 are greatly exaggerated. Actually there is no significant difference between vertical lines and offsets perpendicular to the tangents for the light grades used in practice. Verticals are more convenient and give a smooth curve.

Figures 23–1 and 23–2 show *sag curves.* If the grades are reversed, *summit curves* are formed.

23–3. Computations for an unequal-tangent curve.

In Fig. 23–2, assume that for the two grades of the previous example a 400-ft vertical curve is to be extended back from the vertex, and a 600-ft curve run in forward to better fit the ground conditions.

Connect the midpoints of the two curves, stations 85 and 90, to obtain line *AB.* Draw lines from the B.C. and E.C. to point C.C., station 87. Compute the elevation of the C.C., 747.56, by proportion from the known elevations of *A* and *B.*

Now compute two vertical curves, one from the B.C. to the C.C., and another from the C.C. to the E.C., by the method of section 23–2. Since both curves are tangent to the same line *AB* at point C.C., they will be tangent to each other and form a smooth curve. Critical elevations are shown on the figure.

23–4. High or low point on a vertical curve.

For purposes of investigations of drainage, clearance beneath overhead structures, cover over pipes, and sight distance, it may be necessary to determine the elevation and location of the low (or high) point on a vertical curve. At the low or high point, a tangent to the curve will be horizontal and its slope equal to zero. Based on this fact, the following formula is readily derived:

$$x = \frac{g_1 L}{g_1 - g_2} \qquad (23\text{–}1)$$

in which $x =$ distance, in stations, measured horizontally from the B.C. to the high or low point of the curve;

$g_1 =$ tangent grade through the B.C.;

$g_2 =$ tangent grade through the E.C.;

$L =$ length of the curve, in stations.

If g_2 is substituted for g_1 in the numerator, the distance x is measured from the E.C.

In the problem of Fig. 23–1, $g_1 = -2.00$ per cent, $g_2 = +1.60$ per cent, and $L = 8$ stations. Then

$$x = \frac{-2.00 \times 8}{-2.00 - (+1.60)} = 4.44 \text{ stations}$$

The elevation at this point (station $87 + 44.4$) is

$$(743.24 + 0.444 \times 1.60) + \left(\frac{3.56}{4}\right)^2 \times 3.60 = 746.80 \text{ ft}$$

23–5. Sight distance. The formula for sight distance S with the vehicle on a vertical curve, and S less than the length L, is

$$S^2 = \frac{8Lh}{g_1 - g_2} \qquad (23\text{–}2)$$

where $S =$ sight distance, in stations;

$L =$ length of curve, in stations;

$h =$ height of driver's eye, and the object sighted, above the roadway (usually assumed to be $4\frac{1}{2}$ ft).

Then for a summit curve having a length of 800 ft, and grades of $+2.00$ per cent and -1.60 per cent, if $h = 4\frac{1}{2}$ ft,

$$S = \sqrt{\frac{8 \times 8 \times 4.5}{2.00 - (-1.60)}} = 8.94 \text{ stations} = 894 \text{ ft}$$

Since this distance is greater than the length of curve and thus not in agreement with the assumption used in deriving the formula, a different expression must be employed.

If the vehicle is off the curve and on the tangent to it, the formula

for sight distance which is applicable and derived in a similar manner
is

$$S = \frac{L}{2} + \frac{4h}{g_1 - g_2} \tag{23-3}$$

In the preceding example, with $h = 4\frac{1}{2}$ ft,

$$S = \frac{8}{2} + \frac{4 \times 4.5}{2.00 - (-1.60)} = 9 \text{ stations}$$

23–6. Sources of error.   Some of the sources of error in vertical-
curve work are:

 a. Carrying out grade percentages beyond 0.01 per cent.   Multiples
    of 0.05 per cent or 0.10 per cent are desirable for highways.
 b. Carrying out computed elevations to less than 0.01 ft.
 c. Selecting the vertex at other than a full station.

23–7. Mistakes.   Typical mistakes that are made in computations
for vertical curves include the following:

 a. Arithmetical errors.
 b. Using an incorrect offset at the vertex.
 c. Subtracting the offsets from the tangents for a sag curve, or
    adding them for a summit curve.
 d. Failing to check the computed values for curve elevations, to be
    certain they fit those of the tangents, the P.I., the B.C., and the
    E.C.

PROBLEMS

23– 1. A manhole is 16 ft from the center line of a street that is 40 ft wide and
has a 5-in. parabolic crown.   If the center of the street is at elevation
192.32 ft, what is the elevation of the manhole cover?

23– 2. The width of a street pavement is 36 ft and the average parabolic crown
from the center to each edge is $\frac{1}{4}$ in. per ft.   What is the drop in the pavement surface from the center of the street to a point 10 ft from the edge?

23– 3. A -2.00 per cent grade meets a $+3.00$ per cent grade at station 96 + 00
and elevation 623.00 ft.   Compute and tabulate the elevations on a 600-ft
vertical curve to join the two tangents.

23– 4. A $+4$ per cent grade and a -1 per cent grade are joined by a 250-ft parabolic curve.   The station of the B.C. is 9 + 50 and its elevation is 192.82
ft.   Compute the elevations of 50-ft stations on the curve.   What is the
elevation of station 9 + 75?

23– 5. A -2.00 per cent grade meets a $+1.00$ per cent grade at station 40 + 00,
which has an elevation of 200.00 ft.   The elevation of station 40 + 00 on
the curve must be 201.50.   Compute and tabulate the data required to

lay out a vertical curve which will pass through the designated point at station 40 + 00.

23– 6. A 0.00 per cent grade intersects a +2.00 per cent grade at station 30 + 00 and elevation 350.00 ft. Determine the suitable vertical curve which will join the tangents and pass through a point with an elevation 352.00 at station 30 + 00.

23– 7. A −2.00 per cent grade meets a 0.00 per cent grade at station 15 + 00 and elevation 220.00 The 0.00 per cent grade in turn joins a +1.00 per cent grade at station 18 + 00 and elevation 220.00. Compute and tabulate the notes for an 800-ft vertical curve to fit the given conditions. What is the elevation of station 15 + 50 on the curve?

23– 8. A highway to be built will cross a pipe culvert at right angles. The pipe is located at station 100 + 85, where its top is at elevation 95.6 ft. The vertex of a 500-ft parabolic curve is to be located at station 100 + 00 and have an elevation of 98.60 ft. The grade of the tangent from the B.C. to the P.I. is +1.20 per cent. The grade of the tangent from the P.I. to the E.C. is −1.08 per cent. What is the depth of cover over the pipe?

23– 9. A +4.00 per cent grade meets a −2.00 per cent grade at a summit. What is the minimum length of vertical curve which will provide a sight distance of 500 ft?

23–10. Determine the station and elevation of the high point on the curve in problem 23–4, and of the low point on the curve of problem 23–5.

23–11. Compute and tabulate the elevations on a vertical curve which has tangents of 600 ft and 1000 ft. The first tangent grade is +1.80 per cent and the second is −2.20 per cent. The vertex is at station 44 + 00 and elevation 100.00 ft.

23–12. It is proposed to use a vertical parabolic curve at the summit of a hill to connect a grade of +4.00 per cent and a grade of −3.00 per cent to obtain a clear sight distance of 800 ft when the H.I. of approaching automobiles is 5 ft. The grades intersect at station 82 + 00 and elevation 1009.73 ft. (a) What is the required length of curve? (b) A practical curve length is taken as the multiple of 100 ft nearest the theoretical length, and an equal number of 50-ft stations are placed on each side of the vertex. Tabulate the elevations of the curve stations.

Chapter 24

VOLUMES

24-1. General. Surveyors are called upon to measure volumes of earthwork and concrete for various types of construction projects. Volume computations are required to determine the capacity of bins, tanks, reservoirs, and buildings, and to check the quantities in stockpiles.

The unit of volume is a cube having edges of unit length. Both the cubic foot and the cubic yard are used in surveying calculations but the latter is the standard unit for earthwork. One cubic yard equals 27 cubic feet.

24-2. Methods of measurement. Direct measurement of volumes is rarely made in surveying, since it is difficult to actually apply a unit of the material involved. Indirect measurements are obtained by measuring lines and areas which have a relation to the volume desired.

Two principal methods are used: (a) the cross-section method and (b) the unit-area, or borrow-pit, method.

24-3. The cross-section method. When the cross-section method is used for computing volumes, vertical cross sections are taken (usually at right angles to the center line) at intervals of 50 or 100 ft. The areas of these sections can be found by calculation from the field data, or by planimetering the plotted cross sections. The volume is computed by the *average-end-area formula* or by the *prismoidal formula*.

24-4. Types of cross sections. The types of cross sections commonly used on route surveys are shown in Fig. 24-1. In flat terrain the *level section* in *a* is suitable. The *three-level section* in *b* is generally employed where ordinary ground conditions prevail. Rough topography may require a *five-level section*, as in *c*, or an *irregular section*, as in *d*. A *transition section*, as in *e* and a *side-hill section*, as in *f*, occur in passing from *cut* (excavation) to *fill* (embankment), and on side-hill locations.

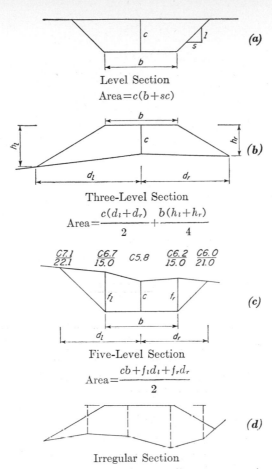

Level Section
Area $= c(b + sc)$

Three-Level Section
$$\text{Area} = \frac{c(d_l + d_r)}{2} + \frac{b(h_l + h_r)}{4}$$

Five-Level Section
$$\text{Area} = \frac{cb + f_l d_l + f_r d_r}{2}$$

Irregular Section

Area found by triangles, coordinates, or matrix method.

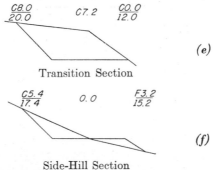

Transition Section

Side-Hill Section

Fig. 24–1.   Earthwork sections.

The width b of the base or finished roadway is fixed by the project requirements. The base is usually wider in cuts than on fills, to provide for drainage ditches. The side slope s depends upon the type of soil encountered. Side slopes in fill must be flatter than those in cuts where the soil remains in its natural state.

Cut slopes of 1 to 1 and fill slopes of $1\frac{1}{2}$ (horizontal) to 1 (vertical) are satisfactory for ordinary loam soils.

Formulas for the areas of the different sections are readily derived. Formulas are listed beside some of the sketches in Fig. 24–1.

24–5. End-area formulas. The volume between two vertical cross sections A_1 and A_2 is equal to the average of the end areas multiplied by the horizontal distance L between them. Thus

$$V = \frac{L(A_1 + A_2)}{2} \tag{24-1}$$

This formula is approximate and gives answers which generally are slightly larger than the true prismoidal volumes. It is used in practice because of its simplicity. Increased accuracy is obtained by decreasing the distance L between the sections. When the ground is irregular, cross sections must be taken close together.

24–6. Prismoidal formula. The prismoidal formula applies to the volumes of all geometric solids which can be considered prismoids. Most earthwork volumes fit this classification but relatively few of them warrant the precision of the prismoidal formula, which is

$$V = \frac{L(A_1 + 4A_m + A_2)}{6} \tag{24-2}$$

where V = volume;
A_1 and A_2 = areas of successive cross sections taken in the field;
A_m = area of a section midway between A_1 and A_2;
L = horizontal distance between A_1 and A_2.

Various handbooks give tables and diagrams to facilitate computations of areas and volumes.

To illustrate the computation of area for the section shown in Fig. 24–2, assume that the following set of notes was obtained in the field (the letters A, B, C, D, E, F, and G, and the values at A and G were not recorded in the field; they are added for this discussion):

Station	A	B	C	D	E	F	G
24 + 00	$\dfrac{0}{15}$	$\dfrac{C\ 8}{27}$	$\dfrac{C\ 16}{20}$	$\dfrac{C\ 18}{0}$	$\dfrac{C\ 10}{14}$	$\dfrac{C\ 12}{33}$	$\dfrac{0}{15}$

The numerators are cuts, in feet, and the denominators are distances out from the center line. Fills are noted by the letter F. Using C instead of plus for cut, and F instead of minus for fill, eliminates confusion. On many projects the measurements are carried out to tenths of a foot. In computing areas by coordinates, cut values are considered plus, distances to the right of the center line are plus, and distances to the left of the center line are minus.

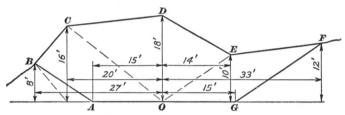

Fig. 24–2. Irregular section.

The area of the cross section in Fig. 24–2 will be found in three ways: (a) by coordinates, (b) by dividing the area into simple figures (triangles), and (c) by the matrix system.

Area by Coordinates

$$0(-27 - 15) = \quad 0$$
$$8(-20 + 15) = -\ 40$$
$$16(\quad 0 + 27) = +\ 432$$
$$18(\quad 14 + 20) = +\ 612$$
$$10(\quad 33 + \quad 0) = +\ 330$$
$$12(\quad 15 - 14) = +\ 12$$
$$0(-15 - 33) = \quad 0$$

$$\overline{2)\ +\ 1346}$$
$$\text{Area} \quad 673$$

Area by Triangles

$$18(34) = \quad 612$$
$$10(33) = \quad 330$$
$$12(\ 1) = \quad 12$$
$$16(27) = \quad 432$$
$$-8(\ 5) = -\ 40$$

$$\overline{2)1346}$$
$$\text{Area} \quad 673$$

Area by matrix system. The matrix system for computing earthwork can be used for any type of section and has many engineering applications.

Using the notes obtained in the field for points B, C, D, E, and F, place half the roadway width beneath zero on both ends of the data. This produces the same expression used in the coordinate method, since the coordinates of A and G are 0/15.

Then beginning at the center, multiply diagonally downward and add the results as shown. Again, beginning at the center, multiply diagonally upward and add the results. Subtract the upward sum from the downward sum to obtain the double area. Divide by 2. The computations may be arranged as follows:

Downward:
$$18(20) + 16(27) + \ 8(15) + 18(14) + 10(33) + 12(15) = 1674$$
Upward:
$$0(16) + 20(8) \ + 27(0) \ + \ 0(10) + 14(12) + 33(0) \ \ = \ \ 328$$
$$2\overline{)1346}$$
$$673$$

It is best to make separate computations for cut and fill if they occur in the same section, since they must always be tabulated independently for pay purposes.

To find the volume between this section at station 24 and another at the next station, 25, which is 100 ft distant, assume that the area of the section at station 25 is 515 sq ft. Then the volume in cubic yards, by the end-area formula, is

$$V = \frac{100}{2 \times 27}(A_1 + A_2) = \frac{100}{54}(673 + 515) = 2200 \text{ cu yd}$$

In order to use the prismoidal formula it is necessary to know the area of the section halfway between the stations. This area is found by the usual computation after averaging the heights and widths of the end sections. Obviously the middle area is not the average of the end areas, since there would then be no difference between the results of the end-area formula and the prismoidal formula.

The prismoidal formula generally gives a volume less than that found by the end-area formula. For example, the volume of a pyramid by the prismoidal formula is $Ah/3$, whereas by the average-end-area method it is $Ah/2$. An exception occurs when the center height is great but the width narrow at one station, and the center height is small but the width large at the adjacent station. Figure 24-3 illustrates this condition. The difference between the volume obtained by the average-end-area formula and that by the prismoidal formula is called the *prismoidal correction*.

Various books on route surveying give formulas and tables for computing prismoidal corrections which can be applied to the average-end-area volumes to get prismoidal volumes.   Except in rock-excavation and in concrete work, the use of the prismoidal formula is not normally justified by the low precision of the field data.   Frequently it is easier to compute the end-area volume and the prismoidal correction than to calculate the prismoidal volume directly.

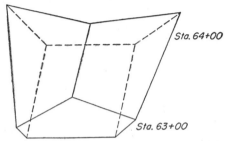

Fig. 24-3. Sections for which the prismoidal correction is added to the end area volume.

24–7. Unit-area, or borrow-pit, method.   Calculations of volumes by the unit-area, or borrow-pit, method were discussed in section 5–29.

Greater accuracy can be obtained in rough terrain by using triangular areas instead of rectangular blocks.   The volume is then equal to the area of each triangle times the average of its three corner heights.   Thus

$$V = \frac{A(a + b + c)}{3} \tag{24-3}$$

24–8. Sources of error.   Some of the common errors in computing areas of sections and volumes of earthwork are:

a. Carrying out areas of cross sections beyond the nearest square foot, or beyond the limit justified by the field data.
b. Carrying out volumes beyond the nearest cubic yard.
c. Failing to correct for the effect of curvature when a section on a horizontal curve has cut on one side of the center line and fill on the other side.

24–9. Mistakes.   Typical mistakes that are made in earthwork calculations are the following:

a. Errors in arithmetic.
b. Using the prismoidal formula when end-area volumes are sufficiently accurate.

c. Using end-area volumes for pyramidal or wedge-shaped solids.

d. Mixing cut quantities and fill quantities.

e. Not considering transition sections when passing from cut to fill, or from fill to cut.

PROBLEMS

24– 1. Compute the end-area volume of earthwork between two level sections in cut having center heights of 3.0 ft and 4.0 ft. The base width is 20 ft and the side slopes are 1 to 1.

24– 2. Same as problem 24–1, but compute the prismoidal volume.

24– 3. An irrigation ditch will be excavated to give a base width of 10 ft and side slopes of 1 to 1. Compute the average-end-area volume of earthwork for the following field notes:

Sta. 38	$\dfrac{C\ 6.2}{11.2}$	C 5.8	$\dfrac{C\ 5.6}{10.6}$
Sta. 37	$\dfrac{C\ 7.0}{12.0}$	C 6.5	$\dfrac{C\ 6.0}{11.0}$

24– 4. Compute the areas of the sections in problem 24–3 by the matrix system.

24– 5. Compute the volume in problem 24–3 by the prismoidal formula.

24– 6. Compute the average-end-area volume of earthwork for a section of highway. The base width is 30 ft and the side slope in fill is $1\frac{1}{2}$ to 1. The field notes follow:

Sta. 72	$\dfrac{F\ 4.0}{21.0}$	F 3.2	$\dfrac{F\ 4.4}{21.6}$
Sta. 71 + 60	$\dfrac{F\ 3.6}{20.4}$	F 2.5	$\dfrac{F\ 0.0}{15.0}$

24– 7. Compute the areas of the sections in problem 24–6 by the matrix system and check by calculation from coordinates.

24– 8. Compute the total volume of earthwork between the sections shown in Figs. 24–1e and 24–1f. Assume that the sections are 50 ft apart and have base widths of 24 ft in both cut and fill.

24– 9. Compute the average-end-area volume and the prismoidal volume for the sections shown in Fig. 24–3 which have a base width of 40 ft and side slopes of 1 to 1. Notes for the sections are as follows:

Sta. 64	$\dfrac{C\ 12.8}{32.8}$	C 6.5	$\dfrac{C\ 12.0}{32.0}$
Sta. 63 + 00	$\dfrac{C\ 3.0}{23.0}$	C 14.4	$\dfrac{C\ 4.6}{24.6}$

24–10. Compute the volume in problem 5–21, using triangular areas instead of rectangular areas.

24–11. Compute the volume of a reservoir between contours 100 and 125, the areas measured by a planimeter on a topographic map being as follows:

Elevation	Area (sq ft)	Elevation	Area (sq ft)
100	1215	115	4680
105	2220	120	6800
110	3590	125	8240

Chapter 25

INDUSTRIAL APPLICATIONS

25–1. General. The increase in the size of manufactured items, and the decrease in tolerance limits in both individual parts and final assembly in mass production, necessitate precise measurements. The toolmaker's old stand-bys—taut wires and hanging plumb bobs, trammels and steel scales, insulated micrometer rods, gages, surface plates, and jo blocks—are no longer good enough. A new and rapidly developing field, *optical tooling*, is providing the equipment capable of meeting the close tolerances specified for large mock-ups, jigs, and end products. The term "optical tooling" is already well-established although somewhat of a misnomer.

Exact alignment, precise linear and angular measurements, and perfect level for vertical control can be obtained with a properly adjusted surveyor's level and transit. When measurements to thousandths of a foot were sufficient for shop practice, standard surveying equipment could meet the requirements. Today, however, tolerances of only a few thousandths of an inch have resulted in refinements of even the better surveying instruments.

The fundamental theory of measurements discussed in previous chapters applies directly to optical tooling in shop work. Optics provide a line of sight that is absolutely straight, has no weight, and serves as a perfect base from which to make accurate measurements.

Layout in a shop requires the establishment of (a) a reference line, (b) lines parallel with or perpendicular to the reference line, and (c) consistent elevations over large surfaces. These are the equivalent of line and grade in construction surveying.

25–2. Basic equipment. Three basic instruments are used in industrial applications of surveying methods:

    a. Alignment telescope, or jig alignment telescope.

    b. Jig transit.

    c. Precise level.

The alignment telescope, Fig. 25–1,[1] provides permanent reference lines on a jig or other structure. The jig transit, Fig. 25–7, establishes an absolutely vertical plane exactly where desired—on line with two marks, or precisely at right angles to any other line of sight. The precise (tilting) level, Fig. 5–11 and Fig. 5–12, fixes a true horizontal plane at any desired height. All three instruments are self-checking, and they can be tested quickly and adjusted exactly.

FIG. 25–1. Jig alignment telescope. (Courtesy of Keuffel and Esser Company.)

Two *optical micrometers*, built into the alignment telescope as indicated in Figs. 25–1 and 25–2, permit the line of sight to be moved parallel to itself sideways or vertically. The jig transit and precise level also can be equipped with an optical micrometer. The motions are controlled by micrometer knobs that show the extent of the movement in thousandths of an inch.

Measurements from the line of sight are made with a precision *optical tooling scale*, one type of which is represented in Fig. 25–12. This scale provides a definite target at every 0.1 in. The remaining decimal part is measured with the optical micrometer to 0.001 in.

25–3. Sighting telescope. The fundamental element of the alignment telescope, jig transit, and tilting level is the sighting telescope.

[1] The illustrations in this chapter, and some of the text material, are from *Optical Tooling Equipment*, published by Keuffel and Esser Company, and are reprinted here by permission.

It must be skillfully designed and perfectly manufactured to combine proper resolving power, definition, magnification, eye distance, size of pupil, and field of view. Some of these features were discussed in section 5–8.

FIG. 25–2. Eyepiece end of jig alignment telescope. (Courtesy of Keuffel and Esser Company.)

The telescope on a jig transit and on a tilting level is mounted in the same manner as that on standard surveying equipment. The alignment telescope usually is supported by the jig itself.

25–4. Alignment telescope. The alignment telescope, Fig. 25–1, can be focused for any distance from practically zero (the point sighted being actually in contact with the front end of the telescope), to infinity. It can be mounted directly within a jig frame, since it requires a minimum of space. The telescope shown has a field of view of approximately 30 min at infinity focus; a resolving power of 3.4 sec; a magnification varying automatically from about 4 power at zero focus to 46 power at infinity focus; an open cross-line pattern for the reticule; and a 90° prismatic-eyepiece attachment that can be rotated through 360°. It is $17\frac{3}{4}$ in. long.

The support provided is either a permanently attached sphere or a spherical adapter which slides over the telescope tube and can be removed to permit use of the telescope in special fixtures. Typical

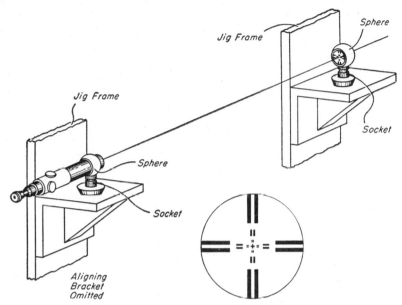

Fig. 25-3. Use of alignment telescope. (Courtesy of Keuffel and Esser Company.)

supports are shown in Fig. 25–3. The adapter gives greater flexibility in positioning the telescope to clear jig parts.

25–5. Use of alignment telescope. The alignment telesope provides a long, absolutely straight, permanent optical reference line for a jig or other structure on which measurements are to be made. A bracket to support a socket for mounting the telescope or a target is built at each end of the jig, as indicated in Fig. 25–3. The telescope, mounted in a sphere, is held in one socket. A target, centered in another sphere, is held by the second socket. A special device with adjusting screws, called an aligning bracket, is supplied for aiming the telescope. The optical reference line is then established by setting the cross lines of the telescope on the target. This line can be recovered readily as long as the sockets remain on the jig.

The sockets have adjustable mounts by which the line of sight is positioned originally. Accurate setting is necessary only when more than one line of sight is to be used, or when the line of sight must be level.

Usually it is convenient to have the line of sight exactly level. To accomplish this, a sphere with a target is placed in each socket and one of the sockets is adjusted to place the two targets at exactly the same elevation determined by means of a tilting level. One target is then replaced by the alignment telescope, which is tilted until the other target appears to coincide with the cross lines when the micrometers are set at zero. The line of sight generally is located to establish either the center line or a line parallel with it.

The line of sight is picked up by targets wherever needed. A target consists of a glass circle mounted in a steel ring ground to a specified diameter. Etched on the glass is a design which marks the center of the ring and which may include scales giving distances from the center. Usually the target is illuminated from behind. Station positions—distances parallel to the line of sight—are measured, with an inside micrometer and measuring rods, from a reference button on the socket support to a reference button on the piece to be positioned. A precise tape is used for longer distances.

25–6. Positioning a part. Parts may be positioned by (a) two targets on line, (b) autoreflection, and (c) measuring from the line of sight.

Two targets on line. When a small jig part is to be positioned on or near the line of sight, as indicated in Fig. 25–4, it is built with a

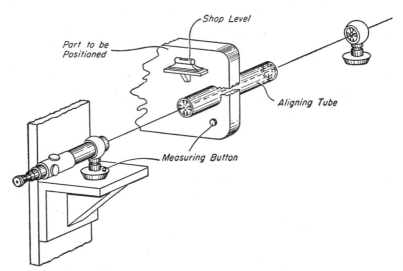

Fig. 25-4. Positioning by two targets on line and a shop level. (Courtesy of Keuffel and Esser Company.)

bracket to hold a square-setting aligning tube containing a target in each end; a bracket to hold a shop level perpendicular to the line of sight; and a button to give the correct station. The part is positioned by adjusting it until the two targets are on line, the bubble of the shop level centers when placed on the bracket, and the button is at the correct station.

Autoreflection. When greater accuracy is necessary, an optically flat mirror target is mounted on the part to be positioned so that its reflecting surface is parallel to the proper reference plane on the part and it is also in the line of sight of the alignment telescope. The part is positioned, as indicated in Fig. 25–5, by placing the mirror target on line; setting the button at the proper station; and turning and tilting the part until the cross lines in the alignment telescope appear to coincide with the reflection of a target mounted on the end of the telescope, this reflection being produced by the mirror target.

Measuring from the line of sight. When the optical-micrometer

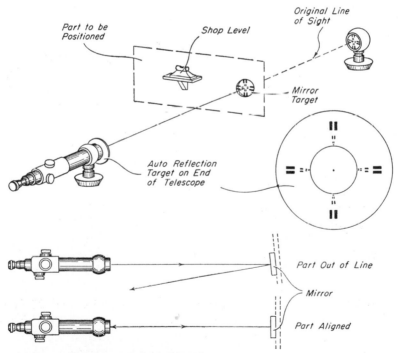

Fig. 25–5. Positioning by autoreflection and a shop level. (Courtesy of Keuffel and Esser Company.)

knobs of the alignment telescope are turned, the line of sight is moved parallel to itself by the number of thousandths of an inch shown on the graduated drums.   Optical micrometers are used to determine any error in positioning the target, and thus to check the tolerances. Tolerance stops are provided for repeated checking of the same tolerance.   Under most circumstances, however, measurements of distances greater than the range covered by the micrometers should be made from the line of sight with a precision scale, a special vernier caliper, or a height gage that has a target attached to the movable section. Possible arrangements are illustrated in Fig. 25–6.   Sometimes a target is placed on the line of sight and measurements are made with an inside micrometer and measuring rods.

A special device, Fig. 25–6, may be built with a target at one end; a measuring button on the other end at a predetermined distance from the target center; and a bracket to hold a shop level.   The bracket holding the level can be placed to accommodate measurements vertically, horizontally, or at any desired angle in a plane perpendicular to the line of sight.

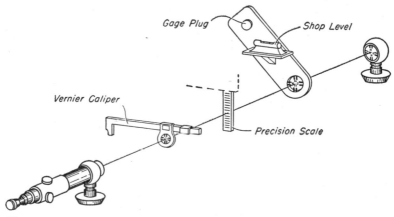

Fig. 25–6.   Measuring from line of sight with special vernier caliper, precise scale, and special fixture.   (Courtesy of Keuffel and Esser Company.)

25–7. The jig transit.   The jig transit, Figs. 25–7 and 25–8, is designed especially for optical tooling.   Its basic operation and functions are like those of an engineer's transit, but the instrument does not have a circle or arc for measuring angles.   Particular features essential to optical tooling are listed.

Precise plate level. The plate level perpendicular to the telescope is as long and sensitive as the telescope level on a standard transit.

Special telescope. The telescope has a minimum focus of 3 ft from the instrument center (instead of the normal 5 ft for transits) and an erecting eyepiece.

FIG. 25–7. Jig transit with optical micrometer, counterweight, and telescope-axle mirror. (Courtesy of Keuffel and Esser Company.)

Adjustable line of sight. The vertical plane of the line of sight can be adjusted laterally to make it pass through the vertical axis. It is then possible to reverse the instrument without shifting the vertical plane of the line of sight horizontally.

Measuring button. A measuring button is mounted on the standard $2\frac{1}{2}$ in. below the center of the mirror on each side. Its face is exactly 3.250 in. from the vertical axis of the instrument and there-

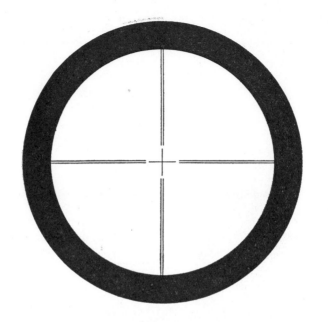

FIG. 25-8.   Top view of jig transit, and glass reticule.   (Courtesy of Keuffel and Esser Company.)

fore 3.250 in. from the vertical plane of the line of sight. The position of the plane of the line of sight can therefore be determined with measuring rods and inside micrometers.

Prismatic eyepiece. This facilitates sighting to high points. Also, it may be rotated 360° to permit use of the instrument near an obstruction.

Additional attachments that are usually furnished on a jig transit include the following:

1) An optical micrometer, with counterweight, to reduce the time of setup when *bucking-in,* and to measure the actual position of any part of the jig, both vertically and horizontally, in any plane perpendicular to the line of sight.

2) Striding level and collars.

3) Finder sights on the striding level to assist in positioning the jig transit at right angles to the line of sight of the alignment telescope.

4) A telescope-axle mirror, which has an optically flat front surface and can be attached on either end of the telescope axle so as to be parallel to the line of sight. With this device the plane of the line of sight of the jig transit can be set perpendicular to any optical line by means of autoreflection, as indicated in Fig. 25–9.

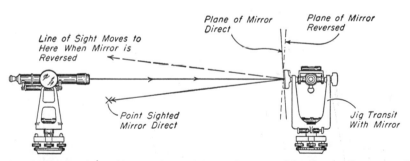

Fig. 25–9. Setting a jig transit at right angles to a sight line. (Courtesy of Keuffel and Esser Company.)

25–8. Use of the jig transit.

25–8. Use of the jig transit. The jig transit is designed to establish a precise vertical plane wherever desired, and to serve as a level when ordinary accuracy is sufficient. It can be used for a variety of purposes, both in original layout and in precise control.

The jig transit should be mounted on a mechanical lateral adjuster supported on a rigid stand, or on an adjustable mount. An optical micrometer greatly facilitates operation of the instrument. When the micrometer is not used, the sunshade should be placed on the telescope to reduce the unfocused light that tends to dim the image.

It is essential that the jig transit be set up with the telescope axle exactly horizontal and with the line of sight in the desired plane. When in this position, the line of sight will sweep the vertical plane required.

Usually the desired vertical plane is marked by two scribed points. The transit is placed in line with them by a process called bucking-in, the procedure being illustrated in Fig. 25–10.   After the instrument is set up in line as judged by eye, the procedure is as follows:

a. Loosen a pair of adjacent leveling screws and rotate the leveling head until a pair of opposite screws is in line with the vertical plane to be established.

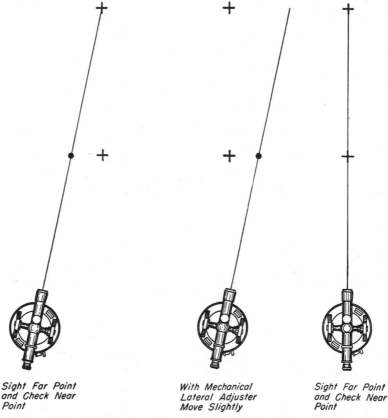

Sight Far Point
and Check Near
Point

With Mechanical
Lateral Adjuster
Move Slightly

Sight Far Point
and Check Near
Point

FIG. 25–10.   Bucking-in.   (Courtesy of Keuffel and Esser Company.)

b. Center the two plate bubbles.

c. Aim at the far point.

d. Aim at the near point without turning the instrument about its vertical axis, and note where the line of sight falls.

e. Move the instrument with the mechanical lateral adjuster until the line of sight has moved in the direction of, and slightly beyond, the near point.

f. Center the plate bubbles.

g. Aim at the far point.

h. Check the near point.

i. Continue until the line of sight checks on both points. Level the instrument each time it is moved.

The striding level and optical micrometer also can be used for bucking-in, but the methods will not be described here.

25–9. The tilting level. The tilting level was described in Chapter 5. Essentially the same type is used in shop work.

Fig. 25–11. Optical micrometer. (Courtesy of Keuffel and Esser Company.)

25–10. Optical micrometers. Optical micrometers are manufactured as attachments for levels and transits to be used for precise leveling and alignment in shop work. Measurements to 0.001 in. can be made with them.

An optical micrometer consists of a disk of optical glass with flat parallel faces; such a disk is called a *planoparallel plate*. It is designed to permit precise tilting by moving a graduated drum, located as shown in Fig. 25–11. The device is mounted on the instrument in place of the sunshade, with the plate in front of the objective lens. The lower right-hand screw clamps the micrometer in position. A knob and a drum control the planoparallel plate. Figure 25–11 shows the line of sight moved 0.081 in. to the right as read on the drum.

25–11. Use of the optical micrometer. Figure 25–12 illustrates schematically the use of an optical micrometer for measuring a verti-

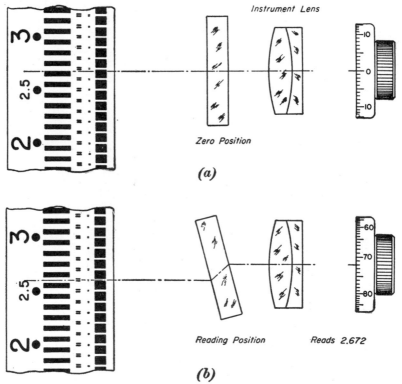

Fig. 25–12. The principle of the optical micrometer. (Courtesy of Keuffel and Esser Company.)

cal distance. The sights are taken on an accurately graduated steel scale divided into tenths of an inch. Figure 25–12a shows the line of sight falling between 2.6 and 2.7 in. for the zero position of the micrometer. The drum is graduated in both directions from 0 to 100. To avoid turning in the wrong direction, the drum is first set to zero and then rotated to make the line of sight move toward the graduation with the lesser value on the steel scale—2.6 in. in Fig. 25–12b. The drum always records the movement of the line of sight from its zero position. Figure 25–12b shows a movement of 72.0 thousandths, thus making the reading 2.6 + 0.072 = 2.672 in.

25–12. Other equipment. Additional items of equipment used in optical tooling include the following:

Optical tooling scales. The design of one type of scale, based upon extensive tests, is shown in Fig. 25–12. Each 0.1-in. graduation and separation is positioned correctly to within ±0.001 in. at 68 F. The design is based upon the principle that a cross line can be set most accurately by centering it between two black lines on a white surface, provided that the white areas between the lines and the cross line are the optimum width. Accordingly the spacing is selected to serve over a certain range of distances for the width of cross lines in a particular telescope.

Optical tooling targets. A typical arrangement of graduations on optical tooling targets is shown in Fig. 25–3.

Spherical adapters. A fixed or movable sphere is useful in positioning alignment telescopes and targets. Figure 25–3 illustrates one type of arrangement of spherical adapters.

Trivet. A trivet is a special device for supporting a transit or level near the floor when the line of sight must be low. Steel-pointed shoes on the three short legs can be removed to allow the trivet to be bolted directly to a jig or other fixture.

Autoreflection angle mirror. An autoreflection angle mirror reflects the line of sight of a telescope equipped with an autoreflection target at any appropriate angle up to about 160°. The device consists of a mirror with an optically flat front surface mounted vertically on the base of an engineer's transit. The mirror is adjusted to make the plane of its surface pass exactly through the vertical axis of the transit. It can therefore be turned through any horizontal angle like a transit.

Rapid developments in the field of optical tooling have produced many instruments which cannot be described in this text. Manufacturers' catalogues and other technical publications are sources of information on the design and use of such equipment.

25–13. Sources of error in optical tooling. Some of the sources of error in optical tooling are:

a. Using poorly graduated scales.

b. Bubble not exactly centered at the time of sighting.

c. Targets not perfectly placed.

25–14. Mistakes. Typical mistakes in using optical tooling equipment include the following:

a. Movement of targets before sights have been completed.

b. Line of sight incorrectly relocated.

c. Micrometer read in wrong direction.

PROBLEMS

25–1. Are the shafts of various pieces of equipment in a shop aligned by using a jig transit, or by using an engineer's transit, or by using other instruments? Explain the reason for the selection of equipment.

25–2. By means of a sketch, show how the jig transit and tilting level can be set up outside a work area to align and position parts readily without interfering with the erection personnel.

25–3. Check the flatness, straightness, and parallel alignment of the planers in a shop.

25–4. Sketch and outline a procedure for checking the straightness of a machine part 10 ft long by using three optical tooling scales and a jig transit. (NOTE: First align two of the scales with the transit).

25–5. By means of a sketch and tabulation, demonstrate how the level can be used to check the flatness of a surface 15 ft by 100 ft.

25–6. Determine whether the four corners of a bedplate on a machine are at the same elevation. Check the bedways.

25–7. Sketch the position of optical tooling equipment which can be employed to check the main shafts of electric generators for levelness.

25–8. Sketch and outline a procedure for checking the 90° angle between a vertical column face and the run of the bedways on a large machine. Use a jig transit and a precise level.

25–9. Check a grinder in the shop for flatness and level of bed, for horizontal travel of the tool guide bar, and for vertical straightness of the machine faces.

APPENDIX A

SUGGESTED ORDER OF FIELD ASSIGNMENTS
(Based on Three-Hour Field Periods and Three-Man Parties)

Period   Problem

1. Measuring distances with a steel tape. Referencing hubs.
2. Measuring distances with a steel tape. Pacing.
3. Differential leveling between two bench marks.
4. Differential leveling. Reciprocal leveling.
5. Profile levels.
6. Closing the horizon. Measurement and layout of angles with a tape.
7. Compass and pacing survey of a five-sided area.
8. Double direct angles, and bearings, of a closed traverse.
9. Prolonging a line by double centering. Prolonging a line past an obstacle.
10. Double deflection angles of a closed traverse (same traverse as in Period 8).
11. Determination of stadia interval factor.
12. Azimuth stadia traverse.
13. Topographic details by transit-stadia (planimetric).
14. Topographic details by transit-stadia (planimetric).
15. Trigonometric leveling.
16. Staking out a building.
17. Layout and leveling of shop equipment.
18. Borrow-pit leveling.
19. Layout of simple circular curve.
20. Contours by transit-stadia.
21. Topographic details by plane table.
22. Topographic details and three-point location by plane table.
23. Property survey.
24. Observation on the sun for azimuth. Observation on Polaris for azimuth.
25. Field test on use of equipment.

NOTES

a) This list of field problems covers sufficient material for a two-quarter or one-semester program. Assignments 1 through 18 are adequate for the typical first course in surveying given to civil and non-civil engineering students. A few deletions may be desirable to fit the particular group involved.

b) The suggested order permits a quick start on drafting-room computations and mapping if inclement weather is experienced early in the school term.

c) Many of the assignments can be carried out on the traverse used during the first field period. A sustained project rather than a series of unrelated problems results.

d) Pacing, and closing the horizon, are done individually while the other two men in the party are taping.

e) The compass and pacing survey, and the layout of shop equipment, are appropriate for certain students.

MEASURING DISTANCES WITH A

Hub	Sto.	Dist.			
A	0+00				
		321.20'			
B	3+21.42				
		276.57'			
C	5+97.99				
		100.30'			
D	6+98.29				
.		306.79'			
E	10+05.16				
		255.48			
A	12+60.64				
Σ	1260.64	1260.34			
	Ratio of error =	$\dfrac{0.30}{1260.49}$	$= \dfrac{1}{4300}$		

Plate

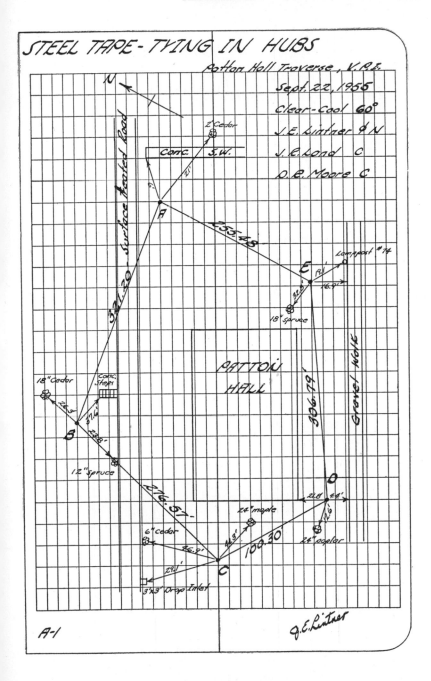

STEEL TAPE - TYING IN HUBS

Patton Hall Traverse, V.P.I.

Sept. 22, 1955

Clear-Cool 60°

J.E.Lintner ϕ N

J.E.Lond   C

O.E.Moore C

A-1   J.E.Lintner

			DISTANCES		
No. of Paces	Direction	Taped Dist.			
154	S	400'			
155	N	400'			
155	S	400'			
156	N	400'			
155	Average				
	Length of pace =		$\frac{400}{155}$ =	2.58'	
	No. of paces per 100' =		39⁻		
				Plate	

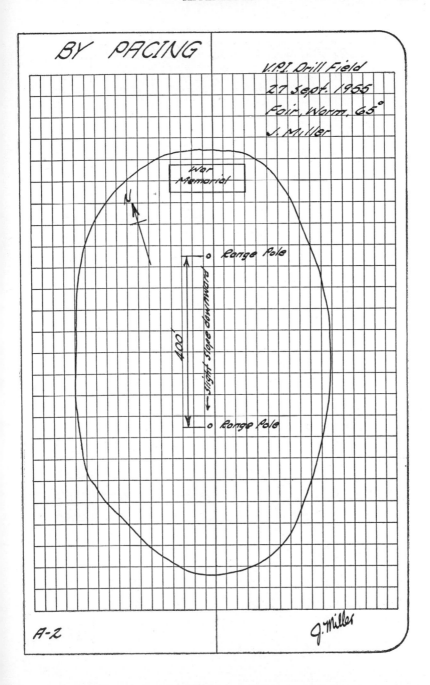

DIFFERENTIAL LEVELS					
Sta.	+ sight	H.I.	− sight	Elev.	Dist.
B.M. Mil.				100.00	
	1.33	101.33			150
T.P. 1			8.37	92.96	150
	0.22	93.18			135
T.P. 2			7.91 / 8.91	85.27	135
	0.96	86.23			160
T.P. 3			11.72	74.51	160
	0.46	74.97			160
B.M. Rutgers			8.71	66.26	160
	2.97		36.71		1210
B.M. Rutgers				66.26	
	11.95	78.21			180
T.P. 1			2.61	75.60	180
	12.55	88.15			180
T.P. 2			0.68	87.47	180
	12.77	100.24			155
B.M. Mil.			0.21	100.03	155
	37.27		3.50		1030
B.M. Rutgers	True elev. above MSL			2053.18	
	Elev.	diff.		33.75	
B.M. Mil.	MSL	elev.		2086.93	
					Plate

V.P.I.   CAMPUS

B.M. Mil. to B.M. Rutgers

29 Sept. 1955

Clear, Warm, 70°

B.M. Mil. on V.P.I. Campus   H.W. Mills   N

SW of Old Military Bldg.   J.F. King   Ø

9.4 ft. north of sidewalk   O.R. Moore   π

to instrument room and   Gurley Level #6

1.6 ft. from bldg. Bronze

disc in pipe flush with ground.

B.M. Rutgers SE of Patton Hall

opposite main entrance and

8 ft. from curb around drill

field. Bronze disc flush with

ground set in 6" concrete

cylinder and stamped Rutgers.

Rod	Sums	Elev.	Checks
−36.71	+37.27	+100.00	+66.26
+2.97	−3.50	−33.74	+33.77
−33.74	+33.77	+66.26	+100.03
	−33.74		

Loop Closure 0.03

Permissible closure = 0.05 $\sqrt{M}$

$= 0.05 \sqrt{2240/5280} = 0.03'$

A-3

H.W. Mills

RECIPROCAL LEVELING

Station	+ Sight		– Sight	Elev. Diff.	Elev.
B.M. Rutgers	2.605				2053.182
B.M. Eagle.			12.304		
			12.302		
			12.293		
			12.297		
B.M. Eagle.		Aver.	12.299	9.694	2043.488
B.M. Eagle.	11.203				2043.488
B.M. Rutgers			1.528		
			1.517		
			1.519		
			1.522		
B.M. Rutgers		Aver.	1.522	9.681	2053.169
Σ	13.808		13.821		
			13.808		
		Closure	0.013		
		Mean		9.688	
B.M. Eagle.		Mean	Elev.		2043.494
					Plate

ACROSS DRILL FIELD

V.P.I. Campus

4 Oct 1955

Clear, Hot 80°

Description on page A-3

H.W. Mills ∅

J.F. King N.

R.C. Rowe π

K & E Level #7

B.M. Eggle. N.E. corner of
2nd step of entrance to
Eggleston Hall. An "X"
chiseled in concrete.

A-4

J.F. King

PROFILE LEVELS

Station	+ Sight	H.I.	− Sight	Int. Sight	Elev.
B.M. Road	10.14	370.62			360.48
0+00				9.36	361.26
0+20				9.8	360.8
1+00				6.5	364.1
2+00				4.3	366.3
2+60				3.7	366.9
3+00				7.1	363.5
3+90				11.7	358.9
4+00				11.2	359.4
4+35				9.5	361.1
T.P. 1	7.33	366.48	11.47		359.15
5+00				8.4	358.1
5+54				11.08	355.40
5+74				10.66	355.82
5+94				11.06	355.42
6+00				10.5	356.0
7+00				4.4	362.1
T.P. 2	2.55	363.77	5.26		361.22
8+00				1.2	362.6
9+00				3.9	359.9
9+25.2				3.4	360.4
9+25.3				4.6	359.2
9+43.2				2.2	361.6
B.M. Store			0.76		363.01
Σ	20.02		17.49		Plate

B.M. ROAD to B.M. STORE

SW Minneapolis on Hwy 169

B.M. Road 3 miles SW of Mpls. 200 yards N. of Pine St overpass. 40 ft. E of E Hwy. 169. Top of R.W. conc. post NS. 268	16 Oct., 1955	
	Cool, Sunny, 50°	
E Hwy. 169, painted X	B.K. Harris	N
West drainage ditch	N.E. Olson	φ
	E.C. Perry	⊼
	Wild Level	#3
Summit		
Sag		
Summit		
E gutter, Maple St.		
E, Maple St.		
W gutter, Maple St.	+ 20.02	
	– 17.49	
	+ 2.53	
	360.48	
Summit	363.01	
Top of E curb, Elm St.		
Bottom of E curb, Elm St.		
E Elm St.		
B.M. Store. NE corner Elm St. & 4th Ave. SE corner Store foundation wall. 3" brass disc set in grout.		

A-5

BORROW PIT LEVELING

Point	+ sight	H.I.	− sight	Elev.	Cut
B.M. Road	4.22	364.70		360.48	
A,0			5.2	359.5	1.5
B,0			5.4	359.3	1.3
C,0			5.7	359.0	1.0
D,0			5.9	358.8	0.8
E,0			6.2	358.5	0.5
A,1			4.7	360.0	2.0
B,1			4.8	359.9	1.9
C,1			5.2	359.5	1.5
D,1			5.5	359.2	1.2
E,1			5.8	358.9	0.9
A,2			4.2	360.5	2.5
B,2			4.7	360.0	2.0
C,2			4.8	359.9	1.9
D,2			5.0	359.7	1.7
A,3			3.8	360.9	2.9
B,3			4.0	360.7	2.7
C,3			4.6	360.1	2.1
D,3			4.6	360.1	2.1
A,4			3.4	361.3	3.3
B,4			3.7	361.0	3.0
C,4			4.2	360.5	2.5
B.M. Road	4.23				
					Plate

SECOND & OAK STREETS

Minneapolis, Minn.

Xn		18 Oct., 1965
B.M. Road - Description page A-5		Cool, Cloudy, 60°
1.5		R.C. Perry N
2.6		B.L. Harris Ø
2.0		N.P. Olson π
1.6		Kern Level #4
0.5		
4.0		
7.6		Second Street
6.0		A 20' B C D E
3.6		
0.9		
5.0		
8.0		
7.6		
3.4		
5.8		
10.8		
6.3		
2.1		Grade elevation 368.0
3.3		
6.0		
2.5		

Oak Street

20'

1

2

3

4

Volume = Area of base × $\dfrac{h_1 + h_2 + h_3 + h_4}{4}$

91.1   4

$22.8 \times \dfrac{400}{27} = 337$ cu. yd.

A-6   R.C. Perry

DOUBLE DIRECT ANGLES

Hub	Dist.	Single ∠	Double ∠	Aver. ∠	Mag. Bearing
A		38°58'00"	77°56'40"	38°58'20"	
	321.31'				S71°-30'W
B		148°53'40"	297°47'00"	148°53'30"	
	276.57'				N41°-00'E
C		84°28'00"	168°56'00"	84°28'00"	
	100.30'				S66°-00'E
D		114°40'20"	229°21'00"	114°40'30"	
	306.83'				N58°-30'E
E		152°60'00"	305°58'00"	152°59'00"	
	255.48'				N32°-00'E
A					
Σ	1260.49'			539°-59'-20"	
			Closure	0°-00'-40"	
		Σ interior ∠ = (N-2)180°			
		= (5-2)180°			
		= 540°-00'			
		Permissible closure = √N × least count			
		of vernier			
		= √5 ×⅓min.			
		= 0.7 min.			
					Plate

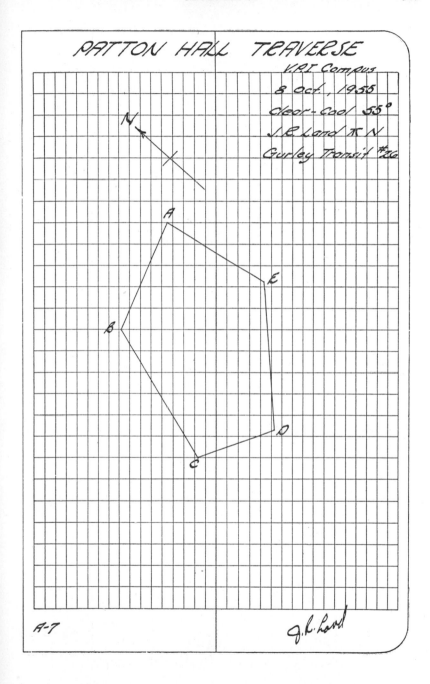

PATTON HALL TRAVERSE

V.P.I. Campus
8 Oct., 1955
Clear - Cool 55°
J.R. Land ⚡ N
Gurley Transit #26

A-7

J.R. Land

DETERMINATION OF

i = Dist. between upper & lower cross-hairs

f = Focal length

f_1 = Dist. from objective lens to plane of cross-hairs

f_2 = Dist. from objective lens to rod

$f_1 + f_2 = f$ Practically, f_2 small f ∴ $f_1 = f$

C = Dist. from plumb bob to lens

s = Dist. from focal point to rod

D = Dist. from plumb bob to rod

e = Rod interval

$$s = D - (C+f), \quad \frac{f}{i} = \frac{s}{e} \text{ or } s = e\frac{f}{i}$$

No.	D	c	f	$c+f = C$	Rod upper
1	100.00'	0.48	0.69	1.17	0.49
2	200.00'	0.49	0.70	1.19	0.99
3	300.00'	0.49	0.70	1.19	1.49
4	400.00'	0.49	0.70	1.19	2.02
5	500.00'	0.49	0.70	1.19	2.52
Means or Sums				1.19	

Sample computation of No. 3

$D = 300.00'$

$c + f = 1.19$

$s = 298.81$

$e = 3.00$

$$\frac{f}{i} = \frac{s}{e} = \frac{298.81}{3.00} = 99.60$$

Plate

STADIA INTERVAL

V.P.I. Campus

12 Oct. 1956

Clear-Cool 55°

J.H. Bell ✕ N

W.H. Vipperman ⌀ C

J.E. Holloway C

Gurley Transit #24

Interval			$\frac{f}{i} = \frac{S}{R}$	Residual Diff.		V^2
Lower	Overall	$S=D-(c+f)$		+V	-V	
0.50	0.99	98.83	99.82	0.22		0.05
0.99	1.98	198.81	100.41	0.81		0.66
1.51	3.00	298.81	99.60			
2.00	4.02	398.81	99.21		0.39	0.15
2.52	5.04	498.81	98.97		0.63	0.40
			99.60	1.03	1.02	1.26

$$E_s = 0.6745 \sqrt{\frac{\Sigma V^2}{(n-1)}} = \sqrt{\frac{1.26}{4}} = \pm 0.38$$

$$E_m = 0.6745 \sqrt{\frac{\Sigma V^2}{n(n-1)}} = \sqrt{\frac{1.26}{20}} = \pm 0.17$$

A-8

J.H. Bell

STADIA SURVEY

Sta.	Azimuth	Stadia	Vert. Angle	Hor. Dist.	Elev.
	Readings from ⊿B Elev. 177.42				
⊿ A	148°04′	6.74	−0°34′	675	170.7
⊿ C	60°00′	4.21	−1°35′	422	165.77
1	90°43′	0.91	−2°04′	92	174.1
2	120°18′	1.66	−2°12′	167	171.0
3	126°31′	3.15	−2°06′	316	165.8
4	143°43′	4.60	−1°25′	461	166.0
5	141°32′	7.85	−0°38′	786	168.7
6	167°19′	2.47	−0°50′	248	173.8
7	172°22′	1.97	−1°20′	198	172.8
8	181°17′	4.99	+0°12′	500	179.2
9	221°45′	5.79	+1°02′	580	187.8
10	256°01′	3.47	+1°50′	348	188.5
11	342°03′	1.17	+1°16′	118	180.0
12	350°16′	1.71	+0°52′	172	180.0
⊿ A	148°04′	6.74	−0.34′	675	170.7
	Readings from ⊿C Elev. 165.77				
⊿ B	240°00′	4.21	+1°34′	422	177.3
13	286°01′	3.21	+2°01′	322	177.1
14	32°02′	2.36	−0°48′	237	162.5
15	41°49′	2.60	−1°03′	261	161.0
16	68°32′	4.61	−1°22′	462	154.8
⊿ B	240°00′	4.21	+1°34′	422	165.77
					Plate

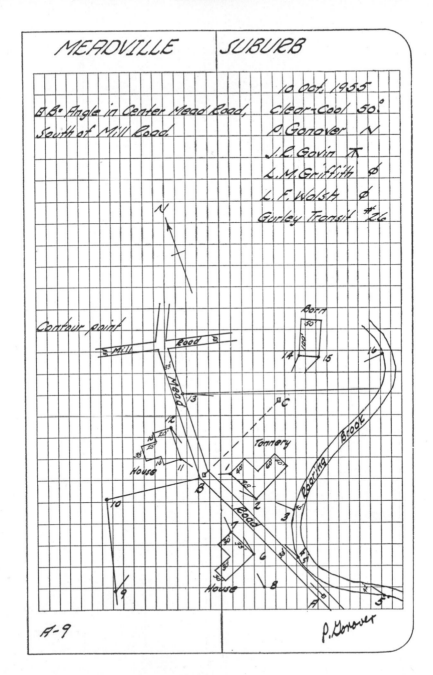

CROSS SECTION LEVELING

Sta.	+ sight	H.I.	− sight	Elev.	
5+00			9.5		
4+00			12.6		
T.P.-1	10.25	106.61	1.87	96.36	
3+00			2.1		
2+50			5.8		
2+00			7.4		
1+35			9.7		
1+00			5.6		
0+50			7.6		
0+00			8.5		
B.M.Rod	8.51	98.23		89.72	
					Plate

HONOLULU-KAILUA HIGHWAY

26 Oct 1955

Warm-Sunny 76

A.C.Chun K

J.E.Kaawa N

S.P.Smith φC

M.L.Hozawa C

	99.2	101.5	97.4	97.1	95.8	97.0	102.8
	7.4	5.1	9.2	9.5	10.8	9.6	2.3
	52	30	10		12	28	45
	102.3	99.9	98.4	94.0	100.1	101.5	98.1
	4.3	6.7	8.2	12.6	4.8	5.1	2.3
	48	24	8		10	25	50
	95.2	95.8	96.6	96.1	94.4	91.1	95.7
	2.0	2.4	1.6	2.1	3.8	7.1	2.5
	50	26	10		8	31	48
95.1	92.8	89.5	93.8	92.4	90.7	93.4	96.6
3.1	5.4	8.7	4.7	5.8	2.5	4.8	1.6
48	32	15	8		10	26	50
	92.3	90.0	90.8	90.8	91.3	93.2	95.9
	5.9	8.2	7.4	7.4	6.9	5.0	2.3
	54	30	10		9	25	40
	85.4	88.7	85.7	88.5	89.8	91.7	94.1
	14.8	9.3	12.5	9.7	8.8	6.5	4.1
	48	25	10		8	15	45
	88.6	97.2	92.2	92.6	95.8	93.6	95.4
	9.6	1.0	6.0	5.6	2.4	4.6	2.8
	52	28	12		10	28	50
	90.0	97.0	92.7	90.6	94.4	95.4	85.5
	8.2	1.2	5.5	7.6	3.8	2.8	12.7
	50	25	8		9	24	4.2
	88.6	96.1	92.0	89.7	93.5	97.0	91.5
	7.6	2.1	6.2	8.5	4.7	1.2	6.7
	50	25	10		8	25	50

B.M.Pod-Kalihi Valley, Oahu, Ewa-makai corner Hibiscus and
Kiawe Drives. Spike in 30" monkey pod tree, 2 ft. above ground.

A-10

J.E.Kaawa

	STAKING OUT		
steps			
1	Set hubs A and B 5' inside curb line, hub A 20' from South property line, hub B 70.00' from A.		
2	Set ⚹ at hub A. B.S. on hub B. Turn 90° L. Set batter board nails 1 and 2, stakes C and D.		
3	Set ⚹ at hub B. B.S. on hub A. Turn 90° L. Set batter board nails 3 and 4, stakes E and F		
4	Measure diagonals CF and DE Adjust error if small, restake if large.		
5	Set ⚹ at C. B.S. on E. Set batter board nail 5. Plunge and set nail 6		
6	Set ⚹ at D. B.S. on F. Set nail 7. Plunge and set nail 8.		
7	Set batter board nails 9,10,11 and 12 by measurements from established points		
			Plate

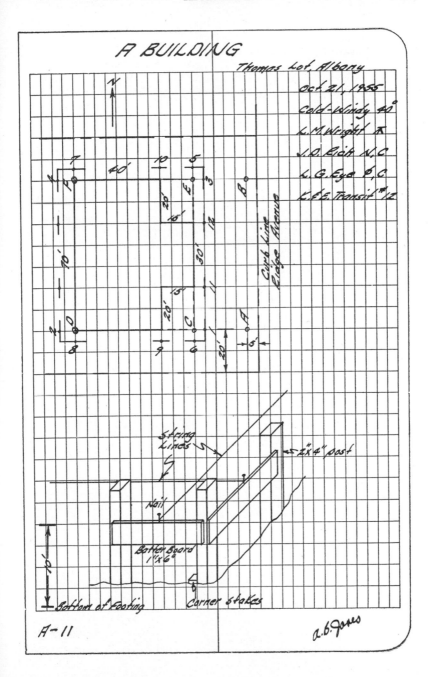

A BUILDING

Thomas Lot, Albany

Oct. 21, 1955
Cold-Windy 40°
L. M. Wright ⋏
J. O. Eck N.C.
L. G. Eye P.C.
C.E.E. Transit #12

A-11

a.b.jones

Station	Point	Total Defl.	Calc. Bearing	Mag. Bearing	Curve Data
ALIGNMENT			**OF**		
68	⊙ P.O.T.				
67					
			N24°42'E	N24°45'E	Δ=8°24'
66+37.06	⊙ E.C.	4°-12'-00"			R=2864.79'
66		3°-49'-45" 3°-49'-48"			D=2°-00' L=420.00'
65	⊙ P.O.C.	2°-49'-46"			T=210.40' E=7.70'
64		1°-49'-45"			M=7.69'
63		0°-49'-46"			
62+17.06	⊙ B.C.	0°-00'-00"			
62			N16°18'E	N16°30'E	
61					
60					
59	⊙ P.O.T.				
					Plate

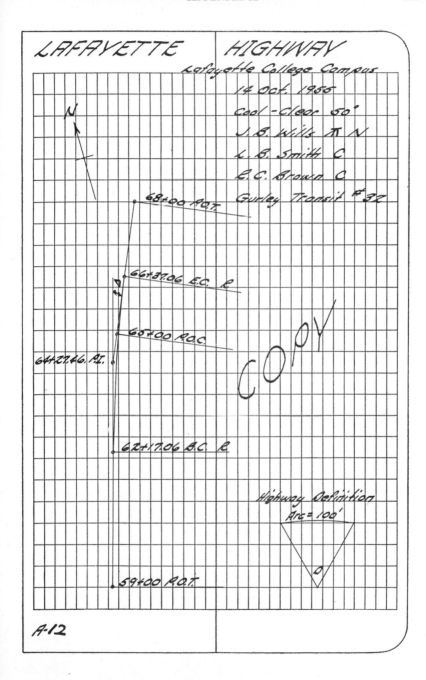

APPENDIX B

Tables

TABLE I.   SAMPLE PAGES FROM TRAVERSE TABLE*

Distance.	15°.		15¼°.		15½°.		15¾°.		Distance.
	Lat.	Dep.	Lat.	Dep.	Lat.	Dep.	Lat.	Dep.	
1	0.97	0.26	0.96	0.26	0.96	0.27	0.96	0.27	1
2	1.93	0.52	1.93	0.53	1.93	0.53	1.92	0.54	2
3	2.90	0.78	2.89	0.79	2.89	0.80	2.89	0.81	3
4	3.86	1.04	3.86	1.05	3.85	1.07	3.85	1.09	4
5	4.83	1.29	4.82	1.32	4.82	1.34	4.81	1.36	5
6	5.80	1.55	5.79	1.58	5.78	1.60	5.77	1.63	6
7	6.76	1.81	6.75	1.84	6.75	1.87	6.74	1.90	7
8	7.73	2.07	7.72	2.10	7.71	2.14	7.70	2.17	8
9	8.69	2.33	8.68	2.37	8.67	2.41	8 66	2.44	9
10	9.66	2.59	9.65	2.63	9.64	2.67	9.62	2.71	10
11	10.63	2.85	10.61	2.89	10.60	2.94	10.59	2.99	11
12	11.59	3.11	11.58	3.16	11.56	3.21	11.55	3.26	12
13	12.56	3.36	12.54	3.42	12.53	3.47	12.51	3.53	13
14	13.52	3.62	13.51	3.68	13.49	3.74	13.47	3.80	14
15	14.49	3.88	14.47	3.95	14.45	4.01	14.44	4.07	15
16	15.45	4.14	15.44	4.21	15.42	4.28	15.40	4.34	16
17	16.42	4.40	16.40	4.47	16.38	4.54	16.36	4.61	17
18	17.39	4.66	17.37	4.73	17.35	4.81	17.32	4.89	18
19	18.35	4.92	18.33	5.00	18.31	5.08	18.29	5.16	19
20	19.32	5.18	19.30	5.26	19.27	5.34	19.25	5.43	20
21	20.28	5.44	20.26	5.52	20.24	5.61	20.21	5.70	21
22	21.25	5.69	21.23	5.79	21.20	5.88	21.17	5.97	22
23	22.22	5.95	22.19	6.05	22.16	6.15	22.14	6.24	23
24	23.18	6.21	23.15	6.31	23.13	6.41	23.10	6.51	24
25	24.15	6.47	24.12	6.58	24.09	6.68	24.06	6.79	25
26	25.11	6.73	25.08	6.84	25.05	6.95	25.02	7.06	26
27	26.08	6.99	26.05	7.10	26.02	7.22	25.99	7.33	27
28	27.05	7.25	27.01	7.36	26.98	7.48	26.95	7.60	28
29	28.01	7.51	27.98	7.63	27.95	7.75	27.91	7.87	29
30	28.98	7.76	28.94	7.89	28.91	8.02	28.87	8.14	30
31	29.94	8.02	29.91	8.15	29.87	8.28	29.84	8.41	31
32	30.91	8.28	30.87	8.42	30.84	8.55	30.80	8.69	32
33	31.88	8.54	31.84	8.68	31.80	8.82	31.76	8.96	33
34	32.84	8.80	32.80	8.94	32.76	9.09	32.72	9.23	34
35	33.81	9.06	33.77	9.21	33.73	9.35	33.69	9.50	35
36	34.77	9.32	34.73	9.47	34.69	9.62	34.65	9.77	36
37	35.74	9.58	35.70	9.73	35.65	9.89	35.61	10.04	37
38	36.71	9.84	36.66	10.00	36.62	10.16	36.57	10.31	38
39	37.67	10.09	37.63	10.26	37.58	10.42	37.54	10.59	39
40	38.64	10.35	38.59	10.52	39.51	10.69	38.50	10.86	40
41	39.60	10.61	39.56	10.78	39.51	10.96	39.46	11.13	41
42	40.57	10.87	40.52	11.05	40.47	11.22	40.42	11.40	42
43	41.53	11.13	41.49	11.31	41.44	11.49	41.39	11.67	43
44	42.50	11.39	42.45	11.57	42.40	11.76	42.35	11.94	44
45	43.47	11.65	43.42	11.84	43.36	12.03	43.31	12.21	45
46	44.43	11.91	44.38	12.10	44.33	12.29	44.27	12.49	46
47	45.40	12.16	45.35	12.36	45.29	12.56	45.24	12.76	47
48	46.36	12.42	46.31	12.63	46.25	12.83	46.20	13.03	48
49	47.33	12.68	47.27	12.89	47.22	13.09	47.16	13.30	49
50	48.30	12.94	48.24	13.15	48.18	13.36	48.12	13.57	50
Distance.	Dep.	Lat.	Dep.	Lat.	Dep.	Lat.	Dep.	Lat.	Distance.
	75°.		74¾°.		74½°.		74¼°.		

* From U.S. Department of the Interior, *Standard Field Tables and Trigonometric Formulas*, 8th ed. (GPO. 1950).

TABLE I. SAMPLE PAGES FROM TRAVERSE TABLE

Distance.	15°.		15¼°.		15½°.		15¾°.		Distance.
	Lat.	Dep.	Lat.	Dep.	Lat.	Dep.	Lat.	Dep.	
51	49.26	13.20	49.20	13.41	49.15	13.63	49.09	13.84	51
52	50.23	13.46	50.17	13.68	50.11	13.90	50.05	14.11	52
53	51.19	13.72	51.13	13.94	51.07	14.16	51.01	14.39	53
54	52.16	13.98	52.10	14.20	52.04	14.43	51.97	14.66	54
55	53.13	14.24	53.06	14.47	53.00	14.70	52.94	14.93	55
56	54.09	14.49	54.03	14.73	53.96	14.97	53.90	15.20	56
57	55.06	14.75	54.99	14.99	54.93	15.23	54.86	15.47	57
58	56.02	15.01	55.96	15.26	55.89	15.50	55.82	15.74	58
59	56.99	15.27	56.92	15.52	56.85	15.77	56.78	16.01	59
60	57.96	15.53	57.89	15.78	57.82	16.03	57.75	16.29	60
61	58.92	15.79	58.85	16.04	58.78	16.30	58.71	16.56	61
62	59.89	16.05	59.82	16.31	59.75	16.57	59.67	16.83	62
63	60.85	16.31	60.78	16.57	60.71	16.84	60.63	17.10	63
64	61.82	16.56	61.75	16.83	61.67	17.10	61.60	17.37	64
65	62.79	16.82	62.71	17.10	62.64	17.37	62.56	17.64	65
66	63.75	17.08	63.68	17.36	63.60	17.64	63.52	17.92	66
67	64.72	17.34	64.64	17.62	64.56	17.90	64.48	18.19	67
68	65.68	17.60	65.61	17.89	65.53	18.17	65.45	18.46	68
69	66.65	17.86	66.57	18.15	66.49	18.44	66.41	18.73	69
70	67.61	18.12	67.54	18.41	67.45	18.71	67.37	19.00	70
71	68.58	18.38	68.50	18.68	68.42	18.97	68.33	19.27	71
72	69.55	18.63	69.46	18.94	69.38	19.24	69.30	19.54	72
73	70.51	18.89	70.43	19.20	70.35	19.51	70.26	19.82	73
74	71.48	19.15	71.39	19.46	71.31	19.78	71.22	20.09	74
75	72.44	19.41	72.36	19.73	72.27	20.04	72.18	20.36	75
76	73.41	19.67	73.32	19.99	73.24	20.31	73.15	20.63	76
77	74.38	19.93	74.29	20.25	74.20	20.58	74.11	20.90	77
78	75.34	20.19	75.25	20.52	75.16	20.84	75.07	21.17	78
79	76.31	20.45	76.22	20.78	76.13	21.11	76.03	21.44	79
80	77.27	20.71	77.18	21.04	77.09	21.38	77.00	21.72	80
81	78.24	20.96	78.15	21.31	78.05	21.65	77.96	21.99	81
82	79.21	21.22	79.11	21.57	79.02	21.91	78.92	22.26	82
83	80.17	21.48	80.08	21.83	79.98	22.18	79.88	22.53	83
84	81.14	21.74	81.04	22.09	80.94	22.45	80.85	22.80	84
85	82.10	22.00	82.01	22.36	81.91	22.72	81.81	23.07	85
86	83.07	22.26	82.97	22.62	82.87	22.98	82.77	23.34	86
87	84.04	22.52	83.94	22.88	83.84	23.25	83.73	23.62	87
88	85.00	22.78	84.90	23.15	84.80	23.52	84.70	23.89	88
89	85.97	23.03	85.87	23.41	85.76	23.78	85.66	24.16	89
90	86.93	23.29	86.83	23.67	86.73	24.05	86.62	24.43	90
91	87.90	23.55	87.80	23.94	87.69	24.32	87.58	24.70	91
92	88.87	23.81	88.76	24.20	88.65	24.59	88.55	24.97	92
93	89.83	24.07	89.73	24.46	89.62	24.85	89.51	25.24	93
94	90.80	24.33	90.69	24.72	90.58	25.12	90.47	25.52	94
95	91.76	24.59	91.65	24.99	91.54	25.39	91.43	25.79	95
96	92.73	24.85	92.62	25.25	92.51	25.65	92.40	26.06	96
97	93.69	25.11	93.58	25.51	93.47	25.92	93.36	26.33	97
98	94.66	25.36	94.55	25.78	94.44	26.19	94.32	26.60	98
99	95.63	25.62	95.51	26.04	95.40	26.46	95.28	26.87	99
100	96.59	25.88	96.48	26.30	96.36	26.72	96.25	27.14	100
Distance.	Dep.	Lat.	Dep.	Lat.	Dep.	Lat.	Dep.	Lat.	Distance.
	75°.		74¾°.		74½°.		74¼°.		

TABLE II. STADIA REDUCTIONS

Minutes	0°		1°		2°		3°	
	Hor. Dist.	Diff. Elev.	Hor. Dist.	Diff. Elev.	Hor. Dist.	Diff. Elev.	Hor. Dist.	Diff. Elev.
0	100.00	.00	99.97	1.74	99.88	3.49	99.73	5.23
2	100.00	.06	99.97	1.80	99.87	3.55	99.72	5.28
4	100.00	.12	99.97	1.86	99.87	3.60	99.71	5.34
6	100.00	.17	99.96	1.92	99.87	3.66	99.71	5.40
8	100.00	.23	99.96	1.98	99.86	3.72	99.70	5.46
10	100.00	.29	99.96	2.04	99.86	3.78	99.69	5.52
12	100.00	.35	99.96	2.09	99.85	3.84	99.69	5.57
14	100.00	.41	99.95	2.15	99.85	3.89	99.68	5.63
16	100.00	.47	99.95	2.21	99.84	3.95	99.68	5.69
18	100.00	.52	99.95	2.27	99.84	4.01	99.67	5.75
20	100.00	.58	99.95	2.33	99.83	4.07	99.66	5.80
22	100.00	.64	99.94	2.38	99.83	4.13	99.66	5.86
24	100.00	.70	99.94	2.44	99.82	4.18	99.65	5.92
26	99.99	.76	99.94	2.50	99.82	4.24	99.64	5.98
28	99.99	.81	99.93	2.56	99.81	4.30	99.63	6.04
30	99.99	.87	99.93	2.62	99.81	4.36	99.63	6.09
32	99.99	.93	99.93	2.67	99.80	4.42	99.62	6.15
34	99.99	.99	99.93	2.73	99.80	4.47	99.61	6.21
36	99.99	1.05	99.92	2.79	99.79	4.53	99.61	6.27
38	99.99	1.11	99.92	2.85	99.79	4.59	99.60	6.32
40	99.99	1.16	99.92	2.91	99.78	4.65	99.59	6.38
42	99.99	1.22	99.91	2.97	99.78	4.71	99.58	6.44
44	99.98	1.28	99.91	3.02	99.77	4.76	99.58	6.50
46	99.98	1.34	99.90	3.08	99.77	4.82	99.57	6.56
48	99.98	1.40	99.90	3.14	99.76	4.88	99.56	6.61
50	99.98	1.45	99.90	3.20	99.76	4.94	99.55	6.67
52	99.98	1.51	99.89	3.26	99.75	4.99	99.55	6.73
54	99.98	1.57	99.89	3.31	99.74	5.05	99.54	6.79
56	99.97	1.63	99.89	3.37	99.74	5.11	99.53	6.84
58	99.97	1.69	99.88	3.43	99.73	5.17	99.52	6.90
60	99.97	1.74	99.88	3.49	99.73	5.23	99.51	6.96
$C = .75$	.75	.01	.75	.02	.75	.03	.75	.05
$C = 1.00$	1.00	.01	1.00	.03	1.00	.04	1.00	.06
$C = 1.25$	1.25	.02	1.25	.03	1.25	.05	1.25	.08

TABLE II. STADIA REDUCTIONS

Minutes	4°		5°		6°		7°	
	Hor. Dist.	Diff. Elev.	Hor. Dist.	Diff. Elev.	Hor. Dist.	Diff. Elev.	Hor. Dist.	Diff. Elev.
0	99.51	6.96	99.24	8.68	98.91	10.40	98.51	12.10
2	99.51	7.02	99.23	8.74	98.90	10.45	98.50	12.15
4	99.50	7.07	99.22	8.80	98.88	10.51	98.49	12.21
6	99.49	7.13	99.21	8.85	98.87	10.57	98.47	12.27
8	99.48	7.19	99.20	8.91	98.86	10.62	98.46	12.32
10	99.47	7.25	99.19	8.97	98.85	10.68	98.44	12.38
12	99.46	7.30	99.18	9.03	98.83	10.74	98.43	12.43
14	99.46	7.36	99.17	9.08	98.82	10.79	98.41	12.49
16	99.45	7.42	99.16	9.14	98.81	10.85	98.40	12.55
18	99.44	7.48	99.15	9.20	98.80	10.91	98.39	12.60
20	99.43	7.53	99.14	9.25	98.78	10.96	98.37	12.66
22	99.42	7.59	99.13	9.31	98.77	11.02	98.36	12.72
24	99.41	7.65	99.11	9.37	98.76	11.08	98.34	12.77
26	99.40	7.71	99.10	9.43	98.74	11.13	98.33	12.83
28	99.39	7.76	99.09	9.48	98.73	11.19	98.31	12.88
30	99.38	7.82	99.08	9.54	98.72	11.25	98.30	12.94
32	99.38	7.88	99.07	9.60	98.71	11.30	98.28	13.00
34	99.37	7.94	99.06	9.65	98.69	11.36	98.27	13.05
36	99.36	7.99	99.05	9.71	98.68	11.42	98.25	13.11
38	99.35	8.05	99.04	9.77	98.67	11.47	98.24	13.17
40	99.34	8.11	99.03	9.83	98.65	11.53	98.22	13.22
42	99.33	8.17	99.01	9.88	98.64	11.59	98.20	13.28
44	99.32	8.22	99.00	9.94	98.63	11.64	98.19	13.33
46	99.31	8.28	98.99	10.00	98.61	11.70	98.17	13.39
48	99.30	8.34	98.98	10.05	98.60	11.76	98.16	13.45
50	99.29	8.40	98.97	10.11	98.58	11.81	98.14	13.50
52	99.28	8.45	98.96	10.17	98.57	11.87	98.13	13.56
54	99.27	8.51	98.94	10.22	98.56	11.93	98.11	13.61
56	99.26	8.57	98.93	10.28	98.54	11.98	98.10	13.67
58	99.25	8.63	98.92	10.34	98.53	12.04	98.08	13.73
60	99.24	8.68	98.91	10.40	98.51	12.10	98.06	13.78
$C = .75$	.75	.06	.75	.07	.75	.08	.74	.10
$C = 1.00$	1.00	.08	1.00	.10	.99	.11	.99	.13
$C = 1.25$	1.25	.10	1.24	.12	1.24	.14	1.24	.16

TABLE II. STADIA REDUCTIONS

Minutes	8°		9°		10°		11°	
	Hor. Dist.	Diff. Elev.	Hor. Dist.	Diff. Elev.	Hor. Dist.	Diff. Elev.	Hor. Dist.	Diff. Elev.
0	98.06	13.78	97.55	15.45	96.98	17.10	96.36	18.73
2	98.05	13.84	97.53	15.51	96.96	17.16	96.34	18.78
4	98.03	13.89	97.52	15.56	96.94	17.21	96.32	18.84
6	98.01	13.95	97.50	15.62	96.92	17.26	96.29	18.89
8	98.00	14.01	97.48	15.67	96.90	17.32	96.27	18.95
10	97.98	14.06	97.46	15.73	96.88	17.37	96.25	19.00
12	97.97	14.12	97.44	15.78	96.86	17.43	96.23	19.05
14	97.95	14.17	97.43	15.84	96.84	17.48	96.21	19.11
16	97.93	14.23	97.41	15.89	96.82	17.54	96.18	19.16
18	97.92	14.28	97.39	15.95	96.80	17.59	96.16	19.21
20	97.90	14.34	97.37	16.00	96.78	17.65	96.14	19.27
22	97.88	14.40	97.35	16.06	96.76	17.70	96.12	19.32
24	97.87	14.45	97.33	16.11	96.74	17.76	96.09	19.38
26	97.85	14.51	97.31	16.17	96.72	17.81	96.07	19.43
28	97.83	14.56	97.29	16.22	96.70	17.86	96.05	19.48
30	97.82	14.62	97.28	16.28	96.68	17.92	96.03	19.54
32	97.80	14.67	97.26	16.33	96.66	17.97	96.00	19.59
34	97.78	14.73	97.24	16.39	96.64	18.03	95.98	19.64
36	97.76	14.79	97.22	16.44	96.62	18.08	95.96	19.70
38	97.75	14.84	97.20	16.50	96.60	18.14	95.93	19.75
40	97.73	14.90	97.18	16.55	96.57	18.19	95.91	19.80
42	97.71	14.95	97.16	16.61	96.55	18.24	95.89	19.86
44	97.69	15.01	97.14	16.66	96.53	18.30	95.86	19.91
46	97.68	15.06	97.12	16.72	96.51	18.35	95.84	19.96
48	97.66	15.12	97.10	16.77	96.49	18.41	95.82	20.02
50	97.64	15.17	97.08	16.83	96.47	18.46	95.79	20.07
52	97.62	15.23	97.06	16.88	96.45	18.51	95.77	20.12
54	97.61	15.28	97.04	16.94	96.42	18.57	95.75	20.18
56	97.59	15.34	97.02	16.99	96.40	18.62	95.72	20.23
58	97.57	15.40	97.00	17.05	96.38	18.68	95.70	20.28
60	97.55	15.45	96.98	17.10	96.36	18.73	95.68	20.34
$C = .75$	.74	.11	.74	.12	.74	.14	.73	.15
$C = 1.00$	.99	.15	.99	.17	.98	.18	.98	.20
$C = 1.25$	1.24	.18	1.23	.21	1.23	.23	1.22	.25

TABLE II. STADIA REDUCTIONS

Minutes	12°		13°		14°		15°	
	Hor. Dist.	Diff. Elev.	Hor. Dist.	Diff. Elev.	Hor. Dist.	Diff. Elev.	Hor. Dist.	Diff. Elev.
0	95.68	20.34	94.94	21.92	94.15	23.47	93.30	25.00
2	95.65	20.39	94.91	21.97	94.12	23.52	93.27	25.05
4	95.63	20.44	94.89	22.02	94.09	23.58	93.24	25.10
6	95.61	20.50	94.86	22.08	94.07	23.63	93.21	25.15
8	95.58	20.55	94.84	22.13	94.04	23.68	93.18	25.20
10	95.56	20.60	94.81	22.18	94.01	23.73	93.16	25.25
12	95.53	20.66	94.79	22.23	93.98	23.78	93.13	25.30
14	95.51	20.71	94.76	22.28	93.95	23.83	93.10	25.35
16	95.49	20.76	94.73	22.34	93.93	23.88	93.07	25.40
18	95.46	20.81	94.71	22.39	93.90	23.93	93.04	25.45
20	95.44	20.87	94.68	22.44	93.87	23.99	93.01	25.50
22	95.41	20.92	94.66	22.49	93.84	24.04	92.98	25.55
24	95.39	20.97	94.63	22.54	93.82	24.09	92.95	25.60
26	95.36	21.03	94.60	22.60	93.79	24.14	92.92	25.65
28	95.34	21.08	94.58	22.65	93.76	24.19	92.89	25.70
30	95.32	21.13	94.55	22.70	93.73	24.24	92.86	25.75
32	95.29	21.18	94.52	22.75	93.70	24.29	92.83	25.80
34	95.27	21.24	94.50	22.80	93.67	24.34	92.80	25.85
36	95.24	21.29	94.47	22.85	93.65	24.39	92.77	25.90
38	95.22	21.34	94.44	22.91	93.62	24.44	92.74	25.95
40	95.19	21.39	94.42	22.96	93.59	24.49	92.71	26.00
42	95.17	21.45	94.39	23.01	93.56	24.55	92.68	26.05
44	95.14	21.50	94.36	23.06	93.53	24.60	92.65	26.10
46	95.12	21.55	94.34	23.11	93.50	24.65	92.62	26.15
48	95.09	21.60	94.31	23.16	93.47	24.70	92.59	26.20
50	95.07	21.66	94.28	23.22	93.45	24.75	92.56	26.25
52	95.04	21.71	94.26	23.27	93.42	24.80	92.53	26.30
54	95.02	21.76	94.23	23.32	93.39	24.85	92.49	26.35
56	94.99	21.81	94.20	23.37	93.36	24.90	92.46	26.40
58	94.97	21.87	94.17	23.42	93.33	24.95	92.43	26.45
60	94.94	21.92	94.15	23.47	93.30	25.00	92.40	26.50
$C = .75$	.73	.16	.73	.18	.73	.19	.72	.20
$C = 1.00$	.98	.22	.97	.23	.97	.25	.96	.27
$C = 1.25$	1.22	.27	1.22	.29	1.21	.31	1.20	.33

TABLE II. STADIA REDUCTIONS

Minutes	16°		17°		18°		19°	
	Hor. Dist.	Diff. Elev.	Hor. Dist.	Diff. Elev.	Hor. Dist.	Diff. Elev.	Hor. Dist.	Diff. Elev.
0	92.40	26.50	91.45	27.96	90.45	29.39	89.40	30.78
2	92.37	26.55	91.42	28.01	90.42	29.44	89.36	30.83
4	92.34	26.59	91.39	28.06	90.38	29.48	89.33	30.87
6	92.31	26.64	91.35	28.10	90.35	29.53	89.29	30.92
8	92.28	26.69	91.32	28.15	90.31	29.58	89.26	30.97
10	92.25	26.74	91.29	28.20	90.28	29.62	89.22	31.01
12	92.22	26.79	91.26	28.25	90.24	29.67	89.18	31.06
14	92.19	26.84	91.22	28.30	90.21	29.72	89.15	31.10
16	92.15	26.89	91.19	28.34	90.18	29.76	89.11	31.15
18	92.12	26.94	91.16	28.39	90.14	29.81	89.08	31.19
20	92.09	26.99	91.12	28.44	90.11	29.86	89.04	31.24
22	92.06	27.04	91.09	28.49	90.07	29.90	89.00	31.28
24	92.03	27.09	91.06	28.54	90.04	29.95	88.97	31.33
26	92.00	27.13	91.02	28.58	90.00	30.00	88.93	31.38
28	91.97	27.18	90.99	28.63	89.97	30.04	88.89	31.42
30	91.93	27.23	90.96	28.68	89.93	30.09	88.86	31.47
32	91.90	27.28	90.92	28.73	89.90	30.14	88.82	31.51
34	91.87	27.33	90.89	28.77	89.86	30.18	88.78	31.56
36	91.84	27.38	90.86	28.82	89.83	30.23	88.75	31.60
38	91.81	27.43	90.82	28.87	89.79	30.28	88.71	31.65
40	91.77	27.48	90.79	28.92	89.76	30.32	88.67	31.69
42	91.74	27.52	90.76	28.96	89.72	30.37	88.64	31.74
44	91.71	27.57	90.72	29.01	89.69	30.41	88.60	31.78
46	91.68	27.62	90.69	29.06	89.65	30.46	88.56	31.83
48	91.65	27.67	90.66	29.11	89.61	30.51	88.53	31.87
50	91.61	27.72	90.62	29.15	89.58	30.55	88.49	31.92
52	91.58	27.77	90.59	29.20	89.54	30.60	88.45	31.96
54	91.55	27.81	90.55	29.25	89.51	30.65	88.41	32.01
56	91.52	27.86	90.52	29.30	89.47	30.69	88.38	32.05
58	91.48	27.91	90.49	29.34	89.44	30.74	88.34	32.09
60	91.45	27.96	90.45	29.39	89.40	30.78	88.30	32.14
$C = .75$	.72	.21	.72	.23	.71	.24	.71	.25
$C = 1.00$	.96	.28	.95	.30	.95	.32	.94	.33
$C = 1.25$	1.20	.36	1.19	.38	1.19	.40	1.18	.42

TABLE II. STADIA REDUCTIONS

Minutes	20°		21°		22°		23°	
	Hor. Dist.	Diff. Elev.	Hor. Dist.	Diff. Elev.	Hor. Dist.	Diff. Elev.	Hor. Dist.	Diff. Elev.
0	88.30	32.14	87.16	33.46	85.97	34.73	84.73	35.97
2	88.26	32.18	87.12	33.50	85.93	34.77	84.69	36.01
4	88.23	32.23	87.08	33.54	85.89	34.82	84.65	36.05
6	88.19	32.27	87.04	33.59	85.85	34.86	84.61	36.09
8	88.15	32.32	87.00	33.63	85.80	34.90	84.57	36.13
10	88.11	32.36	86.96	33.67	85.76	34.94	84.52	36.17
12	88.08	32.41	86.92	33.72	85.72	34.98	84.48	36.21
14	88.04	32.45	86.88	33.76	85.68	35.02	84.44	36.25
16	88.00	32.49	86.84	33.80	85.64	35.07	84.40	36.29
18	87.96	32.54	86.80	33.84	85.60	35.11	84.35	36.33
20	87.93	32.58	86.77	33.89	85.56	35.15	84.31	36.37
22	87.89	32.63	86.73	33.93	85.52	35.19	84.27	36.41
24	87.85	32.67	86.69	33.97	85.48	35.23	84.23	36.45
26	87.81	32.72	86.65	34.01	85.44	35.27	84.18	36.49
28	87.77	32.76	86.61	34.06	85.40	35.31	84.14	36.53
30	87.74	32.80	86.57	34.10	85.36	35.36	84.10	36.57
32	87.70	32.85	86.53	34.14	85.31	35.40	84.06	36.61
34	87.66	32.89	86.49	34.18	85.27	35.44	84.01	36.65
36	87.62	32.93	86.45	34.23	85.23	35.48	83.97	36.69
38	87.58	32.98	86.41	34.27	85.19	35.52	83.93	36.73
40	87.54	33.02	86.37	34.31	85.15	35.56	83.89	36.77
42	87.51	33.07	86.33	34.35	85.11	35.60	83.84	36.80
44	87.47	33.11	86.29	34.40	85.07	35.64	83.80	36.84
46	87.43	33.15	86.25	34.44	85.02	35.68	83.76	36.88
48	87.39	33.20	86.21	34.48	84.98	35.72	83.72	36.92
50	87.35	33.24	86.17	34.52	84.94	35.76	83.67	36.96
52	87.31	33.28	86.13	34.57	84.90	35.80	83.63	37.00
54	87.27	33.33	86.09	34.61	84.86	35.85	83.59	37.04
56	87.24	33.37	86.05	34.65	84.82	35.89	83.54	37.08
58	87.20	33.41	86.01	34.69	84.77	35.93	83.50	37.12
60	87.16	33.46	85.97	34.73	84.73	35.97	83.46	37.16
$C = .75$	.70	.26	.70	.27	.69	.29	.69	.30
$C = 1.00$	.94	.35	.93	.37	.92	.38	.92	.40
$C = 1.25$	1.17	.44	1.16	.46	1.15	.48	1.15	.50

TABLE II. STADIA REDUCTIONS

Minutes	24°		25°		26°		27°	
	Hor. Dist.	Diff. Elev.	Hor. Dist.	Diff. Elev.	Hor. Dist.	Diff. Elev.	Hor. Dist.	Diff. Elev.
0	83.46	37.16	82.14	38.30	80.78	39.40	79.39	40.45
2	83.41	37.20	82.09	38.34	80.74	39.44	79.34	40.49
4	83.37	37.23	82.05	38.38	80.69	39.47	79.30	40.52
6	83.33	37.27	82.01	38.41	80.65	39.51	79.25	40.55
8	83.28	37.31	81.96	38.45	80.60	39.54	79.20	40.59
10	83.24	37.35	81.92	38.49	80.55	39.58	79.15	40.62
12	83.20	37.39	81.87	38.53	80.51	39.61	79.11	40.66
14	83.15	37.43	81.83	38.56	80.46	39.65	79.06	40.69
16	83.11	37.47	81.78	38.60	80.41	39.69	79.01	40.72
18	83.07	37.51	81.74	38.64	80.37	39.72	78.96	40.76
20	83.02	37.54	81.69	38.67	80.32	39.76	78.92	40.79
22	82.98	37.58	81.65	38.71	80.28	39.79	78.87	40.82
24	82.93	37.62	81.60	38.75	80.23	39.83	78.82	40.86
26	82.89	37.66	81.56	38.78	80.18	39.86	78.77	40.89
28	82.85	37.70	81.51	38.82	80.14	39.90	78.73	40.92
30	82.80	37.74	81.47	38.86	80.09	39.93	78.68	40.96
32	82.76	37.77	81.42	38.89	80.04	39.97	78.63	40.99
34	82.72	37.81	81.38	38.93	80.00	40.00	78.58	41.02
36	82.67	37.85	81.33	38.97	79.95	40.04	78.54	41.06
38	82.63	37.89	81.28	39.00	79.90	40.07	78.49	41.09
40	82.58	37.93	81.24	39.04	79.86	40.11	78.44	41.12
42	82.54	37.96	81.19	39.08	79.81	40.14	78.39	41.16
44	82.49	38.00	81.15	39.11	79.76	40.18	78.34	41.19
46	82.45	38.04	81.10	39.15	79.72	40.21	78.30	41.22
48	82.41	38.08	81.06	39.18	79.67	40.24	78.25	41.26
50	82.36	38.11	81.01	39.22	79.62	40.28	78.20	41.29
52	82.32	38.15	80.97	39.26	79.58	40.31	78.15	41.32
54	82.27	38.19	80.92	39.29	79.53	40.35	78.10	41.35
56	82.23	38.23	80.87	39.33	79.48	40.38	78.06	41.39
58	82.18	38.26	80.83	39.36	79.44	40.42	78.01	41.42
60	82.14	38.30	80.78	39.40	79.39	40.45	77.96	41.45
C = .75	.68	.31	.68	.32	.67	.33	.67	.35
C = 1.00	.91	.41	.90	.43	.89	.45	.89	.46
C = 1.25	1.14	.52	1.13	.54	1.12	.56	1.11	.58

TABLE II. STADIA REDUCTIONS

Minutes	28°		29°		30°	
	Hor. Dist.	Diff. Elev.	Hor. Dist.	Diff. Elev.	Hor. Dist.	Diff. Elev.
0	77.96	41.45	76.50	42.40	75.00	43.30
2	77.91	41.48	76.45	42.43	74.95	43.33
4	77.86	41.52	76.40	42.46	74.90	43.36
6	77.81	41.55	76 35	42.49	74.85	43.39
8	77.77	41.58	76.30	42.53	74.80	43.42
10	77.72	41.61	76.25	42.56	74.75	43.45
12	77.67	41.65	76.20	42.59	74.70	43.47
14	77.62	41.68	76.15	42.62	74.65	43.50
16	77.57	41.71	76.10	42.65	74.60	43.53
18	77.52	41.74	76.05	42.68	74.55	43.56
20	77.48	41.77	76.00	42.71	74.49	43.59
22	77.42	41.81	75.95	42.74	74.44	43.62
24	77.38	41.84	75.90	42.77	74.39	43.65
26	77.33	41.87	75.85	42.80	74.34	43.67
28	77.28	41.90	75.80	42.83	74.29	43.70
30	77.23	41.93	75.75	42.86	74.24	43.73
32	77.18	41.97	75.70	42.89	74.19	43.76
34	77.13	42.00	75.65	42.92	74.14	43.79
36	77.09	42.03	75.60	42.95	74.09	43.82
38	77.04	42.06	75.55	42.98	74.04	43.84
40	76.99	42.09	75.50	43.01	73.99	43.87
42	76.94	42.12	75.45	43.04	73.93	43.90
44	76.89	42.15	75.40	43.07	73.88	43.93
46	76.84	42.19	75.35	43.10	73.83	43.95
48	76.79	42.22	75.30	43.13	73.78	43.98
50	76.74	42.25	75.25	43.16	73.73	44.01
52	76.69	42.28	75.20	43.18	73.68	44.04
54	76.64	42.31	75.15	43.21	73.63	44.07
56	76.59	42.34	75.10	43.24	73.58	44.09
58	76.55	42.37	75.05	43.27	73.52	44.12
60	76.50	42.40	75.00	43.30	73.47	44.15
$C = .75$	.66	.36	.65	.37	.65	.38
$C = 1.00$	.88	.48	.87	.49	.86	.51
$C = 1.25$	1.10	.60	1.09	.62	1.08	.63

TABLE III. TABLE OF DISTANCES FOR SUBTENSE BAR (IN FEET)*
(Sample Pages, for Interval 0° 30' to 0° 38' Only)

0°	0''	1''	2''	3''	4''	5''	6''	7''	8''	9''
30'00''	751.9	751.5	751.5	750.7	750.2	749.8	749.4	749.0	748.6	748.2
10	747.7	747.3	746.9	746.5	746.1	745.7	745.3	744.9	744.5	744.0
20	743.6	743.2	742.8	742.4	742.0	741.6	741.2	740.8	740.4	740.0
30	739.6	739.2	738.8	738.4	738.0	737.6	737.2	736.8	736.4	736.0
40	735.6	735.2	734.8	734.4	734.0	733.6	733.2	732.8	732.4	732.0
50	731.6	731.2	730.8	730.4	730.0	729.6	729.2	728.9	728.5	728.1
31'00''	727.7	727.3	726.9	726.5	726.1	725.7	725.3	724.9	724.6	724.2
10	723.8	723.4	723.0	722.6	722.2	721.8	721.5	721.1	720.7	720.3
20	719.9	719.5	719.2	718.8	718.4	718.0	717.6	717.2	716.9	716.5
30	716.1	715.7	715.4	715.0	714.6	714.2	713.9	713.5	713.1	712.7
40	712.3	712.0	711.6	711.2	710.8	710.5	710.1	709.7	709.4	709.0
50	708.6	708.2	707.9	707.5	707.1	706.8	706.4	706.0	705.7	705.3
32'00''	704.9	704.5	704.2	703.8	703.5	703.1	702.7	702.4	702.0	701.6
10	710.3	700.9	700.5	700.2	699.8	699.5	699.1	698.7	698.4	698.0
20	697.7	697.3	696.9	696.6	696.2	695.9	695.5	695.2	694.8	694.4
30	694.1	693.7	693.4	693.0	692.7	692.3	691.9	691.6	691.3	690.9
40	690.5	690.2	689.8	689.5	689.1	688.8	688.4	688.1	687.7	687.4
50	687.0	686.7	686.3	686.0	685.6	685.3	685.0	684.6	684.3	683.9
33'00''	683.6	683.2	682.9	682.5	682.2	681.8	681.5	681.1	680.8	680.5
10	680.1	679.8	679.4	679.1	678.8	678.4	678.1	677.7	677.4	677.0
20	676.7	676.4	676.0	675.7	675.3	675.0	674.7	674.4	674.0	673.7
30	673.4	673.0	672.7	672.4	672.0	671.7	671.4	671.0	670.7	670.4
40	670.0	669.7	669.4	669.0	668.7	668.4	668.1	667.7	667.4	667.0
50	666.7	666.4	666.1	665.7	665.4	665.1	664.8	664.4	664.1	663.8

34'00"	660.5	660.9	661.2	661.5	661.8	662.2	662.5	662.8	663.1	663.5	
10	657.3	657.7	658.0	658.3	658.6	658.9	659.3	659.6	659.9	660.2	10
20	654.2	654.5	654.8	655.1	655.4	655.8	656.1	656.4	656.7	657.0	20
30	651.0	651.3	651.6	651.9	652.3	652.6	652.9	653.2	653.5	653.9	30
40	647.9	648.2	648.5	648.8	649.1	649.4	649.7	650.1	650.4	650.7	40
50	644.8	645.1	645.4	645.7	646.0	646.3	646.6	647.0	647.3	647.6	50
35'00"	641.7	642.1	642.4	642.7	643.0	643.3	643.6	643.9	644.2	644.5	**35'00"**
10	638.7	639.0	639.3	639.6	639.9	640.2	640.5	640.8	641.1	641.4	10
20	635.7	636.0	636.3	636.6	636.9	637.2	637.5	637.8	638.1	638.4	20
30	632.8	633.0	633.3	633.6	633.9	634.2	634.5	634.8	635.1	635.4	30
40	629.8	630.1	630.4	630.7	631.0	631.3	631.6	631.9	632.2	632.5	40
50	626.9	627.2	627.5	627.8	628.1	628.4	628.6	628.9	629.2	629.5	50
36'00"	624.0	624.3	624.6	624.9	625.1	625.4	625.7	626.0	626.3	626.6	**36'00"**
10	621.1	621.4	621.7	622.0	622.3	622.6	622.8	623.1	623.4	623.7	10
20	618.3	618.6	618.8	619.1	619.4	619.7	620.0	620.3	620.5	620.8	20
30	615.5	615.8	616.1	616.3	616.6	616.9	617.2	617.5	617.7	618.0	30
40	612.7	613.0	613.2	613.5	613.8	614.1	614.3	614.6	614.9	615.2	40
50	609.9	610.2	610.5	610.8	611.0	611.3	611.6	611.9	612.1	612.4	50
37'00"	607.2	607.5	607.8	608.0	608.3	608.6	608.8	609.1	609.4	609.7	**37'00"**
10	604.5	604.8	605.0	605.3	605.6	605.8	606.1	606.4	606.6	606.9	10
20	601.8	602.1	602.3	602.6	602.9	603.1	603.4	603.7	603.9	604.2	20
30	599.1	599.4	599.7	599.9	600.2	600.5	600.7	601.0	601.3	601.5	30
40	596.5	596.8	597.0	597.3	597.6	597.8	598.1	598.3	598.6	598.9	40
50	593.9	594.1	594.4	594.7	594.9	595.2	595.5	595.7	596.0	596.2	50
38'00"	591.3	591.5	591.8	592.1	592.3	592.6	592.8	593.1	593.4	593.6	**38'00"**
0°	9"	8"	7"	6"	5"	4"	3"	2"	1"	0"	**0°**

* Courtesy of Kern Instruments, Inc.   The original of these two pages also includes values for 39', and 40'.

TABLE IV. CONVERGENCY OF RANGE LINES

Latitude Degrees	Difference Between South and North Boundaries of Township Links	Angle of Convergency of Adjacent Range Lines ' "	Difference of Longitude per Range		Difference of Latitude, in Minutes of Arc, for	
			Arc ' "	Time Seconds	1 Mile in Arc	6 Miles in Arc
25	33.9	2 25	5 44.34	22.96		
26	35.4	2 32	5 47.20	23.15		
27	37.0	2 39	5 50.22	23.35	0.871	5.229
28	38.6	2 46	5 53.40	23.56		
29	40.2	2 53	5 56.74	23.78		
30	41.9	3 0	6 0.36	24.02		
31	43.6	3 7	6 4.02	24.27		
32	45.4	3 15	6 7.93	24.53	0.871	5.225
33	47.2	3 23	6 12.00	24.80		
34	49.1	3 30	6 16.31	25.09		
35	50.9	3 38	6 20.95	25.40		
36	52.7	3 46	6 25.60	25.71		
37	54.7	3 55	6 30.59	26.04	0.870	5.221
38	56.8	4 4	6 35.81	26.39		
39	58.8	4 13	6 41.34	26.76		
40	60.9	4 22	6 47.13	27.14		
41	63.1	4 31	6 53.22	27.55		
42	65.4	4 41	6 59.62	27.97	0.869	5.217
43	67.7	4 51	7 6.27	28.42		
44	70.1	5 1	7 13.44	28.90		
45	72.6	5 12	7 20.93	29.39		
46	75.2	5 23	7 28.81	29.92		
47	77.8	5 34	7 37.10	30.47	0.869	5.212
48	80.6	5 46	7 45.79	31.05		
49	83.5	5 59	7 55.12	31.67		
50	86.4	6 12	8 4.83	32.32		
51	89.6	6 25	8 15.17	33.01		
52	92.8	6 39	8 26.13	33.74	0.868	5.207
53	96.2	6 54	8 37.75	34.52		
54	99.8	7 9	8 50.07	35.34		
55	103.5	7 25	9 3.18	36.22		
56	107.5	7 42	9 17.12	37.14		
57	111.6	8 0	9 31.97	38.13	0.867	5.202
58	116.0	8 19	9 47.83	39.19		
59	120.6	8 38	10 4.78	40.32		
60	125.5	8 59	10 22.94	41.52		
61	130.8	9 22	10 42.42	42.83		
62	136.3	9 46	11 3.38	44.22	0.866	5.198
63	142.2	10 11	11 25.97	45.73		
64	148.6	10 38	11 50.37	47.36		
65	155.0	11 8	12 16.82	49.12		
66	162.8	11 39	12 45.55	51.04		
67	170.7	12 13	13 16.88	53.12	0.866	5.195
68	179.3	12 51	13 51.15	55.41		
69	188.7	13 31	14 28.77	57.92		
70	199.1	14 15	15 10.26	60.68	0.866	5.193

TABLE V. AZIMUTHS OF THE SECANT*

Lat.	0 mi.	1 mi.	2 mi.	3 mi.	Deflection angle 6 mi.
°	° ′	° ′	° ′		′ ″
25	89 58.8	89 59.2	89 59.6	90°	2 25
26	58.7	59.2	59.6	E or W.	2 32
27	58.7	59.1	59.6	" " "	2 39
28	58.6	59.1	59.5	" " "	2 46
29	58.6	59.0	59.5	" " "	2 53
30	58.5	59.0	59.5	" " "	3 0
31	58.4	59.0	59.5	" " "	3 7
32	58.4	58.9	59.5	" " "	3 15
33	58.3	58.9	59.4	" " "	3 23
34	58.2	58.8	59.4	" " "	3 30
35	58.2	58.8	59.4	" " "	3 38
36	58.1	58.7	59.4	" " "	3 46
37	58.0	58.7	59.3	" " "	3 55
38	58.0	58.6	59.3	" " "	4 4
39	57.9	58.6	59.3	" " "	4 13
40	57.8	58.5	59.3	" " "	4 22
41	57.7	58.5	59.2	" " "	4 31
42	57.7	58.4	59.2	" " "	4 41
43	57.6	58.4	59.2	" " "	4 51
44	57.5	58.3	59.2	" " "	5 1
45	57.4	58.3	59.1	" " "	5 12
46	57.3	58.2	59.1	" " "	5 23
47	57.2	58.1	59.1	" " "	5 34
48	57.1	58.1	59.0	" " "	5 46
49	57.0	58.0	59.0	" " "	5 59
50	56.9	57.9	59.0	" " "	6 12
51	56.8	57.9	58.9	" " "	6 25
52	56.7	57.8	58.9	" " "	6 39
53	56.6	57.7	58.8	" " "	6 54
54	56.4	57.6	58.8	" " "	7 9
55	56.3	57.5	58.8	" " "	7 25
56	56.2	57.4	58.7	" " "	7 42
57	56.0	57.3	58.7	" " "	8 0
58	55.8	57.2	58.6	" " "	8 19
59	55.7	57.1	58.6	" " "	8 38
60	55.5	57.0	58.5	" " "	8 59
61	55.3	56.9	58.4	" " "	9 22
62	55.1	56.7	58.4	" " "	9 46
63	54.9	56.6	58.3	" " "	10 11
64	54.7	56.5	58.2	" " "	10 38
65	54.4	56.3	58.1	" " "	11 8
66	54.2	56.1	58.1	" " "	11 39
67	53.9	55.9	58.0	" " "	12 13
68	53.6	55.7	57.9	" " "	12 51
69	53.2	55.5	57.8	" " "	13 31
70	89 52.9	89 55.3	89 57.6	" " "	14 15
	6 mi.	5 mi.	4 mi.	3 mi.	

* From U.S. Department of the Interior, *Standard Field Tables and Trigonometric Formulas*, 8th ed. (GPO, 1950).

TABLE VI
OFFSETS, IN LINKS, FROM THE SECANT TO THE PARALLEL*

Lat.	0 mi.	½ mi.	1 mi.	1½ mi.	2 mi.	2½ mi.	3 mi.
°							
25	2 N.	1 N.	0	1 S.	1 S.	2 S.	2 S.
26	2	1	0	1	1	2	2
27	3	1	0	1	2	2	2
28	3	1	0	1	2	2	2
29	3	1	0	1	2	2	2
30	3	1	0	1	2	2	2
31	3	1	0	1	2	2	2
32	3	1	0	1	2	2	3
33	3	1	0	1	2	2	3
34	3	2	0	1	2	3	3
35	4	2	0	1	2	3	3
36	4	2	0	1	2	3	3
37	4	2	0	1	2	3	3
38	4	2	0	1	2	3	3
39	4	2	0	1	2	3	3
40	4	2	0	1	3	3	3
41	4	2	0	2	3	3	4
42	5	2	0	2	3	3	4
43	5	2	0	2	3	4	4
44	5	2	0	2	3	4	4
45	5	2	0	2	3	4	4
46	5	2	0	2	3	4	4
47	5	2	0	2	3	4	4
48	6	3	0	2	3	4	4
49	6	3	0	2	3	4	5
50	6	3	0	2	4	4	5
51	6	3	0	2	4	5	5
52	6	3	0	2	4	5	5
53	7	3	0	2	4	5	5
54	7	3	0	2	4	5	6
55	7	3	0	3	4	5	6
56	7	3	0	3	4	6	6
57	8	3	0	3	5	6	6
58	8	4	0	3	5	6	6
59	8	4	0	3	5	6	7
60	9	4	0	3	5	7	7
61	9	4	0	3	5	7	7
62	9	4	0	3	6	7	8
63	10	4	0	3	6	7	8
64	10	5	0	4	6	8	8
65	11	5	0	4	6	8	9
66	11	5	0	4	7	8	9
67	12	5	0	4	7	9	9
68	12	6	0	4	7	9	10
69	13	6	0	5	8	10	10
70	14 N.	6 N.	0	5 S.	8 S.	10 S.	11 S.
	6 mi.	5½ mi.	5 mi.	4½ mi.	4 mi.	3½ mi.	3 mi.

* From U.S. Department of the Interior, *Standard Field Tables and Trigonometric Formulas*, 8th ed. (GPO, 1950).

TABLE VII. FUNCTIONS OF CIRCULAR CURVES

Degree of Curve D	Defl. Per Ft of Sta. (Min)	Chord Definition			Arc Definition	
		Radius R	log R	C.O. 1 Sta.	Radius R	log R
0° 0'		Infinite	Infin.		Infinite	Infin.
1'	0.005	343775.	5.536274	0.03	343775.	5.536274
2'	0.01	171887.	5.235244	0.06	171887.	5.235244
3'	0.015	114592.	5.059153	0.09	114592.	5.059153
4'	0.02	85943.7	4.934214	0.12	85943.7	4.934214
5'	0.025	68754.9	4.837304	0.15	68754.9	4.837304
6'	0.03	57295.8	4.758123	0.17	57295.8	4.758123
7'	0.035	49110.7	4.691176	0.20	49110.7	4.691176
8'	0.04	42971.8	4.633184	0.23	42971.8	4.633184
9'	0.045	38197.2	4.582031	0.26	38197.2	4.582031
10'	0.05	34377.5	4.536274	0.29	34377.5	4.536274
11'	0.055	31252.3	4.494881	0.32	31252.2	4.494881
12'	0.06	28647.8	4.457093	0.35	28647.8	4.457093
13'	0.065	26444.2	4.422331	0.38	26444.2	4.422331
14'	0.07	24555.4	4.390146	0.41	24555.3	4.390146
15'	0.075	22918.3	4.360183	0.44	22918.3	4.360183
16'	0.08	21485.9	4.332154	0.47	21485.9	4.332154
17'	0.085	20222.1	4.305825	0.49	20222.0	4.305825
18'	0.09	19098.6	4.281002	0.52	19098.6	4.281001
19'	0.095	18093.4	4.257521	0.55	18093.4	4.257520
20'	0.1	17188.8	4.235244	0.58	17188.7	4.235244
21'	0.105	16370.2	4.214055	0.61	16370.2	4.214055
22'	0.11	15626.1	4.193852	0.64	15626.1	4.193851
23'	0.115	14946.8	4.174547	0.67	14946.7	4.174546
24'	0.12	14324.0	4.156064	0.70	14323.9	4.156063
25'	0.125	13751.0	4.138335	0.73	13751.0	4.138334
26'	0.13	13222.1	4.121302	0.76	13222.1	4.121300
27'	0.135	12732.4	4.104911	0.79	12732.4	4.104910
28'	0.14	12277.7	4.089117	0.81	12277.7	4.089116
29'	0.145	11854.3	4.073877	0.84	11854.3	4.073876
30'	0.15	11459.2	4.059154	0.87	11459.2	4.059153
31'	0.155	11089.6	4.044914	0.90	11089.5	4.044912
32'	0.16	10743.0	4.031125	0.93	10743.0	4.031124
33'	0.165	10417.5	4.017762	0.96	10417.4	4.017760
34'	0.17	10111.1	4.004797	0.99	10111.0	4.004795
35'	0.175	9822.18	3.992208	1.02	9822.13	3.992206
36'	0.18	9549.34	3.979973	1.05	9549.29	3.979971
37'	0.185	9291.25	3.968074	1.07	9291.21	3.968072
38'	0.19	9046.75	3.956493	1.11	9046.70	3.956490
39'	0.195	8814.78	3.945212	1.13	8814.73	3.945209
40'	0.2	8594.42	3.934216	1.16	8594.37	3.934214
41'	0.205	8384.80	3.923493	1.19	8384.75	3.923490
42'	0.21	8185.16	3.913027	1.21	8185.11	3.913025
43'	0.215	7994.81	3.902808	1.25	7994.76	3.902805
44'	0.22	7813.11	3.892824	1.28	7813.06	3.892821
45'	0.225	7639.49	3.883065	1.31	7639.44	3.883061
46'	0.23	7473.42	3.873519	1.34	7473.36	3.873516
47'	0.235	7314.41	3.864179	1.37	7314.35	3.864176
48'	0.24	7162.03	3.855036	1.39	7161.97	3.855033
49'	0.245	7015.87	3.846082	1.43	7015.81	3.846078
50'	0.25	6875.55	3.837308	1.45	6875.49	3.837304
51'	0.255	6740.74	3.828708	1.48	6740.68	3.828704
52'	0.26	6611.12	3.820275	1.51	6611.05	3.820270
53'	0.265	6486.38	3.812002	1.54	6486.31	3.811998
54'	0.27	6366.26	3.803885	1.57	6366.20	3.803880
55'	0.275	6250.51	3.795916	1.60	6250.45	3.795911
56'	0.28	6138.90	3.788091	1.63	6138.83	3.788086
57'	0.285	6031.20	3.780404	1.66	6031.14	3.780399
58'	0.29	5927.22	3.772851	1.69	5927.15	3.772846
59'	0.295	5826.76	3.765427	1.72	5826.69	3.765422

TABLE VII. FUNCTIONS OF CIRCULAR CURVES

Degree of Curve D	Defl. Per Ft of Sta. (Min)	Chord Definition			Arc Definition	
		Radius R	log R	C.O. 1 Sta.	Radius R	log R
1° 0'	0.3	5729.65	3.758128	1.75	5729.58	3.758123
1'	0.305	5635.72	3.750950	1.77	5635.65	3.750944
2'	0.31	5544.83	3.743888	1.80	5544.75	3.743882
3'	0.315	5456.82	3.736939	1.83	5456.74	3.736933
4'	0.32	5371.56	3.730100	1.86	5371.48	3.730094
5'	0.325	5288.92	3.723367	1.89	5288.84	3.723360
6'	0.33	5208.79	3.716737	1.92	5208.71	3.716730
7'	0.335	5131.05	3.710206	1.95	5130.97	3.710199
8'	0.34	5055.59	3.703772	1.98	5055.51	3.703765
9'	0.345	4982.33	3.697432	2.01	4982.24	3.697425
10'	0.35	4911.15	3.691183	2.03	4911.07	3.691176
11'	0.355	4841.98	3.685023	2.07	4841.90	3.685015
12'	0.36	4774.74	3.678949	2.09	4774.65	3.678941
13'	0.365	4709.33	3.672959	2.12	4709.24	3.672951
14'	0.37	4645.69	3.667051	2.15	4645.60	3.667042
15'	0.375	4583.75	3.661221	2.18	4583.66	3.661213
16'	0.38	4523.44	3.655469	2.21	4523.35	3.655460
17'	0.385	4464.70	3.649792	2.24	4464.61	3.649783
18'	0.39	4407.46	3.644189	2.27	4407.37	3.644179
19'	0.395	4351.67	3.638656	2.30	4351.58	3.638647
20'	0.4	4297.28	3.633194	2.33	4297.18	3.633184
21'	0.405	4244.23	3.627799	2.35	4244.13	3.627789
22'	0.41	4192.47	3.622470	2.39	4192.37	3.622460
23'	0.415	4141.96	3.617206	2.41	4141.86	3.617196
24'	0.42	4092.66	3.612005	2.44	4092.56	3.611995
25'	0.425	4044.51	3.606866	2.47	4044.41	3.606855
26'	0.43	3997.49	3.601787	2.50	3997.38	3.601775
27'	0.435	3951.54	3.596766	2.53	3951.43	3.596755
28'	0.44	3906.64	3.591803	2.56	3906.53	3.591791
29'	0.445	3862.74	3.586896	2.59	3862.64	3.586884
30'	0.45	3819.83	3.582044	2.62	3819.71	3.582031
31'	0.455	3777.85	3.577245	2.65	3777.74	3.577232
32'	0.46	3736.79	3.572499	2.68	3736.68	3.572486
33'	0.465	3696.61	3.567804	2.71	3696.50	3.567791
34'	0.47	3657.29	3.563160	2.73	3657.18	3.563146
35'	0.475	3618.80	3.558564	2.76	3618.68	3.558550
36'	0.48	3581.10	3.554017	2.79	3580.99	3.554003
37'	0.485	3544.19	3.549517	2.82	3544.07	3.549502
38'	0.49	3508.02	3.545063	2.85	3507.91	3.545048
39'	0.495	3472.59	3.540654	2.88	3472.47	3.540638
40'	0.5	3437.87	3.536289	2.91	3437.75	3.536274
41'	0.505	3403.83	3.531968	2.94	3403.71	3.531952
42'	0.51	3370.46	3.527690	2.97	3370.34	3.527673
43'	0.515	3337.74	3.523453	3.00	3337.62	3.523437
44'	0.52	3305.65	3.519257	3.03	3305.53	3.519241
45'	0.525	3274.17	3.515101	3.05	3274.04	3.515085
46'	0.53	3243.29	3.510985	3.08	3243.16	3.510968
47'	0.535	3212.98	3.506908	3.11	3212.85	3.506890
48'	0.54	3183.23	3.502868	3.14	3183.10	3.502850
49'	0.545	3154.03	3.498866	3.17	3153.90	3.498847
50'	0.55	3125.36	3.494900	3.20	3125.22	3.494881
51'	0.555	3097.20	3.490970	3.23	3097.07	3.490951
52'	0.56	3069.55	3.487075	3.26	3069.42	3.487056
53'	0.565	3042.39	3.483215	3.29	3042.25	3.483195
54'	0.57	3015.71	3.479389	3.32	3015.57	3.479369
55'	0.575	2989.48	3.475596	3.35	2989.34	3.475576
56'	0.58	2963.72	3.471836	3.37	2963.58	3.471816
57'	0.585	2938.39	3.468109	3.40	2938.25	3.468087
58'	0.59	2913.49	3.464413	3.43	2913.34	3.464392
59'	0.595	2889.01	3.460749	3.46	2888.86	3.460727

TABLE VII. FUNCTIONS OF CIRCULAR CURVES

Degree of Curve D	Defl. Per Ft of Sta. (Min)	Chord Definition			Arc Definition	
		Radius R	log R	C.O. 1 Sta.	Radius R	log R
2° 0'	0.6	2864.93	3.457115	3.49	2864.79	3.457093
1'	0.605	2841.26	3.453511	3.52	2841.11	3.453488
2'	0.61	2817.97	3.449937	3.55	2817.83	3.449914
3'	0.615	2795.06	3.446392	3.58	2794.92	3.446369
4'	0.62	2772.53	3.442876	3.61	2772.38	3.442852
5'	0.625	2750.35	3.439388	3.64	2750.20	3.439364
6'	0.63	2728.52	3.435928	3.66	2728.37	3.435903
7'	0.635	2707.04	3.432495	3.69	2706.89	3.432470
8'	0.64	2685.89	3.429089	3.72	2685.74	3.429064
9'	0.645	2665.08	3.425710	3.75	2664.92	3.425684
10'	0.65	2644.58	3.422356	3.78	2644.42	3.422330
11'	0.655	2624.39	3.419029	3.81	2624.23	3.419002
12'	0.66	2604.51	3.415727	3.84	2604.35	3.415700
13'	0.665	2584.93	3.412449	3.87	2584.77	3.412422
14'	0.67	2565.65	3.409197	3.90	2565.48	3.409169
15'	0.675	2546.64	3.405968	3.93	2546.48	3.405940
16'	0.68	2527.92	3.402763	3.96	2527.75	3.402735
17'	0.685	2509.47	3.399582	3.98	2509.30	3.399553
18'	0.69	2491.29	3.396424	4.01	2491.12	3.396395
19'	0.695	2473.37	3.393289	4.04	2473.20	3.393259
20'	0.7	2455.70	3.390176	4.07	2455.53	3.390145
21'	0.705	2438.29	3.387085	4.10	2438.12	3.387055
22'	0.71	2421.12	3.384016	4.13	2420.95	3.383985
23'	0.715	2404.19	3.380969	4.16	2404.02	3.380938
24'	0.72	2387.50	3.377943	4.19	2387.32	3.377911
25'	0.725	2371.04	3.374938	4.22	2370.86	3.374905
26'	0.73	2354.80	3.371954	4.25	2354.62	3.371921
27'	0.735	2338.78	3.368990	4.28	2338.60	3.368956
28'	0.74	2322.98	3.366046	4.30	2322.80	3.366012
29'	0.745	2307.39	3.363122	4.33	2307.21	3.363087
30'	0.75	2292.01	3.360217	4.36	2291.83	3.360183
31'	0.755	2276.84	3.357332	4.39	2276.65	3.357297
32'	0.76	2261.86	3.354466	4.42	2261.68	3.354430
33'	0.765	2247.08	3.351618	4.45	2246.89	3.351582
34'	0.77	2232.49	3.348789	4.48	2232.30	3.348753
35'	0.775	2218.09	3.345797	4.51	2217.90	3.345942
36'	0.78	2203.87	3.343187	4.54	2203.68	3.343149
37'	0.785	2189.84	3.340412	4.57	2189.65	3.340374
38'	0.79	2175.98	3.337655	4.60	2175.79	3.337617
39'	0.795	2162.30	3.334916	4.62	2162.10	3.334877
40'	0.8	2148.79	3.332193	4.65	2148.59	3.332154
41'	0.805	2135.44	3.329488	4.68	2135.25	3.329448
42'	0.81	2122.26	3.326799	4.71	2122.07	3.326759
43'	0.815	2109.24	3.324127	4.74	2109.05	3.324086
44'	0.82	2096.39	3.321471	4.77	2096.19	3.321430
45'	0.825	2083.68	3.318832	4.80	2083.48	3.318790
46'	0.83	2071.13	3.316208	4.83	2070.93	3.316166
47'	0.835	2058.73	3.313600	4.86	2058.53	3.313557
48'	0.84	2046.48	3.311008	4.89	2046.28	3.310964
49'	0.845	2034.37	3.308431	4.92	2034.17	3.308387
50'	0.85	2022.41	3.305869	4.94	2022.20	3.305825
51'	0.855	2010.59	3.303323	4.97	2010.38	3.303278
52'	0.86	1998.90	3.300791	5.00	1998.69	3.300745
53'	0.865	1987.35	3.298274	5.03	1987.14	3.298228
54'	0.87	1975.93	3.295771	5.06	1975.72	3.295725
55'	0.875	1964.64	3.293283	5.09	1964.43	3.293236
56'	0.88	1953.48	3.290809	5.12	1953.27	3.290761
57'	0.885	1942.44	3.288349	5.15	1942.23	3.288301
58'	0.89	1931.53	3.285902	5.18	1931.32	3.285854
59'	0.895	1920.75	3.283470	5.21	1920.53	3.283421

TABLE VII. FUNCTIONS OF CIRCULAR CURVES

Degree of Curve D	Defl. Per Ft of Sta. (Min)	Chord Definition			Arc Definition	
		Radius R	log R	C.O. 1 Sta.	Radius R	log R
3° 0'	0.9	1910.08	3.281051	5.24	1909.86	3.281001
1'	0.905	1899.53	3.278646	5.26	1899.31	3.278595
2'	0.91	1889.09	3.276253	5.29	1888.87	3.276203
3'	0.915	1878.77	3.273874	5.32	1878.55	3.273823
4'	0.92	1868.56	3.271508	5.35	1868.34	3.271456
5'	0.925	1858.47	3.269155	5.38	1858.24	3.269102
6'	0.93	1848.48	3.266814	5.41	1848.25	3.266761
7'	0.935	1838.59	3.264486	5.44	1838.37	3.264432
8'	0.94	1828.82	3.262170	5.47	1828.59	3.262116
9'	0.945	1819.14	3.259867	5.50	1818.91	3.259812
10'	0.95	1809.57	3.257576	5.53	1809.34	3.257520
11'	0.955	1800.10	3.255296	5.56	1799.87	3.255240
12'	0.96	1790.73	3.253029	5.58	1790.49	3.252973
13'	0.965	1781.45	3.250774	5.61	1781.22	3.250716
14'	0.97	1772.27	3.248530	5.64	1772.03	3.248472
15'	0.975	1763.18	3.246297	5.67	1762.95	3.246239
16'	0.98	1754.19	3.244077	5.70	1753.95	3.244018
17'	0.985	1745.29	3.241867	5.73	1745.05	3.241808
18'	0.99	1736.48	3.239669	5.76	1736.24	3.239609
19'	0.995	1727.75	3.237481	5.79	1727.51	3.237421
20'	1.0	1719.12	3.235305	5.82	1718.87	3.235244
21'	1.005	1710.57	3.233140	5.85	1710.32	3.233078
22'	1.01	1702.10	3.230985	5.88	1701.85	3.230922
23'	1.015	1693.72	3.228841	5.90	1693.47	3.228778
24'	1.02	1685.42	3.226707	5.93	1685.17	3.226644
25'	1.025	1677.20	3.224584	5.96	1676.95	3.224520
26'	1.03	1669.06	3.222472	5.99	1668.81	3.222407
27'	1.035	1661.00	3.220369	6.02	1660.75	3.220303
28'	1.04	1653.01	3.218277	6.05	1652.76	3.218210
29'	1.045	1645.11	3.216195	6.08	1644.85	3.216128
30'	1.05	1637.28	3.214122	6.11	1637.02	3.214055
31'	1.055	1629.52	3.212060	6.14	1629.26	3.211991
32'	1.06	1621.84	3.210007	6.17	1621.58	3.209938
33'	1.065	1614.22	3.207964	6.19	1613.96	3.207894
34'	1.07	1606.68	3.205930	6.22	1606.42	3.205860
35'	1.075	1599.21	3.203906	6.25	1598.95	3.203835
36'	1.08	1591.81	3.201892	6.28	1591.55	3.201820
37'	1.085	1584.48	3.199886	6.31	1584.21	3.199814
38'	1.09	1577.21	3.197890	6.34	1576.95	3.197817
39'	1.095	1570.01	3.195903	6.37	1569.75	3.195830
40'	1.1	1562.88	3.193925	6.40	1562.61	3.193851
41'	1.105	1555.81	3.191956	6.43	1555.54	3.191881
42'	1.11	1548.80	3.189996	6.46	1548.53	3.189921
43'	1.115	1541.86	3.188045	6.49	1541.59	3.187969
44'	1.12	1534.98	3.186103	6.51	1534.71	3.186026
45'	1.125	1528.16	3.184169	6.54	1527.89	3.184091
46'	1.13	1521.40	3.182244	6.57	1521.13	3.182165
47'	1.135	1514.17	3.180327	6.60	1514.43	3.180248
48'	1.14	1508.06	3.178419	6.63	1507.78	3.178339
49'	1.145	1501.48	3.176519	6.66	1501.20	3.176438
50'	1.15	1494.95	3.174627	6.69	1494.67	3.174546
51'	1.155	1488.48	3.172744	6.72	1488.20	3.172661
52'	1.16	1482.07	3.170868	6.75	1481.79	3.170786
53'	1.165	1475.71	3.169001	6.78	1475.43	3.168918
54'	1.17	1469.41	3.167142	6.81	1469.12	3.167058
55'	1.175	1463.16	3.165291	6.83	1462.87	3.165206
56'	1.18	1456.96	3.163447	6.86	1456.67	3.163362
57'	1.185	1450.81	3.161612	6.89	1450.53	3.161526
58'	1.19	1444.72	3.159784	6.92	1444.43	3.159697
59'	1.195	1438.68	3.157963	6.95	1438.39	3.157876

TABLE VII. FUNCTIONS OF CIRCULAR CURVES

Degree of Curve D	Defl. Per Ft of Sta. (Min)	Chord Definition			Arc Definition	
		Radius R	log R	C.O. 1 Sta.	Radius R	log R
4° 0'	1.2	1432.69	3.156151	6.98	1432.39	3.156063
1'	1.205	1426.74	3.154346	7.01	1426.45	3.154257
2'	1.21	1420.85	3.152548	7.04	1420.56	3.152458
3'	1.215	1415.01	3.150758	7.07	1414.71	3.150667
4'	1.22	1409.21	3.148975	7.10	1408.91	3.148884
5'	1.225	1403.46	3.147200	7.13	1403.16	3.147108
6'	1.23	1397.76	3.145431	7.15	1397.46	3.145339
7'	1.235	1392.10	3.143670	7.18	1391.80	3.143577
8'	1.24	1386.49	3.141916	7.21	1386.19	3.141822
9'	1.245	1380.92	3.140170	7.24	1380.62	3.140074
10'	1.25	1375.40	3.138430	7.27	1375.10	3.138334
11'	1.255	1369.92	3.136697	7.30	1369.62	3.136600
12'	1.26	1364.49	3.134971	7.33	1364.19	3.134873
13'	1.265	1359.10	3.133251	7.36	1358.79	3.133153
14'	1.27	1353.75	3.131539	7.39	1353.44	3.131440
15'	1.275	1348.45	3.129833	7.42	1348.14	3.129734
16'	1.28	1343.18	3.128134	7.45	1342.87	3.128034
17'	1.285	1337.96	3.126442	7.47	1337.64	3.126341
18'	1.29	1332.77	3.124756	7.50	1332.46	3.124654
19'	1.295	1327.63	3.123077	7.53	1327.32	3.122974
20'	1.3	1322.53	3.121404	7.56	1322.21	3.121300
21'	1.305	1317.46	3.119738	7.59	1317.14	3.119633
22'	1.31	1312.43	3.118078	7.62	1312.12	3.117972
23'	1.315	1307.45	3.116424	7.65	1307.13	3.116318
24'	1.32	1302.50	3.114777	7.68	1302.18	3.114669
25'	1.325	1297.58	3.113136	7.71	1297.26	3.113028
26'	1.33	1292.71	3.111501	7.74	1292.39	3.111392
27'	1.335	1287.87	3.109872	7.76	1287.55	3.109762
28'	1.34	1283.07	3.108249	7.79	1282.74	3.108139
29'	1.345	1278.30	3.106632	7.82	1277.97	3.106521
30'	1.35	1273.57	3.105022	7.85	1273.24	3.104910
31'	1.355	1268.87	3.103417	7.88	1268.54	3.103304
32'	1.36	1264.21	3.101818	7.91	1263.88	3.101705
33'	1.365	1259.58	3.100225	7.94	1259.25	3.100111
34'	1.37	1254.98	3.098638	7.97	1254.65	3.098523
35'	1.375	1250.42	3.097057	8.00	1250.09	3.096941
36'	1.38	1245.89	3.095481	8.03	1245.56	3.095365
37'	1.385	1241.40	3.093912	8.06	1241.06	3.093974
38'	1.39	1236.94	3.092347	8.08	1236.60	3.092229
39'	1.395	1232.51	3.090789	8.11	1232.17	3.090670
40'	1.4	1228.11	3.089236	8.14	1227.77	3.089116
41'	1.405	1223.74	3.087689	8.17	1223.40	3.087566
42'	1.41	1219.40	3.086147	8.20	1219.06	3.086025
43'	1.415	1215.09	3.084610	8.23	1214.75	3.084487
44'	1.42	1210.82	3.083079	8.26	1210.47	3.082955
45'	1.425	1206.57	3.081553	8.29	1206.23	3.081429
46'	1.43	1202.36	3.080033	8.32	1202.01	3.079908
47'	1.435	1198.17	3.078518	8.35	1197.82	3.078392
48'	1.44	1194.01	3.077008	8.38	1193.66	3.076881
49'	1.445	1189.88	3.075504	8.40	1189.53	3.075376
50'	1.45	1185.78	3.074005	8.43	1185.43	3.073876
51'	1.455	1181.71	3.072511	8.46	1181.36	3.072381
52'	1.46	1177.66	3.071022	8.49	1177.31	3.070891
53'	1.465	1173.65	3.069538	8.52	1173.29	3.069406
54'	1.47	1169.66	3.068059	8.55	1169.30	3.067927
55'	1.475	1165.70	3.066585	8.58	1165.34	3.066452
56'	1.48	1161.76	3.065116	8.61	1161.40	3.064982
57'	1.485	1157.85	3.063653	8.64	1157.49	3.063517
58'	1.49	1153.97	3.062194	8.67	1153.61	3.062057
59'	1.495	1150.11	3.060740	8.69	1149.75	3.060603

TABLE VII.   FUNCTIONS OF CIRCULAR CURVES

Degree of Curve D	Defl. Per Ft of Sta. (Min)	Chord Definition			Arc Definition	
		Radius R	log R	C.O. 1 Sta.	Radius R	log R
5° 0'	1.5	1146.28	3.059290	8.72	1145.92	3.059153
1'	1.505	1142.47	3.057846	8.75	1142.11	3.057707
2'	1.51	1138.69	3.056407	8.78	1138.33	3.056267
3'	1.515	1134.94	3.054972	8.81	1134.57	3.054831
4'	1.52	1131.21	3.053542	8.84	1130.84	3.053400
5'	1.525	1127.50	3.052116	8.87	1127.13	3.051974
6'	1.53	1123.82	3.050696	8.90	1123.45	3.050553
7'	1.535	1120.16	3.049280	8.93	1119.79	3.049135
8'	1.54	1116.52	3.047868	8.96	1116.15	3.047723
9'	1.545	1112.91	3.046462	8.99	1112.54	3.046315
10'	1.55	1109.33	3.045059	9.01	1108.95	3.044912
11'	1.555	1105.76	3.043662	9.04	1105.38	3.043514
12'	1.56	1102.22	3.042268	9.07	1101.84	3.042119
13'	1.565	1098.70	3.040880	9.10	1098.32	3.040729
14'	1.57	1095.20	3.039495	9.13	1094.82	3.039343
15'	1.575	1091.73	3.038115	9.16	1091.35	3.037963
16'	1.58	1088.28	3.036740	9.19	1087.89	3.036587
17'	1.585	1084.85	3.035368	9.22	1084.46	3.035215
18'	1.59	1081.44	3.034002	9.25	1081.05	3.033847
19'	1.595	1078.05	3.032639	9.28	1077.66	3.032483
20'	1.6	1074.68	3.031281	9.31	1074.30	3.031124
21'	1.605	1071.34	3.029927	9.33	1070.95	3.029769
22'	1.61	1068.01	3.028577	9.36	1067.62	3.028418
23'	1.615	1064.71	3.027231	9.39	1064.32	3.027071
24'	1.62	1061.43	3.025890	9.42	1061.03	3.025729
25'	1.625	1058.16	3.024552	9.45	1057.77	3.024390
26'	1.63	1054.92	3.023219	9.48	1054.52	3.023056
27'	1.635	1051.70	3.021890	9.51	1051.30	3.021726
28'	1.64	1048.49	3.020565	9.54	1048.09	3.020400
29'	1.645	1045.31	3.019244	9.57	1044.91	3.019078
30'	1.65	1042.14	3.017927	9.60	1041.74	3.017760
31'	1.655	1039.00	3.016614	9.62	1038.59	3.016446
32'	1.66	1035.87	3.015305	9.65	1035.47	3.015136
33'	1.665	1032.76	3.013999	9.68	1032.36	3.013829
34'	1.67	1029.67	3.012698	9.71	1029.27	3.012527
35'	1.675	1026.60	3.011401	9.74	1026.19	3.011229
36'	1.68	1023.55	3.010107	9.77	1023.14	3.009935
37'	1.685	1020.51	3.008818	9.80	1020.10	3.008644
38'	1.69	1017.49	3.007532	9.83	1017.08	3.007357
39'	1.695	1014.50	3.006250	9.86	1014.08	3.006074
40'	1.7	1011.51	3.004972	9.89	1011.10	3.004795
41'	1.705	1008.55	3.003698	9.92	1008.14	3.003520
42'	1.71	1005.60	3.002427	9.94	1005.19	3.002248
43'	1.715	1002.67	3.001160	9.97	1002.26	3.000980
44'	1.72	999.762	2.999897	10.00	999.345	2.999715
45'	1.725	996.867	2.998637	10.03	996.448	2.998455
46'	1.73	993.988	2.997381	10.06	993.568	2.997198
47'	1.735	991.126	2.996129	10.09	990.705	2.995944
48'	1.74	988.280	2.994880	10.12	987.858	2.994695
49'	1.745	985.451	2.993635	10.15	985.028	2.993448
50'	1.75	982.638	2.992393	10.18	982.213	2.992206
51'	1.755	979.840	2.991155	10.21	979.415	2.990967
52'	1.76	977.060	2.989921	10.23	976.632	2.989731
53'	1.765	974.294	2.988690	10.26	973.866	2.988499
54'	1.77	971.544	2.987463	10.29	971.115	2.987271
55'	1.775	968.810	2.986239	10.32	968.379	2.986045
56'	1.78	966.091	2.985018	10.35	965.659	2.984824
57'	1.785	963.387	2.983801	10.38	962.954	2.983606
58'	1.79	960.698	2.982587	10.41	960.264	2.982391
59'	1.795	958.025	2.981377	10.44	957.590	2.981179

TABLE VIII. LOGARITHMS OF NUMBERS

No. 100—Log. 000   No. 109—Log. 040

N.	0	1	2	3	4	5	6	7	8	9	Diff.
100	000000	0434	0868	1301	1734	2166	2598	3029	3461	3891	432
101	4321	4751	5181	5609	6038	6466	6894	7321	7748	8174	428
102	8600	9026	9451	9876	*0300	*0724	*1147	*1570	*1993	*2415	424
103	012837	3259	3680	4100	4521	4940	5360	5779	6197	6616	420
104	7033	7451	7868	8284	8700	9116	9532	9947	*0361	*0775	416
105	021189	1603	2016	2428	2841	3252	3664	4075	4486	4896	412
106	5306	5715	6125	6533	6942	7350	7757	8164	8571	8978	408
107	9384	9789	*0195	*0600	*1004	*1408	*1812	*2216	*2619	*3021	404
108	033424	3826	4227	4628	5029	5430	5830	6230	6629	7028	400
109	7426	7825	8223	8620	9017	9414	9811	*0207	*0602	*0998	397

PROPORTIONAL PARTS

Diff.	1	2	3	4	5	6	7	8	9	Diff.
434	43	87	130	174	217	260	304	347	391	434
433	43	87	130	173	217	260	303	346	390	433
432	43	86	130	173	216	259	302	346	389	432
431	43	86	129	172	216	259	302	345	388	431
430	43	86	129	172	215	258	301	344	387	430
429	43	86	129	172	215	257	300	343	386	429
428	43	86	128	171	214	257	300	342	385	428
427	43	85	128	171	214	256	299	342	384	427
426	43	85	128	170	213	256	298	341	383	426
425	43	85	128	170	213	255	298	340	383	425
424	42	85	127	170	212	254	297	339	382	424
423	42	85	127	169	212	254	296	338	381	423
422	42	84	127	169	211	253	295	338	380	422
421	42	84	126	168	211	253	295	337	379	421
420	42	84	126	168	210	252	294	336	378	420
419	42	84	126	168	210	251	293	335	377	419
418	42	84	125	167	209	251	293	334	376	418
417	42	83	125	167	209	250	292	334	375	417
416	42	83	125	166	208	250	291	333	374	416
415	42	83	125	166	208	249	291	332	374	415
414	41	83	124	166	207	248	290	331	373	414
413	41	83	124	165	207	248	289	330	372	413
412	41	82	124	165	206	247	288	330	371	412
411	41	82	123	164	206	247	288	329	370	411
410	41	82	123	164	205	246	287	328	369	410
409	41	82	123	164	205	245	286	327	368	409
408	41	82	122	163	204	245	286	326	367	408
407	41	81	122	163	204	244	285	326	366	407
406	41	81	122	162	203	244	284	325	365	406
405	41	81	122	162	203	243	284	324	365	405
404	40	81	121	162	202	242	283	323	364	404
403	40	81	121	161	202	242	282	322	363	403
402	40	80	121	161	201	241	281	322	362	402
401	40	80	120	160	201	241	281	321	361	401
400	40	80	120	160	200	240	280	320	360	400
399	40	80	120	160	200	239	279	319	359	399
398	40	80	119	159	199	239	279	318	358	398
397	40	79	119	159	199	238	278	318	357	397
396	40	79	119	158	198	238	277	317	356	396
395	40	79	119	158	198	237	277	316	356	395
394	39	79	118	158	197	236	276	315	355	394
393	39	79	118	157	197	236	275	314	354	393
392	39	78	118	157	196	235	274	314	353	392
391	39	78	117	156	196	235	274	313	352	391
390	39	78	117	156	195	234	273	312	351	390
389	39	78	117	156	195	233	272	311	350	389
388	39	78	116	155	194	233	272	310	349	388

TABLE VIII. LOGARITHMS OF NUMBERS

No. 110—Log. 041   No. 124—Log. 096

N.	0	1	2	3	4	5	6	7	8	9	Diff.
110	041393	1787	2182	2576	2969	3362	3755	4148	4540	4932	333
111	5323	5714	6105	6495	6885	7275	7664	8053	8442	8830	390
112	9218	9606	9993	*0380	*0766	*1153	*1538	*1924	*2309	*2694	386
113	053078	3463	3846	4230	4613	4996	5378	5760	6142	6524	383
114	6905	7286	7666	8046	8426	8805	9185	9563	9942	*0320	379
115	060698	1075	1452	1829	2206	2582	2958	3333	3709	4083	376
116	4458	4832	5206	5580	5953	6326	6699	7071	7443	7815	373
117	8186	8557	8928	9298	9668	*0038	*0407	*0776	*1145	*1514	370
118	071882	2250	2617	2985	3352	3718	4085	4451	4816	5182	366
119	5547	5912	6276	6640	7004	7368	7731	8094	8457	8819	363
120	079181	9543	9904	*0266	*0626	*0987	*1347	*1707	*2067	*2426	360
121	082785	3144	3503	3861	4219	4576	4934	5291	5647	6004	357
122	6360	6716	7071	7426	7781	8136	8490	8845	9198	9552	355
123	9905	*0258	*0611	*0963	*1315	*1667	*2018	*2370	*2721	*3071	352
124	093422	3772	4122	4471	4820	5169	5518	5866	6215	6562	349

PROPORTIONAL PARTS

Diff.	1	2	3	4	5	6	7	8	9	Diff.
387	39	77	116	155	194	232	271	310	348	387
386	39	77	116	154	193	232	270	309	347	386
385	39	77	116	154	193	231	270	308	347	385
384	38	77	115	154	192	230	269	307	346	384
383	38	77	115	153	192	230	268	306	345	383
382	38	76	115	153	191	229	267	306	344	382
381	38	76	114	152	191	229	267	305	343	381
380	38	76	114	152	190	228	266	304	342	380
379	38	76	114	152	190	227	265	303	341	379
378	38	76	113	151	189	227	265	302	340	378
377	38	75	113	151	189	226	264	302	339	377
376	38	75	113	150	188	226	263	301	338	376
375	38	75	113	150	188	225	263	300	338	375
374	37	75	112	150	187	224	262	299	337	374
373	37	75	112	149	187	224	261	298	336	373
372	37	74	112	149	186	223	260	298	335	372
371	37	74	111	148	186	223	260	297	334	371
370	37	74	111	148	185	222	259	296	333	370
369	37	74	111	148	185	221	258	295	332	369
368	37	74	110	147	184	221	258	294	331	368
367	37	73	110	147	184	220	257	294	330	367
366	37	73	110	146	183	220	256	293	329	366
365	37	73	110	146	183	219	256	292	329	365
364	36	73	109	146	182	218	255	291	328	364
363	36	73	109	145	182	218	254	290	327	363
362	36	72	109	145	181	217	253	290	326	362
361	36	72	108	144	181	217	253	289	325	361
360	36	72	108	144	180	216	252	288	324	360
359	36	72	108	144	180	215	251	287	323	359
358	36	72	107	143	179	215	251	286	322	358
357	36	71	107	143	179	214	250	286	321	357
356	36	71	107	142	178	214	249	285	320	356
355	36	71	107	142	178	213	249	284	320	355
354	35	71	106	142	177	212	248	283	319	354
353	35	71	106	141	177	212	247	282	318	353
352	35	70	106	141	176	211	246	282	317	352
351	35	70	105	140	176	211	246	281	316	351
350	35	70	105	140	175	210	245	280	315	350
349	35	70	105	140	175	209	244	279	314	349
348	35	70	104	139	174	209	244	278	313	348
347	35	69	104	139	174	208	243	278	312	347

TABLE VIII.   LOGARITHMS OF NUMBERS

No. 125—Log. 097   No. 139—Log. 145

N.	0	1	2	3	4	5	6	7	8	9	Diff.
125	096910	7257	7604	7951	8298	8644	8990	9335	9681	*0026	346
126	100371	0715	1059	1403	1747	2091	2434	2777	3119	3462	343
127	3804	4146	4487	4828	5169	5510	5851	6191	6531	6871	341
128	7210	7549	7888	8227	8565	8903	9241	9579	9916	*0253	338
129	110590	0926	1263	1599	1934	2270	2605	2940	3275	3609	335
130	113943	4277	4611	4944	5278	5611	5943	6276	6608	6940	333
131	7271	7603	7934	8265	8595	8926	9256	9586	9915	*0245	330
132	120574	0903	1231	1560	1888	2216	2544	2871	3198	3525	328
133	3852	4178	4504	4830	5156	5481	5806	6131	6456	6781	325
134	7105	7429	7753	8076	8399	8722	9045	9368	9690	*0012	323
135	130334	0655	0977	1298	1619	1939	2260	2580	2900	3219	321
136	3539	3858	4177	4496	4814	5133	5451	5769	6086	6403	318
137	6721	7037	7354	7671	7987	8303	8618	8934	9249	9564	316
138	9879	*0194	*0508	*0822	*1136	*1450	*1763	*2076	*2389	*2702	314
139	143015	3327	3639	3951	4263	4574	4885	5196	5507	5818	311

PROPORTIONAL PARTS

Diff.	1	2	3	4	5	6	7	8	9	Diff.
347	35	69	104	139	174	208	243	278	312	347
346	35	69	104	138	173	208	242	277	311	346
345	35	69	104	138	173	207	242	276	311	345
344	34	69	103	138	172	206	241	275	310	344
343	34	69	103	137	172	206	240	274	309	343
342	34	68	103	137	171	205	239	274	308	342
341	34	68	102	136	171	205	239	273	307	341
340	34	68	102	136	170	204	238	272	306	340
339	34	68	102	136	170	203	237	271	305	339
338	34	68	101	135	169	203	237	270	304	338
337	34	67	101	135	169	202	236	270	303	337
336	34	67	101	134	168	202	235	269	302	336
335	34	67	101	134	168	201	235	268	302	335
334	33	67	100	134	167	200	234	267	301	334
333	33	67	100	133	167	200	233	266	300	333
332	33	66	100	133	166	199	232	266	299	332
331	33	66	99	132	166	199	232	265	298	331
330	33	66	99	132	165	198	231	264	297	330
329	33	66	99	132	165	197	230	263	296	329
328	33	66	98	131	164	197	230	262	295	328
327	33	65	98	131	164	196	229	262	294	327
326	33	65	98	130	163	196	228	261	293	326
325	33	65	98	130	163	195	228	260	293	325
324	32	65	97	130	162	194	227	259	292	324
323	32	65	97	129	162	194	226	258	291	323
322	32	64	97	129	161	193	225	258	290	322
321	32	64	96	128	161	193	225	257	289	321
320	32	64	96	128	160	192	224	256	288	320
319	32	64	96	128	160	191	223	255	287	319
318	32	64	95	127	159	191	223	254	286	318
317	32	63	95	127	159	190	222	254	285	317
316	32	63	95	126	158	190	221	253	284	316
315	32	63	95	126	158	189	221	252	284	315
314	31	63	94	126	157	188	220	251	283	314
313	31	63	94	125	157	188	219	250	282	313
312	31	62	94	125	156	187	218	250	281	312
311	31	62	93	124	156	187	218	249	280	311
310	31	62	93	124	155	186	217	248	279	310
309	31	62	93	124	155	185	216	247	278	309
308	31	62	92	123	154	185	216	246	277	308
307	31	61	92	123	154	184	215	246	276	307

TABLE VIII. LOGARITHMS OF NUMBERS

No. 140—Log. 146   No. 159—Log. 203

N.	0	1	2	3	4	5	6	7	8	9	Diff.
140	146128	6438	6748	7058	7367	7676	7985	8294	8603	8911	309
141	9219	9527	9835	*0142	*0449	*0756	*1063	*1370	*1676	*1982	307
142	152288	2594	2900	3205	3510	3815	4120	4424	4728	5032	305
143	5336	5640	5943	6246	6549	6852	7154	7457	7759	8061	303
144	8362	8664	8965	9266	9567	9868	*0168	*0469	*0769	*1068	301
145	161368	1667	1967	2266	2564	2863	3161	3460	3758	4055	299
146	4353	4650	4947	5244	5541	5838	6134	6430	6726	7022	297
147	7317	7613	7908	8203	8497	8792	9086	9380	9674	9968	295
148	170262	0555	0848	1141	1434	1726	2019	2311	2603	2895	293
149	3186	3478	3769	4060	4351	4641	4932	5222	5512	5802	291
150	176091	6381	6670	6959	7248	7536	7825	8113	8401	8689	289
151	8977	9264	9552	9839	*0126	*0413	*0699	*0986	*1272	*1558	287
152	181844	2129	2415	2700	2985	3270	3555	3839	4123	4407	285
153	4691	4975	5259	5542	5825	6108	6391	6674	6956	7239	283
154	7521	7803	8084	8366	8647	8928	9209	9490	9771	*0051	281
155	190332	0612	0892	1171	1451	1730	2010	2289	2567	2846	279
156	3125	3403	3681	3959	4237	4514	4792	5069	5346	5623	278
157	5900	6176	6453	6729	7005	7281	7556	7832	8107	8382	276
158	8657	8932	9206	9481	9755	*0029	*0303	*0577	*0850	*1124	274
159	201397	1670	1943	2216	2488	2761	3033	3305	3577	3848	272

PROPORTIONAL PARTS

Diff.	1	2	3	4	5	6	7	8	9	Diff.
306	31	61	92	122	153	184	214	245	275	306
305	31	61	92	122	153	183	214	244	275	305
304	30	61	91	122	152	182	213	243	274	304
303	30	61	91	121	152	182	212	242	273	303
302	30	60	91	121	151	181	211	242	272	302
301	30	60	90	120	151	181	211	241	271	301
300	30	60	90	120	150	180	210	240	270	300
299	30	60	90	120	150	179	209	239	269	299
298	30	60	89	119	149	179	209	238	268	298
297	30	59	89	119	149	178	208	238	267	297
296	30	59	89	118	148	178	207	237	266	296
295	30	59	89	118	148	177	207	236	266	295
294	29	59	88	118	147	176	206	235	265	294
293	29	59	88	117	147	176	205	234	264	293
292	29	58	88	117	146	175	204	234	263	292
291	29	58	87	116	146	175	204	233	262	291
290	29	58	87	116	145	174	203	232	261	290
289	29	58	87	116	145	173	202	231	260	289
288	29	58	86	115	144	173	202	230	259	288
287	29	57	86	115	144	172	201	230	258	287
286	29	57	86	114	143	172	200	229	257	286
285	29	57	86	114	143	171	200	228	257	285
284	28	57	85	114	142	170	199	227	256	284
283	28	57	85	113	142	170	198	226	255	283
282	28	56	85	113	141	169	197	226	254	282
281	28	56	84	112	141	169	197	225	253	281
280	28	56	84	112	140	168	196	224	252	280
279	28	56	84	112	140	167	195	223	251	279
278	28	56	83	111	139	167	195	222	250	278
277	28	55	83	111	139	166	194	222	249	277
276	28	55	83	110	138	166	193	221	248	276
275	28	55	83	110	138	165	193	220	248	275
274	27	55	82	110	137	164	192	219	247	274
273	27	55	82	109	137	164	191	218	246	273
272	27	54	82	109	136	163	190	218	245	272
271	27	54	81	108	136	163	190	217	244	271

TABLE VIII. LOGARITHMS OF NUMBERS

No. 160—Log. 204   No. 179—Log. 255

N.	0	1	2	3	4	5	6	7	8	9	Diff.
160	204120	4391	4663	4934	5204	5475	5746	6016	6286	6556	271
161	6826	7096	7365	7634	7904	8173	8441	8710	8979	9247	269
162	9515	9783	*0051	*0319	*0586	*0853	*1121	*1388	*1654	*1921	267
163	212188	2454	2720	2986	3252	3518	3783	4049	4314	4579	266
164	4844	5109	5373	5638	5902	6166	6430	6694	6957	7221	264
165	217484	7747	8010	8273	8536	8798	9060	9323	9585	9846	262
166	220108	0370	0631	0892	1153	1414	1675	1936	2196	2456	261
167	2716	2976	3236	3496	3755	4015	4274	4533	4792	5051	259
168	5309	5568	5826	6084	6342	6600	6858	7115	7372	7630	258
169	7887	8144	8400	8657	8913	9170	9426	9682	9938	*0193	256
170	230449	0704	0960	1215	1470	1724	1979	2234	2488	2742	255
171	2996	3250	3504	3757	4011	4264	4517	4770	5023	5276	253
172	5528	5781	6033	6285	6537	6789	7041	7292	7544	7795	252
173	8046	8297	8548	8799	9049	9299	9550	9800	*0050	*0300	250
174	240549	0799	1048	1297	1546	1795	2044	2293	2541	2790	249
175	243038	3286	3534	3782	4030	4277	4525	4772	5019	5266	248
176	5513	5759	6006	6252	6499	6745	6991	7237	7482	7728	246
177	7973	8219	8464	8709	8954	9198	9443	9687	9932	*0176	245
178	250420	0664	0908	1151	1395	1638	1881	2125	2368	2610	243
179	2853	3096	3338	3580	3822	4064	4306	4548	4790	5031	242

PROPORTIONAL PARTS

Diff.	1	2	3	4	5	6	7	8	9	Diff.
272	27	54	82	109	136	163	190	218	245	272
271	27	54	81	108	136	163	190	217	244	271
270	27	54	81	108	135	162	189	216	243	270
269	27	54	81	108	135	161	188	215	242	269
268	27	54	80	107	134	161	188	214	241	268
267	27	53	80	107	134	160	187	214	240	267
266	27	53	80	106	133	160	186	213	239	266
265	27	53	80	106	133	159	186	212	239	265
264	26	53	79	106	132	158	185	211	238	264
263	26	53	79	105	132	158	184	210	237	263
262	26	52	79	105	131	157	183	210	236	262
261	26	52	78	104	131	157	183	209	235	261
260	26	52	78	104	130	156	182	208	234	260
259	26	52	78	104	130	155	181	207	233	259
258	26	52	77	103	129	155	181	206	232	258
257	26	51	77	103	129	154	180	206	231	257
256	26	51	77	102	128	154	179	205	230	256
255	26	51	77	102	128	153	179	204	230	255
254	25	51	76	102	127	152	178	203	229	254
253	25	51	76	101	127	152	177	202	228	253
252	25	50	76	101	126	151	176	202	227	252
251	25	50	75	100	126	151	176	201	226	251
250	25	50	75	100	125	150	175	200	225	250
249	25	50	75	100	125	149	174	199	224	249
248	25	50	74	99	124	149	174	198	223	248
247	25	49	74	99	124	148	173	198	222	247
246	25	49	74	98	123	148	172	197	221	246
245	25	49	74	98	123	147	172	196	221	245
244	24	49	73	98	122	146	171	195	220	244
243	24	49	73	97	122	146	170	194	219	243
242	24	48	73	97	121	145	169	194	218	242
241	24	48	72	96	121	145	169	193	217	241
240	24	48	72	96	120	144	168	192	216	240

TABLE VIII. LOGARITHMS OF NUMBERS

No. 180—Log. 255   No. 204—Log. 311

N.	0	1	2	3	4	5	6	7	8	9	Diff.
180	255273	5514	5755	5996	6237	6477	6718	6958	7198	7439	241
181	7679	7918	8158	8398	8637	8877	9116	9355	9594	9833	239
182	260071	0310	0548	0787	1025	1263	1501	1730	1976	2214	238
183	2451	2688	2925	3162	3399	3636	3873	4109	4346	4582	237
184	4818	5054	5290	5525	5761	5996	6232	6467	6702	6937	235
185	267172	7406	7641	7875	8110	8344	8578	8812	9046	9279	234
186	9513	9746	9980	*0213	*0446	*0679	*0912	*1144	*1377	*1609	233
187	271842	2074	2306	2538	2770	3001	3233	3464	3696	3927	232
188	4158	4389	4620	4850	5081	5311	5542	5772	6002	6232	230
189	6462	6692	6921	7151	7380	7609	7838	8067	8296	8525	229
190	278754	8982	9211	9439	9667	9895	*0123	*0351	*0578	*0806	228
191	281033	1261	1488	1715	1942	2169	2396	2622	2849	3075	227
192	3301	3527	3753	3979	4205	4431	4656	4882	5107	5332	226
193	5557	5782	6007	6232	6456	6681	6905	7130	7354	7578	225
194	7802	8026	8249	8473	8696	8920	9143	9366	9589	9812	223
195	290035	0257	0480	0702	0925	1147	1369	1591	1813	2034	222
196	2256	2478	2699	2920	3141	3363	3584	3804	4025	4246	221
197	4466	4687	4907	5127	5347	5567	5787	6007	6226	6446	220
198	6665	6884	7104	7323	7542	7761	7979	8198	8416	8635	219
199	8853	9071	9289	9507	9725	9943	*0161	*0378	*0595	*0813	218
200	301030	1247	1464	1681	1898	2114	2331	2547	2764	2980	217
201	3196	3412	3628	3844	4059	4275	4491	4706	4921	5136	216
202	5351	5566	5781	5996	6211	6425	6639	6854	7068	7282	215
203	7496	7710	7924	8137	8351	8564	8778	8991	9204	9417	213
204	9630	9843	*0056	*0268	*0481	*0693	*0906	*1118	*1330	*1542	212

PROPORTIONAL PARTS

Diff.	1	2	3	4	5	6	7	8	9	Diff.
239	24	48	72	96	120	143	167	191	215	239
238	24	48	71	95	119	143	167	190	214	238
237	24	47	71	95	119	142	166	190	213	237
236	24	47	71	94	118	142	165	189	212	236
235	24	47	71	94	118	141	165	188	212	235
234	23	47	70	94	117	140	164	187	211	234
233	23	47	70	93	117	140	163	186	210	233
232	23	46	70	93	116	139	162	186	209	232
231	23	46	69	92	116	139	162	185	208	231
230	23	46	69	92	115	138	161	184	207	230
229	23	46	69	92	115	137	160	183	206	229
228	23	46	68	91	114	137	160	182	205	228
227	23	45	68	91	114	136	159	182	204	227
226	23	45	68	90	113	136	158	181	203	226
225	23	45	68	90	113	135	158	180	203	225
224	22	45	67	90	112	134	157	179	202	224
223	22	45	67	89	112	134	156	178	201	223
222	22	44	67	89	111	133	155	178	200	222
221	22	44	66	88	111	133	155	177	199	221
220	22	44	66	88	110	132	154	176	198	220
219	22	44	66	88	110	131	153	175	197	219
218	22	44	65	87	109	131	153	174	196	218
217	22	43	65	87	109	130	152	174	195	217
216	22	43	65	86	108	130	151	173	194	216
215	22	43	65	86	108	129	151	172	194	215
214	21	43	64	86	107	128	150	171	193	214
213	21	43	64	85	107	128	149	170	192	213
212	21	42	64	85	106	127	148	170	191	212

TABLE VIII. LOGARITHMS OF NUMBERS
No. 205—Log. 311   No. 234—Log. 370

N.	0	1	2	3	· 4	5	6	7	8	9	Diff.
205	311754	1966	2177	2389	2600	2812	3023	3234	3445	3656	211
206	3867	4078	4289	4499	4710	4920	5130	5340	5551	5760	210
207	5970	6180	6390	6599	6809	7018	7227	7436	7646	7854	209
208	8063	8272	8481	8689	8898	9106	9314	9522	9730	9938	208
209	320146	0354	0562	0769	0977	1184	1391	1598	1805	2012	207
210	322219	2426	2633	2839	3046	3252	3458	3665	3871	4077	206
211	4282	4488	4694	4899	5105	5310	5516	5721	5926	6131	205
212	6336	6541	6745	6950	7155	7359	7563	7767	7972	8176	204
213	8380	8583	8787	8991	9194	9398	9601	9805	*0008	*0211	203
214	330414	0617	0819	1022	1225	1427	1630	1832	2034	2236	202
215	332138	2610	2842	3044	3246	3447	3649	3850	4051	4253	202
216	4454	4655	4856	5057	5257	5458	5658	5859	6059	6260	201
217	6460	6660	6860	7060	7260	7459	7659	7858	8058	8257	200
218	8456	8656	8855	9054	9253	9451	9650	9849	*0047	*0246	199
219	340444	0642	0841	1039	1237	1435	1632	1830	2028	2225	198
220	342423	2620	2817	3014	3212	3409	3606	3802	3999	4196	197
221	4392	4589	4785	4981	5178	5374	5570	5766	5962	6157	196
222	6353	6549	6744	6939	7135	7330	7525	7720	7915	8110	195
223	8305	8500	8694	8889	9083	9278	9472	9666	9860	*0054	194
224	350248	0442	0636	0829	1023	1216	1410	1603	1796	1989	193
225	352183	2375	2568	2761	2954	3147	3339	3532	3724	3916	193
226	4108	4301	4493	4685	4876	5068	5260	5452	5643	5834	192
227	6026	6217	6408	6599	6790	6981	7172	7363	7554	7744	191
228	7935	8125	8316	8506	8696	8886	9076	9266	9456	9646	190
229	9835	*0025	*0215	*0404	*0593	*0783	*0972	*1161	*1350	*1539	189
230	361728	1917	2105	2294	2482	2671	2859	3048	3236	3424	188
231	3612	3800	3988	4176	4363	4551	4739	4926	5113	5301	188
232	5488	5675	5862	6049	6236	6423	6610	6796	6983	7169	187
233	7356	7542	7729	7915	8101	8287	8473	8659	8845	9030	186
234	9216	9401	9587	9772	9958	*0143	*0328	*0513	*0698	*0883	185

PROPORTIONAL PARTS

Diff.	1	2	3	4	5	6	7	8	9	Diff.
212	21	42	64	85	106	127	148	170	191	212
211	21	42	63	84	106	127	148	169	190	211
210	21	42	63	84	105	126	147	168	189	210
209	21	42	63	84	105	125	146	167	188	209
208	21	42	62	83	104	125	146	166	187	208
207	21	41	62	83	104	124	145	166	186	207
206	21	41	62	82	103	124	144	165	185	206
205	21	41	62	82	103	123	144	164	185	205
204	20	41	61	82	102	122	143	163	184	204
203	20	41	61	81	102	122	142	162	183	203
202	20	40	61	81	101	121	141	162	182	202
201	20	40	60	80	101	121	141	161	181	201
200	20	40	60	80	100	120	140	160	180	200
199	20	40	60	80	100	119	139	159	179	199
198	20	40	59	79	99	119	139	158	178	198
197	20	39	59	79	99	118	138	158	177	197
196	20	39	59	78	98	118	137	157	176	196
195	20	39	59	78	98	117	137	156	176	195
194	19	39	58	78	97	116	136	155	175	194
193	19	39	58	77	97	116	135	154	174	193
192	19	38	58	77	96	115	134	154	173	192
191	19	38	57	76	96	115	134	153	172	191
190	19	38	57	76	95	114	133	152	171	190
189	19	38	57	76	95	113	132	151	170	189
188	19	38	56	75	94	113	132	150	169	188

TABLE VIII.   LOGARITHMS OF NUMBERS

No. 235—Log. 371   No. 264—Log. 423

N.	0	1	2	3	4	5	6	7	8	9	Diff.
235	371068	1253	1437	1622	1806	1991	2175	2360	2544	2728	184
236	2912	3096	3280	3464	3647	3831	4015	4198	4382	4565	184
237	4748	4932	5115	5298	5481	5664	5846	6029	6212	6394	183
238	6577	6759	6942	7124	7306	7488	7670	7852	8034	8216	182
239	8398	8580	8761	8943	9124	9306	9487	9668	9849	*0030	181
240	380211	0392	0573	0754	0934	1115	1296	1476	1656	1837	181
241	2017	2197	2377	2557	2737	2917	3097	3277	3456	3636	180
242	3815	3995	4174	4353	4533	4712	4891	5070	5249	5428	179
243	5606	5785	5964	6142	6321	6499	6677	6856	7034	7212	178
244	7390	7568	7746	7923	8101	8279	8456	8634	8811	8989	178
245	389166	9343	9520	9698	9875	*0051	*0228	*0405	*0582	*0759	177
246	390935	1112	1288	1464	1641	1817	1993	2169	2345	2521	176
247	2697	2873	3048	3224	3400	3575	3751	3926	4101	4277	176
248	4452	4627	4802	4977	5152	5326	5501	5676	5850	6025	175
249	6199	6374	6548	6722	6896	7071	7245	7419	7592	7766	174
250	397940	8114	8287	8461	8634	8808	8981	9154	9328	9501	173
251	9674	9847	*0020	*0192	*0365	*0538	*0711	*0883	*1056	*1228	173
252	401401	1573	1745	1917	2089	2261	2433	2605	2777	2949	172
253	3121	3292	3464	3635	3807	3978	4149	4320	4492	4663	171
254	4834	5005	5176	5346	5517	5688	5858	6029	6199	6370	171
255	406540	6710	6881	7051	7221	7391	7561	7731	7901	8070	170
256	8240	8410	8579	8749	8918	9087	9257	9426	9595	9764	169
257	9933	*0102	*0271	*0440	*0609	*0777	*0946	*1114	*1283	*1451	169
258	411620	1788	1956	2124	2293	2461	2629	2796	2964	3132	168
259	3300	3467	3635	3803	3970	4137	4305	4472	4639	4806	167
260	414973	5140	5307	5474	5641	5808	5974	6141	6308	6474	167
261	6641	6807	6973	7139	7306	7472	7638	7804	7970	8135	166
262	8301	8467	8633	8798	8964	9129	9295	9460	9625	9791	165
263	9956	*0121	*0286	*0451	*0616	*0781	*0945	*1110	*1275	*1439	165
264	421604	1768	1933	2097	2261	2426	2590	2754	2918	3082	164

PROPORTIONAL PARTS

Diff.	1	2	3	4	5	6	7	8	9	Diff.
187	19	37	56	75	94	112	131	150	168	187
186	19	37	56	74	93	112	130	149	167	186
185	19	37	56	74	93	111	130	148	167	185
184	18	37	55	74	92	110	129	147	166	184
183	18	37	55	73	92	110	128	146	165	183
182	18	36	55	73	91	109	127	146	164	182
181	18	36	54	72	91	109	127	145	163	181
180	18	36	54	72	90	108	126	144	162	180
179	18	36	54	72	90	107	125	143	161	179
178	18	36	53	71	89	107	125	142	160	178
177	18	35	53	71	89	106	124	142	159	177
176	18	35	53	70	88	106	123	141	158	176
175	18	35	53	70	88	105	123	140	158	175
174	17	35	52	70	87	104	122	139	157	174
173	17	35	52	69	87	104	121	138	156	173
172	17	34	52	69	86	103	120	138	155	172
171	17	34	51	68	86	103	120	137	154	171
170	17	34	51	68	85	102	119	136	153	170
169	17	34	51	68	85	101	118	135	152	169
168	17	34	50	67	84	101	118	134	151	168
167	17	33	50	67	84	100	117	134	150	167
166	17	33	50	66	83	100	116	133	149	166
165	17	33	50	66	83	99	116	132	149	165
164	16	33	49	66	82	98	115	131	148	164

TABLE VIII. LOGARITHMS OF NUMBERS

No. 265—Log. 423   No. 299—Log. 476

N.	0	1	2	3	4	5	6	7	8	9	Diff.
265	423246	3410	3574	3737	3901	4065	4228	4392	4555	4718	164
266	4882	5045	5208	5371	5534	5697	5860	6023	6186	6349	163
267	6511	6674	6836	6999	7161	7324	7486	7648	7811	7973	162
268	8135	8297	8459	8621	8783	8944	9106	9268	9429	9591	162
269	9752	9914	*0075	*0236	*0398	*0559	*0720	*0881	*1042	*1203	161
270	431364	1525	1685	1846	2007	2167	2328	2488	2649	2809	161
271	2969	3130	3290	3450	3610	3770	3930	4090	4249	4409	160
272	4569	4729	4888	5048	5207	5367	5526	5685	5844	6004	159
273	6163	6322	6481	6640	6799	6957	7116	7275	7433	7592	159
274	7751	7909	8067	8226	8384	8542	8701	8859	9017	9175	158
275	439333	9491	9648	9806	9964	*0122	*0279	*0437	*0594	*0752	158
276	440909	1066	1224	1381	1538	1695	1852	2009	2166	2323	157
277	2480	2637	2793	2950	3106	3263	3419	3576	3732	3889	157
278	4045	4201	4357	4513	4669	4825	4981	5137	5293	5449	156
279	5604	5760	5915	6071	6226	6382	6537	6692	6848	7003	156
280	447158	7313	7468	7623	7778	7933	8088	8242	8397	8552	155
281	8706	8861	9015	9170	9324	9478	9633	9787	9941	*0095	154
282	450249	0403	0557	0711	0865	1018	1172	1326	1479	1633	154
283	1786	1940	2093	2247	2400	2553	2706	2859	3012	3165	153
284	3318	3471	3624	3777	3930	4082	4235	4387	4540	4692	153
285	454845	4997	5150	5302	5454	5606	5758	5910	6062	6214	152
286	6366	6518	6670	6821	6973	7125	7276	7428	7579	7731	152
287	7882	8033	8184	8336	8487	8638	8789	8940	9091	9242	151
288	9392	9543	9694	9845	9995	*0146	*0296	*0447	*0597	*0748	151
289	460898	1048	1198	1348	1499	1649	1799	1948	2098	2248	150
290	462398	2548	2697	2847	2997	3146	3296	3445	3594	3744	150
291	3893	4042	4191	4340	4490	4639	4788	4930	5085	5234	149
292	5383	5532	5680	5829	5977	6126	6274	6423	6571	6719	149
293	6868	7016	7164	7312	7460	7608	7756	7904	8052	8200	148
294	8347	8495	8643	8790	8938	9085	9233	9380	9527	9675	148
295	469822	9969	*0116	*0263	*0410	*0557	*0704	*0851	*0998	*1145	147
296	471292	1438	1585	1732	1878	2025	2171	2318	2464	2610	146
297	2756	2903	3049	3195	3341	3487	3633	3779	3925	4071	146
298	4216	4362	4508	4653	4799	4944	5090	5235	5381	5526	146
299	5671	5816	5962	6107	6252	6397	6542	6687	6832	6976	145

PROPORTIONAL PARTS

Diff.	1	2	3	4	5	6	7	8	9	Diff.
164	16	33	49	66	82	98	115	131	148	164
163	16	33	49	65	82	98	114	130	147	163
162	16	32	49	65	81	97	113	130	146	162
161	16	32	48	64	81	97	113	129	145	161
160	16	32	48	64	80	96	112	128	144	160
159	16	32	48	64	80	95	111	127	143	159
158	16	32	47	63	79	95	111	126	142	158
157	16	31	47	63	79	94	110	126	141	157
156	16	31	47	62	78	94	109	125	140	156
155	16	31	47	62	78	93	109	124	140	155
154	15	31	46	62	77	92	108	123	139	154
153	15	31	46	61	77	92	107	122	138	153
152	15	30	46	61	76	91	106	122	137	152
151	15	30	45	60	76	91	106	121	136	151
150	15	30	45	60	75	90	105	120	135	150
149	15	30	45	60	75	89	104	119	134	149
148	15	30	44	59	74	89	104	118	133	148
147	15	29	44	59	74	88	103	118	132	147
146	15	29	44	58	73	88	102	117	131	146
145	15	29	44	58	73	87	102	116	131	145
144	14	29	43	58	72	86	101	115	130	144
143	14	29	43	57	72	86	100	114	129	143

TABLE VIII.   LOGARITHMS OF NUMBERS

No. 300—Log. 477   No. 339—Log. 531

N.	0	1	2	3	4	5	6	7	8	9	Diff.
300	477121	7266	7411	7555	7700	7844	7989	8133	8278	8422	145
301	8566	8711	8855	8999	9143	9287	9431	9575	9719	9863	144
302	480007	0151	0294	0438	0582	0725	0869	1012	1156	1299	144
303	1443	1586	1729	1872	2016	2159	2302	2445	2588	2731	143
304	2874	3016	3159	3302	3445	3587	3730	3872	4015	4157	143
305	484300	4442	4585	4727	4869	5011	5153	5295	5437	5579	142
306	5721	5863	6005	6147	6289	6430	6572	6714	6855	6997	142
307	7138	7280	7421	7563	7704	7845	7986	8127	8269	8410	141
308	8551	8692	8833	8974	9114	9255	9396	9537	9677	9818	141
309	9958	*0099	*0239	*0380	*0520	*0661	*0801	*0941	*1081	*1222	140
310	491362	1502	1642	1782	1922	2062	2201	2341	2481	2621	140
311	2760	2900	3040	3179	3319	3458	3597	3737	3876	4015	139
312	4155	4294	4433	4572	4711	4850	4989	5128	5267	5406	139
313	5544	5683	5822	5960	6099	6238	6376	6515	6653	6791	139
314	6930	7068	7206	7344	7483	7621	7759	7897	8035	8173	138
315	498311	8448	8556	8724	8862	8999	9137	9275	9412	9550	138
316	9687	9824	9962	*0099	*0236	*0374	*0511	*0648	*0785	*0922	137
317	501059	1196	1333	1470	1607	1744	1880	2017	2154	2291	137
318	2427	2564	2700	2837	2973	3109	3246	3382	3518	3655	136
319	3791	3927	4063	4199	4335	4471	4607	4743	4878	5014	136
320	505150	5286	5421	5557	5693	5828	5964	6099	6234	6370	136
321	6505	6640	6776	6911	7046	7181	7316	7451	7586	7721	135
322	7856	7991	8126	8260	8395	8530	8664	8799	8934	9068	135
323	9203	9337	9471	9606	9740	9874	*0009	*0143	*0277	*0411	134
324	510545	0679	0813	0947	1081	1215	1349	1482	1616	1750	134
325	511883	2017	2151	2284	2418	2551	2684	2818	2951	3084	133
326	3218	3351	3484	3617	3750	3883	4016	4149	4282	4415	133
327	4548	4681	4813	4946	5079	5211	5344	5476	5609	5741	133
328	5874	6006	6139	6271	6403	6535	6668	6800	6932	7064	132
329	7196	7328	7460	7592	7724	7855	7987	8119	8251	8382	132
330	518514	8646	8777	8909	9040	9171	9303	9434	9566	9697	131
331	9828	9959	*0090	*0221	*0353	*0484	*0615	*0745	*0876	*1007	131
332	521138	1269	1400	1530	1661	1792	1922	2053	2183	2314	131
333	2444	2575	2705	2835	2966	3096	3226	3356	3486	3616	130
334	3746	3876	4006	4136	4266	4396	4526	4656	4785	4915	130
335	525045	5174	5304	5434	5563	5693	5822	5951	6081	6210	129
336	6339	6469	6598	6727	6856	6985	7114	7243	7372	7501	129
337	7630	7759	7888	8016	8145	8274	8402	8531	8660	8788	129
338	8917	9045	9174	9302	9430	9559	9687	9815	9943	*0072	128
339	530200	0328	0456	0584	0712	0840	0968	1096	1223	1351	128

PROPORTIONAL PARTS

Diff.	1	2	3	4	5	6	7	8	9	Diff.
142	14	28	43	57	71	85	99	114	128	142
141	14	28	42	56	71	85	99	113	127	141
140	14	28	42	56	70	84	98	112	126	140
139	14	28	42	56	70	83	97	111	125	139
138	14	28	41	55	69	83	97	110	124	138
137	14	27	41	55	69	82	96	110	123	137
136	14	27	41	54	68	82	95	109	122	136
135	14	27	41	54	68	81	95	108	122	135
134	13	27	40	54	67	80	94	107	121	134
133	13	27	40	53	67	80	93	106	120	133
132	13	26	40	53	66	79	92	106	119	132
131	13	26	39	52	66	79	92	105	118	131
130	13	26	39	52	65	78	91	104	117	130
129	13	26	39	52	65	77	90	103	116	129
128	13	26	38	51	64	77	90	102	115	128
127	13	25	38	51	64	76	89	102	114	127

TABLE VIII. LOGARITHMS OF NUMBERS
No. 340—Log. 531   No. 379—Log. 579

N.	0	1	2	3	4	5	6	7	8	9	Diff.
340	531479	1607	1734	1862	1990	2117	2245	2372	2500	2627	128
341	2754	2882	3009	3136	3264	3391	3518	3645	3772	3899	127
342	4026	4153	4280	4407	4534	4661	4787	4914	5041	5167	127
343	5294	5421	5547	5674	5800	5927	6053	6180	6306	6432	126
344	6558	6685	6811	6937	7063	7189	7315	7441	7567	7693	126
345	537819	7945	8071	8197	8322	8448	8574	8699	8825	8951	126
346	9076	9202	9327	9452	9578	9703	9829	9954	*0079	*0204	125
347	540329	0455	0580	0705	0830	0955	1080	1205	1330	1454	125
348	1579	1704	1829	1953	2078	2203	2327	2452	2576	2701	125
349	2825	2950	3074	3199	3323	3447	3571	3696	3820	3944	124
350	544068	4192	4316	4440	4564	4688	4812	4936	5060	5183	124
351	5307	5431	5555	5678	5802	5925	6049	6172	6296	6419	124
352	6543	6666	6789	6913	7036	7159	7282	7405	7529	7652	123
353	7775	7898	8021	8144	8267	8389	8512	8635	8758	8881	123
354	9003	9126	9249	9371	9494	9616	9739	9861	9984	*0106	123
355	550228	0351	0473	0595	0717	0840	0962	1084	1206	1328	122
356	1450	1572	1694	1816	1938	2060	2181	2303	2425	2547	122
357	2668	2790	2911	3033	3155	3276	3398	3519	3640	3762	121
358	3883	4004	4126	4247	4368	4489	4610	4731	4852	4973	121
359	5094	5215	5336	5457	5578	5699	5820	5940	6061	6182	121
360	556303	6423	6544	6664	6785	6905	7026	7146	7267	7387	120
361	7507	7627	7748	7868	7988	8108	8228	8349	8469	8589	120
362	8709	8829	8948	9068	9188	9308	9428	9548	9667	9787	120
363	9907	*0026	*0146	*0265	*0385	*0504	*0624	*0743	*0863	*0982	119
364	561101	1221	1340	1459	1578	1698	1817	1936	2055	2174	119
365	562293	2412	2531	2650	2769	2887	3006	3125	3244	3362	119
366	3481	3600	3718	3837	3955	4074	4192	4311	4429	4548	119
367	4666	4784	4903	5021	5139	5257	5376	5494	5612	5730	118
368	5848	5966	6084	6202	6320	6437	6555	6673	6791	6909	118
369	7026	7144	7262	7379	7497	7614	7732	7849	7967	8084	118
370	568202	8319	8436	8554	8671	8788	8905	9023	9140	9257	117
371	9374	9491	9608	9725	9842	9959	*0076	*0193	*0309	*0426	117
372	570543	0000	0776	0893	1010	1126	1243	1350	1476	1592	117
373	1709	1825	1942	2058	2174	2291	2407	2523	2639	2755	116
374	2872	2988	3104	3220	3336	3452	3568	3684	3800	3915	116
375	574031	4147	4263	4379	4494	4610	4726	4841	4957	5072	116
376	5188	5303	5419	5534	5650	5765	5880	5996	6111	6226	115
377	6341	6457	6572	6687	6802	6917	7032	7147	7262	7377	115
378	7492	7607	7722	7836	7951	8066	8181	8295	8410	8525	115
379	8639	8754	8868	8983	9097	9212	9326	9441	9555	9669	114

PROPORTIONAL PARTS

Diff.	1	2	3	4	5	6	7	8	9	Diff.
128	13	26	38	51	64	77	90	102	115	128
127	13	25	38	51	64	76	89	102	114	127
126	13	25	38	50	63	76	88	101	113	126
125	13	25	38	50	63	75	88	100	113	125
124	12	25	37	50	62	74	87	99	112	124
123	12	25	37	49	62	74	86	98	111	123
122	12	24	37	49	61	73	85	98	110	122
121	12	24	36	48	61	73	85	97	109	121
120	12	24	36	48	60	72	84	96	108	120
119	12	24	36	48	60	71	83	95	107	119
118	12	24	35	47	59	71	83	94	106	118
117	12	23	35	47	59	70	82	94	105	117
116	12	23	35	46	58	70	81	93	104	116

TABLE VIII. LOGARITHMS OF NUMBERS

No. 380—Log. 579   No. 419—Log. 623

N.	0	1	2	3	4	5	6	7	8	9	Diff.
380	579784	9898	*0012	*0126	*0241	*0355	*0469	*0583	*0697	*0811	114
381	580925	1039	1153	1267	1381	1495	1608	1722	1836	1950	114
382	2063	2177	2291	2404	2518	2631	2745	2858	2972	3085	114
383	3199	3312	3426	3539	3652	3765	3879	3992	4105	4218	113
384	4331	4444	4557	4670	4783	4896	5009	5122	5235	5348	113
385	585461	5574	5686	5799	5912	6024	6137	6250	6362	6475	113
386	6587	6700	6812	6925	7037	7149	7262	7374	7486	7599	112
387	7711	7823	7935	8047	8160	8272	8384	8496	8608	8720	112
388	8832	8944	9056	9167	9279	9391	9503	9615	9726	9838	112
389	9950	*0061	*0173	*0284	*0396	*0507	*0619	*0730	*0842	*0953	112
390	591065	1176	1287	1399	1510	1621	1732	1843	1955	2066	111
391	2177	2288	2399	2510	2621	2732	2843	2954	3064	3175	111
392	3286	3397	3508	3618	3729	3840	3950	4061	4171	4282	111
393	4393	4503	4614	4724	4834	4945	5055	5165	5276	5386	110
394	5496	5606	5717	5827	5937	6047	6157	6267	6377	6487	110
395	596597	6707	6817	6927	7037	7146	7256	7366	7476	7586	110
396	7695	7805	7914	8024	8134	8243	8353	8462	8572	8681	110
397	8791	8900	9009	9119	9228	9337	9446	9556	9665	9774	109
398	9883	9992	*0101	*0210	*0319	*0428	*0537	*0646	*0755	*0864	109
399	600973	1082	1191	1299	1408	1517	1625	1734	1843	1951	109
400	602060	2169	2277	2386	2494	2603	2711	2819	2928	3036	108
401	3144	3253	3361	3469	3577	3686	3794	3902	4010	4118	108
402	4226	4334	4442	4550	4658	4766	4874	4982	5089	5197	108
403	5305	5413	5521	5628	5736	5844	5951	6059	6166	6274	108
404	6381	6489	6596	6704	6811	6919	7026	7133	7241	7348	107
405	607455	7562	7669	7777	7884	7991	8098	8205	8312	8419	107
406	8526	8633	8740	8847	8954	9061	9167	9274	9381	9488	107
407	9594	9701	9808	9914	*0021	*0128	*0234	*0341	*0447	*0554	107
408	610660	0767	0873	0979	1086	1192	1298	1405	1511	1617	106
409	1723	1829	1936	2042	2148	2254	2360	2466	2572	2678	106
410	612784	2890	2996	3102	3207	3313	3419	3525	3630	3736	106
411	3842	3947	4053	4159	4264	4370	4475	4581	4686	4792	106
412	4897	5003	5108	5213	5319	5424	5529	5634	5740	5845	105
413	5950	6055	6160	6265	6370	6476	6581	6686	6790	6895	105
414	7000	7105	7210	7315	7420	7525	7629	7734	7839	7943	105
415	618048	8153	8257	8362	8466	8571	8676	8780	8884	8989	105
416	9093	9198	9302	9406	9511	9615	9719	9824	9928	*0032	104
417	620136	0240	0344	0448	0552	0656	0760	0864	0968	1072	104
418	1176	1280	1384	1488	1592	1695	1799	1903	2007	2110	104
419	2214	2318	2421	2525	2628	2732	2835	2939	3042	3146	104

PROPORTIONAL PARTS

Diff.	1	2	3	4	5	6	7	8	9	Diff.
115	12	23	35	46	58	69	81	92	104	115
114	11	23	34	46	57	68	80	91	103	114
113	11	23	34	45	57	68	79	90	102	113
112	11	22	34	45	56	67	78	90	101	112
111	11	22	33	44	56	67	78	89	100	111
110	11	22	33	44	55	66	77	88	99	110
109	11	22	33	44	55	65	76	87	98	109
108	11	22	32	43	54	65	76	86	97	108
107	11	21	32	43	54	64	75	86	96	107
106	11	21	32	42	53	64	74	85	95	106
105	11	21	32	42	53	63	74	84	95	105
104	10	21	31	42	52	62	73	83	94	104
103	10	21	31	41	52	62	72	82	93	103

TABLE VIII. LOGARITHMS OF NUMBERS

No. 420—Log. 623   No. 464—Log. 667

N.	0	1	2	3	4	5	6	7	8	9	Diff.
420	623249	3353	3456	3559	3663	3766	3869	3973	4076	4179	103
421	4282	4385	4488	4591	4695	4798	4901	5004	5107	5210	103
422	5312	5415	5518	5621	5724	5827	5929	6032	6135	6238	103
423	6340	6443	6546	6648	6751	6853	6956	7058	7161	7263	103
424	7366	7468	7571	7673	7775	7878	7980	8082	8185	8287	102
425	628389	8491	8593	8695	8797	8900	9002	9104	9206	9308	102
426	9410	9512	9613	9715	9817	9919	*0021	*0123	*0224	*0326	102
427	630428	0530	0631	0733	0835	0936	1038	1139	1241	1342	102
428	1444	1545	1647	1748	1849	1951	2052	2153	2255	2356	101
429	2457	2559	2660	2761	2862	2963	3064	3165	3266	3367	101
430	633468	3569	3670	3771	3872	3973	4074	4175	4276	4376	101
431	4477	4578	4679	4779	4880	4981	5081	5182	5283	5383	101
432	5484	5584	5685	5785	5886	5986	6087	6187	6287	6388	100
433	6488	6588	6688	6789	6889	6989	7089	7189	7290	7390	100
434	7490	7590	7690	7790	7890	7990	8090	8190	8290	8389	100
435	638489	8589	8689	8789	8888	8988	9088	9188	9287	9387	100
436	9486	9586	9686	9785	9885	9984	*0084	*0183	*0283	*0382	99
437	640481	0581	0680	0779	0879	0978	1077	1177	1276	1375	99
438	1474	1573	1672	1771	1871	1970	2069	2168	2267	2366	99
439	2465	2563	2662	2761	2860	2959	3058	3156	3255	3354	99
440	643453	3551	3650	3749	3847	3946	4044	4143	4242	4340	98
441	4439	4537	4636	4734	4832	4931	5029	5127	5226	5324	98
442	5422	5521	5619	5717	5815	5913	6011	6110	6208	6306	98
443	6404	6502	6600	6698	6796	6894	6992	7089	7187	7285	98
444	7383	7481	7579	7676	7774	7872	7969	8067	8165	8262	98
445	648360	8458	8555	8653	8750	8848	8945	9043	9140	9237	97
446	9335	9432	9530	9627	9724	9821	9919	*0016	*0113	*0210	97
447	650308	0405	0502	0599	0696	0793	0890	0987	1084	1181	97
448	1278	1375	1472	1569	1666	1762	1859	1956	2053	2150	97
449	2246	2343	2440	2536	2633	2730	2826	2923	3019	3116	97
450	653213	3309	3405	3502	3598	3695	3791	3888	3984	4080	96
451	4177	4273	4369	4465	4562	4658	4754	4850	4946	5042	96
452	5138	5235	5331	5427	5523	5619	5715	5810	5906	6002	96
453	6098	6194	6290	6386	6482	6577	6673	6769	6864	6960	96
454	7056	7152	7247	7343	7438	7534	7629	7725	7820	7916	96
455	658011	8107	8202	8298	8393	8488	8584	8679	8774	8870	95
456	8965	9060	9155	9250	9346	9441	9536	9631	9726	9821	95
457	9916	*0011	*0106	*0201	*0296	*0391	*0486	*0581	*0676	*0771	95
458	660865	0960	1055	1150	1245	1339	1434	1529	1623	1718	95
459	1813	1907	2002	2096	2191	2286	2380	2475	2569	2663	95
460	662758	2852	2947	3041	3135	3230	3324	3418	3512	3607	94
461	3701	3795	3889	3983	4078	4172	4266	4360	4454	4548	94
462	4642	4736	4830	4924	5018	5112	5206	5299	5393	5487	94
463	5581	5675	5769	5862	5956	6050	6143	6237	6331	6424	94
464	6518	6612	6705	6799	6892	6986	7079	7173	7266	7360	94

PROPORTIONAL PARTS

Diff.	1	2	3	4	5	6	7	8	9	Diff.
104	10	21	31	42	52	62	73	83	94	104
103	10	21	31	41	52	62	72	82	93	103
102	10	20	31	41	51	61	71	82	92	102
101	10	20	30	40	51	61	71	81	91	101
100	10	20	30	40	50	60	70	80	90	100
99	10	20	30	40	50	59	69	79	89	99
98	10	20	29	39	49	59	69	78	88	98
97	10	19	29	39	49	58	68	78	87	97
96	10	19	29	38	48	58	67	77	86	96
95	10	19	29	38	48	57	67	76	86	95

TABLE VIII. LOGARITHMS OF NUMBERS
No. 465—Log. 667   No. 509—Log. 707

N.	0	1	2	3	4	5	6	7	8	9	Diff.
465	667453	7546	7640	7733	7826	7920	8013	8106	8199	8293	93
466	8386	8479	8572	8665	8759	8852	8945	9038	9131	9224	93
467	9317	9410	9503	9596	9689	9782	9875	9967	*0060	*0153	93
468	670246	0339	0431	0524	0617	0710	0802	0895	0988	1080	93
469	1173	1265	1358	1451	1543	1636	1728	1821	1913	2005	93
470	672098	2190	2283	2375	2467	2560	2652	2744	2836	2929	92
471	3021	3113	3205	3297	3390	3482	3574	3666	3758	3850	92
472	3942	4034	4126	4218	4310	4402	4494	4586	4677	4769	92
473	4861	4953	5045	5137	5228	5320	5412	5503	5595	5687	92
474	5778	5870	5962	6053	6145	6236	6328	6419	6511	6602	92
475	676694	6785	6876	6968	7059	7151	7242	7333	7424	7516	91
476	7607	7698	7789	7881	7972	8063	8154	8245	8336	8427	91
477	8518	8609	8700	8791	8882	8973	9064	9155	9246	9337	91
478	9428	9519	9610	9700	9791	9882	9973	*0063	*0154	*0245	91
479	680336	0426	0517	0607	0698	0789	0879	0970	1060	1151	91
480	681241	1332	1422	1513	1603	1693	1784	1874	1964	2055	90
481	2145	2235	2326	2416	2506	2596	2686	2777	2867	2957	90
482	3047	3137	3227	3317	3407	3497	3587	3677	3767	3857	90
483	3947	4037	4127	4217	4307	4396	4486	4576	4666	4756	90
484	4845	4935	5025	5114	5204	5294	5383	5473	5563	5652	90
485	685742	5831	5921	6010	6100	6189	6279	6368	6458	6547	89
486	6636	6726	6815	6904	6994	7083	7172	7261	7351	7440	89
487	7529	7618	7707	7796	7886	7975	8064	8153	8242	8331	89
488	8420	8509	8598	8687	8776	8865	8953	9042	9131	9220	89
489	9309	9398	9486	9575	9664	9753	9841	9930	*0019	*0107	89
490	690196	0285	0373	0462	0550	0639	0728	0816	0905	0993	89
491	1081	1170	1258	1347	1435	1524	1612	1700	1789	1877	88
492	1965	2053	2142	2230	2318	2406	2494	2583	2671	2759	88
493	2847	2935	3023	3111	3199	3287	3375	3463	3551	3639	88
494	3727	3815	3903	3991	4078	4166	4254	4342	4430	4517	88
495	694605	4693	4781	4868	4956	5044	5131	5219	5307	5394	88
496	5482	5569	5657	5744	5832	5919	6007	6094	6182	6269	87
497	6356	6444	6531	6618	6706	6793	6880	6968	7055	7142	87
498	7229	7317	7404	7491	7578	7665	7752	7839	7926	8014	87
499	8101	8188	8275	8362	8449	8535	8622	8709	8796	8883	87
500	698970	9057	9144	9231	9317	9404	9491	9578	9664	9751	87
501	9838	9924	*0011	*0098	*0184	*0271	*0358	*0444	*0531	*0617	87
502	700704	0790	0877	0963	1050	1136	1222	1309	1395	1482	86
503	1568	1654	1741	1827	1913	1999	2086	2172	2258	2344	86
504	2431	2517	2603	2689	2775	2861	2947	3033	3119	3205	86
505	703291	3377	3463	3549	3635	3721	3807	3893	3979	4065	86
506	4151	4236	4322	4408	4494	4579	4665	4751	4837	4922	86
507	5008	5094	5179	5265	5350	5436	5522	5607	5693	5778	86
508	5864	5949	6035	6120	6206	6291	6376	6462	6547	6632	85
509	6718	6803	6888	6974	7059	7144	7229	7315	7400	7485	85

PROPORTIONAL PARTS

Diff.	1	2	3	4	5	6	7	8	9	Diff.
94	9	19	28	38	47	56	66	75	85	94
93	9	19	28	37	47	56	65	74	84	93
92	9	18	28	37	46	55	64	74	83	92
91	9	18	27	36	46	55	64	73	82	91
90	9	18	27	36	45	54	63	72	81	90
89	9	18	27	36	45	53	62	71	80	89
88	9	18	26	35	44	53	62	70	79	88
87	9	17	26	35	44	52	61	70	78	87
86	9	17	26	34	43	52	60	69	77	86
85	9	17	26	34	43	51	60	68	77	85

TABLE VIII. LOGARITHMS OF NUMBERS

No. 510—Log. 707   No. 554—Log. 744

N.	0	1	2	3	4	5	6	7	8	9	Diff.
510	707570	7655	7740	7826	7911	7996	8081	8166	8251	8336	85
511	8421	8506	8591	8676	8761	8846	8931	9015	9100	9185	85
512	9270	9355	9440	9524	9609	9694	9779	9863	9948	*0033	85
513	710117	0202	0287	0371	0456	0540	0625	0710	0794	0879	85
514	0963	1048	1132	1217	1301	1385	1470	1554	1639	1723	84
515	711807	1892	1976	2060	2144	2229	2313	2397	2481	2566	84
516	2650	2734	2818	2902	2986	3070	3154	3238	3323	3407	84
517	3491	3575	3659	3742	3826	3910	3994	4078	4162	4246	84
518	4330	4414	4497	4581	4665	4749	4833	4916	5000	5084	84
519	5167	5251	5335	5418	5502	5586	5669	5753	5836	5920	84
520	716003	6087	6170	6254	6337	6421	6504	6588	6671	6754	83
521	6838	6921	7004	7088	7171	7254	7338	7421	7504	7587	83
522	7671	7754	7837	7920	8003	8086	8169	8253	8336	8419	83
523	8502	8585	8668	8751	8834	8917	9000	9083	9165	9248	83
524	9331	9414	9497	9580	9663	9745	9828	9911	9994	*0077	83
525	720159	0242	0325	0407	0490	0573	0655	0738	0821	0903	83
526	0986	1068	1151	1233	1316	1398	1481	1563	1646	1728	82
527	1811	1893	1975	2058	2140	2222	2305	2387	2469	2552	82
528	2634	2716	2798	2881	2963	3045	3127	3209	3291	3374	82
529	3456	3538	3620	3702	3784	3866	3948	4030	4112	4194	82
530	724276	4358	4440	4522	4604	4685	4767	4849	4931	5013	82
531	5095	5176	5258	5340	5422	5503	5585	5667	5748	5830	82
532	5912	5993	6075	6156	6238	6320	6401	6483	6564	6646	82
533	6727	6809	6890	6972	7053	7134	7216	7297	7379	7460	81
534	7541	7623	7704	7785	7866	7948	8029	8110	8191	8273	81
535	728354	8435	8516	8597	8678	8759	8841	8922	9003	9084	81
536	9165	9246	9327	9408	9489	9570	9651	9732	9813	9893	81
537	9974	*0055	*0136	*0217	*0298	*0378	*0459	*0540	*0621	*0702	81
538	730782	0863	0944	1024	1105	1186	1266	1347	1428	1508	81
539	1589	1669	1750	1830	1911	1991	2072	2152	2233	2313	81
540	732394	2474	2555	2635	2715	2796	2876	2956	3037	3117	80
541	3197	3278	3358	3438	3518	3598	3679	3759	3839	3919	80
542	3999	4079	4160	4240	4320	4400	4480	4560	4640	4720	80
543	4800	4880	4960	5040	5120	5200	5279	5359	5439	5519	80
544	5599	5679	5759	5838	5918	5998	6078	6157	6237	6317	80
545	736397	6476	6556	6635	6715	6795	6874	6954	7034	7113	80
546	7193	7272	7352	7431	7511	7590	7670	7749	7829	7908	79
547	7987	8067	8146	8225	8305	8384	8463	8543	8622	8701	79
548	8781	8860	8939	9018	9097	9177	9256	9335	9414	9493	79
549	9572	9651	9731	9810	9889	9968	*0047	*0126	*0205	*0284	79
550	740363	0442	0521	0600	0678	0757	0836	0915	0994	1073	79
551	1152	1230	1309	1388	1467	1546	1624	1703	1782	1860	79
552	1939	2018	2096	2175	2254	2332	2411	2489	2568	2647	79
553	2725	2804	2882	2961	3039	3118	3196	3275	3353	3431	78
554	3510	3588	3667	3745	3823	3902	3980	4058	4136	4215	78

PROPORTIONAL PARTS

Diff.	1	2	3	4	5	6	7	8	9	Diff.
86	9	17	26	34	43	52	60	69	77	86
85	9	17	26	34	43	51	60	68	77	85
84	8	17	25	34	42	50	59	67	76	84
83	8	17	25	33	42	50	58	66	75	83
82	8	16	25	33	41	49	57	66	74	82
81	8	16	24	32	41	49	57	65	73	81
80	8	16	24	32	40	48	56	64	72	80
79	8	16	24	32	40	47	55	63	71	79

TABLE VIII. LOGARITHMS OF NUMBERS
No. 555—Log. 744   No. 599—Log. 778

N.	0	1	2	3	4	5	6	7	8	9	Diff.
555	744293	4371	4449	4528	4606	4684	4762	4840	4919	4997	78
556	5075	5153	5231	5309	5387	5465	5543	5621	5699	5777	78
557	5855	5933	6011	6089	6167	6245	6323	6401	6479	6556	78
558	6634	6712	6790	6868	6945	7023	7101	7179	7256	7334	78
559	7412	7489	7567	7645	7722	7800	7878	7955	8033	8110	78
560	748188	8266	8343	8421	8498	8576	8653	8731	8808	8885	77
561	8963	9040	9118	9195	9272	9350	9427	9504	9582	9659	77
562	9736	9814	9891	9968	*0045	*0123	*0200	*0277	*0354	*0431	77
563	750508	0586	0663	0740	0817	0894	0971	1048	1125	1202	77
564	1279	1356	1433	1510	1587	1664	1741	1818	1895	1972	77
565	752048	2125	2202	2279	2356	2433	2509	2586	2663	2740	77
566	2816	2893	2970	3047	3123	3200	3277	3353	3430	3506	77
567	3583	3660	3736	3813	3889	3966	4042	4119	4195	4272	77
568	4348	4425	4501	4578	4654	4730	4807	4883	4960	5036	76
569	5112	5189	5265	5341	5417	5494	5570	5646	5722	5799	76
570	755875	5951	6027	6103	6180	6256	6332	6408	6484	6560	76
571	6636	6712	6788	6864	6940	7016	7092	7168	7244	7320	76
572	7396	7472	7548	7624	7700	7775	7851	7927	8003	8079	76
573	8155	8230	8306	8382	8458	8533	8609	8685	8761	8836	76
574	8912	8988	9063	9139	9214	9290	!9366	9441	9517	9592	76
575	759668	9743	9819	9894	9970	*0045	*0121	*0196	*0272	*0347	75
576	760422	0498	0573	0649	0724	0799	0875	0950	1025	1101	75
577	1176	1251	1326	1402	1477	1552	1627	1702	1778	1853	75
578	1928	2003	2078	2153	2228	2303	2378	2453	2529	2604	75
579	2679	2754	2829	2904	2978	3053	3128	3203	3278	3353	75
580	763428	3503	3578	3653	3727	3802	3877	3952	4027	4101	75
581	4176	4251	4326	4400	4475	4550	4624	4699	4774	4848	75
582	4923	4998	5072	5147	5221	5296	5370	5445	5520	5594	75
583	5669	5743	5818	5892	5966	6041	6115	6190	6264	6338	74
584	6413	6487	6562	6636	6710	6785	6859	6933	7007	7082	74
585	767156	7230	7304	7379	7453	7527	7601	7675	7749	7823	74
586	7898	7972	8046	8120	8194	8268	8342	8416	8490	8564	74
587	8638	8712	8786	8860	8934	9008	9082	9156	9230	9303	74
588	9377	9451	9525	9599	9673	9746	9820	9894	9968	*0042	74
589	770115	0189	0263	0336	0410	0484	0557	0631	0705	0778	74
590	770852	0926	0999	1073	1146	1220	1293	1367	1440	1514	74
591	1587	1661	1734	1808	1881	1955	2028	2102	2175	2248	73
592	2322	2395	2468	2542	2615	2688	2762	2835	2908	2981	73
593	3055	3128	3201	3274	3348	3421	3494	3567	3640	3713	73
594	3786	3860	3933	4006	4079	4152	4225	4298	4371	4444	73
595	774517	4590	4663	4736	4809	4882	4955	5028	5100	5173	73
596	5246	5319	5392	5465	5538	5610	5683	5756	5829	5902	73
597	5974	6047	6120	6193	6265	6338	6411	6483	6556	6629	73
598	6701	6774	6846	6919	6992	7064	7137	7209	7282	7354	73
599	7427	7499	7572	7644	7717	7789	7862	7934	8006	8079	72

PROPORTIONAL PARTS

Diff.	1	2	3	4	5	6	7	8	9	Diff.
78	8	16	23	31	39	47	55	62	70	78
77	8	15	23	31	39	46	54	62	69	77
76	8	15	23	30	38	46	53	61	68	76
75	8	15	23	30	38	45	53	60	68	75
74	7	15	22	30	37	44	52	59	67	74
73	7	15	22	29	37	44	51	58	66	73
72	7	14	22	29	36	43	50	58	65	72

TABLE VIII. LOGARITHMS OF NUMBERS
No. 600—Log. 778   No. 649—Log. 812

N.	0	1	2	3	4	5	6	7	8	9	Diff.
600	778151	8224	8296	8368	8441	8513	8585	8658	8730	8802	72
601	8874	8947	9019	9091	9163	9236	9308	9380	9452	9524	72
602	9596	9669	9741	9813	9885	9957	*0029	*0101	*0173	*0245	72
603	780317	0389	0461	0533	0605	0677	0749	0821	0893	0965	72
604	1037	1109	1181	1253	1324	1396	1468	1540	1612	1684	72
605	781755	1827	1899	1971	2042	2114	2186	2258	2329	2401	72
606	2473	2544	2616	2688	2759	2831	2902	2974	3046	3117	72
607	3189	3260	3332	3403	3475	3546	3618	3689	3761	3832	71
608	3904	3975	4046	4118	4189	4261	4332	4403	4475	4546	71
609	4617	4689	4760	4831	4902	4974	5045	5116	5187	5259	71
610	785330	5401	5472	5543	5615	5686	5757	5828	5899	5970	71
611	6041	6112	6183	6254	6325	6396	6467	6538	6609	6680	71
612	6751	6822	6893	6964	7035	7106	7177	7248	7319	7390	71
613	7460	7531	7602	7673	7744	7815	7885	7956	8027	8098	71
614	8168	8239	8310	8381	8451	8522	8593	8663	8734	8804	71
615	788875	8946	9016	9087	9157	9228	9299	9369	9440	9510	71
616	9581	9651	9722	9792	9863	9933	*0004	*0074	*0144	*0215	70
617	790285	0356	0426	0496	0567	0637	0707	0778	0848	0918	70
618	0988	1059	1129	1199	1269	1340	1410	1480	1550	1620	70
619	1691	1761	1831	1901	1971	2041	2111	2181	2252	2322	70
620	792392	2462	2532	2602	2672	2742	2812	2882	2952	3022	70
621	3092	3162	3231	3301	3371	3441	3511	3581	3651	3721	70
622	3790	3860	3930	4000	4070	4139	4209	4279	4349	4418	70
623	4488	4558	4627	4697	4767	4836	4906	4976	5045	5115	70
624	5185	5254	5324	5393	5463	5532	5602	5672	5741	5811	70
625	795880	5949	6019	6088	6158	6227	6297	6366	6436	6505	69
626	6574	6644	6713	6782	6852	6921	6990	7060	7129	7198	69
627	7268	7337	7406	7475	7545	7614	7683	7752	7821	7890	69
628	7960	8029	8098	8167	8236	8305	8374	8443	8513	8582	69
629	8651	8720	8789	8858	8927	8996	9065	9134	9203	9272	69
630	799341	9409	9478	9547	9616	9685	9754	9823	9892	9961	69
631	800029	0098	0167	0236	0305	0373	0442	0511	0580	0648	69
632	0717	0786	0854	0923	0992	1061	1129	1198	1266	1335	69
633	1404	1472	1541	1609	1678	1747	1815	1884	1952	2021	69
634	2089	2158	2226	2295	2363	2432	2500	2568	2637	2705	68
635	802774	2842	2910	2979	3047	3116	3184	3252	3321	3389	68
636	3457	3525	3594	3662	3730	3798	3867	3935	4003	4071	68
637	4139	4208	4276	4344	4412	4480	4548	4616	4685	4753	68
638	4821	4889	4957	5025	5093	5161	5229	5297	5365	5433	68
639	5501	5569	5637	5705	5773	5841	5908	5976	6044	6112	68
640	806180	6248	6316	6384	6451	6519	6587	6655	6723	6790	68
641	6858	6926	6994	7061	7129	7197	7264	7332	7400	7467	68
642	7535	7603	7670	7738	7806	7873	7941	8008	8076	8143	68
643	8211	8279	8346	8414	8481	8549	8616	8684	8751	8818	67
644	8886	8953	9021	9088	9156	9223	9290	9358	9425	9492	67
645	809560	9627	9694	9762	9829	9896	9964	*0031	*0098	*0165	67
646	810233	0300	0367	0434	0501	0569	0636	0703	0770	0837	67
647	0904	0971	1039	1106	1173	1240	1307	1374	1441	1508	67
648	1575	1642	1709	1776	1843	1910	1977	2044	2111	2178	67
649	2245	2312	2379	2445	2512	2579	2646	2713	2780	2847	67

PROPORTIONAL PARTS

Diff.	1	2	3	4	5	6	7	8	9	Diff.
73	7	15	22	29	37	44	51	58	66	73
72	7	14	22	29	36	43	50	58	65	72
71	7	14	21	28	36	43	50	57	64	71
70	7	14	21	28	35	42	49	56	63	70
69	7	14	21	28	35	41	48	55	62	69
68	7	14	20	27	34	41	48	54	61	68

TABLE VIII. LOGARITHMS OF NUMBERS

No. 650—Log. 812   No. 699—Log. 845

N.	0	1	2	3	4	5	6	7	8	9	Diff.
650	812913	2980	3047	3114	3181	3247	3314	3381	3448	3514	67
651	3581	3648	3714	3781	3848	3914	3981	4048	4114	4181	67
652	4248	4314	4381	4447	4514	4581	4647	4714	4780	4847	67
653	4913	4980	5046	5113	5179	5246	5312	5378	5445	5511	66
654	5578	5644	5711	5777	5843	5910	5976	6042	6109	6175	66
655	816241	6308	6374	6440	6506	6573	6639	6705	6771	6838	66
656	6904	6970	7036	7102	7169	7235	7301	7367	7433	7499	66
657	7565	7631	7698	7764	7830	7896	7962	8028	8094	8160	66
658	8226	8292	8358	8424	8490	8556	8622	8688	8754	8820	66
659	8885	8951	9017	9083	9149	9215	9281	9346	9412	9478	66
660	819544	9610	9676	9741	9807	9873	9939	*0004	*0070	*0136	66
661	820201	0267	0333	0399	0464	0530	0595	0661	0727	0792	66
662	0858	0924	0989	1055	1120	1186	1251	1317	1382	1448	66
663	1514	1579	1645	1710	1775	1841	1906	1972	2037	2103	65
664	2168	2233	2299	2364	2430	2495	2560	2626	2691	2756	65
665	822822	2887	2952	3018	3083	3148	3213	3279	3344	3409	65
666	3474	3539	3605	3670	3735	3800	3865	3930	3996	4061	65
667	4126	4191	4256	4321	4386	4451	4516	4581	4646	4711	65
668	4776	4841	4906	4971	5036	5101	5166	5231	5296	5361	65
669	5426	5491	5556	5621	5686	5751	5815	5880	5945	6010	65
670	826075	6140	6204	6269	6334	6399	6464	6528	6593	6658	65
671	6723	6787	6852	6917	6981	7046	7111	7175	7240	7305	65
672	7369	7434	7499	7563	7628	7692	7757	7821	7886	7951	65
673	8015	8080	8144	8209	8273	8338	8402	8467	8531	8595	64
674	8660	8724	8789	8853	8918	8982	9046	9111	9175	9239	64
675	829304	9368	9432	9497	9561	9625	9690	9754	9818	9882	64
676	9947	*0011	*0075	*0139	*0204	*0268	*0332	*0396	*0460	*0525	64
677	830589	0653	0717	0781	0845	0909	0973	1037	1102	1166	64
678	1230	1294	1358	1422	1486	1550	1614	1678	1742	1806	64
679	1870	1934	1998	2062	2126	2189	2253	2317	2381	2445	64
680	832509	2573	2637	2700	2764	2828	2892	2956	3020	3083	64
681	3147	3211	3275	3338	3402	3466	3530	3593	3657	3721	64
682	3784	3848	3912	3975	4039	4103	4166	4230	4294	4357	64
683	4421	4484	4548	4611	4675	4739	4802	4866	4929	4993	64
684	5056	5120	5183	5247	[5310	5373	5437	5500	5564	5627	63
685	835691	5754	5817	5881	5944	6007	6071	6134	6197	6261	63
686	6324	6387	6451	6514	6577	6641	6704	6767	6830	6894	63
687	6957	7020	7083	7146	7210	7273	7336	7399	7462	7525	63
688	7588	7652	7715	7778	7841	7904	7967	8030	8093	8156	63
689	8219	8282	8345	8408	8471	8534	8597	8660	8723	8786	63
690	838849	8912	8975	9038	9101	9164	9227	9289	9352	9415	63
691	9478	9541	9604	9667	9729	9792	9855	9918	9981	*0043	63
692	840106	0169	0232	0294	0357	0420	0482	0545	0608	0671	63
693	0733	0796	0859	0921	0984	1046	1109	1172	1234	1297	63
694	1359	1422	1485	1547	1610	1672	1735	1797	1860	1922	63
695	841985	2047	2110	2172	2235	2297	2360	2422	2484	2547	62
696	2609	2672	2734	2796	2859	2921	2983	3046	3108	3170	62
697	3233	3295	3357	3420	3482	3544	3606	3669	3731	3793	62
698	3855	3918	3980	4042	4104	4166	4229	4291	4353	4415	62
699	4477	4539	4601	4664	4726	4788	4850	4912	4974	5036	62

PROPORTIONAL PARTS

Diff.	1	2	3	4	5	6	7	8	9	Diff.
67	7	13	20	27	34	40	47	54	60	67
66	7	13	20	26	33	40	46	53	59	66
65	7	13	20	26	33	39	46	52	59	65
64	6	13	19	26	32	38	45	51	58	64
63	6	13	19	25	32	38	44	50	57	63
62	6	12	19	25	31	37	43	50	56	62

TABLE VIII.   LOGARITHMS OF NUMBERS

No. 700—Log. 845   No. 749—Log. 875

N.	0	1	2	3	4	5	6	7	8	9	Diff.
700	845098	5160	5222	5284	5346	5408	5470	5532	5504	5656	62
701	5718	5780	5842	5904	5966	6028	6090	6151	6213	6275	62
702	6337	6399	6461	6523	6585	6646	6708	6770	6832	6894	62
703	6955	7017	7079	7141	7202	7264	7326	7388	7449	7511	62
704	7573	7634	7696	7758	7819	7881	7943	8004	8066	8128	62
705	848189	8251	8312	8374	8435	8497	8559	8620	8682	8743	62
706	8805	8866	8928	8989	9051	9112	9174	9235	9297	9358	61
707	9419	9481	9542	9604	9665	9726	9788	9849	9911	9972	61
708	850033	0095	0156	0217	0279	0340	0401	0462	0524	0585	61
709	0646	0707	0769	0830	0891	0952	1014	1075	1136	1197	61
710	851258	1320	1381	1442	1503	1564	1625	1686	1747	1809	61
711	1870	1931	1992	2053	2114	2175	2236	2297	2358	2419	61
712	2480	2541	2602	2663	2724	2785	2846	2907	2968	3029	61
713	3090	3150	3211	3272	3333	3394	3455	3516	3577	3637	61
714	3698	3759	3820	3881	3941	4002	4063	4124	4185	4245	61
715	854306	4367	4428	4488	4549	4610	4670	4731	4792	4852	61
716	4913	4974	5034	5095	5156	5216	5277	5337	5398	5459	61
717	5519	5580	5640	5701	5761	5822	5882	5943	6003	6064	61
718	6124	6185	6245	6306	6366	6427	6487	6548	6608	6668	60
719	6729	6789	6850	6910	6970	7031	7091	7152	7212	7272	60
720	857332	7393	7453	7513	7574	7634	7694	7755	7815	7875	60
721	7935	7995	8056	8116	8176	8236	8297	8357	8417	8477	60
722	8537	8597	8657	8718	8778	8838	8898	8958	9018	9078	60
723	9138	9198	9258	9318	9379	9439	9499	9559	9619	9679	60
724	9739	9799	9859	9918	9978	*0038	*0098	*0158	*0218	*0278	60
725	860338	0398	0458	0518	0578	0637	0697	0757	0817	0877	60
726	0937	0996	1056	1116	1176	1236	1295	1355	1415	1475	60
727	1534	1594	1654	1714	1773	1833	1893	1952	2012	2072	60
728	2131	2191	2251	2310	2370	2430	2489	2549	2608	2668	60
729	2728	2787	2847	2906	2966	3025	3085	3144	3204	3263	60
730	863323	3382	3442	3501	3561	3620	3680	3739	3799	3858	59
731	3917	3977	4036	4096	4155	4214	4274	4333	4392	4452	59
732	4511	4570	4630	4689	4748	4808	4867	4926	4985	5045	59
733	5104	5163	5222	5282	5341	5400	5459	5519	5578	5637	59
734	5696	5755	5814	5874	5933	5992	6051	6110	6169	6228	59
735	866287	6346	6405	6465	6524	6583	6642	6701	6760	6819	59
736	6878	6937	6996	7055	7114	7173	7232	7291	7350	7409	59
737	7467	7526	7585	7644	7703	7762	7821	7880	7939	7998	59
738	8056	8115	8174	8233	8292	8350	8409	8468	8527	8586	59
739	8644	8703	8762	8821	8879	8938	8997	9056	9114	9173	59
740	869232	9290	9349	9408	9466	9525	9584	9642	9701	9760	59
741	9818	9877	9935	9994	*0053	*0111	*0170	*0228	*0287	*0345	59
742	870404	0462	0521	0579	0638	0696	0755	0813	0872	0930	58
743	0989	1047	1106	1164	1223	1281	1339	1398	1456	1515	58
744	1573	1631	1690	1748	1806	1865	1923	1981	2040	2098	58
745	872156	2215	2273	2331	2389	2448	2506	2564	2622	2681	58
746	2739	2797	2855	2913	2972	3030	3088	3146	3204	3262	58
747	3321	3379	3437	3495	3553	3611	3669	3727	3785	3844	58
748	3902	3960	4018	4076	4134	4192	4250	4308	4366	4424	58
749	4482	4540	4598	4656	4714	4772	4830	4888	4945	5003	58

PROPORTIONAL PARTS

Diff.	1	2	3	4	5	6	7	8	9	Diff.
62	6	12	19	25	31	37	43	50	56	62
61	6	12	18	24	31	37	43	49	55	61
60	6	12	18	24	30	36	42	48	54	60
59	6	12	18	24	30	35	41	47	53	59
58	6	12	17	23	29	35	41	46	52	58

TABLE VIII. LOGARITHMS OF NUMBERS

No. 750—Log. 875   No. 799—Log. 903

N.	0	1	2	3	4	5	6	7	8	9	Diff.
750	875061	5119	5177	5235	5293	5351	5409	5466	5524	5582	58
751	5640	5698	5756	5813	5871	5929	5987	6045	6102	6160	58
752	6218	6276	6333	6391	6449	6507	6564	6622	6680	6737	58
753	6795	6853	6910	6968	7026	7083	7141	7199	7256	7314	58
754	7371	7429	7487	7544	7602	7659	7717	7774	7832	7889	58
755	877947	8004	8062	8119	8177	8234	8292	8349	8407	8464	57
756	8522	8579	8637	8694	8752	8809	8866	8924	8981	9039	57
757	9096	9153	9211	9268	9325	9383	9440	9497	9555	9612	57
758	9669	9726	9784	9841	9898	9956	*0013	*0070	*0127	*0185	57
759	880242	0299	0356	0413	0471	0528	0585	0642	0699	0756	57
760	880814	0871	0928	0985	1042	1099	1156	1213	1271	1328	57
761	1385	1442	1499	1556	1613	1670	1727	1784	1841	1898	57
762	1955	2012	2069	2126	2183	2240	2297	2354	2411	2468	57
763	2525	2581	2638	2695	2752	2809	2866	2923	2980	3037	57
764	3093	3150	3207	3264	3321	3377	3434	3491	3548	3605	57
765	883661	3718	3775	3832	3888	3945	4002	4059	4115	4172	57
766	4229	4285	4342	4399	4455	4512	4569	4625	4682	4739	57
767	4795	4852	4909	4965	5022	5078	5135	5192	5248	5305	57
768	5361	5418	5474	5531	5587	5644	5700	5757	5813	5870	57
769	5926	5983	6039	6096	6152	6209	6265	6321	6378	6434	56
770	886491	6547	6604	6660	6716	6773	6829	6885	6942	6998	56
771	7054	7111	7167	7223	7280	7336	7392	7449	7505	7561	56
772	7617	7674	7730	7786	7842	7898	7955	8011	8067	8123	56
773	8179	8236	8292	8348	8404	8460	8516	8573	8629	8685	56
774	8741	8797	8853	8909	8965	9021	9077	9134	9190	9246	56
775	889302	9358	9414	9470	9526	9582	9638	9694	9750	9806	56
776	9862	9918	9974	*0030	*0086	*0141	*0197	*0253	*0309	*0365	56
777	890421	0477	0533	0589	0645	0700	0756	0812	0868	0924	56
778	0980	1035	1091	1147	1203	1259	1314	1370	1426	1482	56
779	1537	1593	1649	1705	1760	1816	1872	1928	1983	2039	56
780	892095	2150	2206	2262	2317	2373	2429	2484	2540	2595	56
781	2651	2707	2762	2818	2873	2929	2985	3040	3096	3151	56
782	3207	3262	3318	3373	3429	3484	3540	3595	3651	3706	56
783	3762	3817	3873	3928	3984	4039	4094	4150	4205	4261	55
784	4316	4371	4427	4482	4538	4593	4648	4704	4759	4814	55
785	894870	4925	4980	5036	5091	5146	5201	5257	5312	5367	55
786	5423	5478	5533	5588	5644	5699	5754	5809	5864	5920	55
787	5975	6030	6085	6140	6195	6251	6306	6361	6416	6471	55
788	6526	6581	6636	6692	6747	6802	6857	6912	6967	7022	55
789	7077	7132	7187	7242	7297	7352	7407	7462	7517	7572	55
790	897627	7682	7737	7792	7847	7902	7957	8012	8067	8122	55
791	8176	8231	8286	8341	8396	8451	8506	8561	8615	8670	55
792	8725	8780	8835	8890	8944	8999	9054	9109	9164	9218	55
793	9273	9328	9383	9437	9492	9547	9602	9656	9711	9766	55
794	9821	9875	9930	9985	*0039	*0094	*0149	*0203	*0258	*0312	55
795	900367	0422	0476	0531	0586	0640	0695	0749	0804	0859	55
796	0913	0968	1022	1077	1131	1186	1240	1295	1349	1404	55
797	1458	1513	1567	1622	1676	1731	1785	1840	1894	1948	54
798	2003	2057	2112	2166	2221	2275	2329	2384	2438	2492	54
799	2547	2601	2655	2710	2764	2818	2873	2927	2981	3036	54

PROPORTIONAL PARTS

Diff.	1	2	3	4	5	6	7	8	9	Diff.
57	6	11	17	23	29	34	40	46	51	57
56	6	11	17	22	28	34	39	45	50	56
55	6	11	17	22	28	33	39	44	50	55
54	5	11	16	22	27	32	38	43	49	54

TABLE VIII. LOGARITHMS OF NUMBERS

No. 800—Log. 903   No. 849—Log. 929

N.	0	1	2	3	4	5	6	7	8	9	Diff.
800	903090	3144	3199	3253	3307	3361	3416	3470	3524	3578	54
801	3633	3687	3741	3795	3849	3904	3958	4012	4066	4120	54
802	4174	4229	4283	4337	4391	4445	4499	4553	4607	4661	54
803	4716	4770	4824	4878	4932	4986	5040	5094	5148	5202	54
804	5256	5310	5364	5418	5472	5526	5580	5634	5688	5742	54
805	905796	5850	5904	5958	6012	6066	6119	6173	6227	6281	54
806	6335	6389	6443	6497	6551	6604	6658	6712	6766	6820	54
807	6874	6927	6981	7035	7089	7143	7196	7250	7304	7358	54
808	7411	7465	7519	7573	7626	7680	7734	7787	7841	7895	54
809	7949	8002	8056	8110	8163	8217	8270	8324	8378	8431	54
810	908485	8539	8592	8646	8699	8753	8807	8860	8914	8967	54
811	9021	9074	9128	9181	9235	9289	9342	9396	9449	9503	54
812	9556	9610	9663	9716	9770	9823	9877	9930	9984	*0037	53
813	910091	0144	0197	0251	0304	0358	0411	0464	0518	0571	53
814	0624	0678	0731	0784	0838	0891	0944	0998	1051	1104	53
815	911158	1211	1264	1317	1371	1424	1477	1530	1584	1637	53
816	1690	1743	1797	1850	1903	1956	2009	2063	2116	2169	53
817	2222	2275	2328	2381	2435	2488	2541	2594	2647	2700	53
818	2753	2806	2859	2913	2966	3019	3072	3125	3178	3231	53
819	3284	3337	3390	3443	3496	3549	3602	3655	3708	3761	53
820	913814	3867	3920	3973	4026	4079	4132	4184	4237	4290	53
821	4343	4396	4449	4502	4555	4608	4660	4713	4766	4819	53
822	4872	4925	4977	5030	5083	5136	5189	5241	5294	5347	53
823	5400	5453	5505	5558	5611	5664	5716	5769	5822	5875	53
824	5927	5980	6033	6085	6138	6191	6243	6296	6349	6401	53
825	916454	6507	6559	6612	6664	6717	6770	6822	6875	6927	53
826	6980	7033	7085	7138	7190	7243	7295	7348	7400	7453	53
827	7506	7558	7611	7663	7716	7768	7820	7873	7925	7978	52
828	8030	8083	8135	8188	8240	8293	8345	8397	8450	8502	52
829	8555	8607	8659	8712	8764	8816	8869	8921	8973	9026	52
830	919078	9130	9183	9235	9287	9340	9392	9444	9496	9549	52
831	9601	9653	9706	9758	9810	9862	9914	9967	*0019	*0071	52
832	920123	0176	0228	0280	0332	0384	0436	0489	0541	0593	52
833	0645	0697	0749	0801	0853	0906	0958	1010	1062	1114	52
834	1166	1218	1270	1322	1374	1426	1478	1530	1582	1634	52
835	921686	1738	1790	1842	1894	1946	1998	2050	2102	2154	52
836	2206	2258	2310	2362	2414	2466	2518	2570	2622	2674	52
837	2725	2777	2829	2881	2933	2985	3037	3089	3140	3192	52
838	3244	3296	3348	3399	3451	3503	3555	3607	3658	3710	52
839	3762	3814	3865	3917	3969	4021	4072	4124	4176	4228	52
840	924279	4331	4383	4434	4486	4538	4589	4641	4693	4744	52
841	4796	4848	4899	4951	5003	5054	5106	5157	5209	5261	52
842	5312	5364	5415	5467	5518	5570	5621	5673	5725	5776	52
843	5828	5879	5931	5982	6034	6085	6137	6188	6240	6291	51
844	6342	6394	6445	6497	6548	6600	6651	6702	6754	6805	51
845	926857	6908	6959	7011	7062	7114	7165	7216	7268	7319	51
846	7370	7422	7473	7524	7576	7627	7678	7730	7781	7832	51
847	7883	7935	7986	8037	8088	8140	8191	8242	8293	8345	51
848	8396	8447	8498	8549	8601	8652	8703	8754	8805	8857	51
849	8908	8959	9010	9061	9112	9163	9215	9266	9317	9368	51

PROPORTIONAL PARTS

Diff.	1	2	3	4	5	6	7	8	9	Diff.
55	6	11	17	22	28	33	39	44	50	55
54	5	11	16	22	27	32	38	43	49	54
53	5	11	16	21	27	32	37	42	48	53
52	5	10	16	21	26	31	36	42	47	52

TABLE VIII.   LOGARITHMS OF NUMBERS

No. 850—Log. 929   No. 899—Log. 954

N.	0	1	2	3	4	5	6	7	8	9	Diff.
850	929419	9470	9521	9572	9623	9674	9725	9776	9827	9879	51
851	9930	9981	*0032	*0083	*0134	*0185	*0236	*0287	*0338	*0389	51
852	930440	0491	0542	0592	0643	0694	0745	0796	0847	0898	51
853	0949	1000	1051	1102	1153	1204	1254	1305	1356	1407	51
854	1458	1509	1560	1610	1661	1712	1763	1814	1865	1915	51
855	931966	201?	2068	2118	2169	2220	2271	2322	2372	2423	51
856	2474	2524	2575	2626	2677	2727	2778	2829	2879	2930	51
857	2981	3031	3082	3133	3183	3234	3285	3335	3386	3437	51
858	3487	3538	3589	3639	3690	3740	3791	3841	3892	3943	51
859	3993	4044	4094	4145	4195	4246	4296	4347	4397	4448	51
860	934498	4549	4599	4650	4700	4751	4801	4852	4902	4953	50
861	5003	5054	5104	5154	5205	5255	5306	5356	5406	5457	50
862	5507	5558	5608	5658	5709	5759	5809	5860	5910	5960	50
863	6011	6061	6111	6162	6212	6262	6313	6363	6413	6463	50
864	6514	6564	6614	6665	6715	6765	6815	6865	6916	6966	50
865	937016	7066	7117	7167	7217	7267	7317	7367	7418	7468	50
866	7518	7568	7618	7668	7718	7769	7819	7869	7919	7969	50
867	8019	8069	8119	8169	8219	8269	8320	8370	8420	8470	50
868	8520	8570	8620	8670	8720	8770	8820	8870	8920	8970	50
869	9020	9070	9120	9170	9220	9270	9320	9369	9419	9469	50
870	939519	9569	9619	9669	9719	9769	9819	9869	9918	9968	50
871	940018	0068	0118	0168	0218	0267	0317	0367	0417	0467	50
872	0516	0566	0616	0666	0716	0765	0815	0865	0915	0964	50
873	1014	1064	1114	1163	1213	1263	1313	1362	1412	1462	50
874	1511	1561	1611	1660	1710	1760	1809	1859	1909	1958	50
875	942008	2058	2107	2157	2207	2256	2306	2355	2405	2455	50
876	2504	2554	2603	2653	2702	2752	2801	2851	2901	2950	50
877	3000	3049	3099	3148	3198	3247	3297	3346	3396	3445	49
878	3495	3544	3593	3643	3692	3742	3791	3841	3890	3939	49
879	3989	4038	4088	4137	4186	4236	4285	4335	4384	4433	49
880	944483	4532	4581	4631	4680	4729	4779	4828	4877	4927	49
881	4976	5025	5074	5124	5173	5222	5272	5321	5370	5419	49
882	5469	5518	5567	5616	5665	5715	5764	5813	5862	5912	49
883	5961	6010	6059	6108	6157	6207	6256	6305	6354	6403	49
884	6452	6501	6551	6600	6649	6698	6747	6796	6845	6894	49
885	946943	6992	7041	7090	7140	7189	7238	7287	7336	7385	49
886	7434	7483	7532	7581	7630	7679	7728	7777	7826	7875	49
887	7924	7973	8022	8070	8119	8168	8217	8266	8315	8364	49
888	8413	8462	8511	8560	8609	8657	8706	8755	8804	8853	49
889	8902	8951	8999	9048	9097	9146	9195	9244	9292	9341	49
890	949390	9439	9488	9536	9585	9634	9683	9731	9780	9829	49
891	9878	9926	9975	*0024	*0073	*0121	*0170	*0219	*0267	*0316	49
892	950365	0414	0462	0511	0560	0608	0657	0706	0754	0803	49
893	0851	0900	0949	0997	104b	1095	1143	1192	1240	1289	49
894	1338	1386	1435	1483	1532	1580	1629	1677	1726	1775	49
895	951823	1872	1920	1969	2017	2066	2114	2163	2211	2260	48
896	2308	2356	2405	2453	2502	2550	2599	2647	2696	2744	48
897	2792	2841	2889	2938	2986	3034	3083	3131	3180	3228	48
898	3276	3325	3373	3421	3470	3518	3566	3615	3663	3711	48
899	3760	3808	3856	3905	3953	4001	4049	4098	4146	4194	48

PROPORTIONAL PARTS

Diff.	1	2	3	4	5	6	7	8	9	Diff.
51	5	10	15	20	26	31	36	41	46	51
50	5	10	15	20	25	30	35	40	45	50
49	5	10	15	20	25	29	34	39	44	49
48	5	10	14	19	24	29	34	38	43	48

TABLE VIII.   LOGARITHMS OF NUMBERS

No. 900—Log. 954   No. 949—Log. 977

N.	0	1	2	3	4	5	6	7	8	9	Diff.
900	954243	4291	4339	4387	4435	4484	4532	4580	4628	4677	48
901	4725	4773	4821	4869	4918	4966	5014	5062	5110	5158	48
902	5207	5255	5303	5351	5399	5447	5495	5543	5592	5640	48
903	5688	5736	5784	5832	5880	5928	5976	6024	6072	6120	48
904	6168	6216	6265	6313	6361	6409	6457	6505	6553	6601	48
905	956649	6697	6745	6793	6840	6888	6936	6984	7032	7080	48
906	7128	7176	7224	7272	7320	7368	7416	7464	7512	7559	48
907	7607	7655	7703	7751	7799	7847	7894	7942	7990	8038	48
908	8086	8134	8181	8229	8277	8325	8373	8421	8468	8516	48
909	8564	8612	8659	8707	8755	8803	8850	8898	8946	8994	48
910	959041	9089	9137	9185	9232	9280	9328	9375	9423	9471	48
911	9518	9566	9614	9661	9709	9757	9804	9852	9900	9947	48
912	9995	*0042	*0090	*0138	*0185	*0233	*0280	*0328	*0376	*0423	48
913	960471	0518	0566	0613	0661	0709	0756	0804	0851	0899	48
914	0946	0994	1041	1089	1136	1184	1231	1279	1326	1374	48
915	961421	1469	1516	1563	1611	1658	1706	1753	1801	1848	47
916	1895	1943	1990	2038	2085	2132	2180	2227	2275	2322	47
917	2369	2417	2464	2511	2559	2606	2653	2701	2748	2795	47
918	2843	2890	2937	2985	3032	3079	3126	3174	3221	3268	47
919	3316	3363	3410	3457	3504	3552	3599	3646	3693	3741	47
920	963788	3835	3882	3929	3977	4024	4071	4118	4165	4212	47
921	4260	4307	4354	4401	4448	4495	4542	4590	4637	4684	47
922	4731	4778	4825	4872	4919	4966	5013	5061	5108	5155	47
923	5202	5249	5296	5343	5390	5437	5484	5531	5578	5625	47
924	5672	5719	5766	5813	5860	5907	5954	6001	6048	6095	47
925	966142	6189	6236	6283	6329	6376	6423	6470	6517	6564	47
926	6611	6658	6705	6752	6799	6845	6892	6939	6986	7033	47
927	7080	7127	7173	7220	7267	7314	7361	7408	7454	7501	47
928	7548	7595	7642	7688	7735	7782	7829	7875	7922	7969	47
929	8016	8062	8109	8156	8203	8249	8296	8343	8390	8436	47
930	968483	8530	8576	8623	8670	8716	8763	8810	8856	8903	47
931	8950	8996	9043	9090	9136	9183	9229	9276	9323	9369	47
932	9416	9463	9509	9556	9602	9649	9695	9742	9789	9835	47
933	9882	9928	9975	*0021	*0068	*0114	*0161	*0207	*0254	*0300	47
934	970347	0393	0440	0486	0533	0579	0626	0672	0719	0765	46
935	970812	0858	0904	0951	0997	1044	1090	1137	1183	1229	46
936	1276	1322	1369	1415	1461	1508	1554	1601	1647	1693	46
937	1740	1786	1832	1879	1925	1971	2018	2064	2110	2157	46
938	2203	2249	2295	2342	2388	2434	2481	2527	2573	2619	46
939	2666	2712	2758	2804	2851	2897	2943	2989	3035	3082	46
940	973128	3174	3220	3266	3313	3359	3405	3451	3497	3543	46
941	3590	3636	3682	3728	3774	3820	3866	3913	3959	4005	46
942	4051	4097	4143	4189	4235	4281	4327	4374	4420	4466	46
943	4512	4558	4604	4650	4696	4742	4788	4834	4880	4926	46
944	4972	5018	5064	5110	5156	5202	5248	5294	5340	5386	46
945	975432	5478	5524	5570	5616	5662	5707	5753	5799	5845	46
946	5891	5937	5983	6029	6075	6121	6167	6212	6258	6304	46
947	6350	6396	6442	6488	6533	6579	6625	6671	6717	6763	46
948	6808	6854	6900	6946	6992	7037	7083	7129	7175	7220	46
949	7266	7312	7358	7403	7449	7495	7541	7586	7632	7678	46

PROPORTIONAL PARTS

Diff.	1	2	3	4	5	6	7	8	9	Diff.
49	5	10	15	20	25	29	34	39	44	49
48	5	10	14	19	24	29	34	38	43	48
47	5	9	14	19	24	28	33	38	42	47
46	5	9	14	18	23	28	32	37	41	46

TABLE VIII. LOGARITHMS OF NUMBERS

No. 950—Log. 977   No. 999—Log. 999

N.	0	1	2	3	4	5	6	7	8	9	Diff.
950	977724	7769	7815	7861	7906	7952	7998	8043	8089	8135	46
951	8181	8226	8272	8317	8363	8409	8454	8500	8546	8591	46
952	8637	8683	8728	8774	8819	8865	8911	8956	9002	9047	46
953	9093	9138	9184	9230	9275	9321	9366	9412	9457	9503	46
954	9548	9594	9639	9685	9730	9776	9821	9867	9912	9958	46
955	980003	0049	0094	0140	0185	0231	0276	0322	0367	0412	45
956	0458	0503	0549	0594	0640	0685	0730	0776	0821	0867	45
957	0912	0957	1003	1048	1093	1139	1184	1229	1275	1320	45
958	1366	1411	1456	1501	1547	1592	1637	1683	1728	1773	45
959	1819	1864	1909	1954	2000	2045	2090	2135	2181	2226	45
960	982271	2316	2362	2407	2452	2497	2543	2588	2633	2678	45
961	2723	2769	2814	2859	2904	2949	2994	3040	3085	3130	45
962	3175	3220	3265	3310	3356	3401	3446	3491	3536	3581	45
963	3626	3671	3716	3762	3807	3852	3897	3942	3987	4032	45
964	4077	4122	4167	4212	4257	4302	4347	4392	4437	4482	45
965	984527	4572	4617	4662	4707	4752	4797	4842	4887	4932	45
966	4977	5022	5067	5112	5157	5202	5247	5292	5337	5382	45
967	5426	5471	5516	5561	5606	5651	5696	5741	5786	5830	45
968	5875	5920	5965	6010	6055	6100	6144	6189	6234	6279	45
969	6324	6369	6413	6458	6503	6548	6593	6637	6682	6727	45
970	986772	6817	6861	6906	6951	6996	7040	7085	7130	7175	45
971	7219	7264	7309	7353	7398	7443	7488	7532	7577	7622	45
972	7666	7711	7756	7800	7845	7890	7934	7979	8024	8068	45
973	8113	8157	8202	8247	8291	8336	8381	8425	8470	8514	45
974	8559	8604	8648	8693	8737	8782	8826	8871	8916	8960	45
975	989005	9049	9094	9138	9183	9227	9272	9316	9361	9405	45
976	9450	9494	9539	9583	9628	9672	9717	9761	9806	9850	44
977	9895	9939	9983	*0028	*0072	*0117	*0161	*0206	*0250	*0294	44
978	990339	0383	0428	0472	0516	0561	0605	0650	0694	0738	44
979	0783	0827	0871	0916	0960	1004	1049	1093	1137	1182	44
980	991226	1270	1315	1359	1403	1448	1492	1536	1580	1625	44
981	1669	1713	1758	1802	1846	1890	1935	1979	2023	2067	44
982	2111	2156	2200	2244	2288	2333	2377	2421	2465	2509	44
983	2554	2598	2642	2686	2730	2774	2819	2863	2907	2951	44
984	2995	3039	3083	3127	3172	3216	3260	3304	3348	3392	44
985	993436	3480	3524	3568	3613	3657	3701	3745	3789	3833	44
986	3877	3921	3965	4009	4053	4097	4141	4185	4229	4273	44
987	4317	4361	4405	4449	4493	4537	4581	4625	4669	4713	44
988	4757	4801	4845	4889	4933	4977	5021	5065	5108	5152	44
989	5196	5240	5284	5328	5372	5416	5460	5504	5547	5591	44
990	995635	5679	5723	5767	5811	5854	5898	5942	5986	6030	44
991	6074	6117	6161	6205	6249	6293	6337	6380	6424	6468	44
992	6512	6555	6599	6643	6687	6731	6774	6818	6862	6906	44
993	6949	6993	7037	7080	7124	7168	7212	7255	7299	7343	44
994	7386	7430	7474	7517	7561	7605	7648	7692	7736	7779	44
995	997823	7867	7910	7954	7998	8041	8085	8129	8172	8216	44
996	8259	8303	8347	8390	8434	8477	8521	8564	8608	8652	44
997	8695	8739	8782	8826	8869	8913	8956	9000	9043	9087	44
998	9131	9174	9218	9261	9305	9348	9392	9435	9479	9522	44
999	9565	9609	9652	9696	9739	9783	9826	9870	9913	9957	43

PROPORTIONAL PARTS

Diff.	1	2	3	4	5	6	7	8	9	Diff.
46	5	9	14	18	23	28	32	37	41	46
45	5	9	14	18	23	27	32	36	41	45
44	4	9	13	18	22	26	31	35	40	44
43	4	9	13	17	22	26	30	34	39	43

TABLE IX.   LOGARITHMIC SIN., COS., TAN., AND COT.

0°   179°

M.	Sin.	D. 1″.	Cos.	D. 1″.	Tan.	D. 1″.	Cot.	
0	− Inf.		10.000000	.00	− Inf.		+ Inf.	60
1	6.463726	5017.17	.000000	.00	6.463726	5017.17	3.536274	59
2	.764756	2934.85	.000000	.00	.764756	2934.85	.235244	58
3	.940847	2082.32	.000000	.00	.940847	2082.32	.059153	57
4	7.065786	1615.17	.000000	.00	7.065786	1615.17	2.934214	56
5	7.162696	1319.68	10.000000	.02	7.162696	1319.70	2.837304	55
6	.241877	1115.78	9.999999	.00	.241878	1115.78	.758122	54
7	.308824	966.53	.999999	.00	.308825	966.53	.691175	53
8	.366816	852.53	.999999	.00	.366817	852.55	.633183	52
9	.417968	762.63	.999999	.02	.417970	762.62	.582030	51
10	7.463726	689.87	9.999998	.00	7.463727	689.88	2.536273	50
11	.505118	629.80	.999998	.02	.505120	629.82	.494880	49
12	.542906	579.37	.999997	.00	.542909	579.38	.457091	48
13	.577668	536.42	.999997	.02	.577672	536.42	.422328	47
14	.609853	499.38	.999996	.00	.609857	499.38	.390143	46
15	7.639816	467.15	9.999996	.02	7.639820	467.15	2.360180	45
16	.667845	438.80	.999995	.00	.667849	438.83	.332151	44
17	.694173	413.73	.999995	.02	.694179	413.73	.305821	43
18	.718997	391.35	.999994	.02	.719003	391.35	.280997	42
19	.742478	371.27	.999993	.00	.742484	371.28	.257516	41
20	7.764754	353.15	9.999993	.02	7.764761	353.17	2.235239	40
21	.785943	336.72	.999992	.02	.785951	336.73	.214049	39
22	.806146	321.75	.999991	.02	.806155	321.75	.193845	38
23	.825451	308.05	.999990	.02	.825460	308.07	.174540	37
24	.843934	295.47	.999989	.00	.843944	295.50	.156056	36
25	7.861662	283.88	9.999989	.02	7.861674	283.90	2.138326	35
26	.878695	273.17	.999988	.02	.878708	273.18	.121292	34
27	.895085	263.23	.999987	.02	.895099	263.25	.104901	33
28	.910879	254.00	.999986	.02	.910894	254.00	.089106	32
29	.926119	245.38	.999985	.03	.926134	245.40	.073866	31
30	7.940842	237.33	9.999983	.02	7.940858	237.37	2.059142	30
31	.955082	229.80	.999982	.02	.955100	229.82	.044900	29
32	.968870	222.72	.999981	.02	.968889	222.73	.031111	28
33	.982233	216.08	.999980	.02	.982253	216.10	.017747	27
34	.995198	209.82	.999979	.03	.995219	209.83	.004781	26
35	8.007787	203.90	9.999977	.02	8.007809	203.92	1.992191	25
36	.020021	198.30	.999976	.02	.020044	198.35	.979956	24
37	.031919	193.03	.999975	.03	.031945	193.03	.968055	23
38	.043501	188.00	.999973	.02	.043527	188.03	.956473	22
39	.054781	183.25	.999972	.02	.054809	183.28	.945191	21
40	8.065776	178.73	9.999971	.03	8.065806	178.75	1.934194	20
41	.076500	174.42	.999969	.02	.076531	174.43	.923469	19
42	.086965	170.30	.999966	.03	.086997	170.33	.913003	18
43	.097183	166.40	.999964	.03	.097217	166.43	.902783	17
44	.107167	162.65	.999964	.02	.107203	162.67	.892797	16
45	8.116926	159.08	9.999963	.03	8.116963	159.12	1.883037	15
46	.126471	155.65	.999961	.03	.126510	155.68	.873490	14
47	.135810	152.38	.999959	.02	.135861	152.42	.864149	13
48	.144953	149.23	.999958	.03	.144996	149.27	.855004	12
49	.153907	146.23	.999956	.03	.153952	146.25	.846048	11
50	8.162681	143.32	9.999954	.03	8.162727	143.35	1.837273	10
51	.171280	140.55	.999952	.03	.171328	140.58	.828672	9
52	.179713	137.87	.999950	.03	.179763	137.88	.820237	8
53	.187985	135.28	.999948	.03	.188036	135.33	.811964	7
54	.196102	132.80	.999946	.03	.196156	132.83	.803844	6
55	8.204070	130.42	9.999944	.03	8.204126	130.45	1.795874	5
56	.211895	128.10	.999942	.03	.211953	128.13	.788047	4
57	.219581	125.88	.999940	.03	.219641	125.90	.780359	3
58	.227134	123.72	.999938	.03	.227195	123.77	.772805	2
59	.234557	121.63	.999936	.03	.234621	121.67	.765379	1
60	8.241855		9.999934		8.241921		1.758079	0
	Cos.	D. 1″.	Sin.	D. 1″.	Cot.	D. 1″.	Tan.	M.

90°   89°

TABLE IX. LOGARITHMIC SINES,

M.	Sin.	D. 1″.	Cos.	D. 1″.	Tan.	D. 1″	Cot.	
0	8.241855	119.63	9.999934	.03	8.241921	119.68	1.758079	60
1	.249033	117.68	.999932	.05	.249102	117.72	.750898	59
2	.256094	115.80	.999929	.03	.256165	115.83	.743835	58
3	.263042	113.98	.999927	.03	.263115	114.02	.736885	57
4	.269881	112.22	.999925	.05	.269956	112.25	.730044	56
5	8.276614	110.48	9.999922	.03	8.276691	110.53	1.723309	55
6	.283243	108.83	.999920	.03	.283323	108.88	.716677	54
7	.289773	107.23	.999918	.03	.289856	107.27	.710144	53
8	.296207	105.65	.999915	.03	.296292	105.70	.703708	52
9	.302546	104.13	.999913	.05	.302634	104.17	.697366	51
10	8.308794	102.67	9.999910	.05	8.308884	102.70	1.691116	50
11	.314954	101.22	.999907	.03	.315046	101.27	.684954	49
12	.321027	99.82	.999905	.05	.321122	99.87	.678878	48
13	.327016	98.47	.999902	.05	.327114	98.52	.672886	47
14	.332924	97.15	.999899	.03	.333025	97.18	.666975	46
15	8.338753	95.85	9.999897	.05	8.338856	95.90	1.661144	45
16	.344504	94.62	.999894	.05	.344610	94.65	.655390	44
17	.350181	93.37	.999891	.05	.350289	93.43	.649711	43
18	.355783	92.20	.999888	.05	.355895	92.25	.644105	42
19	.361315	91.03	.999885	.05	.361430	91.08	.638570	41
20	8.366777	89.90	9.999882	.05	8.366895	89.95	1.633105	40
21	.372171	88.80	.999879	.05	.372292	88.83	.627708	39
22	.377499	87.72	.999876	.05	.377622	87.78	.622378	38
23	.382762	86.67	.999873	.05	.382889	86.72	.617111	37
24	.387962	85.65	.999870	.05	.388092	85.70	.611908	36
25	8.393101	84.63	9.999867	.05	8.393234	84.68	1.606766	35
26	.398179	83.67	.999864	.05	.398315	83.72	.601685	34
27	.403199	82.70	.999861	.05	.403338	82.77	.596662	33
28	.408161	81.78	.999858	.07	.408304	81.82	.591696	32
29	.413068	80.85	.999854	.05	.413213	80.92	.586787	31
30	8.417919	79.97	9.999851	.05	8.418068	80.02	1.581932	30
31	.422717	79.08	.999848	.07	.422869	79.15	.577131	29
32	.427462	78.23	.999844	.05	.427618	78.28	.572382	28
33	.432156	77.40	.999841	.05	.432315	77.45	.567685	27
34	.436800	76.57	.999838	.07	.436962	76.63	.563038	26
35	8.441394	75.78	9.999834	.05	8.441560	75.83	1.558440	25
36	.445941	74.98	.999831	.07	.446110	75.05	.553890	24
37	.450440	74.22	.999827	.05	.450613	74.28	.549387	23
38	.454893	73.47	.999824	.07	.455070	73.52	.544930	22
39	.459301	72.73	.999820	.07	.459481	72.80	.540519	21
40	8.463665	72.00	9.999816	.05	8.463849	72.05	1.536151	20
41	.467985	71.30	.999813	.07	.468172	71.37	.531828	19
42	.472263	70.58	.999809	.07	.472454	70.65	.527546	18
43	.476498	69.92	.999805	.07	.476693	69.98	.523307	17
44	.480693	69.25	.999801	.07	.480892	69.30	.519108	16
45	8.484848	68.58	9.999797	.05	8.485050	68.67	1.514950	15
46	.488963	67.95	.999794	.07	.489170	68.00	.510830	14
47	.493040	67.30	.999790	.07	.493250	67.38	.506750	13
48	.497078	66.70	.999786	.07	.497293	66.75	.502707	12
49	.501080	66.08	.999782	.07	.501298	66.15	.498702	11
50	8.505045	65.48	9.999778	.07	8.505267	65.55	1.494733	10
51	.508974	64.88	.999774	.08	.509200	64.97	.490800	9
52	.512867	64.32	.999769	.07	.513098	64.38	.486902	8
53	.516726	63.75	.999765	.07	.516961	63.82	.483039	7
54	.520551	63.20	.999761	.07	.520790	63.27	.479210	6
55	8.524343	62.65	9.999757	.07	8.524586	62.72	1.475414	5
56	.528102	62.10	.999753	.08	.528349	62.18	.471651	4
57	.531828	61.58	.999748	.07	.532080	61.65	.467920	3
58	.535523	61.05	.999744	.07	.535779	61.13	.464221	2
59	.539186	60.55	.999740	.08	.539447	60.62	.460553	1
60	8.542819		9.999735		8.543084		1.456916	0
	Cos.	D. 1″.	Sin.	D. 1″.	Cot.	D. 1″.	Tan.	M.

COSINES, TANGENTS, AND COTANGENTS

M.	Sin.	D. 1″.	Cos.	D. 1″.	Tan.	D. 1″.	Cot.	
0	8.542819	60.05	9.999735	.07	8.543084	60.12	1.456916	60
1	.546422	59.55	.999731	.08	.546691	59.62	.453309	59
2	.549995	59.07	.999726	.07	.550268	59.15	.449732	58
3	.553539	58.58	.999722	.08	.553817	58.65	.446183	57
4	.557054	58.10	.999717	.07	.557336	58.20	.442664	56
5	8.560540	57.65	9.999713	.08	8.560828	57.72	1.439172	55
6	.563999	57.20	.999708	.07	.564291	57.27	.435709	54
7	.567431	56.75	.999704	.08	.567727	56.83	.432273	53
8	.570836	56.30	.999699	.08	.571137	56.38	.428863	52
9	.574214	55.87	.999694	.08	.574520	55.95	.425480	51
10	8.577566	55.43	9.999689	.07	8.577877	55.52	1.422123	50
11	.580892	55.02	.999685	.08	.581208	55.10	.418792	49
12	.584193	54.60	.999680	.08	.584514	54.68	.415486	48
13	.587469	54.20	.999675	.08	.587795	54.27	.412205	47
14	.590721	53.78	.999670	.08	.591051	53.87	.408949	46
15	8.593948	53.40	9.999665	.08	8.594283	53.48	1.405717	45
16	.597152	53.00	.999660	.08	.597492	53.08	.402508	44
17	.600332	52.62	.999655	.08	.600677	52.70	.399323	43
18	.603489	52.23	.999650	.08	.603839	52.32	.396161	42
19	.606623	51.85	.999645	.08	.606978	51.93	.393022	41
20	8.609734	51.48	9.999640	.08	8.610094	51.58	1.389906	40
21	.612823	51.13	.999635	.10	.613189	51.22	.386811	39
22	.615891	50.77	.999629	.08	.616262	50.85	.383738	38
23	.618937	50.42	.999624	.08	.619313	50.50	.380687	37
24	.621962	50.05	.999619	.08	.622343	50.15	.377657	36
25	8.624965	49.72	9.999614	.10	8.625352	49.80	1.374648	35
26	.627948	49.38	.999608	.08	.628340	49.47	.371660	34
27	.630911	49.05	.999603	.10	.631308	49.13	.368692	33
28	.633854	48.70	.999597	.08	.634256	48.80	.365744	32
29	.636776	48.40	.999592	.10	.637184	48.48	.362816	31
30	8.639680	48.05	9.999586	.08	8.640093	48.15	1.359907	30
31	.642563	47.75	.999581	.08	.642982	47.85	.357018	29
32	.645428	47.43	.999575	.08	.645853	47.52	.354147	28
33	.648274	47.13	.999570	.10	.648704	47.22	.351296	27
34	.651102	46.82	.999564	.10	.651537	46.92	.348463	26
35	8.653911	46.52	9.999558	.08	8.654352	46.62	1.345648	25
36	.656702	46.22	.999553	.10	.657149	46.32	.342851	24
37	.659475	45.92	.999547	.10	.659928	46.02	.340072	23
38	.662230	45.63	.999541	.10	.662689	45.73	.337311	22
39	.664968	45.35	.999535	.10	.665433	45.45	.334567	21
40	8.667689	45.07	9.999529	.08	8.668160	45.17	1.331840	20
41	.670393	44.78	.999524	.10	.670870	44.88	.329130	19
42	.673080	44.52	.999518	.10	.673563	44.60	.326437	18
43	.675751	44.23	.999512	.10	.676239	44.35	.323761	17
44	.678405	43.97	.999506	.10	.678900	44.07	.321100	16
45	8.681043	43.70	9.999500	.12	8.681544	43.80	1.318456	15
46	.683665	43.45	.999493	.10	.684172	43.53	.315828	14
47	.686272	43.18	.999487	.10	.686784	43.28	.313216	13
48	.688863	42.92	.999481	.10	.689381	43.03	.310619	12
49	.691438	42.67	.999475	.10	.691963	42.77	.308037	11
50	8.693998	42.42	9.999469	.10	8.694529	42.53	1.305471	10
51	.696543	42.17	.999463	.12	.697081	42.27	.302919	9
52	.699073	41.93	.999456	.10	.699617	42.03	.300383	8
53	.701589	41.68	.999450	.12	.702139	41.78	.297861	7
54	.704090	41.45	.999443	.10	.704646	41.57	.295354	6
55	8.706577	41.20	9.999437	.10	8.707140	41.30	1.292860	5
56	.709049	40.97	.999431	.12	.709618	41.08	.290382	4
57	.711507	40.75	.999424	.10	.712083	40.85	.287917	3
58	.713952	40.52	.999418	.12	.714534	40.63	.285466	2
59	.716383	40.28	.999411	.12	.716972	40.40	.283028	1
60	8.718800		9.999404	.12	8.719396		1.280604	0
	Cos.	D. 1″.	Sin.	D. 1″.	Cot.	D. 1″.	Tan.	M.

TABLE IX. LOGARITHMIC SINES,

M.	Sin.	D. 1″.	Cos.	D. 1″.	Tan.	D. 1″.	Cot.	
0	8.718800	40.07	9.999404	.10	8.719396	40.17	1.280604	60
1	.721204	39.85	.999398	.12	.721806	39.97	.278194	59
2	.723595	39.62	.999391	.12	.724204	39.73	.275793	58
3	.725972	39.42	.999384	.10	.726588	39.52	.273412	57
4	.728337	39.18	.999378	.12	.728959	39.30	.271041	56
5	8.730688	38.98	9.999371	.12	8.731317	39.10	1.268683	55
6	.733027	38.78	.999364	.12	.733663	38.88	.266337	54
7	.735354	38.55	.999357	.12	.735996	38.68	.264004	53
8	.737667	38.37	.999350	.12	.738317	38.48	.261683	52
9	.739969	38.17	.999343	.12	.740626	38.27	.259374	51
10	8.742259	37.95	9.999336	.12	8.742922	38.08	1.257078	50
11	.744536	37.77	.999329	.12	.745207	37.87	.254793	49
12	.746802	37.55	.999322	.12	.747479	37.68	.252521	48
13	.749055	37.37	.999315	.12	.749740	37.48	.250260	47
14	.751297	37.18	.999308	.12	.751989	37.30	.248011	46
15	8.753528	36.98	9.999301	.12	8.754227	37.10	1.245773	45
16	.755747	36.80	.999294	.12	.756453	36.92	.243547	44
17	.757955	36.60	.999287	.13	.758668	36.73	.241332	43
18	.760151	36.43	.999279	.12	.760872	36.55	.239128	42
19	.762337	36.23	.999272	.12	.763065	36.35	.236935	41
20	8.764511	36.07	9.999265	.13	8.765246	36.18	1.234754	40
21	.766675	35.88	.999257	.12	.767417	36.02	.232583	39
22	.768828	35.70	.999250	.13	.769578	35.82	.230422	38
23	.770970	35.52	.999242	.12	.771727	35.65	.228273	37
24	.773101	35.37	.999235	.13	.773866	35.48	.226134	36
25	8.775223	35.17	9.999227	.12	8.775995	35.32	1.224005	35
26	.777333	35.02	.999220	.13	.778114	35.13	.221886	34
27	.779434	34.83	.999212	.12	.780222	34.97	.219778	33
28	.781524	34.68	.999205	.13	.782320	34.80	.217680	32
29	.783605	34.50	.999197	.13	.784408	34.63	.215592	31
30	8.785675	34.35	9.999189	.13	8.786486	34.47	1.213514	30
31	.787736	34.18	.999181	.12	.788554	34.32	.211446	29
32	.789787	34.02	.999174	.13	.790613	34.15	.209387	28
33	.791828	33.85	.999166	.13	.792662	33.98	.207338	27
34	.793859	33.70	.999158	.13	.794701	33.83	.205299	26
35	8.795881	33.55	9.999150	.13	8.796731	33.68	1.203269	25
36	.797894	33.38	.999142	.13	.798752	33.52	.201248	24
37	.799897	33.25	.999134	.13	.800763	33.37	.199237	23
38	.801892	33.07	.999126	.13	.802765	33.22	.197235	22
39	.803876	32.93	.999118	.13	.804758	33.07	.195242	21
40	8.805852	32.78	9.999110	.13	8.806742	32.92	1.193258	20
41	.807819	32.63	.999102	.13	.808717	32.77	.191283	19
42	.809777	32.48	.999094	.13	.810683	32.63	.189317	18
43	.811726	32.35	.999086	.15	.812641	32.47	.187359	17
44	.813667	32.20	.999077	.13	.814589	32.33	.185411	16
45	8.815599	32.05	9.999069	.13	8.816529	32.20	1.183471	15
46	.817522	31.90	.999061	.13	.818461	32.05	.181539	14
47	.819436	31.78	.999053	.15	.820384	31.90	.179616	13
48	.821343	31.62	.999044	.13	.822298	31.78	.177702	12
49	.823240	31.50	.999036	.15	.824205	31.63	.175795	11
50	8.825130	31.35	9.999027	.13	8.826103	31.48	1.173897	10
51	.827011	31.22	.999019	.15	.827992	31.37	.172008	9
52	.828884	31.08	.999010	.13	.829874	31.23	.170126	8
53	.830749	30.97	.999002	.15	.831748	31.08	.168252	7
54	.832607	30.82	.998993	.15	.833613	30.97	.166387	6
55	8.834456	30.68	9.998984	.13	8.835471	30.83	1.164529	5
56	.836297	30.55	.998976	.15	.837321	30.70	.162679	4
57	.838130	30.43	.998967	.15	.839163	30.58	.160837	3
58	.839956	30.30	.998958	.13	.840998	30.45	.159002	2
59	.841774	30.18	.998950	.15	.842825	30.32	.157175	1
60	8.843585		9.998941		8.844644		1.155356	0
	Cos.	D. 1″.	Sin.	D. 1″.	Cot.	D. 1″.	Tan.	M.

COSINES, TANGENTS, AND COTANGENTS

4°   175°

M.	Sin.	D. 1″.	Cos.	D. 1″.	Tan.	D. 1″.	Cot.	
0	8.843585	30.03	9.998941	.15	8.844644	30.18	1.155356	60
1	.845387	29.93	.998932	.15	.846455	30.08	.153545	59
2	.847183	29.80	.998923	.15	.848260	29.95	.151740	58
3	.848971	29.67	.998914	.15	.850057	29.82	.149943	57
4	.850751	29.57	.998905	.15	.851846	29.70	.148154	56
5	8.852525	29.43	9.998896	.15	8.853628	29.58	1.146372	55
6	.854291	29.30	.998887	.15	.855403	29.47	.144597	54
7	.856049	29.20	.998878	.15	.857171	29.35	.142829	53
8	.857801	29.08	.998869	.15	.858932	29.23	.141068	52
9	.859546	28.95	.998860	.15	.860686	29.12	.139314	51
10	8.861283	28.85	9.998851	.17	8.862433	29.00	1.137567	50
11	.863014	28.73	.998841	.15	.864173	28.88	.135827	49
12	.864738	28.62	.998832	.15	.865906	28.77	.134094	48
13	.866455	28.50	.998823	.17	.867632	28.65	.132368	47
14	.868165	28.38	.998813	.15	.869351	28.55	.130649	46
15	8.869868	28.28	9.998804	.15	8.871064	28.43	1.128936	45
16	.871565	28.17	.998795	.17	.872770	28.32	.127230	44
17	.873255	28.05	.998785	.15	.874469	28.22	.125531	43
18	.874938	27.95	.998776	.17	.876162	28.12	.123838	42
19	.876615	27.83	.998766	.15	.877849	28.00	.122151	41
20	8.878285	27.73	9.998757	.17	8.879529	27.88	1.120471	40
21	.879949	27.63	.998747	.15	.881202	27.78	.118798	39
22	.881607	27.52	.998738	.17	.882869	27.68	.117131	38
23	.883258	27.42	.998728	.17	.884530	27.58	.115470	37
24	.884903	27.32	.998718	.17	.886185	27.47	.113815	36
25	8.886542	27.20	9.998708	.15	8.887833	27.38	1.112167	35
26	.888174	27.12	.998699	.17	.889476	27.27	.110524	34
27	.889801	27.00	.998689	.17	.891112	27.17	.108888	33
28	.891421	26.90	.998679	.17	.892742	27.07	.107258	32
29	.893035	26.80	.998669	.17	.894366	26.97	.105634	31
30	8.894643	26.72	9.998659	.17	8.895984	26.87	1.104016	30
31	.896246	26.60	.998649	.17	.897596	26.78	.102404	29
32	.897842	26.50	.998639	.17	.899203	26.67	.100797	28
33	.899432	26.42	.998629	.17	.900803	26.58	.099197	27
34	.901017	26.32	.998619	.17	.902398	26.48	.097602	26
35	8.902596	26.22	9.998609	.17	8.903987	26.38	1.096013	25
36	.904169	26.12	.998599	.17	.905570	26.28	.094430	24
37	.905736	26.02	.998589	.18	.907147	26.20	.092853	23
38	.907297	25.93	.998578	.17	.908719	26.10	.091281	22
39	.908853	25.85	.998568	.17	.910285	26.02	.089715	21
40	8.910404	25.75	9.998558	.17	8.911846	25.92	1.088154	20
41	.911949	25.65	.998548	.18	.913401	25.83	.086599	19
42	.913488	25.57	.998537	.17	.914951	25.73	.085049	18
43	.915022	25.47	.998527	.18	.916495	25.65	.083505	17
44	.916550	25.38	.998516	.17	.918034	25.57	.081966	16
45	8.918073	25.30	9.998506	.18	8.919568	25.47	1.080432	15
46	.919591	25.20	.998495	.17	.921096	25.38	.078904	14
47	.921103	25.12	.998485	.18	.922619	25.28	.077381	13
48	.922610	25.03	.998474	.17	.924136	25.22	.075864	12
49	.924112	24.95	.998464	.18	.925649	25.12	.074351	11
50	8.925609	24.85	9.998453	.18	8.927156	25.03	1.072844	10
51	.927100	24.78	.998442	.18	.928658	24.95	.071342	9
52	.928587	24.68	.998431	.17	.930155	24.87	.069845	8
53	.930068	24.60	.998421	.18	.931647	24.78	.068353	7
54	.931544	24.52	.998410	.18	.933134	24.70	.066866	6
55	8.933015	24.43	9.998399	.18	8.934616	24.62	1.065384	5
56	.934481	24.35	.998388	.18	.936093	24.53	.063907	4
57	.935942	24.27	.998377	.18	.937565	24.45	.062435	3
58	.937398	24.20	.998366	.18	.939032	24.37	.060968	2
59	.938850	24.10	.998355	.18	.940494	24.30	.059506	1
60	8.940296		9.998344	.18	8.941952		1.058048	0
	Cos.	D. 1″.	Sin.	D. 1″.	Cot.	D. 1″.	Tan.	M.

94°   85°

TABLE IX. LOGARITHMIC SINES,

5°   174°

M.	Sin.	D. 1".	Cos.	D. 1".	Tan.	D. 1".	Cot.	
0	8.940296	24.03	9.998344	.18	8.941952	24.20	1.058048	60
1	.941738	23.93	.998333	.18	.943404	24.13	056596	59
2	.943174	23.87	.998322	.18	.944852	24.05	.055148	58
3	.944606	23.80	.998311	.18	.946295	23.98	.053705	57
4	.946034	23.70	.998300	.18	.947734	23.90	.052266	56
5	8.947456	23.63	9.998289	.20	8.949168	23.82	1.050832	55
6	.948874	23.55	.998277	.18	.950597	23.73	.049403	54
7	.950287	23.48	.998266	.18	.952021	23.67	.047979	53
8	.951696	23.40	.998255	.20	.953441	23.58	.046559	52
9	.953100	23.32	.998243	.18	.954856	23.52	.045144	51
10	8.954499	23.25	9.998232	.20	8.956267	23.45	1.043733	50
11	.955894	23.17	.998220	.18	.957674	23.35	.042326	49
12	.957284	23.10	.998209	.20	.959075	23.30	.040925	48
13	.958670	23.03	.998197	.18	.960473	23.22	.039527	47
14	.960052	22.95	.998186	.20	.961866	23.15	.038134	46
15	8.961429	22.87	9.998174	.18	8.963255	23.07	1.036745	45
16	.962801	22.82	.998163	.20	.964639	23.00	.035361	44
17	.964170	22.73	.998151	.20	.966019	22.92	.033981	43
18	.965534	22.65	.998139	.18	.967394	22.87	.032606	42
19	.966893	22.60	.998128	.20	.968766	22.78	.031234	41
20	8.968249	22.52	9.998116	.20	8.970133	22.72	1.029867	40
21	.969600	22.45	.998104	.20	.971496	22.65	.028504	39
22	.970947	22.37	.998092	.20	.972855	22.57	.027145	38
23	.972289	22.32	.998080	.20	.974209	22.52	.025791	37
24	.973628	22.23	.998068	.20	.975560	22.43	.024440	36
25	8.974962	22.18	9.998056	.20	8.976906	22.37	1.023094	35
26	.976293	22.10	.998044	.20	.978248	22.30	.021752	34
27	.977619	22.03	.998032	.20	.979586	22.25	.020414	33
28	.978941	21.97	.998020	.20	.980921	22.17	.019079	32
29	.980259	21.90	.998008	.20	.982251	22.10	.017749	31
30	8.981573	21.83	9.997996	.20	8.983577	22.03	1.016423	30
31	.982883	21.77	.997984	.20	.984899	21.97	.015101	29
32	.984189	21.70	.997972	.22	.986217	21.92	.013783	28
33	.985491	21.63	.997959	.20	.987532	21.83	.012468	27
34	.986789	21.57	.997947	.20	.988842	21.78	.011158	26
35	8.988083	21.52	9.997935	.22	8.990149	21.70	1.009851	25
36	.989374	21.43	.997922	.20	.991451	21.65	.008549	24
37	.990660	21.38	.997910	.22	.992750	21.58	.007250	23
38	.991943	21.32	.997897	.20	.994045	21.53	.005955	22
39	.993222	21.25	.997885	.22	.995337	21.45	.004663	21
40	8.994497	21.18	9.997872	.20	8.996624	21.40	1.003376	20
41	.995768	21.13	.997860	.22	.997908	21.33	.002092	19
42	.997036	21.05	.997847	.20	.999188	21.28	.000812	18
43	.998209	21.02	.997835	.22	9.000465	21.22	0.999535	17
44	.999560	20.93	.997822	.22	.001738	21.15	.998262	16
45	9.000816	20.88	9.997809	.20	9.003007	21.08	0.996993	15
46	.002069	20.82	.997797	.22	.004272	21.03	.995728	14
47	.003318	20.75	.997784	.22	.005534	20.97	.994466	13
48	.004563	20.70	.997771	.22	.006792	20.92	.993208	12
49	.005805	20.65	.997758	.22	.008047	20.85	.991953	11
50	9.007044	20.57	9.997745	.22	9.009298	20.80	0.990702	10
51	.008278	20.53	.997732	.22	.010546	20.73	.989454	9
52	.009510	20.45	.997719	.22	.011790	20.68	.988210	8
53	.010737	20.42	.997706	.22	.013031	20.62	.986969	7
54	.011962	20.33	.997693	.22	.014268	20.57	.985732	6
55	9.013182	20.30	9.997680	.22	9.015502	20.50	0.984498	5
56	.014400	20.22	.997667	.22	.016732	20.45	.983268	4
57	.015613	20.18	.997654	.22	.017959	20.40	.982041	3
58	.016824	20.12	.997641	.22	.019183	20.33	.980817	2
59	.018031	20.07	.997628	.22	.020403	20.28	.979597	1
60	9.019235		9.997614	.23	9.021620		0.978380	0
	Cos.	D. 1".	Sin.	D. 1".	Cot.	D. 1".	Tan.	M.

95°   84°

COSINES, TANGENTS, AND COTANGENTS

6°   173°

M.	Sin.	D. 1″.	Cos.	D. 1″.	Tan.	D. 1″.	Cot.	
0	9.019235	20.00	9.997614	.22	9.021620	20.23	0.978380	60
1	.020435	19.95	.997601	.22	.022834	20.17	.977166	59
2	.021632	19.88	.997588	.23	.024044	20.12	.975956	58
3	.022825	19.85	.997574	.22	.025251	20.07	.974749	57
4	.024016	19.78	.997561	.23	.026455	20.00	.973545	56
5	9.025203	19.72	9.997547	.22	9.027655	19.95	0.972345	55
6	.026386	19.68	.997534	.23	.028852	19.90	.971148	54
7	.027567	19.62	.997520	.22	.030046	19.85	.969954	53
8	.028744	19.57	.997507	.23	.031237	19.80	.968763	52
9	.029918	19.52	.997493	.22	.032425	19.73	.967575	51
10	9.031089	19.47	9.997480	.23	9.033609	19.70	0.966391	50
11	.032257	19.40	.997466	.23	.034791	19.63	.965209	49
12	.033421	19.35	.997452	.22	.035969	19.58	.964031	48
13	.034582	19.32	.997439	.23	.037144	19.53	.962856	47
14	.035741	19.25	.997425	.23	.038316	19.48	.961684	46
15	9.036896	19.20	9.997411	.23	9.039485	19.43	0.960515	45
16	.038048	19.15	.997397	.23	.040651	19.37	.959349	44
17	.039197	19.08	.997383	.23	.041813	19.33	.958187	43
18	.040342	19.05	.997369	.23	.042973	19.28	.957027	42
19	.041485	19.00	.997355	.23	.044130	19.23	.955870	41
20	9.042625	18.95	9.997341	.23	9.045284	19.17	0.954716	40
21	.043762	18.88	.997327	.23	.046434	19.13	.953566	39
22	.044895	18.85	.997313	.23	.047582	19.08	.952418	38
23	.046026	18.80	.997299	.23	.048727	19.03	.951273	37
24	.047154	18.75	.997285	.23	.049869	18.98	.950131	36
25	9.048279	18.68	9.997271	.23	9.051008	18.93	0.948992	35
26	.049400	18.65	.997257	.25	.052144	18.88	.947856	34
27	.050519	18.60	.997242	.23	.053277	18.83	.946723	33
28	.051635	18.57	.997228	.23	.054407	18.80	.945593	32
29	.052749	18.50	.997214	.25	.055535	18.73	.944465	31
30	9.053859	18.45	9.997199	.23	9.056659	18.70	0.943341	30
31	.054966	18.42	.997185	.25	.057781	18.65	.942219	29
32	.056071	18.35	.997170	.23	.058900	18.60	.941100	28
33	.057172	18.32	.997156	.25	.060016	18.57	.939984	27
34	.058271	18.27	.997141	.23	.061130	18.50	.938870	26
35	9.059367	18.22	9.997127	.25	9.062240	18.47	0.937760	25
36	.060460	18.18	.997112	.23	.063348	18.42	.936652	24
37	.061551	18.13	.997098	.25	.064453	18.38	.935547	23
38	.062639	18.08	.997083	.25	.065556	18.32	.934444	22
39	.063724	18.03	.997068	.25	.066655	18.28	.933345	21
40	9.064806	17.98	9.997053	.23	9.067752	18.23	0.932248	20
41	.065885	17.95	.997039	.25	.068846	18.20	.931154	19
42	.066962	17.90	.997024	.25	.069938	18.15	.930062	18
43	.068036	17.85	.997009	.25	.071027	18.10	.928973	17
44	.069107	17.82	.996994	.25	.072113	18.07	.927887	16
45	9.070176	17.77	9.996979	.25	9.073197	18.02	0.926803	15
46	.071242	17.73	.996964	.25	.074278	17.97	.925722	14
47	.072306	17.67	.996949	.25	.075356	17.93	.924644	13
48	.073366	17.63	.996934	.25	.076432	17.88	.923568	12
49	.074424	17.60	.996919	.25	.077505	17.85	.922495	11
50	9.075480	17.55	9.996904	.25	9.078576	17.80	0.921424	10
51	.076533	17.50	.996889	.25	.079644	17.77	.920356	9
52	.077583	17.47	.996873	.27	.080710	17.72	.919290	8
53	.078631	17.42	.996858	.25	.081773	17.67	.918227	7
54	.079676	17.38	.996843	.25	.082833	17.63	.917167	6
55	9.080719	17.33	9.996828	.27	9.083891	17.60	0.916109	5
56	.081759	17.30	.996812	.25	.084947	17.55	.915053	4
57	.082797	17.25	.996797	.25	.086000	17.50	.914000	3
58	.083832	17.20	.996782	.27	.087050	17.47	.912950	2
59	.084864	17.17	.996766	.25	.088098	17.43	.911902	1
60	9.085894		9.996751		9.089144		0.910856	0
	Cos.	D. 1″.	Sin.	D. 1″.	Cot.	D. 1″.	Tan.	M.

96°   83°

TABLE IX. LOGARITHMIC SINES,

7°   172°

M.	Sin.	D. 1".	Cos.	D. 1".	Tan.	D. 1".	Cot.	
0	9.085894	17.13	9.996751	.27	9.089144	17.38	0.910856	60
1	.086922	17.08	.996735	.25	.090187	17.35	.909813	59
2	.087947	17.05	.996720	.27	.091228	17.30	.908772	58
3	.088970	17.00	.996704	.27	.092266	17.27	.907734	57
4	.089990	16.97	.996688	.25	.093302	17.23	.906698	56
5	9.091008	16.93	9.996673	.27	9.094336	17.18	0.905664	55
6	.092024	16.88	.996657	.27	.095367	17.13	.904633	54
7	.093037	16.83	.996641	.27	.096395	17.13	.903605	53
8	.094047	16.82	.996625	.27	.097422	17.12	.902578	52
9	.095056	16.77	.996610	.25	.098446	17.07	.901554	51
10	9.096062	16.72	9.996594	.27	9.099468	17.03	0.900532	50
11	.097065	16.68	.996578	.27	.100487	16.98	.899513	49
12	.098066	16.65	.996562	.27	.101504	16.95	.898496	48
13	.099065	16.62	.996546	.27	.102519	16.92	.897481	47
14	.100062	16.57	.996530	.27	.103532	16.88	.896468	46
15	9.101056	16.53	9.996514	.27	9.104542	16.83	0.895458	45
16	.102048	16.48	.996498	.27	.105550	16.80	.894450	44
17	.103037	16.47	.996482	.28	.106556	16.77	.893444	43
18	.104025	16.42	.996465	.27	.107559	16.72	.892441	42
19	.105010	16.37	.996449	.27	.108560	16.68	.891440	41
20	9.105992	16.35	9.996433	.27	9.109559	16.65	0.890441	40
21	.106973	16.30	.996417	.28	.110556	16.62	.889444	39
22	.107951	16.27	.996400	.27	.111551	16.58	.888449	38
23	.108927	16.23	.996384	.27	.112543	16.53	.887457	37
24	.109901	16.20	.996368	.28	.113533	16.50	.886467	36
25	9.110873	16.15	9.996351	.27	9.114521	16.47	0.885479	35
26	.111842	16.12	.996335	.28	.115507	16.43	.884493	34
27	.112809	16.08	.996318	.27	.116491	16.40	.883509	33
28	.113774	16.05	.996302	.28	.117472	16.35	.882528	32
29	.114737	16.02	.996285	.27	.118452	16.33	.881548	31
30	9.115698	15.97	9.996269	.28	9.119429	16.28	0.880571	30
31	.116656	15.95	.996252	.28	.120404	16.25	.879596	29
32	.117613	15.90	.996235	.27	.121377	16.22	.878623	28
33	.118567	15.87	.996219	.28	.122348	16.18	.877652	27
34	.119519	15.83	.996202	.28	.123317	16.15	.876683	26
35	9.120469	15.80	9.996185	.28	9.124284	16.12	0.875716	25
36	.121417	15.75	.996168	.28	.125249	16.08	.874751	24
37	.122362	15.73	.996151	.28	.126211	16.03	.873789	23
38	.123306	15.70	.996134	.28	.127172	16.02	.872828	22
39	.124248	15.65	.996117	.28	.128130	15.97	.871870	21
40	9.125187	15.63	9.996100	.28	9.129087	15.95	0.870913	20
41	.126125	15.58	.996083	.28	.130041	15.90	.869959	19
42	.127060	15.55	.996066	.28	.130994	15.88	.869006	18
43	.127993	15.53	.996049	.28	.131944	15.83	.868056	17
44	.128925	15.48	.996032	.28	.132893	15.82	.867107	16
45	9.129854	15.45	9.996015	.28	9.133839	15.77	0.866161	15
46	.130781	15.42	.995998	.30	.134784	15.75	.865216	14
47	.131706	15.40	.995980	.28	.135726	15.70	.864274	13
48	.132630	15.35	.995963	.28	.136667	15.68	.863333	12
49	.133551	15.32	.995946	.30	.137605	15.63	.862395	11
50	9.134470	15.28	9.995928	.28	9.138542	15.62	0.861458	10
51	.135387	15.27	.995911	.28	.139476	15.57	.860524	9
52	.136303	15.22	.995894	.30	.140409	15.55	.859591	8
53	.137216	15.20	.995876	.28	.141340	15.52	.858660	7
54	.138128	15.15	.995859	.30	.142269	15.48	.857731	6
55	9.139037	15.12	9.995841	.30	9.143196	15.45	0.856804	5
56	.139944	15.10	.995823	.28	.144121	15.42	.855879	4
57	.140850	15.07	.995806	.30	.145044	15.38	.854956	3
58	.141754	15.02	.995788	.28	.145966	15.37	.854034	2
59	.142655	15.00	.995771	.30	.146885	15.32	.853115	1
60	9.143555		9.995753		9.147803	15.30	0.852197	0
	Cos.	D. 1".	Sin.	D. 1".	Cot.	D. 1".	Tan.	M.

97°   82°

COSINES, TANGENTS, AND COTANGENTS

8°   171°

M.	Sin.	D. 1″.	Cos.	D. 1″.	Tan.	D. 1″.	Cot.	
0	9.143555	14.97	9.995753	.30	9.147803	15.25	0.852197	60
1	.144453	14.93	.995735	.30	.148718	15.23	.851282	59
2	.145349	14.90	.995717	.30	.149632	15.20	.850368	58
3	.146243	14.88	.995699	.30	.150544	15.17	.849456	57
4	.147136	14.83	.995681	.28	.151454	15.15	.848546	56
5	9.148026	14.82	9.995664	.30	9.152363	15.10	0.847637	55
6	.148915	14.78	.995646	.30	.153269	15.08	.846731	54
7	.149802	14.73	.995628	.30	.154174	15.05	.845826	53
8	.150686	14.72	.995610	.32	.155077	15.02	.844923	52
9	.151569	14.70	.995591	.30	.155978	14.98	.844022	51
10	9.152451	14.65	9.995573	.30	9.156877	14.97	0.843123	50
11	.153330	14.63	.995555	.30	.157775	14.93	.842225	49
12	.154208	14.58	.995537	.30	.158671	14.90	.841329	48
13	.155083	14.57	.995519	.30	.159565	14.87	.840435	47
14	.155957	14.55	.995501	.32	.160457	14.83	.839543	46
15	9.156830	14.50	9.995482	.30	9.161347	14.82	0.838653	45
16	.157700	14.48	.995464	.30	.162236	14.78	.837764	44
17	.158569	14.43	.995446	.32	.163123	14.75	.836877	43
18	.159435	14.43	.995427	.30	.164008	14.73	.835992	42
19	.160301	14.38	.995409	.32	.164892	14.70	.835108	41
20	9.161164	14.35	9.995390	.30	9.165774	14.67	0.834226	40
21	.162025	14.33	.995372	.32	.166654	14.63	.833346	39
22	.162885	14.30	.995353	.32	.167532	14.62	.832468	38
23	.163743	14.28	.995334	.30	.168409	14.58	.831591	37
24	.164600	14.23	.995316	.32	.169284	14.55	.830716	36
25	9.165454	14.22	9.995297	.32	9.170157	14.53	0.829843	35
26	.166307	14.20	.995278	.30	.171029	14.50	.828971	34
27	.167159	14.15	.995260	.32	.171899	14.47	.828101	33
28	.168008	14.13	.995241	.32	.172767	14.45	.827233	32
29	.168856	14.10	.995222	.32	.173634	14.42	.826366	31
30	9.169702	14.08	9.995203	.32	9.174499	14.38	0.825501	30
31	.170547	14.03	.995184	.32	.175362	14.37	.824638	29
32	.171389	14.02	.995165	.32	.176224	14.33	.823776	28
33	.172230	14.00	.995146	.32	.177084	14.30	.822916	27
34	.173070	13.97	.995127	.32	.177942	14.28	.822058	26
35	9.173908	13.93	9.995108	.32	9.178799	14.27	0.821201	25
36	.174744	13.90	.995089	.22	.179655	14.22	.820345	24
37	.175578	13.88	.995070	.32	.180508	14.20	.819492	23
38	.176411	13.85	.995051	.32	.181360	14.18	.818640	22
39	.177242	13.83	.995032	.32	.182211	14.13	.817789	21
40	9.178072	13.80	9.995013	.33	9.183059	14.13	0.816941	20
41	.178900	13.77	.994993	.32	.183907	14.08	.816093	19
42	.179726	13.75	.994974	.32	.184752	14.08	.815248	18
43	.180551	13.72	.994955	.33	.185597	14.03	.814403	17
44	.181374	13.70	.994935	.32	.186439	14.02	.813561	16
45	9.182196	13.67	9.994916	.33	9.187280	14.00	0.812720	15
46	.183016	13.63	.994896	.32	.188120	13.97	.811880	14
47	.183834	13.62	.994877	.33	.188958	13.93	.811042	13
48	.184651	13.58	.994857	.32	.189794	13.92	.810206	12
49	.185466	13.57	.994838	.33	.190629	13.88	.809371	11
50	9.186280	13.53	9.994818	.33	9.191462	13.87	0.808538	10
51	.187092	13.52	.994798	.32	.192294	13.83	.807706	9
52	.187903	13.48	.994779	.33	.193124	13.82	.806876	8
53	.188712	13.45	.994759	.33	.193953	13.78	.806047	7
54	.189519	13.43	.994739	.32	.194780	13.77	.805220	6
55	9.190325	13.42	9.994720	.33	9.195606	13.73	0.804394	5
56	.191130	13.38	.994700	.33	.196430	13.72	.803570	4
57	.191933	13.35	.994680	.33	.197253	13.68	.802747	3
58	.192734	13.33	.994660	.33	.198074	13.67	.801926	2
59	.193534	13.30	.994640	.33	.198894	13.65	.801106	1
60	9.194332		9.994620		9.199713		0.800287	0
	Cos.	D. 1″.	Sin.	D. 1″.	Cot.	D. 1″.	Tan.	M.

APPENDIX B

TABLE IX. LOGARITHMIC SINES,

9°   170°

M.	Sin.	D. 1″.	Cos.	D. 1″.	Tan.	D. 1″.	Cot.	
0	9.194332		9.994620		9.199713		0.800287	60
1	.195129	13.28	.994600	.33	.200529	13.60	.799471	59
2	.195925	13.27	.994580	.33	.201345	13.60	.798655	58
3	.196719	13.23	.994560	.33	.202159	13.57	.797841	57
4	.197511	13.20	.994540	.33	.202971	13.53	.797029	56
5	9.198302	13.18	9.994519	.35	9.203782	13.52	0.796218	55
6	.199091	13.15	.994499	.33	.204592	13.50	.795408	54
7	.199879	13.13	.994479	.33	.205400	13.47	.794600	53
8	.200666	13.12	.994459	.33	.206207	13.45	.793793	52
9	.201451	13.08	.994438	.35	.207013	13.43	.792987	51
10	9.202234	13.05	9.994418	.33	9.207817	13.40	0.792183	50
11	.203017	13.05	.994398	.33	.208619	13.37	.791381	49
12	.203797	13.00	.994377	.35	.209420	13.35	.790580	48
13	.204577	13.00	.994357	.33	.210220	13.33	.789780	47
14	.205354	12.95	.994336	.35	.211018	13.30	.788982	46
15	9.206131	12.95	9.994316	.33	9.211815	13.28	0.788185	45
16	.206906	12.92	.994295	.35	.212611	13.27	.787389	44
17	.207679	12.88	.994274	.33	.213405	13.23	.786595	43
18	.208452	12.88	.994254	.35	.214198	13.22	.785802	42
19	.209222	12.83	.994233	.35	.214989	13.18	.785011	41
20	9.209992	12.83	9.994212	.35	9.215780	13.18	0.784220	40
21	.210760	12.80	.994191	.33	.216568	13.13	.783432	39
22	.211526	12.77	.994171	.35	.217356	13.13	.782644	38
23	.212291	12.75	.994150	.35	.218142	13.10	.781858	37
24	.213055	12.73	.994129	.35	.218926	13.07	.781074	36
25	9.213818	12.72	9.994108	.35	9.219710	13.07	0.780290	35
26	.214579	12.68	.994087	.35	.220492	13.03	.779508	34
27	.215338	12.65	.994066	.35	.221272	13.00	.778728	33
28	.216097	12.65	.994045	.35	.222052	13.00	.777948	32
29	.216854	12.62	.994024	.35	.222830	12.97	.777170	31
30	9.217609	12.58	9.994003	.35	9.223607	12.95	0.776393	30
31	.218363	12.57	.993982	.37	.224382	12.92	.775618	29
32	.219116	12.55	.993960	.35	.225156	12.90	.774844	28
33	.219868	12.53	.993939	.35	.225929	12.88	.774071	27
34	.220618	12.50	.993918	.35	.226700	12.85	.773300	26
35	9.221367	12.48	9.993897	.37	9.227471	12.85	0.772529	25
36	.222115	12.47	.993875	.35	.228239	12.80	.771761	24
37	.222861	12.43	.993854	.37	.229007	12.80	.770993	23
38	.223606	12.42	.993832	.35	.229773	12.77	.770227	22
39	.224349	12.38	.993811	.37	.230539	12.77	.769461	21
40	9.225092	12.38	9.993789	.35	9.231302	12.72	0.768698	20
41	.225833	12.35	.993768	.37	.232065	12.72	.767935	19
42	.226573	12.33	.993746	.35	.232826	12.68	.767174	18
43	.227311	12.30	.993725	.37	.233586	12.67	.766414	17
44	.228048	12.28	.993703	.37	.234345	12.65	.765655	16
45	9.228784	12.27	9.993681	.35	9.235103	12.63	0.764897	15
46	.229518	12.23	.993660	.37	.235859	12.60	.764141	14
47	.230252	12.23	.993638	.37	.236614	12.58	.763386	13
48	.230984	12.20	.993616	.37	.237368	12.57	.762632	12
49	.231715	12.18	.993594	.37	.238120	12.53	.761880	11
50	9.232444	12.15	9.993572	.37	9.238872	12.53	0.761128	10
51	.233172	12.13	.993550	.37	.239622	12.50	.760378	9
52	.233899	12.12	.993528	.37	.240371	12.48	.759629	8
53	.234625	12.10	.993506	.37	.241118	12.45	.758882	7
54	.235349	12.07	.993484	.37	.241865	12.45	.758135	6
55	9.236073	12.07	9.993462	.37	9.242610	12.42	0.757390	5
56	.236795	12.03	.993440	.37	.243354	12.40	.756646	4
57	.237515	12.00	.993418	.37	.244097	12.38	.755903	3
58	.238235	12.00	.993396	.37	.244839	12.37	.755161	2
59	.238953	11.97	.993374	.37	.245579	12.33	.754421	1
60	9.239670	11.95	9.993351	.38	9.246319	12.33	0.753681	0
	Cos.	D. 1″.	Sin.	D. 1″.	Cot.	D. 1″.	Tan.	M.

99°   80°

COSINES, TANGENTS, AND COTANGENTS

10° 169°

M.	Sin.	D. 1″.	Cos.	D. 1″.	Tan.	D. 1″.	Cot.	
0	9.239670	11.93	9.993351	.37	9.246319	12.30	0.753681	60
1	.240386	11.92	.993329	.37	.247057	12.28	.752943	59
2	.241101	11.88	.993307	.37	.247794	12.27	.752206	58
3	.241814	11.87	.993284	.38	.248530	12.23	.751470	57
4	.242526	11.85	.993262	.37	.249264	12.23	.750736	56
5	9.243237	11.83	9.993240	.37	9.249998	12.20	0.750002	55
6	.243947	11.82	.993217	.38	.250730	12.18	.749270	54
7	.244656	11.78	.993195	.37	.251461	12.17	.748539	53
8	.245363	11.77	.993172	.38	.252191	12.15	.747809	52
9	.246069	11.77	.993149	.38	.252920	12.13	.747080	51
10	9.246775	11.72	9.993127	.37	9.253648	12.10	0.746352	50
11	.247478	11.72	.993104	.38	.254374	12.10	.745626	49
12	.248181	11.70	.993081	.38	.255100	12.07	.744900	48
13	.248883	11.67	.993059	.37	.255824	12.05	.744176	47
14	.249583	11.65	.993036	.38	.256547	12.03	.743453	46
15	9.250282	11.63	9.993013	.38	9.257269	12.02	0.742731	45
16	.250980	11.62	.992990	.38	.257990	12.00	.742010	44
17	.251677	11.60	.992967	.38	.258710	11.98	.741290	43
18	.252373	11.57	.992944	.38	.259429	11.95	.740571	42
19	.253067	11.57	.992921	.38	.260146	11.95	.739854	41
20	9.253761	11.53	9.992898	.38	9.260863	11.92	0.739137	40
21	.254453	11.52	.992875	.38	.261578	11.90	.738422	39
22	.255144	11.50	.992852	.38	.262292	11.88	.737708	38
23	.255834	11.48	.992829	.38	.263005	11.87	.736995	37
24	.256523	11.47	.992806	.38	.263717	11.85	.736283	36
25	9.257211	11.45	9.992783	.40	9.264428	11.83	0.735572	35
26	.257898	11.42	.992759	.38	.265138	11.82	.734862	34
27	.258583	11.42	.992736	.38	.265847	11.80	.734153	33
28	.259268	11.38	.992713	.38	.266555	11.77	.733445	32
29	.259951	11.37	.992690	.40	.267261	11.77	.732739	31
30	9.260633	11.35	9.992666	.38	9.267967	11.73	0.732033	30
31	.261314	11.33	.992643	.40	.268671	11.73	.731329	29
32	.261994	11.32	.992619	.38	.269375	11.70	.730625	28
33	.262673	11.30	.992596	.40	.270077	11.70	.729923	27
34	.263351	11.27	.992572	.40	.270779	11.67	.729221	26
35	9.264027	11.27	9.992549	.38	9.271479	11.65	0.728521	25
36	.264703	11.23	.992525	.40	.272178	11.63	.727822	24
37	.265377	11.23	.992501	.40	.272876	11.62	.727124	23
38	.266051	11.20	.992478	.38	.273573	11.60	.726427	22
39	.266723	11.20	.992454	.40	.274269	11.58	.725731	21
40	9.267395	11.17	9.992430	.40	9.274964	11.57	0.725036	20
41	.268065	11.15	.992406	.40	.275658	11.55	.724342	19
42	.268734	11.13	.992382	.38	.276351	11.53	.723649	18
43	.269402	11.12	.992359	.40	.277043	11.52	.722957	17
44	.270069	11.10	.992335	.40	.277734	11.50	.722266	16
45	9.270735	11.08	9.992311	.40	9.278424	11.48	0.721576	15
46	.271400	11.07	.992287	.40	.279113	11.47	.720887	14
47	.272064	11.03	.992263	.40	.279801	11.45	.720199	13
48	.272726	11.03	.992239	.42	.280483	11.43	.719512	12
49	.273388	11.02	.992214	.40	.281174	11.40	.718826	11
50	9.274049	10.98	9.992190	.40	9.281858	11.40	0.718142	10
51	.274708	10.98	.992166	.40	.282542	11.33	.717458	9
52	.275367	10.97	.992142	.40	.283225	11.37	.716775	8
53	.276025	10.93	.992118	.42	.283907	11.35	.716093	7
54	.276681	10.93	.992093	.40	.284588	11.33	.715412	6
55	9.277337	10.90	9.992069	.42	9.285268	11.32	0.714732	5
56	.277991	10.90	.992044	.40	.285947	11.28	.714053	4
57	.278645	10.87	.992020	.40	.286624	11.28	.713376	3
58	.279297	10.85	.991996	.40	.287301	11.27	.712699	2
59	.279948	10.85	.991971	.42	.287977	11.25	.712023	1
60	9.280599		9.991947	.40	9.288652		0.711348	0
	Cos.	D. 1″.	Sin.	D. 1″.	Cot.	D. 1″.	Tan.	M.

100° 79°

TABLE IX. LOGARITHMIC SINES,

11°　　　　　　　　　　　　　　　　　　　　　　　　　　　168°

M.	Sin.	D. 1″.	Cos.	D. 1″.	Tan.	D. 1″.	Cot.	
0	9.280599	10.82	9.991947	.42	9.288652	11.23	0.711348	60
1	.281248	10.82	.991922	.42	.289326	11.22	.710674	59
2	.281897	10.78	.991897	.42	.289999	11.20	.710001	58
3	.282544	10.77	.991873	.40	.290671	11.18	.709329	57
4	.283190	10.77	.991848	.42	.291342	11.18	.708658	56
5	9.283836	10.73	9.991823	.42	9.292013	11.15	0.707987	55
6	.284480	10.73	.991799	.40	.292682	11.13	.707318	54
7	.285124	10.70	.991774	.42	.293350	11.13	.706650	53
8	.285766	10.70	.991749	.42	.294017	11.12	.705983	52
9	.286408	10.67	.991724	.42	.294684	11.12	.705316	51
10	9.287048	10.67	9.991699	.42	9.295349	11.08	0.704651	50
11	.287688	10.63	.991674	.42	.296013	11.07	.703987	49
12	.288326	10.63	.991649	.42	.296677	11.07	.703323	48
13	.288964	10.60	.991624	.42	.297339	11.03	.702661	47
14	.289600	10.60	.991599	.42	.298001	11.03	.701999	46
15	9.290236	10.57	9.991574	.42	9.298662	11.02	0.701338	45
16	.290870	10.57	.991549	.42	.299322	11.00	.700678	44
17	.291504	10.55	.991524	.42	.299980	10.97	.700020	43
18	.292137	10.52	.991498	.43	.300638	10.97	.699362	42
19	.292768	10.52	.991473	.42	.301295	10.95	.698705	41
20	9.293399	10.50	9.991448	.42	9.301951	10.93	0.698049	40
21	.294029	10.48	.991422	.43	.302607	10.93	.697393	39
22	.294658	10.47	.991397	.42	.303261	10.90	.696739	38
23	.295286	10.45	.991372	.42	.303914	10.88	.696086	37
24	.295913	10.43	.991346	.43	.304567	10.88	.695433	36
25	9.296539	10.42	9.991321	.42	9.305218	10.85	0.694782	35
26	.297164	10.40	.991295	.43	.305869	10.85	.694131	34
27	.297788	10.40	.991270	.42	.306519	10.83	.693481	33
28	.298412	10.37	.991244	.43	.307168	10.82	.692832	32
29	.299034	10.35	.991218	.43	.307816	10.80	.692184	31
30	9.299655	10.35	9.991193	.42	9.308463	10.78	0.691537	30
31	.300276	10.32	.991167	.43	.309109	10.77	.690891	29
32	.300895	10.32	.991141	.43	.309754	10.75	.690246	28
33	.301514	10.30	.991115	.43	.310399	10.75	.689601	27
34	.302132	10.27	.991090	.42	.311042	10.72	.688958	26
35	9.302748	10.27	9.991064	.43	9.311685	10.72	0.688315	25
36	.303364	10.25	.991038	.43	.312327	10.70	.687673	24
37	.303979	10.23	.991012	.43	.312968	10.68	.687032	23
38	.304593	10.23	.990986	.43	.313608	10.67	.686392	22
39	.305207	10.20	.990960	.43	.314247	10.65	.685753	21
40	9.305819	10.18	9.990934	.43	9.314885	10.63	0.685115	20
41	.306430	10.18	.990908	.43	.315523	10.63	.684477	19
42	.307041	10.15	.990882	.43	.316159	10.60	.683841	18
43	.307650	10.15	.990855	.45	.316795	10.60	.683205	17
44	.308259	10.13	.990829	.43	.317430	10.58	.682570	16
45	9.308867	10.12	9.990803	.43	9.318064	10.57	0.681936	15
46	.309474	10.10	.990777	.43	.318697	10.55	.681303	14
47	.310080	10.08	.990750	.45	.319330	10.55	.680670	13
48	.310685	10.07	.990724	.43	.319961	10.52	.680039	12
49	.311289	10.07	.990697	.45	.320592	10.52	.679408	11
50	9.311893	10.03	9.990671	.43	9.321222	10.50	0.678778	10
51	.312495	10.03	.990645	.43	.321851	10.48	.678149	9
52	.313097	10.02	.990618	.45	.322479	10.47	.677521	8
53	.313698	9.98	.990591	.45	.323106	10.45	.676894	7
54	.314297	10.00	.990565	.43	.323733	10.45	.676267	6
55	9.314897	9.97	9.990538	.45	9.324358	10.42	0.675642	5
56	.315495	9.95	.990511	.45	.324983	10.42	.675017	4
57	.316092	9.95	.990485	.43	.325607	10.40	.674393	3
58	.316689	9.92	.990458	.45	.326231	10.40	.673769	2
59	.317284	9.92	.990431	.45	.326853	10.37	.673147	1
60	9.317879		9.990404	.45	9.327475	10.37	0.672525	0
	Cos.	D. 1″.	Sin.	D. 1″.	Cot.	D. 1″.	Tan.	M.

101°　　　　　　　　　　　　　　　　　　　　　　　　　　　78°

COSINES, TANGENTS, AND COTANGENTS

12°   167

M.	Sin.	D. 1".	Cos.	D. 1".	Tan.	D. 1".	Cot.	
0	9.317879	9.90	9.990404	.43	9.327475	10.33	0.672525	60
1	.318473	9.88	.990378	.45	.328095	10.33	.671905	59
2	.319066	9.87	.990351	.45	.328715	10.32	.671285	58
3	.319658	9.85	.990324	.45	.329334	10.32	.670666	57
4	.320249	9.85	.990297	.45	.329953	10.28	.670047	56
5	9.320840	9.83	9.990270	.45	9.330570	10.28	0.669430	55
6	.321430	9.82	.990243	.47	.331187	10.27	.668813	54
7	.322019	9.80	.990215	.45	.331803	10.25	.668197	53
8	.322607	9.78	.990188	.45	.332418	10.25	.667582	52
9	.323194	9.77	.990161	.45	.333033	10.22	.666967	51
10	9.323780	9.77	9.990134	.45	9.333646	10.22	0.666354	50
11	.324366	9.73	.990107	.47	.334259	10.20	.665741	49
12	.324950	9.73	.990079	.45	.334871	10.18	.665129	48
13	.325534	9.72	.990052	.45	.335482	10.18	.664518	47
14	.326117	9.72	.990025	.47	.336093	10.15	.663907	46
15	9.326700	9.68	9.989997	.45	9.336702	10.15	0.663298	45
16	.327281	9.68	.989970	.47	.337311	10.13	.662689	44
17	.327862	9.67	.989942	.45	.337919	10.13	.662081	43
18	.328442	9.65	.989915	.47	.338527	10.10	.661473	42
19	.329021	9.63	.989887	.45	.339133	10.10	.660867	41
20	9.329599	9.62	9.989860	.47	9.339739	10.08	0.660261	40
21	.330176	9.62	.989832	.47	.340344	10.07	.659656	39
22	.330753	9.60	.989804	.45	.340948	10.07	.659052	38
23	.331329	9.57	.989777	.47	.341552	10.05	.658448	37
24	.331903	9.58	.989749	.47	.342155	10.03	.657845	36
25	9.332478	9.55	9.989721	.47	9.342757	10.02	0.657243	35
26	.333051	9.55	.989693	.47	.343358	10.00	.656642	34
27	.333624	9.52	.989665	.47	.343958	10.00	.656042	33
28	.334195	9.53	.989637	.47	.344558	9.98	.655442	32
29	.334767	9.50	.989610	.45	.345157	9.97	.654843	31
30	9.335337	9.48	9.989582	.47	9.345755	9.97	0.654245	30
31	.335906	9.48	.989553	.48	.346353	9.93	.653647	29
32	.336475	9.47	.989525	.47	.346949	9.93	.653051	28
33	.337043	9.45	.989497	.47	.347545	9.93	.652455	27
34	.337610	9.43	.989469	.47	.348141	9.90	.651859	26
35	9.338176	9.43	9.989441	.47	9.348735	9.90	0.651265	25
36	.338742	9.42	.989413	.47	.349329	9.88	.650671	24
37	.339307	9.40	.989385	.48	.349922	9.87	.650078	23
38	.339871	9.38	.989356	.47	.350514	9.87	.649486	22
39	.340434	9.37	.989328	.47	.351106	9.85	.648894	21
40	9.340996	9.37	9.989300	.48	9.351697	9.83	0.648303	20
41	.341558	9.35	.989271	.47	.352287	9.82	.647713	19
42	.342119	9.33	.989243	.48	.352876	9.82	.647124	18
43	.342679	9.33	.989214	.47	.353465	9.80	.646535	17
44	.343239	9.30	.989186	.48	.354053	9.78	.645947	16
45	9.343797	9.30	9.989157	.48	9.354640	9.78	0.645360	15
46	.344355	9.28	.989128	.47	.355227	9.77	.644773	14
47	.344912	9.28	.989100	.48	.355813	9.75	.644187	13
48	.345469	9.25	.989071	.48	.356398	9.73	.643602	12
49	.346024	9.25	.989042	.47	.356982	9.73	.643018	11
50	9.346579	9.25	9.989014	.48	9.357566	9.72	0.642434	10
51	.347134	9.22	.988985	.48	.358149	9.70	.641851	9
52	.347687	9.22	.988956	.48	.358731	9.70	.641269	8
53	.348240	9.20	.988927	.48	.359313	9.67	.640687	7
54	.348792	9.18	.988898	.48	.359893	9.68	.640107	6
55	9.349343	9.17	9.988869	.48	9.360474	9.65	0.639526	5
56	.349893	9.17	.988840	.48	.361053	9.65	.638947	4
57	.350443	9.15	.988811	.48	.361632	9.63	.638368	3
58	.350992	9.13	.988782	.48	.362210	9.62	.637790	2
59	.351540	9.13	.988753	.48	.362787	9.62	.637213	1
60	9.352088		9.988724		9.363364		0.636636	0
	Cos.	D. 1".	Sin.	D. 1".	Cot.	D. 1".	Tan.	M.

102°   77°

TABLE IX. LOGARITHMIC SINES,

13°   166°

M.	Sin.	D. 1".	Cos.	D. 1".	Tan.	D. 1".	Cot.	
0	9.352088	9.12	9.988724	.48	9.363364	9.60	0.636636	60
1	.352635	9.10	.988695	.48	.363940	9.58	.636060	59
2	.353181	9.08	.988666	.50	.364515	9.58	.635485	58
3	.353726	9.08	.988636	.48	.365090	9.57	.634910	57
4	.354271	9.07	.988607	.48	.365664	9.55	.634336	56
5	9.354815	9.05	9.988578	.50	9.366237	9.55	0.633763	55
6	.355358	9.05	.988548	.48	.366810	9.53	.633190	54
7	.355901	9.03	.988519	.50	.367382	9.52	.632618	53
8	.356443	9.02	.988489	.48	.367953	9.52	.632047	52
9	.356984	9.00	.988460	.50	.368524	9.50	.631476	51
10	9.357524	9.00	9.988430	.48	9.369094	9.48	0.630906	50
11	.358064	8.98	.988401	.50	.369663	9.48	.630337	49
12	.358603	8.97	.988371	.48	.370232	9.45	.629768	48
13	.359141	8.95	.988342	.50	.370799	9.47	.629201	47
14	.359678	8.95	.988312	.50	.371367	9.43	.628633	46
15	9.360215	8.95	9.988282	.50	9.371933	9.43	0.628067	45
16	.360752	8.92	.988252	.48	.372499	9.42	.627501	44
17	.361287	8.92	.988223	.50	.373064	9.42	.626936	43
18	.361822	8.90	.988193	.50	.373629	9.40	.626371	42
19	.362356	8.88	.988163	.50	.374193	9.38	.625807	41
20	9.362889	8.88	9.988133	.50	9.374756	9.38	0.625244	40
21	.363422	8.87	.988103	.50	.375319	9.37	.624681	39
22	.363954	8.85	.988073	.50	.375881	9.35	.624119	38
23	.364485	8.85	.988043	.50	.376442	9.35	.623558	37
24	.365016	8.83	.988013	.50	.377003	9.33	.622997	36
25	9.365546	8.82	9.987983	.50	9.377563	9.32	0.622437	35
26	.366075	8.82	.987953	.50	.378122	9.32	.621878	34
27	.366604	8.78	.987922	.52	.378681	9.30	.621319	33
28	.367131	8.80	.987892	.50	.379239	9.30	.620761	32
29	.367659	8.77	.987862	.50	.379797	9.28	.620203	31
30	9.368185	8.77	9.987832	.52	9.380354	9.27	0.619646	30
31	.368711	8.75	.987801	.50	.380910	9.27	.619090	29
32	.369236	8.75	.987771	.52	.381466	9.23	.618534	28
33	.369761	8.73	.987740	.50	.382020	9.25	.617980	27
34	.370285	8.72	.987710	.52	.382575	9.23	.617425	26
35	9.370808	8.70	9.987679	.50	9.383129	9.22	0.616871	25
36	.371330	8.70	.987649	.52	.383682	9.20	.616318	24
37	.371852	8.68	.987618	.50	.384234	9.20	.615766	23
38	.372373	8.68	.987588	.52	.384786	9.18	.615214	22
39	.372894	8.67	.987557	.52	.385337	9.18	.614663	21
40	9.373414	8.65	9.987526	.50	9.385888	9.17	0.614112	20
41	.373933	8.65	.987496	.52	.386438	9.15	.613562	19
42	.374452	8.63	.987465	.52	.386987	9.15	.613013	18
43	.374970	8.62	.987434	.52	.387536	9.13	.612464	17
44	.375487	8.60	.987403	.52	.388084	9.12	.611916	16
45	9.376003	8.60	9.987372	.52	9.388631	9.12	0.611369	15
46	.376519	8.60	.987341	.52	.389178	9.10	.610822	14
47	.377035	8.57	.987310	.52	.389724	9.10	.610276	13
48	.377549	8.57	.987279	.52	.390270	9.08	.609730	12
49	.378063	8.57	.987248	.52	.390815	9.08	.609185	11
50	9.378577	8.53	9.987217	.52	9.391360	9.05	0.608640	10
51	.379089	8.53	.987186	.52	.391903	9.07	.608097	9
52	.379601	8.53	.987155	.52	.392447	9.03	.607553	8
53	.380113	8.52	.987124	.53	.392989	9.03	.607011	7
54	.380624	8.50	.987092	.52	.393531	9.03	.606469	6
55	9.381134	8.48	9.987061	.52	9.394073	9.02	0.605927	5
56	.381643	8.48	.987030	.53	.394614	9.00	.605386	4
57	.382152	8.48	.986998	.52	.395154	9.00	.604846	3
58	.382661	8.45	.986967	.52	.395694	8.98	.604306	2
59	.383168	8.45	.986936	.53	.396233	8.97	.603767	1
60	9.383675		9.986904		9.396771		0.603229	0
	Cos.	D. 1".	Sin.	D. 1".	Cot.	D. 1".	Tan.	M.

COSINES, TANGENTS, AND COTANGENTS

14°   165°

M.	Sin.	D. 1″.	Cos.	D. 1″.	Tan.	D. 1″.	Cot.	
0	9.383675	8.45	9.986901	.52	9.396771	8.97	0.603229	60
1	.384182	8.42	.986873	.53	.397309	8.95	.602691	59
2	.384687	8.42	.986841	.53	.397846	8.95	.602154	58
3	.385192	8.42	.986809	.52	.398383	8.93	.601617	57
4	.385697	8.40	.986778	.53	.398919	8.93	.601081	56
5	9.386201	8.38	9.986746	.53	9.399455	8.92	0.600545	55
6	.386704	8.38	.986714	.52	.399990	8.90	.600010	54
7	.387207	8.37	.986683	.53	.400524	8.90	.599476	53
8	.387709	8.35	.986651	.53	.401058	8.88	.598942	52
9	.388210	8.35	.986619	.53	.401591	8.88	.598409	51
10	9.388711	8.33	9.986587	.53	9.402124	8.87	0.597876	50
11	.389211	8.33	.986555	.53	.402656	8.85	.597344	49
12	.389711	8.32	.986523	.53	.403187	8.85	.596813	48
13	.390210	8.30	.986491	.53	.403718	8.85	.596282	47
14	.390708	8.30	.986459	.53	.404249	8.82	.595751	46
15	9.391206	8.28	9.986427	.53	9.404778	8.83	0.595222	45
16	.391703	8.27	.986395	.53	.405308	8.80	.594692	44
17	.392199	8.27	.986363	.53	.405836	8.80	.594164	43
18	.392695	8.27	.986331	.53	.406364	8.80	.593636	42
19	.393191	8.23	.986299	.55	.406892	8.78	.593108	41
20	9.393685	8.23	9.986266	.53	9.407419	8.77	0.592581	40
21	.394179	8.23	.986234	.53	.407945	8.77	.592055	39
22	.394673	8.22	.986202	.55	.408471	8.75	.591529	38
23	.395166	8.20	.986169	.53	.408996	8.75	.591004	37
24	.395658	8.20	.986137	.55	.409521	8.73	.590479	36
25	9.396150	8.18	9.986104	.53	9.410045	8.73	0.589955	35
26	.396641	8.18	.986072	.55	.410569	8.72	.589431	34
27	.397132	8.15	.986039	.53	.411092	8.72	.588908	33
28	.397621	8.17	.986007	.55	.411615	8.70	.588385	32
29	.398111	8.15	.985974	.53	.412137	8.68	.587863	31
30	9.398600	8.13	9.985942	.55	9.412658	8.68	0.587342	30
31	.399088	8.12	.985909	.55	.413179	8.67	.586821	29
32	.399575	8.12	.985876	.55	.413699	8.67	.586301	28
33	.400062	8.12	.985843	.55	.414219	8.65	.585781	27
34	.400549	8.10	.985811	.55	.414738	8.65	.585262	26
35	9.401035	8.08	9.985778	.55	9.415257	8.63	0.584743	25
36	.401520	8.08	.985745	.55	.415775	8.63	.584225	24
37	.402005	8.07	.985712	.55	.416293	8.62	.583707	23
38	.402489	8.05	.985679	.55	.416810	8.60	.583190	22
39	.402972	8.05	.985646	.55	.417326	8.60	.582674	21
40	9.403455	8.05	9.985613	.55	9.417842	8.60	0.582158	20
41	.403938	8.03	.985580	.55	.418358	8.58	.581612	19
42	.404420	8.02	.985547	.55	.418873	8.57	.581127	18
43	.404901	8.02	.985514	.57	.419387	8.57	.580613	17
44	.405382	8.00	.985480	.55	.419901	8.57	.580099	16
45	9.405862	7.98	9.985447	.55	9.420415	8.53	0.579585	15
46	.406341	7.98	.985414	.55	.420927	8.55	.579073	14
47	.406820	7.98	.985381	.57	.421440	8.53	.578560	13
48	.407299	7.97	.985347	.55	.421952	8.52	.578048	12
49	.407777	7.95	.985314	.57	.422463	8.52	.577537	11
50	9.408254	7.95	9.985280	.55	9.422974	8.50	0.577026	10
51	.408731	7.93	.985247	.57	.423484	8.48	.576516	9
52	.409207	7.92	.985213	.55	.423993	8.50	.576007	8
53	.409682	7.92	.985180	.57	.424503	8.47	.575497	7
54	.410157	7.92	.985146	.57	.425011	8.47	.574989	6
55	9.410632	7.90	9.985113	.55	9.425519	8.47	0.574481	5
56	.411106	7.88	.985079	.57	.426027	8.45	.573973	4
57	.411579	7.88	.985045	.57	.426534	8.45	.573466	3
58	.412052	7.87	.985011	.55	.427041	8.43	.572959	2
59	.412524	7.87	.984978	.57	.427547	8.42	.572453	1
60	9.412996		9.984944		9.428052		0.571948	0
	Cos.	D. 1″.	Sin.	D. 1.″	Cot.	D. 1″.	Tan.	M.

104°   75°

TABLE IX. LOGARITHMIC SINES,

15°   164°

M.	Sin.	D. 1″.	Cos.	D. 1″.	Tan.	D. 1″.	Cot.	
0	9.412996	7.85	9.984944	.57	9.428052	8.43	0.571948	60
1	.413467	7.85	.984910	.57	.428558	8.40	.571442	59
2	.413938	7.83	.984876	.57	.429062	8.40	.570938	58
3	.414408	7.83	.984842	.57	.429566	8.40	.570434	57
4	.414878	7.82	.984808	.57	.430070	8.38	.569930	56
5	9.415347	7.80	9.984774	.57	9.430573	8.37	0.569427	55
6	.415815	7.80	.984740	.57	.431075	8.37	.568925	54
7	.416283	7.80	.984706	.57	.431577	8.37	.568423	53
8	.416751	7.77	.984672	.57	.432079	8.35	.567921	52
9	.417217	7.78	.984638	.58	.432580	8.33	.567420	51
10	9.417684	7.77	9.984603	.57	9.433080	8.33	0.566920	50
11	.418150	7.75	.984569	.57	.433580	8.33	.566420	49
12	.418615	7.73	.984535	.58	.434080	8.32	.565920	48
13	.419079	7.75	.984500	.57	.434579	8.32	.565421	47
14	.419544	7.72	.984466	.57	.435078	8.30	.564922	46
15	9.420007	7.72	9.984432	.57	9.435576	8.28	0.564424	45
16	.420470	7.72	.984397	.58	.436073	8.28	.563927	44
17	.420933	7.70	.984363	.57	.436570	8.28	.563430	43
18	.421395	7.70	.984328	.58	.437067	8.27	.562933	42
19	.421857	7.68	.984294	.57	.437563	8.27	.562437	41
20	9.422318	7.67	9.984259	.58	9.438059	8.25	0.561941	40
21	.422778	7.67	.984224	.57	.438554	8.23	.561446	39
22	.423238	7.65	.984190	.58	.439048	8.25	.560952	38
23	.423697	7.65	.984155	.58	.439543	8.22	.560457	37
24	.424156	7.65	.984120	.58	.440036	8.22	.559964	36
25	9.424615	7.63	9.984085	.58	9.440529	8.22	0.559471	35
26	.425073	7.62	.984050	.58	.441022	8.20	.558978	34
27	.425530	7.62	.984015	.57	.441514	8.20	.558486	33
28	.425987	7.60	.983981	.58	.442006	8.18	.557994	32
29	.426443	7.60	.983946	.58	.442497	8.18	.557503	31
30	9.426899	7.58	9.983911	.60	9.442988	8.18	0.557012	30
31	.427354	7.58	.983875	.58	.443479	8.15	.556521	29
32	.427809	7.57	.983840	.58	.443968	8.17	.556032	28
33	.428263	7.57	.983805	.58	.444458	8.15	.555542	27
34	.428717	7.55	.983770	.58	.444947	8.13	.555053	26
35	9.429170	7.55	9.983735	.58	9.445435	8.13	0.554565	25
36	.429623	7.53	.983700	.60	.445923	8.13	.554077	24
37	.430075	7.53	.983664	.58	.446411	8.12	.553589	23
38	.430527	7.52	.983629	.58	.446898	8.10	.553102	22
39	.430978	7.52	.983594	.60	.447384	8.10	.552616	21
40	9.431429	7.50	9.983558	.58	9.447870	8.10	0.552130	20
41	.431879	7.50	.983523	.60	.448356	8.08	.551644	19
42	.432329	7.48	.983487	.58	.448841	8.08	.551159	18
43	.432778	7.47	.983452	.60	.449326	8.07	.550674	17
44	.433226	7.48	.983416	.58	.449810	8.07	.550190	16
45	9.433675	7.45	9.983381	.60	9.450294	8.05	0.549706	15
46	.434122	7.45	.983345	.60	.450777	8.05	.549223	14
47	.434569	7.45	.983309	.60	.451260	8.05	.548740	13
48	.435016	7.43	.983273	.58	.451743	8.03	.548257	12
49	.435462	7.43	.983238	.60	.452225	8.02	.547775	11
50	9.435908	7.42	9.983202	.60	9.452706	8.02	0.547294	10
51	.436353	7.42	.983166	.60	.453187	8.02	.546813	9
52	.436798	7.40	.983130	.60	.453668	8.00	.546332	8
53	.437242	7.40	.983094	.60	.454148	8.00	.545852	7
54	.437686	7.38	.983058	.60	.454628	7.98	.545372	6
55	9.438129	7.38	9.983022	.60	9.455107	7.98	0.544893	5
56	.438572	7.37	.982986	.60	.455586	7.97	.544414	4
57	.439014	7.37	.982950	.60	.456064	7.97	.543936	3
58	.439456	7.35	.982914	.60	.456542	7.95	.543458	2
59	.439897	7.35	.982878	.60	.457019	7.95	.542981	1
60	9.440338		9.982842		9.457496		0.542504	0
	Cos.	D. 1″.	Sin.	D. 1″.	Cot.	D. 1″.	Tan.	M.

COSINES, TANGENTS, AND COTANGENTS

16°   163°

M.	Sin.	D. 1″.	Cos.	D. 1″.	Tan.	D. 1″.	Cot.	
0	9.440338	7.33	9.982842	.62	9.457496	7.95	0.542504	60
1	.440778	7.33	.982805	.60	.457973	7.93	.542027	59
2	.441218	7.33	.982769	.60	.458449	7.93	.541551	58
3	.441658	7.30	.982733	.62	.458925	7.92	.541075	57
4	.442096	7.32	.982696	.60	.459400	7.92	.540600	56
5	9.442535	7.30	9.982660	.60	9.459875	7.90	0.540125	55
6	.442973	7.28	.982624	.62	.460349	7.90	.539651	54
7	.443410	7.28	.982587	.60	.460823	7.90	.539177	53
8	.443847	7.28	.982551	.62	.461297	7.88	.538703	52
9	.444284	7.27	.982514	.62	.461770	7.87	.538230	51
10	9.444720	7.25	9.982477	.60	9.462242	7.88	0.537758	50
11	.445155	7.25	.982441	.62	.462715	7.85	.537285	49
12	.445590	7.25	.982404	.62	.463186	7.87	.536814	48
13	.446025	7.23	.982367	.60	.463658	7.83	.536342	47
14	.446459	7.23	.982331	.62	.464128	7.85	.535872	46
15	9.446893	7.22	9.982294	.62	9.464599	7.83	0.535401	45
16	.447326	7.22	.982257	.62	.465069	7.83	.534931	44
17	.447759	7.20	.982220	.62	.465539	7.82	.534461	43
18	.448191	7.20	.982183	.62	.466008	7.82	.533992	42
19	.448623	7.18	.982146	.62	.466477	7.80	.533523	41
20	9.449054	7.18	9.982109	.62	9.466945	7.80	0.533055	40
21	.449485	7.17	.982072	.62	.467413	7.78	.532587	39
22	.449915	7.17	.982035	.62	.467880	7.78	.532120	38
23	.450345	7.17	.981998	.62	.468347	7.78	.531653	37
24	.450775	7.15	.981961	.62	.468814	7.77	.531186	36
25	9.451204	7.13	9.981924	.63	9.469280	7.77	0.530720	35
26	.451632	7.13	.981886	.62	.469746	7.75	.530254	34
27	.452060	7.13	.981849	.62	.470211	7.75	.529789	33
28	.452488	7.12	.981812	.63	.470676	7.75	.529324	32
29	.452915	7.12	.981774	.62	.471141	7.73	.528859	31
30	9.453342	7.10	9.981737	.62	9.471605	7.73	0.528395	30
31	.453768	7.10	.981700	.63	.472069	7.72	.527931	29
32	.454194	7.08	.981662	.62	.472532	7.72	.527468	28
33	.454619	7.08	.981625	.63	.472995	7.70	.527005	27
34	.455044	7.08	.981587	.63	.473457	7.70	.526543	26
35	9.455469	7.07	9.981549	.62	9.473919	7.70	0.526081	25
36	.455893	7.05	.981512	.63	.474381	7.68	.525619	24
37	.456316	7.05	.981474	.63	.474842	7.68	.525158	23
38	.456739	7.05	.981436	.63	.475303	7.67	.524697	22
39	.457162	7.03	.981399	.62	.475763	7.67	.524237	21
40	9.457584	7.03	9.981361	.63	9.476223	7.67	0.523777	20
41	.458006	7.02	.981323	.63	.476683	7.65	.523317	19
42	.458427	7.02	.981285	.63	.477142	7.65	.522858	18
43	.458848	7.00	.981247	.63	.477601	7.63	.522399	17
44	.459268	7.00	.981209	.63	.478059	7.63	.521941	16
45	9.459688	7.00	9.981171	.63	9.478517	7.63	0.521483	15
46	.460108	6.98	.981133	.63	.478975	7.62	.521025	14
47	.460527	6.98	.981095	.63	.479432	7.62	.520568	13
48	.460946	6.97	.981057	.63	.479889	7.60	.520111	12
49	.461364	6.97	.981019	.63	.480345	7.60	.519655	11
50	9.461782	6.95	9.980981	.65	9.480801	7.60	0.519199	10
51	.462199	6.95	.980942	.63	.481257	7.58	.518743	9
52	.462616	6.93	.980904	.63	.481712	7.58	.518288	8
53	.463032	6.93	.980866	.65	.482167	7.57	.517833	7
54	.463448	6.93	.980827	.63	.482621	7.57	.517379	6
55	9.463864	6.92	9.980789	.65	9.483075	7.57	0.516925	5
56	.464279	6.92	.980750	.63	.483529	7.55	.516471	4
57	.464694	6.90	.980712	.65	.483982	7.55	.516018	3
58	.465108	6.90	.980673	.63	.484435	7.53	.515565	2
59	.465522	6.88	.980635	.65	.484887	7.53	.515113	1
60	9.465935		9.980596		9.485339		0.514661	0
	Cos.	D. 1″.	Sin.	D. 1″.	Cot.	D. 1″.	Tan.	M.

TABLE IX.   LOGARITHMIC SINES,

17°   162°

M.	Sin.	D. 1″.	Cos.	D. 1″.	Tan.	D. 1″.	Cot.	
0	9.465935	6.88	9.980596	.63	9.485339	7.53	0.514661	60
1	.466348	6.88	.980558	.65	.485791	7.52	.514209	59
2	.466761	6.87	.980519	.65	.486242	7.52	.513758	58
3	.467173	6.87	.980480	.63	.486693	7.52	.513307	57
4	.467585	6.85	.980442	.65	.487143	7.50	.512857	56
5	9.467996	6.85	9.980403	.65	9.487593	7.50	0.512407	55
6	.468407	6.83	.980364	.65	.488043	7.50	.511957	54
7	.468817	6.83	.980325	.65	.488492	7.48	.511508	53
8	.469227	6.83	.980286	.65	.488941	7.48	.511059	52
9	.469637	6.82	.980247	.65	.489390	7.48	.510610	51
10	9.470046	6.82	9.980208	.65	9.489838	7.47	0.510162	50
11	.470455	6.80	.980169	.65	.490286	7.47	.509714	49
12	.470863	6.80	.980130	.65	.490733	7.45	.509267	48
13	.471271	6.80	.980091	.65	.491180	7.45	.508820	47
14	.471679	6.78	.980052	.67	.491627	7.45	.508373	46
15	9.472086	6.77	9.980012	.65	9.492073	7.43	0.507927	45
16	.472492	6.77	.979973	.65	.492519	7.43	.507481	44
17	.472898	6.77	.979934	.65	.492965	7.43	.507035	43
18	.473304	6.77	.979895	.67	.493410	7.42	.506590	42
19	.473710	6.75	.979855	.65	.493854	7.40	.506146	41
20	9.474115	6.73	9.979816	.67	9.494299	7.42	0.505701	40
21	.474519	6.73	.979776	.65	.494743	7.40	.505257	39
22	.474923	6.73	.979737	.67	.495186	7.38	.504814	38
23	.475327	6.72	.979697	.65	.495630	7.40	.504370	37
24	.475730	6.72	.979658	.67	.496073	7.38	.503927	36
25	9.476133	6.72	9.979618	.65	9.496515	7.37	0.503485	35
26	.476536	6.70	.979579	.67	.496957	7.37	.503043	34
27	.476938	6.70	.979539	.67	.497399	7.37	.502601	33
28	.477340	6.68	.979499	.67	.497841	7.37	.502159	32
29	.477741	6.68	979459	.65	.498282	7.35	.501718	31
30	9.478142	6.67	9.979420	.67	9.498722	7.33	0.501278	30
31	.478542	6.67	.979380	.67	.499163	7.35	.500837	29
32	.478942	6.67	.979340	.67	.499603	7.33	.500397	28
33	.479342	6.65	.979300	.67	.500042	7.32	.499958	27
34	.479741	6.65	.979260	.67	.500481	7.32	.499519	26
35	9.480140	6.65	9.979220	.67	9.500920	7.32	0.499080	25
36	.480539	6.63	.979180	.67	.501359	7.32	.498641	24
37	.480937	6.62	.979140	.67	.501797	7.30	.498203	23
38	.481334	6.62	.979100	.68	.502235	7.30	.497765	22
39	.481731	6.62	.979059	.67	.502672	7.28	.497328	21
40	9.482128	6.62	9.979019	.67	9.503109	7.28	0.496891	20
41	.482525	6.60	.978979	.67	.503546	7.28	.496454	19
42	.482921	6.58	.978939	.68	.503982	7.27	.496018	18
43	.483316	6.60	.978898	.67	.504418	7.27	.495582	17
44	.483712	6.58	.978858	.68	.504854	7.27	.495146	16
45	9.484107	6.57	9.978817	.67	9.505289	7.25	0.494711	15
46	.484501	6.57	.978777	.67	.505724	7.25	.494276	14
47	.484895	6.57	.978737	.68	.506159	7.25	.493841	13
48	.485289	6.55	.978696	.68	.506593	7.23	.493407	12
49	.485682	6.55	.978655	.67	.507027	7.23	.492973	11
50	9.486075	6.53	9.978615	.68	9.507460	7.22	0.492540	10
51	.486467	6.55	.978574	.68	.507803	7.22	.492107	9
52	.486860	6.52	.978533	.67	.508326	7.22	.491674	8
53	.487251	6.53	.978493	.68	.508759	7.20	.491241	7
54	.487643	6.52	.978452	.68	.509191	7.18	.490809	6
55	9.488034	6.50	9.978411	.68	9.509622	7.20	0.490378	5
56	.488424	6.50	.978370	.68	.510054	7.18	.489946	4
57	.488814	6.50	.978329	.68	.510485	7.18	.489515	3
58	.489204	6.48	.978288	.68	.510916	7.17	.489084	2
59	.489593	6.48	.978247	.68	.511346	7.17	.488654	1
60	9.489982		9.978206		9.511776		0.488224	0
	Cos.	D. 1″.	Sin.	D. 1″.	Cot.	D. 1″.	Tan.	M.

COSINES, TANGENTS, AND COTANGENTS

18°   161°

M.	Sin.	D. 1″.	Cos.	D. 1″.	Tan.	D. 1″.	Cot.	
0	9.489982	6.48	9.978206	.68	9.511776	7.17	0.488224	60
1	.490371	6.47	.978165	.68	.512206	7.15	.487794	59
2	.490759	6.47	.978124	.68	.512635	7.15	.487365	58
3	.491147	6.47	.978083	.68	.513064	7.15	.486936	57
4	.491535	6.45	.978042	.68	.513493	7.13	.486507	56
5	9.491922	6.43	9.978001	.70	9.513921	7.13	0.486079	55
6	.492308	6.45	.977959	.68	.514349	7.13	.485651	54
7	.492695	6.43	.977918	.68	.514777	7.12	.485223	53
8	.493081	6.42	.977877	.70	.515204	7.12	.484796	52
9	.493466	6.42	.977835	.68	.515631	7.10	.484369	51
10	9.493851	6.42	9.977794	.70	9.516057	7.12	0.483943	50
11	.494236	0.42	.977752	.68	.516484	7.10	.483516	49
12	.494621	6.40	.977711	.70	.516910	7.08	.483090	48
13	.495005	6.38	.977669	.68	.517335	7.10	.482665	47
14	.495388	6.40	.977628	.70	.517761	7.08	.482239	46
15	9.495772	6.37	9.977586	.70	9.518186	7.07	0.481814	45
16	.496154	6.38	.977544	.68	.518610	7.07	.481390	44
17	.496537	6.37	.977503	.70	.519034	7.07	.480966	43
18	.496919	6.37	.977461	.70	.519458	7.07	.480542	42
19	.497301	6.35	.977419	.70	.519882	7.05	.480118	41
20	9.497682	6.37	9.977377	.70	9.520305	7.05	0.479695	40
21	.498064	6.33	.977335	.70	.520728	7.05	.479272	39
22	.498444	6.35	.977293	.70	.521151	7.03	.478849	38
23	.498825	6.32	.977251	.70	.521573	7.03	.478427	37
24	.499204	6.33	.977209	.70	.521995	7.03	.478005	36
25	9.499584	6.32	9.977167	.70	9.522417	7.02	0.477583	35
26	.499963	6.32	.977125	.70	.522838	7.02	.477162	34
27	.500342	6.32	.977083	.70	.523259	7.02	.476741	33
28	.500721	6.30	.977041	.70	.523680	7.00	.476320	32
29	.501099	6.28	.976999	.70	.524100	7.00	.475900	31
30	9.501476	6.30	9.976957	.72	9.524520	7.00	0.475480	30
31	.501854	6.28	.976914	.70	.524940	6.98	.475060	29
32	.502231	6.27	.976872	.70	.525359	6.98	.474641	28
33	.502607	6.28	.976830	.72	.525778	6.98	.474222	27
34	.502984	6.27	.976787	.70	.526197	6.97	.473803	26
35	9.503360	6.25	9.976745	.72	9.526615	6.97	0.473385	25
36	.503735	6.25	.976702	.70	.527033	6.97	.472967	24
37	.504110	6.25	.976660	.72	.527451	6.95	.472549	23
38	.504485	6.25	.976617	.72	.527868	6.95	.472132	22
39	.504860	6.23	.976574	.70	.528285	6.95	.471715	21
40	9.505234	6.23	9.976532	.72	9.528702	6.95	0.471298	20
41	.505608	6.22	.976489	.72	.529119	6.93	.470881	19
42	.505981	6.22	.976446	.70	.529535	6.93	.470465	18
43	.506354	6.22	.976404	.72	.529951	6.92	.470049	17
44	.506727	6.20	.976361	.72	.530366	6.92	.469634	16
45	9.507099	6.20	9.976318	.72	9.530781	6.92	0.469219	15
46	.507471	6.20	.976275	.72	.531196	6.92	.468804	14
47	.507843	6.18	.976232	.72	.531611	6.90	.468389	13
48	.508214	6.18	.976189	.72	.532025	6.90	.467975	12
49	.508585	6.18	.976146	.72	.532439	6.90	.467561	11
50	9.508956	6.17	9.976103	.72	9.532853	6.88	0.467147	10
51	.509326	6.17	.976060	.72	.533266	6.88	.466734	9
52	.509696	6.15	.976017	.72	.533679	6.88	.466321	8
53	.510065	6.15	.975974	.72	.534092	6.87	.465908	7
54	.510434	6.15	.975930	.73	.534504	6.87	.465496	6
55	9.510803	6.15	9.975887	.72	9.534916	6.87	0.465084	5
56	.511172	6.13	.975844	.72	.535328	6.85	.464672	4
57	.511540	6.12	.975800	.73	.535739	6.85	.464261	3
58	.511907	6.13	.975757	.72	.536150	6.85	.463850	2
59	.512275	6.12	.975714	.73	.536561	6.85	.463439	1
60	9.512642		9.975670		9.536972		0.463028	0
	Cos.	D. 1″.	Sin.	D. 1″.	Cot.	D. 1″.	Tan.	M.

TABLE IX. LOGARITHMIC SINES,

19°   160°

M.	Sin.	D. 1″.	Cos.	D. 1″.	Tan.	D. 1″.	Cot.	
0	9.512642	6.12	9.975670	.72	9.536972	6.83	0.463028	60
1	.513009	6.10	.975627	.73	.537382	6.83	.462618	59
2	.513375	6.10	.975583	.73	.537792	6.83	.462208	58
3	.513741	6.10	.975539	.72	.538202	6.83	.461798	57
4	.514107	6.08	.975496	.73	.538611	6.82	.461389	56
5	9.514472	6.08	9.975452	.73	9.539020	6.82	0.460980	55
6	.514837	6.08	.975408	.72	.539429	6.82	.460571	54
7	.515202	6.07	.975365	.73	.539837	6.80	.460163	53
8	.515566	6.07	.975321	.73	.540245	6.80	.459755	52
9	.515930	6.07	.975277	.73	.540653	6.80	.459347	51
10	9.516294	6.05	9.975233	.73	9.541061	6.80	0.458939	50
11	.516657	6.05	.975189	.73	.541468	6.78	.458532	49
12	.517020	6.03	.975145	.73	.541875	6.78	.458125	48
13	.517382	6.05	.975101	.73	.542281	6.77	.457719	47
14	.517745	6.03	.975057	.73	.542688	6.78	.457312	46
15	9.518107	6.02	9.975013	.73	9.543094	6.77	0.456906	45
16	.518468	6.02	.974969	.73	.543499	6.75	.456501	44
17	.518829	6.02	.974925	.75	.543905	6.77	.456095	43
18	.519190	6.02	.974880	.73	.544310	6.75	.455690	42
19	.519551	6.00	.974836	.73	.544715	6.75	.455285	41
20	9.519911	6.00	9.974792	.73	9.545119	6.73	0.454881	40
21	.520271	6.00	.974748	.75	.545524	6.75	.454476	39
22	.520631	5.98	.974703	.73	.545928	6.73	.454072	38
23	.520990	5.98	.974659	.75	.546331	6.72	.453669	37
24	.521349	5.97	.974614	.73	.546735	6.73	.453265	36
25	9.521707	5.98	9.974570	.73	9.547138	6.72	0.452862	35
26	.522066	5.97	.974525	.75	.547540	6.70	.452460	34
27	.522424	5.95	.974481	.73	.547943	6.72	.452057	33
28	.522781	5.95	.974436	.75	.548345	6.70	.451655	32
29	.523138	5.95	.974391	.75	.548747	6.70	.451253	31
30	9.523495	5.95	9.974347	.73	9.549149	6.70	0.450851	30
31	.523852	5.93	.974302	.75	.549550	6.68	.450450	29
32	.524208	5.93	.974257	.75	.549951	6.68	.450049	28
33	.524564	5.93	.974212	.75	.550352	6.68	.449648	27
34	.524920	5.92	.974167	.75	.550752	6.67	.449248	26
35	9.525275	5.92	9.974122	.75	9.551153	6.68	0.448847	25
36	.525630	5.90	.974077	.75	.551552	6.65	.448448	24
37	.525984	5.92	.974032	.75	.551952	6.67	.448048	23
38	.526339	5.90	.973987	.75	.552351	6.65	.447649	22
39	.526693	5.88	.973942	.75	.552750	6.65	.447250	21
40	9.527046	5.90	9.973897	.75	9.553149	6.65	0.446851	20
41	.527400	5.88	.973852	.75	.553548	6.63	.446452	19
42	.527753	5.87	.973807	.77	.553946	6.63	.446054	18
43	.528105	5.88	.973761	.75	.554344	6.63	.445656	17
44	.528458	5.87	.973716	.75	.554741	6.62	.445259	16
45	9.528810	5.85	9.973671	.77	9.555139	6.63	0.444861	15
46	.529161	5.87	.973625	.75	.555536	6.62	.444464	14
47	.529513	5.85	.973580	.75	.555933	6.62	.444067	13
48	.529864	5.85	.973535	.77	.556329	6.60	.443671	12
49	.530215	5.83	.973489	.75	.556725	6.60	.443275	11
50	9.530565	5.83	9.973444	.77	9.557121	6.60	0.442879	10
51	.530915	5.83	.973398	.77	.557517	6.60	.442483	9
52	.531265	5.82	.973352	.75	.557913	6.58	.442087	8
53	.531614	5.82	.973307	.77	.558308	6.58	.441692	7
54	.531963	5.82	.973261	.77	.558703	6.57	.441297	6
55	9.532312	5.82	9.973215	.77	9.559097	6.57	0.440903	5
56	.532661	5.80	.973169	.75	.559491	6.57	.440509	4
57	.533009	5.80	.973124	.77	.559885	6.57	.440115	3
58	.533357	5.78	.973078	.77	.560279	6.57	.439721	2
59	.533704	5.80	.973032	.77	.560673	6.55	.439327	1
60	9.534052		9.972986		9.561066		0.438934	0
	Cos.	D. 1″.	Sin.	D. 1″.	Cot.	D. 1″.	Tan.	M.

COSINES, TANGENTS, AND COTANGENTS

20°   159°

M.	Sin.	D. 1″.	Cos.	D. 1″.	Tan.	D. 1″.	Cot.	
0	9.534052	5.78	9.972986	.77	9.561066	6.55	0.438934	60
1	.534399	5.77	.972940	.77	.561459	6.53	.438541	59
2	.534745	5.78	.972894	.77	.561851	6.55	.438149	58
3	.535092	5.77	.972848	.77	.562244	6.53	.437756	57
4	.535438	5.75	.972802	.77	.562636	6.53	.437364	56
5	9.535783	5.77	9.972755	.78	9.563028	6.52	0.436972	55
6	.536129	5.75	.972709	.77	.563419	6.53	.436581	54
7	.536474	5.73	.972663	.77	.563811	6.52	.436189	53
8	.536818	5.75	.972617	.77	.564202	6.52	.435798	52
9	.537163	5.73	.972570	.78	.564593	6.50	.435407	51
10	9.537507	5.73	9.972524	.77	9.564983	6.50	0.435017	50
11	.537851	5.72	.972478	.78	.565373	6.50	.434627	49
12	.538194	5.73	.972431	.77	.565763	6.50	.434237	48
13	.538538	5.70	.972385	.78	.566153	6.48	.433847	47
14	.538880	5.72	.972338	.78	.566542	6.50	.433458	46
15	9.539223	5.70	9.972291	.77	9.566932	6.47	0.433068	45
16	.539565	5.70	.972245	.78	.567320	6.48	.432680	44
17	.539907	5.70	.972198	.78	.567709	6.48	.432291	43
18	.540249	5.68	.972151	.77	.568098	6.47	.431902	42
19	.540590	5.68	.972105	.78	.568486	6.45	.431514	41
20	9.540931	5.68	9.972058	.78	9.568873	6.47	0.431127	40
21	.541272	5.68	.972011	.78	.569261	6.45	.430739	39
22	.541613	5.67	.971964	.78	.569648	6.45	.430352	38
23	.541953	5.67	.971917	.78	.570035	6.45	.429965	37
24	.542293	5.65	.971870	.78	.570422	6.45	.429578	36
25	9.542632	5.65	9.971823	.78	9.570809	6.43	0.429191	35
26	.542971	5.65	.971776	.78	.571195	6.43	.428805	34
27	.543310	5.65	.971729	.78	.571581	6.43	.428419	33
28	.543649	5.63	.971682	.78	.571967	6.42	.428033	32
29	.543987	5.63	.971635	.78	.572352	6.43	.427648	31
30	9.544325	5.63	9.971588	.80	9.572738	6.42	0.427262	30
31	.544663	5.62	.971540	.78	.573123	6.40	.426877	29
32	.545000	5.63	.971493	.78	.573507	6.42	.426493	28
33	.545338	5.60	.971446	.80	.573892	6.40	.426108	27
34	.545674	5.62	.971398	.78	.574276	6.40	.425724	26
35	9.546011	5.60	9.971351	.80	9.574660	6.40	0.425340	25
36	.546347	5.60	.971303	.80	.575044	6.38	.424956	24
37	.546683	5.60	.971256	.78	.575427	6.38	.424573	23
38	.547019	5.58	.971208	.80	.575810	6.38	.424190	22
39	.547354	5.58	.971161	.78	.576193	6.38	.423807	21
40	9.547689	5.58	9.971113	.80	9.576576	6.38	0.423424	20
41	.548024	5.58	.971066	.78	.576959	6.37	.423041	19
42	.548359	5.57	.971018	.80	.577341	6.37	.422659	18
43	.548693	5.57	.970970	.80	.577723	6.35	.422277	17
44	.549027	5.55	.970922	.80	.578104	6.37	.421896	16
45	9.549360	5.55	9.970874	.80	9.578486	6.35	0.421514	15
46	.549693	5.55	.970827	.78	.578867	6.35	.421133	14
47	.550026	5.55	.970779	.80	.579248	6.35	.420752	13
48	.550359	5.55	.970731	.80	.579629	6.33	.420371	12
49	.550692	5.53	.970683	.80	.580009	6.33	.419991	11
50	9.551024	5.53	9.970635	.80	9.580389	6.33	0.419611	10
51	.551356	5.52	.970586	.82	.580769	6.33	.419231	9
52	.551687	5.52	.970538	.80	.581149	6.33	.418851	8
53	.552018	5.52	.970490	.80	.581528	6.32	.418472	7
54	.552349	5.52	.970442	.80	.581907	6.32	.418093	6
55	9.552680	5.50	9.970394	.80	9.582286	6.32	0.417714	5
56	.553010	5.52	.970345	.82	.582665	6.32	.417335	4
57	.553341	5.48	.970297	.80	.583044	6.32	.416956	3
58	.553670	5.50	.970249	.80	.583422	6.30	.416578	2
59	.554000	5.48	.970200	.82	.583800	6.30	.416200	1
60	9.554329		9.970152	.80	9.584177	6.28	0.415823	0
	Cos.	D. 1″.	Sin.	D. 1″.	Cot.	D. 1″.	Tan.	M.

110°   69°

TABLE IX. LOGARITHMIC SINES,

21°   158°

M.	Sin.	D. 1″.	Cos.	D. 1″.	Tan.	D. 1″.	Cot.	
0	9.554329	5.48	9.970152	.82	9.584177	6.30	0.415823	60
1	.554658	5.48	.970103	.80	.584555	6.28	.415445	59
2	.554987	5.47	.970055	.82	.584932	6.28	.415068	58
3	.555315	5.47	.970006	.82	.585309	6.28	.414691	57
4	.555643	5.47	.969957	.80	.585686	6.27	.414314	56
5	9.555971	5.47	9.969909	.82	9.586062	6.28	0.413938	55
6	.556299	5.45	.969860	.82	.586439	6.27	.413561	54
7	.556626	5.45	.969811	.82	.586815	6.25	.413185	53
8	.556953	5.45	.969762	.80	.587190	6.27	.412810	52
9	.557280	5.43	.969714	.82	.587566	6.25	.412434	51
10	9.557606	5.43	9.969665	.82	9.587941	6.25	0.412059	50
11	.557932	5.43	.969616	.82	.588316	6.25	.411684	49
12	.558258	5.42	.969567	.82	.588691	6.25	.411309	48
13	.558583	5.43	.969518	.82	.589066	6.23	.410934	47
14	.558909	5.42	.969469	.82	.589440	6.23	.410560	46
15	9.559234	5.40	9.969420	.83	9.589814	6.23	0.410186	45
16	.559558	5.42	.969370	.82	.590188	6.23	.409812	44
17	.559883	5.40	.969321	.82	.590562	6.22	.409438	43
18	.560207	5.40	.969272	.82	.590935	6.22	.409065	42
19	.560531	5.40	.969223	.83	.591308	6.22	.408692	41
20	9.560855	5.38	9.969173	.82	9.591681	6.22	0.408319	40
21	.561178	5.38	.969124	.82	.592054	6.20	.407946	39
22	.561501	5.38	.969075	.83	.592426	6.22	.407574	38
23	.561824	5.37	.969025	.82	.592799	6.20	.407201	37
24	.562146	5.37	.968976	.83	.593171	6.18	.406829	36
25	9.562468	5.37	9.968926	.82	9.593542	6.20	0.406458	35
26	.562790	5.37	.968877	.83	.593914	6.18	.406086	34
27	.563112	5.35	.968827	.83	.594285	6.18	.405715	33
28	.563433	5.37	.968777	.82	.594656	6.18	.405344	32
29	.563755	5.33	.968728	.83	.595027	6.18	.404973	31
30	9.564075	5.35	9.968678	.83	9.595398	6.17	0.404602	30
31	.564396	5.33	.968628	.83	.595768	6.17	.404232	29
32	.564716	5.33	.968578	.83	.596138	6.17	.403862	28
33	.565036	5.33	.968528	.82	.596508	6.17	.403492	27
34	.565356	5.33	.968479	.83	.596878	6.15	.403122	26
35	9.565676	5.32	9.968429	.83	9.597247	6.15	0.402753	25
36	.565995	5.32	.968379	.83	.597616	6.15	.402384	24
37	.566314	5.30	.968329	.85	.597985	6.15	.402015	23
38	.566632	5.32	.968278	.83	.598354	6.13	.401646	22
39	.566951	5.30	.968228	.83	.598722	6.15	.401278	21
40	9.567269	5.30	9.968178	.83	9.599091	6.13	0.400909	20
41	.567587	5.28	.968128	.83	.599459	6.13	.400541	19
42	.567904	5.30	.968078	.85	.599827	6.12	.400173	18
43	.568222	5.28	.968027	.83	.600194	6.13	.399806	17
44	.568539	5.28	.967977	.83	.600562	6.12	.399438	16
45	9.568856	5.27	9.967927	.85	9.600929	6.12	0.399071	15
46	.569172	5.27	.967876	.83	.601296	6.12	.398704	14
47	.569488	5.27	.967826	.83	.601663	6.10	.398337	13
48	.569804	5.27	.967775	.83	.602029	6.10	.397971	12
49	.570120	5.25	.967725	.85	.602395	6.10	.397605	11
50	9.570435	5.27	9.967674	.83	9.602761	6.10	0.397239	10
51	.570751	5.25	.967624	.85	.603127	6.10	.396873	9
52	.571066	5.23	.967573	.85	.603493	6.08	.396507	8
53	.571380	5.25	.967522	.85	.603858	6.08	−.396142	7
54	.571695	5.23	.967471	.83	.604223	6.08	.395777	6
55	9.572009	5.23	9.967421	.85	9.604588	6.08	0.395412	5
56	.572323	5.22	.967370	.85	.604953	6.07	.395047	4
57	.572636	5.23	.967319	.85	.605317	6.08	.394683	3
58	.572950	5.22	.967268	.85	.605682	6.07	.394318	2
59	.573263	5.20	.967217	.85	.606046	6.07	.393954	1
60	9.573575		9.967166		9.606410		0.393590	0
	Cos.	D. 1″.	Sin.	D. 1″.	Cot.	D. 1″.	Tan.	M.

COSINES, TANGENTS, AND COTANGENTS

22°   157°

M.	Sin.	D. 1".	Cos.	D. 1".	Tan.	D. 1".	Cot.	
0	9.573575	5.22	0.967166	.85	9.600410	6.05	0.393590	60
1	.573888	5.20	.967115	.85	.606773	6.07	.393227	59
2	.574200	5.20	.967064	.85	.607137	6.05	.392863	58
3	.574512	5.20	.967013	.85	.607500	6.05	.392500	57
4	.574824	5.20	.966961	.87	.607863	6.03	.392137	56
5	9.575136	5.18	9.966910	.85	9.608225	6.05	0.391775	55
6	.575447	5.18	.966859	.85	.608588	6.03	.391412	54
7	.575758	5.18	.966808	.87	.608950	6.03	.391050	53
8	.576069	5.17	.966756	.85	.609312	6.03	.390688	52
9	.576379	5.17	.966705	.87	.609674	6.03	.390326	51
10	9.576689	5.17	9.966653	.85	9.610036	6.02	0.389964	50
11	.576999	5.17	.966602	.87	.610397	6.03	.389603	49
12	.577309	5.15	.966550	.85	.610759	6.02	.389241	48
13	.577618	5.15	.966499	.87	.611120	6.02	.388880	47
14	.577927	5.15	.966447	.87	.611480	6.00	.388520	46
15	9.578236	5.15	9.966395	.85	9.611841	6.02	0.388159	45
16	.578545	5.13	.966344	.87	.612201	6.00	.387799	44
17	.578853	5.15	.966292	.87	.612561	6.00	.387439	43
18	.579162	5.13	.966240	.87	.612921	6.00	.387079	42
19	.579470	5.12	.966188	.87	.613281	6.00	.386719	41
20	9.579777	5.13	9.966136	.85	9.613641	5.98	0.386359	40
21	.580085	5.12	.966085	.87	.614000	5.98	.386000	39
22	.580392	5.12	.966033	.87	.614359	5.98	.385641	38
23	.580699	5.10	.965981	.87	.614718	5.98	.385282	37
24	.581005	5.12	.965929	.88	.615077	5.97	.384923	36
25	9.581312	5.10	9.965876	.87	9.615435	5.97	0.384565	35
26	.581618	5.10	.965824	.87	.615793	5.97	.384207	34
27	.581924	5.08	.965772	.87	.616151	5.97	.383849	33
28	.582229	5.10	.965720	.87	.616509	5.97	.383491	32
29	.582535	5.08	.965668	.88	.616867	5.95	.383133	31
30	9.582840	5.08	9.965615	.87	9.617224	5.97	0.382776	30
31	.583145	5.07	.965563	.87	.617582	5.95	.382418	29
32	.583449	5.08	.965511	.88	.617939	5.93	.382061	28
33	.583754	5.07	.965458	.87	.618295	5.95	.381705	27
34	.584058	5.05	.965406	.88	.618652	5.93	.381348	26
35	9.584361	5.07	9.965353	.87	9.619008	5.93	0.380992	25
36	.584665	5.05	.965301	.88	.619364	5.93	.380636	24
37	.584968	5.07	.965248	.88	.619720	5.93	.380280	23
38	.585272	5.03	.965195	.87	.620076	5.03	.379924	22
39	.585574	5.05	.965143	.88	.620432	5.92	.379568	21
40	9.585877	5.03	9.965090	.88	9.620787	5.92	0.379213	20
41	.586179	5.05	.965037	.88	.621142	5.92	.378858	19
42	.586482	5.02	.964984	.88	.621497	5.92	.378503	18
43	.586783	5.03	.964931	.87	.621852	5.92	.378148	17
44	.587085	5.02	.964879	.88	.622207	5.90	.377793	16
45	9.587386	5.03	9.964826	.88	9.622561	5.90	0.377439	15
46	.587688	5.02	.964773	.88	.622915	5.90	.377085	14
47	.587989	5.02	.964720	.90	.623269	5.90	.376731	13
48	.588289	5.00	.964666	.88	.623623	5.88	.376377	12
49	.588590	5.02	.964613	.88	.623976	5.90	.376024	11
50	9.588890	5.00	9.964560	.88	9.624330	5.88	0.375670	10
51	.589190	4.98	.964507	.88	.624683	5.88	.375317	9
52	.589489	5.00	.964454	.90	.625036	5.87	.374964	8
53	.589789	4.98	.964400	.88	.625388	5.88	.374612	7
54	.590088	4.98	.964347	.88	.625741	5.87	.374259	6
55	9.590387	4.98	9.964294	.90	9.626093	5.87	0.373907	5
56	.590686	4.97	.964240	.88	.626445	5.87	.373555	4
57	.590984	4.97	.964187	.90	.626797	5.87	.373203	3
58	.591282	4.97	.964133	.90	.627149	5.87	.372851	2
59	.591580	4.97	.964080	.88	.627501	5.85	.372499	1
60	9.591878	4.97	9.964026	.90	9.627852		0.372148	0
	Cos.	D. 1".	Sin.	D. 1".	Cot.	D. 1".	Tan.	M.

112°   67°

TABLE IX. LOGARITHMIC SINES,

23°   156°

M.	Sin.	D. 1″.	Cos.	D. 1″.	Tan.	D. 1″.	Cot.	
0	9.591878	4.97	9.964026	.90	9.627852	5.85	0.372148	60
1	.592176	4.95	.963972	.88	.628203	5.85	.371797	59
2	.592473	4.95	.963919	.90	.628554	5.85	.371446	58
3	.592770	4.95	.963865	.90	.628905	5.83	.371095	57
4	.593067	4.93	.963811	.90	.629255	5.85	.370745	56
5	9.593363	4.93	9.963757	.88	9.629606	5.83	0.370394	55
6	.593659	4.93	.963704	.90	.629956	5.83	.370044	54
7	.593955	4.93	.963650	.90	.630306	5.83	.369694	53
8	.594251	4.93	.963596	.90	.630656	5.82	.369344	52
9	.594547	4.92	.963542	.90	.631005	5.83	.368995	51
10	9.594842	4.92	9.963488	.90	9.631355	5.82	0.368645	50
11	.595137	4.92	.963434	.92	.631704	5.82	.368296	49
12	.595432	4.92	.963379	.90	.632053	5.82	.367947	48
13	.595727	4.90	.963325	.90	.632402	5.80	.367598	47
14	.596021	4.90	.963271	.90	.632750	5.82	.367250	46
15	9.596315	4.90	9.963217	.90	9.633099	5.80	0.366901	45
16	.596609	4.90	.963163	.92	.633447	5.80	.366553	44
17	.596903	4.88	.963108	.90	.633795	5.80	.366205	43
18	.597196	4.90	.963054	.92	.634143	5.78	.365857	42
19	.597490	4.88	.962999	.90	.634490	5.80	.365510	41
20	9.597783	4.87	9.962945	.92	9.634838	5.78	0.365162	40
21	.598075	4.88	.962890	.90	.635185	5.78	.364815	39
22	.598368	4.87	.962836	.92	.635532	5.78	.364468	38
23	.598660	4.87	.962781	.92	.635879	5.78	.364121	37
24	.598952	4.87	.962727	.92	.636226	5.77	.363774	36
25	9.599244	4.87	9.962672	.92	9.636572	5.78	0.363428	35
26	.599536	4.85	.962617	.92	.636919	5.77	.363081	34
27	.599827	4.85	.962562	.90	.637265	5.77	.362735	33
28	.600118	4.85	.962508	.92	.637611	5.75	.362389	32
29	.600409	4.85	.962453	.92	.637956	5.77	.362044	31
30	9.600700	4.83	9.962398	.92	9.638302	5.75	0.361698	30
31	.600990	4.83	.962343	.92	.638647	5.75	.361353	29
32	.601280	4.83	.962288	.92	.638992	5.75	.361008	28
33	.601570	4.83	.962233	.92	.639337	5.75	.360663	27
34	.601860	4.83	.962178	.92	.639682	5.75	.360318	26
35	9.602150	4.82	9.962123	.93	9.640027	5.73	0.359973	25
36	.602439	4.82	.962067	.92	.640371	5.75	.359629	24
37	.602728	4.82	.962012	.92	.640716	5.73	.359284	23
38	.603017	4.80	.961957	.92	.641060	5.73	.358940	22
39	.603305	4.82	.961902	.93	.641404	5.72	.358596	21
40	9.603594	4.80	9.961846	.92	9.641747	5.73	0.358253	20
41	.603882	4.80	.961791	.93	.642091	5.72	.357909	19
42	.604170	4.78	.961735	.92	.642434	5.72	.357566	18
43	.604457	4.80	.961680	.93	.642777	5.72	.357223	17
44	.604745	4.78	.961624	.92	.643120	5.72	.356880	16
45	9.605032	4.78	9.961569	.93	9.643463	5.72	0.356537	15
46	.605319	4.78	.961513	.92	.643806	5.70	.356194	14
47	.605606	4.77	.961458	.93	.644148	5.70	.355852	13
48	.605892	4.78	.961402	.93	.644490	5.70	.355510	12
49	.606179	4.77	.961346	.93	.644832	5.70	.355168	11
50	9.606465	4.77	9.961290	.92	9.645174	5.70	0.354826	10
51	.606751	4.75	.961235	.93	.645516	5.68	.354484	9
52	.607036	4.77	.961179	.93	.645857	5.70	.354143	8
53	.607322	4.75	.961123	.93	.646199	5.68	.353801	7
54	.607607	4.75	.961067	.93	.646540	5.68	.353460	6
55	9.607892	4.75	9.961011	.93	9.646881	5.68	0.353119	5
56	.608177	4.73	.960955	.93	.647222	5.67	.352778	4
57	.608461	4.73	.960899	.93	.647562	5.68	.352438	3
58	.608745	4.73	.960843	.95	.647903	5.67	.352097	2
59	.609029	4.73	.960786	.93	.648243	5.67	.351757	1
60	9.609313	4.73	9.960730		9.648583	5.67	0.351417	0
	Cos.	D. 1″.	Sin.	D. 1″.	Cot.	D. 1″.	Tan.	M.

COSINES, TANGENTS, AND COTANGENTS

24° 155°

M.	Sin.	D. 1″.	Cos.	D. 1″.	Tan.	D. 1″.	Cot.	
0	9.609313	4.73	9.960730	.93	9.648583	5.67	0.351417	60
1	.609597	4.72	.960674	.93	.648923	5.67	.351077	59
2	.609880	4.73	.960618	.95	.649263	5.65	.350737	58
3	.610164	4.72	.960561	.93	.649602	5.65	.350398	57
4	.610447	4.70	.960505	.95	.649942	5.65	.350058	56
5	9.610729	4.72	9.960448	.93	9.650281	5.65	0.349719	55
6	.611012	4.70	.960392	.95	.650620	5.65	.349380	54
7	.611294	4.70	.960335	.95	.650959	5.63	.349041	53
8	.611576	4.70	.960279	.93	.651297	5.63	.348703	52
9	.611858	4.70	.960222	.95	.651636	5.65	.348364	51
10	9.612140	4.68	9.960165	.95	9.651974	5.63	0.348026	50
11	.612421	4.68	.960109	.93	.652312	5.63	.347688	49
12	.612702	4.68	.960052	.95	.652650	5.63	.347350	48
13	.612983	4.68	.959995	.95	.652988	5.63	.347012	47
14	.613264	4.68	.959938	.95	.653326	5.62	.346674	46
15	9.613545	4.67	9.959882	.93	9.653663	5.62	0.346337	45
16	.613825	4.67	.959825	.95	.654000	5.62	.346000	44
17	.614105	4.67	.959768	.95	.654337	5.62	.345663	43
18	.614385	4.67	.959711	.95	.654674	5.62	.345326	42
19	.614665	4.65	.959654	.95	.655011	5.62	.344989	41
20	9.614944	4.65	9.959596	.97	9.655348	5.60	0.344652	40
21	.615223	4.65	.959539	.95	.655684	5.60	.344316	39
22	.615502	4.65	.959482	.95	.656020	5.60	.343980	38
23	.615781	4.65	.959425	.95	.656356	5.60	.343644	37
24	.616060	4.63	.959368	.95	.656692	5.60	.343308	36
25	9.616338	4.63	9.959310	.97	9.657028	5.60	0.342972	35
26	.616616	4.63	.959253	.95	.657364	5.58	.342636	34
27	.616894	4.63	.959195	.97	.657699	5.58	.342301	33
28	.617172	4.63	.959138	.95	.658034	5.58	.341966	32
29	.617450	4.62	.959080	.97	.658369	5.58	.341631	31
30	9.617727	4.62	9.959023	.95	9.658704	5.58	0.341296	30
31	.618004	4.62	.958965	.97	.659039	5.57	.340961	29
32	.618281	4.62	.958908	.95	.659373	5.58	.340627	28
33	.618558	4.60	.958850	.97	.659708	5.57	.340292	27
34	.618834	4.60	.958792	.97	.660042	5.57	.339958	26
35	9.619110	4.60	9.958734	.97	9.660376	5.57	0.339624	25
36	.619386	4.60	.958677	.95	.660710	5.55	.339290	24
37	.619662	4.60	.958619	.97	.661043	5.57	.338957	23
38	.619938	4.58	.958561	.97	.661377	5.55	.338623	22
39	.620213	4.58	.958503	.97	.661710	5.55	.338290	21
40	9.620488	4.58	9.958445	.97	9.662043	5.55	0.337957	20
41	.620763	4.58	.958387	.97	.662376	5.55	.337624	19
42	.621038	4.58	.958329	.97	.662709	5.55	.337291	18
43	.621313	4.57	.958271	.97	.663042	5.53	.336958	17
44	.621587	4.57	.958213	.98	.663375	5.53	.336625	16
45	9.621861	4.57	9.958154	.97	9.663707	5.53	0.336293	15
46	.622135	4.57	.958096	.97	.664039	5.53	.335961	14
47	.622409	4.55	.958038	.98	.664371	5.53	.335629	13
48	.622682	4.57	.957979	.97	.664703	5.53	.335297	12
49	.622956	4.55	.957921	.97	.665035	5.52	.334965	11
50	9.623229	4.55	9.957863	.98	9.665366	5.53	0.334634	10
51	.623502	4.53	.957804	.97	.665698	5.52	.334302	9
52	.623774	4.55	.957746	.98	.666029	5.52	.333971	8
53	.624047	4.53	.957687	.97	.666360	5.52	.333640	7
54	.624319	4.53	.957628	.98	.666691	5.52	.333309	6
55	9.624591	4.53	9.957570	.97	9.667021	5.52	0.332979	5
56	.624863	4.53	.957511	.98	.667352	5.50	.332648	4
57	.625135	4.52	.957452	.98	.667682	5.52	.332318	3
58	.625406	4.52	.957393	.98	.668013	5.50	.331987	2
59	.625677	4.52	.957335	.97	.668343	5.50	.331657	1
60	9.625948		9.957276	.98	9.668673	5.50	0.331327	0
	Cos.	D. 1″.	Sin.	D. 1″.	Cot.	D. 1″.	Tan.	M.

114° 65°

TABLE IX.   LOGARITHMIC SINES,

25°   154°

M.	Sin.	D. 1″.	Cos.	D. 1.″	Tan.	D. 1″.	Cot.	
0	9.625948	4.52	9.957276	.98	9.668673	5.48	0.331327	60
1	.626219	4.52	.957217	.98	.669002	5.50	.330998	59
2	.626490	4.50	.957158	.98	.669332	5.48	.330668	58
3	.626760	4.50	.957099	.98	.669661	5.50	.330339	57
4	.627030	4.50	.957040	.98	.669991	5.48	.330009	56
5	9.627300	4.50	9.956981	1.00	9.670320	5.48	0.329680	55
6	.627570	4.50	.956921	.98	.670649	5.47	.329351	54
7	.627840	4.48	.956862	.98	.670977	5.48	.329023	53
8	.628109	4.48	.956803	.98	.671306	5.48	.328694	52
9	.628378	4.48	.956744	1.00	.671635	5.47	.328365	51
10	9.628647	4.48	9.956684	.98	9.671963	5.47	0.328037	50
11	.628916	4.48	.956625	.98	.672291	5.47	.327709	49
12	.629185	4.47	.956566	1.00	.672619	5.47	.327381	48
13	.629453	4.47	.956506	.98	.672947	5.45	.327053	47
14	.629721	4.47	.956447	1.00	.673274	5.47	.326726	46
15	9.629989	4.47	9.956387	1.00	9.673602	5.45	0.326398	45
16	.630257	4.45	.956327	.98	.673929	5.47	.326071	44
17	.630524	4.47	.956268	1.00	.674257	5.45	.325743	43
18	.630792	4.45	.956208	1.00	.674584	5.45	.325416	42
19	.631059	4.45	.956148	.98	.674911	5.43	.325089	41
20	9.631326	4.45	9.956089	1.00	9.675237	5.45	0.324763	40
21	.631593	4.43	.956029	1.00	.675564	5.43	.324436	39
22	.631859	4.43	.955969	1.00	.675890	5.45	.324110	38
23	.632125	4.45	.955909	1.00	.676217	5.43	.323783	37
24	.632392	4.43	.955849	1.00	.676543	5.43	.323457	36
25	9.632658	4.42	9.955789	1.00	9.676869	5.42	0.323131	35
26	.632923	4.43	.955729	1.00	.677194	5.43	.322806	34
27	.633189	4.42	.955669	1.00	.677520	5.43	.322480	33
28	.633454	4.42	.955609	1.02	.677846	5.42	.322154	32
29	.633719	4.42	.955548	1.00	.678171	5.42	.321829	31
30	9.633984	4.42	9.955488	1.00	9.678496	5.42	0.321504	30
31	.634249	4.42	.955428	1.00	.678821	5.42	.321179	29
32	.634514	4.40	.955368	1.02	.679146	5.42	.320854	28
33	.634778	4.40	.955307	1.00	.679471	5.40	.320529	27
34	.635042	4.40	.955247	1.02	.679795	5.42	.320205	26
35	9.635306	4.40	9.955186	1.00	9.680120	5.40	0.319880	25
36	.635570	4.40	.955126	1.02	.680444	5.40	.319556	24
37	.635834	4.38	.955065	1.00	.680768	5.40	.319232	23
38	.636097	4.38	.955005	1.02	.681092	5.40	.318908	22
39	.636360	4.38	.954944	1.02	.681416	5.40	.318584	21
40	9.636623	4.38	9.954883	1.00	9.681740	5.38	0.318260	20
41	.636886	4.37	.954823	1.02	.682063	5.40	.317937	19
42	.637148	4.38	.954762	1.02	.682387	5.38	.317613	18
43	.637411	4.37	.954701	1.02	.682710	5.38	.317290	17
44	.637673	4.37	.954640	1.02	.683033	5.38	.316967	16
45	9.637935	4.37	9.954579	1.02	9.683356	5.38	0.316644	15
46	.638197	4.35	.954518	1.02	.683679	5.37	.316321	14
47	.638458	4.37	.954457	1.02	.684001	5.38	.315999	13
48	.638720	4.35	.954396	1.02	.684324	5.37	.315676	12
49	.638981	4.35	.954335	1.02	.684646	5.37	.315354	11
50	9.639242	4.35	9.954274	1.02	9.684968	5.37	0.315032	10
51	.639503	4.35	.954213	1.02	.685290	5.37	.314710	9
52	.639764	4.33	.954152	1.03	.685612	5.37	.314388	8
53	.640024	4.33	.954090	1.02	.685934	5.35	.314066	7
54	.640284	4.33	.954029	1.02	.686255	5.37	.313745	6
55	9.640544	4.33	9.953968	1.03	9.686577	5.35	0.313423	5
56	.640804	4.33	.953906	1.02	.686898	5.35	.313102	4
57	.641064	4.33	.953845	1.03	.687219	5.35	.312781	3
58	.641324	4.32	.953783	1.02	.687540	5.35	.312460	2
59	.641583	4.32	.953722	1.03	.687861	5.35	.312139	1
60	9.641842		9.953660		9.688182		0.311818	0
	Cos.	D. 1″.	Sin.	D. 1″.	Cot.	D. 1″.	Tan.	M.

115°   64°

COSINES, TANGENTS, AND COTANGENTS

26°   153°

M.	Sin.	D. 1″.	Cos.	D. 1″.	Tan.	D. 1″.	Cot.	
0	9.641842	4.32	9.953660	1.02	9.688182	5.33	0.311818	60
1	.642101	4.32	.953599	1.03	.688502	5.35	.311498	59
2	.642360	4.30	.953537	1.03	.688823	5.33	.311177	58
3	.642618	4.32	.953475	1.03	.689143	5.33	.310857	57
4	.642877	4.30	.953413	1.02	.689463	5.33	.310537	56
5	9.643135	4.30	9.953352	1.03	9.689783	5.33	0.310217	55
6	.643393	4.28	.953290	1.03	.690103	5.33	.309897	54
7	.643650	4.30	.953228	1.03	.690423	5.32	.309577	53
8	.643908	4.28	.953166	1.03	.690742	5.33	.309258	52
9	.644165	4.30	.953104	1.03	.691062	5.32	.308938	51
10	9.644423	4.28	9.953042	1.03	9.691381	5.32	0.308619	50
11	.644680	4.27	.952980	1.03	.691700	5.32	.308300	49
12	.644936	4.28	.952918	1.05	.692019	5.32	.307981	48
13	.645193	4.28	.952855	1.03	.692338	5.32	.307662	47
14	.645450	4.27	.952793	1.03	.692656	5.30	.307344	46
15	9.645706	4.27	9.952731	1.03	9.692975	5.32	0.307025	45
16	.645962	4.27	.952669	1.05	.693293	5.30	.306707	44
17	.646218	4.27	.952606	1.03	.693612	5.32	.306388	43
18	.646474	4.25	.952544	1.05	.693930	5.30	.306070	42
19	.646729	4.25	.952481	1.03	.694248	5.30	.305752	41
20	9.646984	4.27	9.952419	1.05	9.694566	5.28	0.305434	40
21	.647240	4.23	.952356	1.03	.694883	5.30	.305117	39
22	.647494	4.25	.952294	1.05	.695201	5.28	.304799	38
23	.647749	4.25	.952231	1.05	.695518	5.30	.304482	37
24	.648004	4.23	.952168	1.03	.695836	5.28	.304164	36
25	9.648258	4.23	9.952106	1.05	9.696153	5.28	0.303847	35
26	.648512	4.23	.952043	1.05	.696470	5.28	.303530	34
27	.648766	4.23	.951980	1.05	.696787	5.27	.303213	33
28	.649020	4.23	.951917	1.05	.697103	5.28	.302897	32
29	.649274	4.22	.951854	1.05	.697420	5.27	.302580	31
30	9.649527	4.23	9.951791	1.05	9.697736	5.28	0.302264	30
31	.649781	4.22	.951728	1.05	.698053	5.27	.301947	29
32	.650034	4.22	.951665	1.05	.698369	5.27	.301631	28
33	.650287	4.20	.951602	1.05	.698685	5.27	.301315	27
34	.650539	4.22	.951539	1.05	.699001	5.25	.300999	26
35	9.650792	4.20	9.951476	1.07	9.699316	5.27	0.300684	25
36	.651044	4.22	.951412	1.05	.699632	5.25	.300368	24
37	.651297	4.20	.951349	1.05	.699947	5.27	.300053	23
38	.651549	4.18	.951286	1.07	.700263	5.25	.299737	22
39	.651800	4.20	.951222	1.05	.700578	5.25	.299422	21
40	9.652052	4.20	9.951159	1.05	9.700893	5.25	0.299107	20
41	.652304	4.18	.951096	1.07	.701208	5.25	.298792	19
42	.652555	4.18	.951032	1.07	.701523	5.23	.298477	18
43	.652806	4.18	.950968	1.05	.701837	5.25	.298163	17
44	.653057	4.18	.950905	1.07	.702152	5.23	.297848	16
45	9.653308	4.17	9.950841	1.05	9.702466	5.25	0.297534	15
46	.653558	4.17	.950778	1.07	.702781	5.23	.297219	14
47	.653808	4.18	.950714	1.07	.703095	5.23	.296905	13
48	.654059	4.17	.950650	1.07	.703409	5.22	.296591	12
49	.654309	4.15	.950586	1.07	.703722	5.23	.296278	11
50	9.654558	4.17	9.950522	1.07	9.704036	5.23	0.295964	10
51	.654808	4.17	.950458	1.07	.704350	5.22	.295650	9
52	.655058	4.15	.950394	1.07	.704663	5.23	.295337	8
53	.655307	4.15	.950330	1.07	.704976	5.22	.295024	7
54	.655556	4.15	.950266	1.07	.705290	5.22	.294710	6
55	9.655805	4.15	9.950202	1.07	9.705603	5.22	0.294397	5
56	.656054	4.13	.950138	1.07	.705916	5.20	.294084	4
57	.656302	4.15	.950074	1.07	.706228	5.22	.293772	3
58	.656551	4.13	.950010	1.08	.706541	5.22	.293459	2
59	.656799	4.13	.949945	1.07	.706854	5.20	.293146	1
60	9.657047		9.949881		9.707166		0.292834	0
	Cos.	D. 1″.	Sin.	D. 1″.	Cot.	D. 1″.	Tan.	M.

116°   63°

TABLE IX. LOGARITHMIC SINES,

27°

152°

M.	Sin.	D. 1″.	Cos.	D. 1″.	Tan.	D. 1″.	Cot.	
0	9.657047	4.13	9.949881	1.08	9.707166	5.20	0.292834	60
1	.657295	4.12	.949816	1.07	.707478	5.20	.292522	59
2	.657542	4.13	.949752	1.07	.707790	5.20	.292210	58
3	.657790	4.12	.949688	1.08	.708102	5.20	.291898	57
4	.658037	4.12	.949623	1.08	.708414	5.20	.291586	56
5	9.658284	4.12	9.949558	1.07	9.708726	5.20	0.291274	55
6	.658531	4.12	.949494	1.08	.709037	5.20	.290963	54
7	.658778	4.12	.949429	1.08	.709349	5.18	.290651	53
8	.659025	4.10	.949364	1.07	.709660	5.18	.290340	52
9	.659271	4.10	.949300	1.08	.709971	5.18	.290029	51
10	9.659517	4.10	9.949235	1.08	9.710282	5.18	0.289718	50
11	.659763	4.10	.949170	1.08	.710593	5.18	.289407	49
12	.660009	4.10	.949105	1.08	.710904	5.18	.289096	48
13	.660255	4.10	.949040	1.08	.711215	5.18	.288785	47
14	.660501	4.08	.948975	1.08	.711525	5.17	.288475	46
15	9.660746	4.08	9.948910	1.08	9.711836	5.18	0.288164	45
16	.660991	4.08	.948845	1.08	.712146	5.17	.287854	44
17	.661236	4.08	.948780	1.08	.712456	5.17	.287544	43
18	.661481	4.08	.948715	1.08	.712766	5.17	.287234	42
19	.661726	4.07	.948650	1.10	.713076	5.17	.286924	41
20	9.661970	4.07	9.948584	1.08	9.713386	5.17	0.286614	40
21	.662214	4.08	.948519	1.08	.713696	5.17	.286304	39
22	.662459	4.07	.948454	1.10	.714005	5.15	.285995	38
23	.662703	4.05	.948388	1.08	.714314	5.15	.285686	37
24	.662946	4.07	.948323	1.10	.714624	5.17	.285376	36
25	9.663190	4.05	9.948257	1.08	9.714933	5.15	0.285067	35
26	.663433	4.07	.948192	1.10	.715242	5.15	.284758	34
27	.663677	4.05	.948126	1.10	.715551	5.15	.284449	33
28	.663920	4.05	.948060	1.08	.715860	5.15	.284140	32
29	.664163	4.05	.947995	1.10	.716168	5.13	.283832	31
30	9.664406	4.03	9.947929	1.10	9.716477	5.13	0.283523	30
31	.664648	4.05	.947863	1.10	.716785	5.13	.283215	29
32	.664891	4.03	.947797	1.10	.717093	5.13	.282907	28
33	.665133	4.03	.947731	1.10	.717401	5.13	.282599	27
34	.665375	4.03	.947665	1.08	.717709	5.13	.282291	26
35	9.665617	4.03	9.947600	1.12	9.718017	5.13	0.281983	25
36	.665859	4.02	.947533	1.10	.718325	5.13	.281675	24
37	.666100	4.03	.947467	1.10	.718633	5.12	.281367	23
38	.666342	4.02	.947401	1.10	.718940	5.13	.281060	22
39	.666583	4.02	.947335	1.10	.719248	5.12	.280752	21
40	9.666824	4.02	9.947269	1.10	9.719555	5.12	0.280445	20
41	.667065	4.00	.947203	1.12	.719862	5.12	.280138	19
42	.667305	4.02	.947136	1.10	.720169	5.12	.279831	18
43	.667546	4.00	.947070	1.10	.720476	5.12	.279524	17
44	.667786	4.02	.947004	1.12	.720783	5.10	.279217	16
45	9.668027	4.00	9.946937	1.10	9.721089	5.12	0.278911	15
46	.668267	3.98	.946871	1.12	.721396	5.10	.278604	14
47	.668506	4.00	.946804	1.10	.721702	5.12	.278298	13
48	.668746	4.00	.946738	1.12	.722009	5.10	.277991	12
49	.668986	3.98	.946671	1.12	.722315	5.10	.277685	11
50	9.669225	3.98	9.946604	1.10	9.722621	5.10	0.277379	10
51	.669464	3.98	.946538	1.12	.722927	5.08	.277073	9
52	.669703	3.98	.946471	1.12	.723232	5.10	.276768	8
53	.669942	3.98	.946404	1.12	.723538	5.10	.276462	7
54	.670181	3.97	.946337	1.12	.723844	5.08	.276156	6
55	9.670419	3.98	9.946270	1.12	9.724149	5.08	0.275851	5
56	.670658	3.97	.946203	1.12	.724454	5.10	.275546	4
57	.670896	3.97	.946136	1.12	.724760	5.08	.275240	3
58	.671134	3.97	.946069	1.12	.725065	5.08	.274935	2
59	.671372	3.95	.946002	1.12	.725370	5.07	.274630	1
60	9.671609		9.945935		9.725674		0.274326	0
	Cos.	D. 1″.	Sin.	D. 1″.	Cot.	D. 1″.	Tan.	M.

COSINES, TANGENTS, AND COTANGENTS

28°   151°

M.	Sin.	D. 1″.	Cos.	D. 1″.	Tan.	D. 1″.	Cot.	
0	9.671609	3.97	9.945935	1.12	9.725674	5.08	0.274326	60
1	.671847	3.95	.945868	1.13	.725979	5.08	.274021	59
2	.672084	3.95	.945800	1.12	.726284	5.07	.273716	58
3	.672321	3.95	.945733	1.12	.726588	5.07	.273412	57
4	.672558	3.95	.945666	1.13	.726892	5.08	.273108	56
5	9.672795	3.95	9.945598	1.12	9.727197	5.07	0.272803	55
6	.673032	3.93	.945531	1.12	.727501	5.07	.272499	54
7	.673268	3.95	.945464	1.13	.727805	5.07	.272195	53
8	.673505	3.93	.945396	1.13	.728109	5.07	.271891	52
9	.673741	3.93	.945328	1.12	.728412	5.05	.271588	51
10	9.673977	3.93	9.945261	1.13	9.728716	5.07	0.271284	50
11	.674213	3.92	.945193	1.13	.729020	5.05	.270980	49
12	.674448	3.93	.945125	1.12	.729323	5.05	.270677	48
13	.674684	3.92	.945058	1.13	.729626	5.05	.270374	47
14	.674919	3.93	.944990	1.13	.729929	5.07	.270071	46
15	9.675155	3.92	9.944922	1.13	9.730233	5.03	0.269767	45
16	.675390	3.90	.944854	1.13	.730535	5.05	.269465	44
17	.675624	3.92	.944786	1.13	.730838	5.05	.269162	43
18	.675859	3.92	.944718	1.13	.731141	5.05	.268859	42
19	.676094	3.90	.944650	1.13	.731444	5.03	.268556	41
20	9.676328	3.90	9.944582	1.13	9.731746	5.03	0.268254	40
21	.676562	3.90	.944514	1.13	.732048	5.05	.267952	39
22	.676796	3.90	.944446	1.15	.732351	5.03	.267649	38
23	.677030	3.90	.944377	1.13	.732653	5.03	.267347	37
24	.677264	3.90	.944309	1.13	.732955	5.03	.267045	36
25	9.677498	3.88	9.944241	1.15	9.733257	5.02	0.266743	35
26	.677731	3.88	.944172	1.13	.733558	5.03	.266442	34
27	.677964	3.88	.944104	1.13	.733860	5.03	.266140	33
28	.678197	3.83	.944036	1.15	.734162	5.02	.265838	32
29	.678430	3.88	.943967	1.13	.734463	5.02	.265537	31
30	9.678663	3.87	9.943899	1.15	9.734764	5.03	0.265236	30
31	.678895	3.88	.943830	1.15	.735066	5.02	.264934	29
32	.679128	3.87	.943761	1.13	.735367	5.02	.264633	28
33	.679360	3.87	.943693	1.15	.735668	5.02	.264332	27
34	.679592	3.87	.943624	1.15	.735969	5.00	.264031	26
35	9.679824	3.87	9.943555	1.15	9.736269	5.02	0.263731	25
36	.680056	3.87	.943486	1.15	.736570	5.02	.263430	24
37	.680288	3.85	.943417	1.15	.736870	5.02	.263130	23
38	.680519	3.85	.943348	1.15	.737171	5.00	.262829	22
39	.680750	3.87	.943279	1.15	.737471	5.00	.262529	21
40	9.680982	3.85	9.943210	1.15	9.737771	5.00	0.262229	20
41	.681213	3.83	.943141	1.15	.738071	5.00	.261929	19
42	.681443	3.85	.943072	1.15	.738371	5.00	.261629	18
43	.681674	3.85	.943003	1.15	.738671	5.00	.261329	17
44	.681905	3.83	.942934	1.17	.738971	5.00	.261029	16
45	9.682135	3.83	9.942864	1.15	9.739271	4.98	0.260729	15
46	.682365	3.83	.942795	1.15	.739570	5.00	.260430	14
47	.682595	3.83	.942726	1.17	.739870	4.98	.260130	13
48	.682825	3.83	.942656	1.15	.740169	4.98	.259831	12
49	.683055	3.82	.942587	1.17	.740468	4.98	.259532	11
50	9.683284	3.83	9.942517	1.15	9.740767	4.98	0.259233	10
51	.683514	3.82	.942448	1.17	.741066	4.98	.258934	9
52	.683743	3.82	.942378	1.17	.741365	4.98	.258635	8
53	.683972	3.82	.942308	1.15	.741664	4.97	.258336	7
54	.684201	3.82	.942239	1.17	.741962	4.98	.258038	6
55	9.684430	3.80	9.942169	1.17	9.742261	4.97	0.257739	5
56	.684658	3.82	.942099	1.17	.742559	4.98	.257441	4
57	.684887	3.80	.942029	1.17	.742858	4.97	.257142	3
58	.685115	3.80	.941959	1.17	.743156	4.97	.256844	2
59	.685343	3.80	.941889	1.17	.743454	4.97	.256546	1
60	9.685571		9.941819	1.17	9.743752	4.97	0.256248	0
	Cos.	D. 1″.	Sin.	D. 1″.	Cot.	D. 1″.	Tan.	M.

TABLE IX. LOGARITHMIC SINES,

29°   150°

M.	Sin.	D. 1″.	Cos.	D. 1″.	Tan.	D. 1″.	Cot.	
0	9.685571	3.80	9.941819	1.17	9.743752	4.97	0.256248	60
1	.685799	3.80	.941749	1.17	.744050	4.97	.255950	59
2	.686027	3.78	.941679	1.17	.744348	4.95	.255652	58
3	.686254	3.80	.941609	1.17	.744645	4.97	.255355	57
4	.686482	3.78	.941539	1.17	.744943	4.95	.255057	56
5	9.686709	3.78	9.941469	1.18	9.745240	4.97	0.254760	55
6	.686936	3.78	.941398	1.17	.745538	4.95	.254462	54
7	.687163	3.77	.941328	1.17	.745835	4.95	.254165	53
8	.687389	3.78	.941258	1.18	.746132	4.95	.253868	52
9	.687616	3.78	.941187	1.17	.746429	4.95	.253571	51
10	9.687843	3.77	9.941117	1.18	9.746726	4.95	0.253274	50
11	.688069	3.77	.941046	1.18	.747023	4.93	.252977	49
12	.688295	3.77	.940975	1.18	.747319	4.95	.252681	48
13	.688521	3.77	.940905	1.17	.747616	4.95	.252384	47
14	.688747	3.75	.940834	1.18	.747913	4.93	.252087	46
15	9.688972	3.77	9.940763	1.18	9.748209	4.93	0.251791	45
16	.689198	3.75	.940693	1.17	.748505	4.93	.251495	44
17	.689423	3.75	.940622	1.18	.748801	4.93	.251199	43
18	.689648	3.75	.940551	1.18	.749097	4.93	.250903	42
19	.689873	3.75	.940480	1.18	.749393	4.93	.250607	41
20	9.690098	3.75	9.940409	1.18	9.749689	4.93	0.250311	40
21	.690323	3.75	.940338	1.18	.749985	4.93	.250015	39
22	.690548	3.73	.940267	1.18	.750281	4.92	.249719	38
23	.690772	3.73	.940196	1.18	.750576	4.93	.249424	37
24	.690996	3.73	.940125	1.18	.750872	4.92	.249128	36
25	9.691220	3.73	9.940054	1.20	9.751167	4.92	0.248833	35
26	.691444	3.73	.939982	1.18	.751462	4.92	.248538	34
27	.691668	3.73	.939911	1.18	.751757	4.92	.248243	33
28	.691892	3.72	.939840	1.20	.752052	4.92	.247948	32
29	.692115	3.73	.939768	1.18	.752347	4.92	.247653	31
30	9.692339	3.72	9.939697	1.20	9.752642	4.92	0.247358	30
31	.692562	3.72	.939625	1.18	.752937	4.90	.247063	29
32	.692785	3.72	.939554	1.20	.753231	4.92	.246769	28
33	.693008	3.72	.939482	1.20	.753526	4.90	.246474	27
34	.693231	3.70	.939410	1.18	.753820	4.92	.246180	26
35	9.693453	3.72	9.939339	1.20	9.754115	4.90	0.245885	25
36	.693676	3.70	.939267	1.20	.754409	4.90	.245591	24
37	.693898	3.70	.939195	1.20	.754703	4.90	.245297	23
38	.694120	3.70	.939123	1.18	.754997	4.90	.245003	22
39	.694342	3.70	.939052	1.20	.755291	4.90	.244709	21
40	9.694564	3.70	9.938980	1.20	9.755585	4.88	0.244415	20
41	.694786	3.68	.938908	1.20	.755878	4.90	.244122	19
42	.695007	3.70	.938836	1.22	.756172	4.88	.243828	18
43	.695229	3.68	.938763	1.20	.756465	4.90	.243535	17
44	.695450	3.68	.938691	1.20	.756759	4.88	.243241	16
45	9.695671	3.68	9.938619	1.20	9.757052	4.88	0.242948	15
46	.695892	3.68	.938547	1.20	.757345	4.88	.242655	14
47	.696113	3.68	.938475	1.22	.757638	4.88	.242362	13
48	.696334	3.67	.938402	1.20	.757931	4.88	.242069	12
49	.696554	3.68	.938330	1.20	.758224	4.88	.241776	11
50	9.696775	3.67	9.938258	1.22	9.758517	4.88	0.241483	10
51	.696995	3.67	.938185	1.20	.758810	4.87	.241190	9
52	.697215	3.67	.938113	1.22	.759102	4.88	.240898	8
53	.697435	3.65	.938040	1.22	.759395	4.87	.240605	7
54	.697654	3.67	.937967	1.20	.759687	4.87	.240313	6
55	9.697874	3.67	9.937895	1.22	9.759979	4.88	0.240021	5
56	.698094	3.65	.937822	1.22	.760272	4.87	.239728	4
57	.698313	3.65	.937749	1.22	.760564	4.87	.239436	3
58	.698532	3.65	.937676	1.20	.760856	4.87	.239144	2
59	.698751	3.65	.937604	1.22	.761148	4.85	.238852	1
60	9.698970	3.65	9.937531	1.22	9.761439		0.238561	0
	Cos.	D. 1″.	Sin.	D. 1″.	Cot.	D. 1″.	Tan.	M.

COSINES, TANGENTS, AND COTANGENTS

30°   149°

M.	Sin.	D. 1".	Cos.	D. 1".	Tan.	D. 1".	Cot.	
0	9.698970	3.65	9.937531	1.22	9.761439	4.87	0.238561	60
1	.699189	3.63	.937458	1.22	.761731	4.87	.238269	59
2	.699407	3.65	.937385	1.22	.762023	4.85	.237977	58
3	.699626	3.63	.937312	1.22	.762314	4.87	.237686	57
4	.699844	3.63	.937238	1.23	.762606	4.85	.237394	56
5	9.700062	3.63	9.937165	1.22	9.762897	4.85	0.237103	55
6	.700280	3.63	.937092	1.22	.763188	4.85	.236812	54
7	.700498	3.63	.937019	1.22	.763479	4.85	.236521	53
8	.700716	3.62	.936946	1.23	.763770	4.85	.236230	52
9	.700933	3.63	.936872	1.22	.764061	4.85	.235939	51
10	9.701151	3.62	9.936799	1.23	9.764352	4.85	0.235648	50
11	.701368	3.62	.936725	1.22	.764643	4.83	.235357	49
12	.701585	3.62	.936652	1.23	.764933	4.85	.235067	48
13	.701802	3.62	.936578	1.22	.765224	4.83	.234776	47
14	.702019	3.62	.936505	1.23	.765514	4.83	.234486	46
15	9.702236	3.60	9.936431	1.23	9.765805	4.85	0.234195	45
16	.702452	3.62	.936357	1.22	.766095	4.83	.233905	44
17	.702669	3.60	.936284	1.23	.766385	4.83	.233615	43
18	.702885	3.60	.936210	1.23	.766675	4.83	.233325	42
19	.703101	3.60	.936136	1.23	.766965	4.83	.233035	41
20	9.703317	3.60	9.936062	1.23	9.767255	4.83	0.232745	40
21	.703533	3.60	.935988	1.23	.767545	4.82	.232455	39
22	.703749	3.58	.935914	1.23	.767834	4.83	.232166	38
23	.703964	3.58	.935840	1.23	.768124	4.83	.231876	37
24	.704179	3.60	.935766	1.23	.768414	4.82	.231586	36
25	9.704395	3.58	9.935692	1.23	9.768703	4.82	0.231297	35
26	.704610	3.58	.935618	1.25	.768992	4.82	.231008	34
27	.704825	3.58	.935543	1.23	.769281	4.83	.230719	33
28	.705040	3.57	.935469	1.23	.769571	4.82	.230429	32
29	.705254	3.58	.935395	1.25	.769860	4.80	.230140	31
30	9.705469	3.57	9.935320	1.23	9.770148	4.82	0.229852	30
31	.705683	3.58	.935246	1.25	.770437	4.82	.229563	29
32	.705898	3.57	.935171	1.23	.770726	4.82	.229274	28
33	.706112	3.57	.935097	1.25	.771015	4.80	.228985	27
34	.706326	3.57	.935022	1.25	.771303	4.82	.228697	26
35	9.706539	3.57	9.934948	1.25	9.771592	4.80	0.228408	25
36	.706753	3.57	.934873	1.25	.771880	4.80	.228120	24
37	.706967	3.55	.934798	1.25	.772168	4.82	.227832	23
38	.707180	3.55	.934723	1.23	.772457	4.80	.227543	22
39	.707393	3.55	.934649	1.25	.772745	4.80	.227255	21
40	9.707606	3.55	9.934574	1.25	9.773033	4.80	0.226967	20
41	.707819	3.55	.934499	1.25	.773321	4.78	.226679	19
42	.708032	3.55	.934424	1.25	.773608	4.80	.226392	18
43	.708245	3.55	.934349	1.25	.773896	4.80	.226104	17
44	.708458	3.53	.934274	1.25	.774184	4.78	.225816	16
45	9.708670	3.53	9.934199	1.27	9.774471	4.80	0.225529	15
46	.708882	3.53	.934123	1.25	.774759	4.78	.225241	14
47	.709094	3.53	.934048	1.25	.775046	4.78	.224954	13
48	.709306	3.53	.933973	1.25	.775333	4.80	.224667	12
49	.709518	3.53	.933898	1.27	.775621	4.78	.224379	11
50	9.709730	3.52	9.933822	1.25	9.775908	4.78	0.224092	10
51	.709941	3.53	.933747	1.27	.776195	4.78	.223805	9
52	.710153	3.52	.933671	1.25	.776482	4.77	.223518	8
53	.710364	3.52	.933596	1.27	.776768	4.78	.223232	7
54	.710575	3.52	.933520	1.25	.777055	4.78	.222945	6
55	9.710786	3.52	9.933445	1.27	9.777342	4.77	0.222658	5
56	.710997	3.52	.933369	1.27	.777628	4.78	.222372	4
57	.711208	3.52	.933293	1.27	.777915	4.77	.222085	3
58	.711419	3.50	.933217	1.27	.778201	4.78	.221799	2
59	.711629	3.50	.933141	1.27	.778488	4.77	.221512	1
60	9.711839		9.933066	1.25	9.778774		0.221226	0
	Cos.	D.1".	Sin.	D. 1".	Cot.	D. 1".	Tan.	M.

120°   59°

TABLE IX. LOGARITHMIC SINES,

31°   148°

M.	Sin.	D. 1″.	Cos.	D. 1″.	Tan.	D. 1″.	Cot.	
0	9.711839	3.52	9.933066	1.27	9.778774	4.77	0.221226	60
1	.712050	3.50	.932990	1.27	.779060	4.77	.220940	59
2	.712260	3.48	.932914	1.27	.779346	4.77	.220654	58
3	.712469	3.50	.932838	1.27	.779632	4.77	.220368	57
4	.712679	3.50	.932762	1.28	.779918	4.77	.220082	56
5	9.712889	3.48	9.932685	1.27	9.780203	4.75	0.219797	55
6	.713008	3.50	.932609	1.27	.780489	4.77	.219511	54
7	.713308	3.48	.932533	1.27	.780775	4.77	.219225	53
8	.713517	3.48	.932457	1.28	.781060	4.77	.218940	52
9	.713726	3.48	.932380	1.27	.781346	4.75	.218654	51
10	9.713935	3.48	9.932304	1.27	9.781631	4.75	0.218369	50
11	.714144	3.47	.932228	1.28	.781916	4.75	.218084	49
12	.714352	3.48	.932151	1.27	.782201	4.75	.217799	48
13	.714561	3.47	.932075	1.28	.782486	4.75	.217514	47
14	.714769	3.48	.931998	1.28	.782771	4.75	.217229	46
15	9.714978	3.47	9.931921	1.27	9.783056	4.75	0.216944	45
16	.715186	3.47	.931845	1.28	.783341	4.75	.216659	44
17	.715394	3.47	.931768	1.28	.783626	4.73	.216374	43
18	.715602	3.45	.931691	1.28	.783910	4.75	.216090	42
19	.715809	3.47	.931614	1.28	.784195	4.73	.215805	41
20	9.716017	3.45	9.931537	1.28	9.784479	4.75	0.215521	40
21	.716224	3.47	.931460	1.28	.784764	4.73	.215236	39
22	.716432	3.45	.931383	1.28	.785048	4.73	.214952	38
23	.716639	3.45	.931306	1.28	.785332	4.73	.214668	37
24	.716846	3.45	.931229	1.28	.785616	4.73	.214384	36
25	9.717053	3.43	9.931152	1.28	9.785900	4.73	0.214100	35
26	.717259	3.45	.931075	1.28	.786184	4.73	.213816	34
27	.717466	3.45	.930998	1.28	.786468	4.73	.213532	33
28	.717673	3.43	.930921	1.30	.786752	4.73	.213248	32
29	.717879	3.43	.930843	1.28	.787036	4.72	.212964	31
30	9.718085	3.43	9.930766	1.30	9.787319	4.73	0.212681	30
31	.718291	3.43	.930688	1.28	.787603	4.72	.212397	29
32	.718497	3.43	.930611	1.30	.787886	4.73	.212114	28
33	.718703	3.43	.930533	1.28	.788170	4.72	.211830	27
34	.718909	3.42	.930456	1.30	.788453	4.72	.211547	26
35	9.719114	3.43	9.930378	1.30	9.788736	4.72	0.211264	25
36	.719320	3.42	.930300	1.28	.789019	4.72	.210981	24
37	.719525	3.42	.930223	1.30	.789302	4.72	.210698	23
38	.719730	3.42	.930145	1.30	.789585	4.72	.210415	22
39	.719935	3.42	.930067	1.30	.789868	4.72	.210132	21
40	9.720140	3.42	9.929989	1.30	9.790151	4.72	0.209849	20
41	.720345	3.40	.929911	1.30	.790434	4.70	.209566	19
42	.720549	3.42	.929833	1.30	.790716	4.72	.209284	18
43	.720754	3.40	.929755	1.30	.790999	4.70	.209001	17
44	.720958	3.40	.929677	1.30	.791281	4.70	.208719	16
45	9.721162	3.40	9.929599	1.30	9.791563	4.72	0.208437	15
46	.721366	3.40	.929521	1.32	.791846	4.70	.208154	14
47	.721570	3.40	.929442	1.30	.792128	4.70	.207872	13
48	.721774	3.40	.929364	1.30	.792410	4.70	.207590	12
49	.721978	3.38	.929286	1.32	.792692	4.70	.207308	11
50	9.722181	3.40	9.929207	1.30	9.792974	4.70	0.207026	10
51	.722385	3.38	.929129	1.32	.793256	4.70	.206744	9
52	.722588	3.38	.929050	1.30	.793538	4.68	.206462	8
53	.722791	3.38	.928972	1.32	.793819	4.70	.206181	7
54	.722994	3.38	.928893	1.30	.794101	4.70	.205899	6
55	9.723197	3.38	9.928815	1.32	9.794383	4.68	0.205617	5
56	.723400	3.38	.928736	1.32	.794664	4.70	.205336	4
57	.723603	3.37	.928657	1.32	.794946	4.68	.205054	3
58	.723805	3.37	.928578	1.32	.795227	4.68	.204773	2
59	.724007	3.38	.928499	1.32	.795508	4.68	.204492	1
60	9.724210		9.928420		9.795789		0.204211	0
	Cos.	D. 1″.	Sin.	D. 1″.	Cot.	D. 1″.	Tan.	M.

121°   58°

COSINES, TANGENTS, AND COTANGENTS

M.	Sin.	D. 1″.	Cos.	D. 1″.	Tan.	D. 1″.	Cot.	
0	9.724210	3.37	9.928420	1.30	9.795789	4.68	0.204211	60
1	.724412	3.37	.928342	1.32	.796070	4.68	.203930	59
2	.724614	3.37	.928263	1.33	.796351	4.68	.203649	58
3	.724816	3.37	.928183	1.32	.796632	4.68	.203368	57
4	.725017	3.37	.928104	1.32	.796913	4.68	.203087	56
5	9.725219	3.35	9.928025	1.32	9.797194	4.67	0.202806	55
6	.725420	3.37	.927946	1.32	.797474	4.68	.202526	54
7	.725622	3.35	.927867	1.33	.797755	4.68	.202245	53
8	.725823	3.35	.927787	1.32	.798036	4.67	.201964	52
9	.726024	3.35	.927708	1.32	.798316	4.67	.201684	51
10	9.726225	3.35	9.927629	1.33	9.798596	4.68	0.201404	50
11	.726426	3.33	.927549	1.32	.798877	4.67	.201123	49
12	.726626	3.35	.927470	1.33	.799157	4.67	.200843	48
13	.726827	3.33	.927390	1.33	.799437	4.67	.200563	47
14	.727027	3.35	.927310	1.32	.799717	4.67	.200283	46
15	9.727228	3.33	9.927231	1.33	9.799997	4.67	0.200003	45
16	.727428	3.33	.927151	1.33	.800277	4.67	.199723	44
17	.727628	3.33	.927071	1.33	.800557	4.65	.199443	43
18	.727828	3.32	.926991	1.33	.800836	4.67	.199164	42
19	.728027	3.33	.926911	1.33	.801116	4.67	.198884	41
20	9.728227	3.33	9.926831	1.33	9.801396	4.65	0.198604	40
21	.728427	3.32	.926751	1.33	.801675	4.67	.198325	39
22	.728626	3.32	.926671	1.33	.801955	4.65	.198045	38
23	.728825	3.32	.926591	1.33	.802234	4.65	.197766	37
24	.729024	3.32	.926511	1.33	.802513	4.65	.197487	36
25	9.729223	3.32	9.926431	1.33	9.802792	4.67	0.197208	35
26	.729422	3.32	.926351	1.35	.803072	4.65	.196928	34
27	.729621	3.32	.926270	1.33	.803351	4.65	.196649	33
28	.729820	3.30	.926190	1.33	.803630	4.65	.196370	32
29	.730018	3.32	.926110	1.35	.803909	4.63	.196091	31
30	9.730217	3.30	9.926029	1.33	9.804187	4.65	0.195813	30
31	.730415	3.30	.925949	1.35	.804466	4.65	.195534	29
32	.730613	3.30	.925868	1.33	.804745	4.63	.195255	28
33	.730811	3.30	.925788	1.35	.805023	4.65	.194977	27
34	.731009	3.28	.925707	1.35	.805302	4.63	.194698	26
35	9.731206	3.30	9.925626	1.35	9.805580	4.65	0.194420	25
36	.731404	3.30	.925545	1.33	.805859	4.63	.194141	24
37	.731602	3.28	.925465	1.35	.806137	4.63	.193863	23
38	.731799	3.28	.925384	1.35	.806415	4.63	.193585	22
39	.731996	3.28	.925303	1.35	.806693	4.63	.193307	21
40	9.732193	3.28	9.925222	1.35	9.806971	4.63	0.193029	20
41	.732390	3.28	.925141	1.35	.807249	4.63	.192751	19
42	.732587	3.28	.925060	1.35	.807527	4.63	.192473	18
43	.732784	3.27	.924979	1.37	.807805	4.63	.192195	17
44	.732980	3.28	.924897	1.35	.808083	4.63	.191917	16
45	9.733177	3.27	9.924816	1.35	9.808361	4.62	0.191639	15
46	.733373	3.27	.924735	1.35	.808638	4.63	.191362	14
47	.733569	3.27	.924654	1.37	.808916	4.62	.191084	13
48	.733765	3.27	.924572	1.35	.809193	4.63	.190807	12
49	.733961	3.27	.924491	1.37	.809471	4.62	.190529	11
50	9.734157	3.27	9.924409	1.35	9.809748	4.62	0.190252	10
51	.734353	3.27	.924328	1.37	.810025	4.62	.189975	9
52	.734549	3.25	.924246	1.37	.810302	4.63	.189698	8
53	.734744	3.25	.924164	1.35	.810580	4.62	.189420	7
54	.734939	3.27	.924083	1.37	.810857	4.62	.189143	6
55	9.735135	3.25	9.924001	1.37	9.811134	4.60	0.188866	5
56	.735330	3.25	.923919	1.37	.811410	4.62	.188590	4
57	.735525	3.23	.923837	1.37	.811687	4.62	.188313	3
58	.735719	3.25	.923755	1.37	.811964	4.62	.188036	2
59	.735914	3.25	.923673	1.37	.812241	4.60	.187759	1
60	9.736109		9.923591		9.812517		0.187483	0
	Cos.	D. 1″.	Sin.	D. 1″.	Cot.	D. 1″.	Tan.	M.

TABLE IX. LOGARITHMIC SINES,

33ᵈ

146°

M.	Sin.	D. 1″.	Cos.	D. 1″.	Tan.	D. 1″.	Cot.	
0	9.736109	3.23	9.923591	1.37	9.812517	4.62	0.187483	60
1	.736308	3.25	.923509	1.37	.812794	4.60	.187206	59
2	.736498	3.23	.923427	1.37	.813070	4.62	.186930	58
3	.736692	3.23	.923345	1.37	.813347	4.60	.186653	57
4	.736886	3.23	.923263	1.37	.813623	4.60	.186377	56
5	9.737080	3.23	9.923181	1.37	9.813899	4.62	0.186101	55
6	.737274	3.22	.923098	1.38	.814176	4.60	.185824	54
7	.737467	3.23	.923016	1.37	.814452	4.60	.185548	53
8	.737661	3.23	.922933	1.38	.814728	4.60	.185272	52
9	.737855	3.22	.922851	1.37	.815004	4.60	.184996	51
10	9.738048	3.22	9.922768	1.38	9.815280	4.58	0.184720	50
11	.738241	3.22	.922686	1.37	.815555	4.60	.184445	49
12	.738434	3.22	.922603	1.38	.815831	4.60	.184169	48
13	.738627	3.22	.922520	1.38	.816107	4.58	.183893	47
14	.738820	3.22	.922438	1.37	.816382	4.60	.183618	46
15	9.739013	3.22	9.922355	1.38	9.816658	4.58	0.183342	45
16	.739206	3.20	.922272	1.38	.816933	4.60	.183067	44
17	.739398	3.20	.922189	1.38	.817209	4.58	.182791	43
18	.739590	3.22	.922106	1.38	.817484	4.58	.182516	42
19	.739783	3.20	.922023	1.38	.817759	4.60	.182241	41
20	9.739975	3.20	9.921940	1.38	9.818035	4.58	0.181965	40
21	.740167	3.20	.921857	1.38	.818310	4.58	.181690	39
22	.740359	3.18	.921774	1.38	.818585	4.58	.181415	38
23	.740550	3.20	.921691	1.38	.818860	4.58	.181140	37
24	.740742	3.20	.921607	1.40	.819135	4.58	.180865	36
25	9.740934	3.18	9.921524	1.38	9.819410	4.57	0.180590	35
26	.741125	3.18	.921441	1.38	.819684	4.58	.180316	34
27	.741316	3.20	.921357	1.40	.819959	4.58	.180041	33
28	.741508	3.18	.921274	1.38	.820234	4.57	.179766	32
29	.741699	3.17	.921190	1.40	.820508	4.58	.179492	31
30	9.741889	3.18	9.921107	1.38	9.820783	4.57	0.179217	30
31	.742080	3.18	.921023	1.40	.821057	4.58	.178943	29
32	.742271	3.18	.920939	1.40	.821332	4.57	.178668	28
33	.742462	3.17	.920856	1.38	.821606	4.57	.178394	27
34	.742652	3.17	.920772	1.40	.821880	4.57	.178120	26
35	9.742842	3.18	9.920688	1.40	9.822154	4.58	0.177846	25
36	.743033	3.17	.920604	1.40	.822429	4.57	.177571	24
37	.743223	3.17	.920520	1.40	.822703	4.57	.177297	23
38	.743413	3.15	.920436	1.40	.822977	4.57	.177023	22
39	.743602	3.17	.920352	1.40	.823251	4.55	.176749	21
40	9.743792	3.17	9.920268	1.40	9.823524	4.57	0.176476	20
41	.743982	3.15	.920184	1.42	.823798	4.57	.176202	19
42	.744171	3.17	.920099	1.40	.824072	4.55	.175928	18
43	.744361	3.15	.920015	1.40	.824345	4.57	.175655	17
44	.744550	3.15	.919931	1.42	.824619	4.57	.175381	16
45	9.744739	3.15	9.919846	1.40	9.824893	4.55	0.175107	15
46	.744928	3.15	.919762	1.42	.825166	4.55	.174834	14
47	.745117	3.15	.919677	1.42	.825439	4.57	.174561	13
48	.745306	3.13	.919593	1.40	.825713	4.55	.174287	12
49	.745494	3.15	.919508	1.42	.825986	4.55	.174014	11
50	9.745683	3.13	9.919424	1.40	9.826259	4.55	0.173741	10
51	.745871	3.15	.919339	1.42	.826532	4.55	.173468	9
52	.746060	3.13	.919254	1.42	.826805	4.55	.173195	8
53	.746248	3.13	.919169	1.42	.827078	4.55	.172922	7
54	.746436	3.13	.919085	1.40	.827351	4.55	.172649	6
55	9.746624	3.13	9.919000	1.42	9.827624	4.55	0.172376	5
56	.746812	3.12	.918915	1.42	.827897	4.55	.172103	4
57	.746999	3.13	.918830	1.42	.828170	4.55	.171830	3
58	.747187	3.12	.918745	1.42	.828442	4.53	.171558	2
59	.747374	3.13	.918659	1.43	.828715	4.55	.171285	1
60	9.747562		9.918574	1.42	9.828987	4.53	0.171013	0
	Cos.	D. 1″.	Sin.	D. 1″.	Cot.	D. 1″.	Tan.	M.

COSINES, TANGENTS, AND COTANGENTS

34°   145°

M.	Sin.	D. 1″.	Cos.	D. 1″.	Tan.	D. 1′.	Cot.	
0	9.747562	3.12	9.918574	1.42	9.828987	4.55	0.171013	60
1	.747749	3.12	.918489	1.42	.829260	4.53	.170740	59
2	.747936	3.12	.918404	1.43	.829532	4.55	.170468	58
3	.748123	3.12	.918318	1.42	.829805	4.53	.170195	57
4	.748310	3.12	.918233	1.43	.830077	4.53	.169923	56
5	9.748497	3.10	9.918147	1.42	9.830349	4.53	0.169651	55
6	.748683	3.12	.918062	1.43	.830621	4.53	.169379	54
7	.748870	3.10	.917976	1.42	.830893	4.53	.169107	53
8	.749056	3.12	.917891	1.43	.831165	4.53	.168835	52
9	.749243	3.10	.917805	1.43	.831437	4.53	.168563	51
10	9.749429	3.10	9.917719	1.42	9.831709	4.53	0.168291	50
11	.749615	3.10	.917634	1.43	.831981	4.53	.168019	49
12	.749801	3.10	.917548	1.43	.832253	4.53	.167747	48
13	.749987	3.10	.917462	1.43	.832525	4.52	.167475	47
14	.750172	3.08	.917376	1.43	.832796	4.53	.167204	46
15	9.750358	3.10	9.917290	1.43	9.833068	4.52	0.166932	45
16	.750543	3.10	.917204	1.43	.833339	4.53	.166661	44
17	.750729	3.08	.917118	1.43	.833611	4.52	.166389	43
18	.750914	3.08	.917032	1.43	.833882	4.53	.166118	42
19	.751099	3.08	.916946	1.45	.834154	4.52	.165846	41
20	9.751284	3.08	9.916859	1.43	9.834425	4.52	0.165575	40
21	.751469	3.08	.916773	1.43	.834696	4.52	.165304	39
22	.751654	3.08	.916687	1.45	.834967	4.52	.165033	38
23	.751839	3.07	.916600	1.43	.835238	4.52	.164762	37
24	.752023	3.08	.916514	1.45	.835509	4.52	.164491	36
25	9.752208	3.07	9.916427	1.43	9.835780	4.52	0.164220	35
26	.752392	3.07	.916341	1.45	.836051	4.52	.163949	34
27	.752576	3.07	.916254	1.45	.836322	4.52	.163678	33
28	.752760	3.07	.916167	1.43	.836593	4.52	.163407	32
29	.752944	3.07	.916081	1.45	.836864	4.50	.163136	31
30	9.753128	3.07	9.915994	1.45	9.837134	4.52	0.162866	30
31	.753312	3.05	.915907	1.45	.837405	4.50	.162595	29
32	.753495	3.07	.915820	1.45	.837675	4.52	.162325	28
33	.753679	3.05	.915733	1.45	.837946	4.50	.162054	27
34	.753862	3.07	.915646	1.45	.838216	4.52	.161784	26
35	9.754046	3.05	9.915559	1.45	9.838487	4.50	0.161513	25
36	.754229	3.05	.915472	1.45	.838757	4.50	.161243	24
37	.754412	3.05	.915385	1.45	.839027	4.50	.160973	23
38	.754595	3.05	.915297	1.47	.839297	4.52	.160703	22
39	.754778	3.03	.915210	1.45	.839568	4.50	.160432	21
40	9.754960	3.05	9.915123	1.45	9.839838	4.50	0.160162	20
41	.755143	3.05	.915035	1.47	.840108	4.50	.159892	19
42	.755326	3.03	.914948	1.45	.840378	4.50	.159622	18
43	.755508	3.03	.914860	1.47	.840648	4.50	.159352	17
44	.755690	3.03	.914773	1.45	.840917	4.48	.159083	16
45	9.755872	3.03	9.914685	1.47	9.841187	4.50	0.158813	15
46	.756054	3.03	.914598	1.45	.841457	4.50	.158543	14
47	.756236	3.03	.914510	1.47	.841727	4.48	.158273	13
48	.756418	3.03	.914422	1.47	.841996	4.50	.158004	12
49	.756600	3.03	.914334	1.47	.842266	4.48	.157734	11
50	9.756782	3.02	9.914246	1.47	9.842535	4.50	0.157465	10
51	.756963	3.02	.914158	1.47	.842805	4.48	.157195	9
52	.757144	3.03	.914070	1.47	.843074	4.48	.156926	8
53	.757326	3.02	.913982	1.47	.843343	4.48	.156657	7
54	.757507	3.02	.913894	1.47	.843612	4.50	.156388	6
55	9.757688	3.02	9.913806	1.47	9.843882	4.48	0.156118	5
56	.757869	3.02	.913718	1.47	.844151	4.48	.155849	4
57	.758050	3.00	.913630	1.48	.844420	4.48	.155580	3
58	.758230	3.02	.913541	1.47	.844689	4.48	.155311	2
59	.758411	3.00	.913453	1.47	.844958	4.48	.155042	1
60	9.758591		9.913365		9.845227		0.154773	0
	Cos.	D. 1″.	Sin.	D. 1″.	Cot.	D. 1″.	Tan.	M.

124°   55°

TABLE IX. LOGARITHMIC SINES,

35°   144°

M.	Sin.	D. 1″.	Cos.	D. 1″.	Tan.	D. 1″.	Cot.	
0	9.758591	3.02	9.913365	1.48	9.845227	4.48	0.154773	60
1	.758772	3.00	.913276	1.48	.845496	4.47	.154504	59
2	.758952	3.00	.913187	1.47	.845764	4.48	.154236	58
3	.759132	3.00	.913099	1.48	.846033	4.48	.153967	57
4	.759312	3.00	.913010	1.47	.846302	4.47	.153698	56
5	9.759492	3.00	9.912922	1.47	9.846570	4.48	0.153430	55
6	.759672	3.00	.912833	1.48	.846839	4.48	.153161	54
7	.759852	2.98	.912744	1.48	.847108	4.47	.152892	53
8	.760021	3.00	.912655	1.48	.847376	4.48	.152624	52
9	.760211	2.98	.912566	1.48	.847644	4.48	.152356	51
10	9.760390	2.98	9.912477	1.48	9.847913	4.47	0.152087	50
11	.760569	2.98	.912388	1.48	.848181	4.47	.151819	49
12	.760748	2.98	.912299	1.48	.848449	4.47	.151551	48
13	.760927	2.98	.912210	1.48	.848717	4.48	.151283	47
14	.761106	2.98	.912121	1.50	.848986	4.47	.151014	46
15	9.761285	2.98	9.912031	1.48	9.849254	4.47	0.150746	45
16	.761464	2.97	.911942	1.48	.849522	4.47	.150478	44
17	.761642	2.98	.911853	1.50	.849790	4.45	.150210	43
18	.761821	2.97	.911763	1.48	.850057	4.47	.149943	42
19	.761999	2.97	.911674	1.50	.850325	4.47	.149675	41
20	9.762177	2.98	9.911584	1.48	9.850593	4.47	0.149407	40
21	.762356	2.97	.911495	1.50	.850861	4.47	.149139	39
22	.762534	2.97	.911405	1.50	.851129	4.45	.148871	38
23	.762712	2.95	.911315	1.48	.851396	4.47	.148604	37
24	.762889	2.97	.911226	1.50	.851664	4.45	.148336	36
25	9.763067	2.97	9.911136	1.50	9.851931	4.47	0.148069	35
26	.763245	2.95	.911046	1.50	.852199	4.45	.147801	34
27	.763422	2.97	.910956	1.50	.852466	4.45	.147534	33
28	.763600	2.95	.910866	1.50	.852733	4.47	.147267	32
29	.763777	2.95	.910776	1.50	.853001	4.45	.146999	31
30	9.763954	2.95	9.910686	1.50	9.853268	4.45	0.146732	30
31	.764131	2.95	.910596	1.50	.853535	4.45	.146465	29
32	.764308	2.95	.910506	1.52	.853802	4.45	.146198	28
33	.764485	2.95	.910415	1.50	.854069	4.45	.145931	27
34	.764662	2.93	.910325	1.50	.854336	4.45	.145664	26
35	9.764838	2.95	9.910235	1.52	9.854603	4.45	0.145397	25
36	.765015	2.93	.910144	1.50	.854870	4.45	.145130	24
37	.765191	2.93	.910054	1.50	.855137	4.45	.144863	23
38	.765367	2.93	.909963	1.52	.855404	4.45	.144596	22
39	.765544	2.95	.909873	1.50	.855671	4.45	.144329	21
40	9.765720	2.93	9.909782	1.52	9.855938	4.43	0.144062	20
41	.765896	2.93	.909691	1.50	.856204	4.45	.143796	19
42	.766072	2.92	.909601	1.52	.856471	4.43	.143529	18
43	.766247	2.93	.909510	1.52	.856737	4.45	.143263	17
44	.766423	2.92	.909419	1.52	.857004	4.43	.142996	16
45	9.766598	2.93	9.909328	1.52	9.857270	4.45	0.142730	15
46	.766774	2.92	.909237	1.52	.857537	4.43	.142463	14
47	.766949	2.92	.909146	1.52	.857803	4.43	.142197	13
48	.767124	2.93	.909055	1.52	.858069	4.45	.141931	12
49	.767300	2.92	.908964	1.52	.858336	4.43	.141664	11
50	9.767475	2.90	9.908873	1.53	9.858602	4.43	0.141398	10
51	.767649	2.92	.908781	1.52	.858868	4.43	.141132	9
52	.767824	2.92	.908690	1.52	.859134	4.43	.140866	8
53	.767999	2.90	.908599	1.53	.859400	4.43	.140600	7
54	.768173	2.92	.908507	1.52	.859666	4.43	.140334	6
55	9.768348	2.90	9.908416	1.53	9.859932	4.43	0.140068	5
56	.768522	2.92	.908324	1.52	.860198	4.43	.139802	4
57	.768697	2.90	.908233	1.53	.860464	4.43	.139536	3
58	.768871	2.90	.908141	1.53	.860730	4.43	.139270	2
59	.769045	2.90	.908049	1.53	.860995	4.42	.139005	1
60	9.769219		9.907958	1.52	9.861261	4.43	0.138739	0
	Cos.	D. 1″.	Sin.	D. 1″.	Cot.	D. 1″.	Tan.	M.

125°   54°

COSINES, TANGENTS, AND COTANGENTS

36°   143°

M.	Sin.	D. 1″.	Cos.	D. 1″.	Tan.	D. 1″.	Cot.	
0	9.769219	2.90	9.907958	1.53	9.861261	4.43	0.138739	60
1	.769393	2.88	.907866	1.53	.861527	4.42	.138473	59
2	.769566	2.90	.907774	1.53	.861792	4.43	.138208	58
3	.769740	2.88	.907682	1.53	.862058	4.42	.137942	57
4	.769913	2.90	.907590	1.53	.862323	4.42	.137677	56
5	9.770087	2.88	9.907498	1.53	9.862589	4.43	0.137411	55
6	.770260	2.88	.907406	1.53	.862854	4.42	.137146	54
7	.770433	2.88	.907314	1.53	.863119	4.43	.136881	53
8	.770606	2.88	.907222	1.55	.863385	4.42	.136615	52
9	.770779	2.88	.907129	1.53	.863650	4.42	.136350	51
10	9.770952	2.88	9.907037	1.53	9.863915	4.42	0.136085	50
11	.771125	2.88	.906945	1.55	.864180	4.42	.135820	49
12	.771298	2.87	.906852	1.53	.864445	4.42	.135555	48
13	.771470	2.88	.906760	1.55	.864710	4.42	.135290	47
14	.771643	2.87	.906667	1.53	.864975	4.42	.135025	46
15	9.771815	2.87	9.906575	1.55	9.865240	4.42	0.134760	45
16	.771987	2.87	.906482	1.55	.865505	4.42	.134495	44
17	.772159	2.87	.906389	1.55	.865770	4.42	.134230	43
18	.772331	2.87	.906296	1.53	.866035	4.42	.133965	42
19	.772503	2.87	.906204	1.55	.866300	4.40	.133700	41
20	9.772675	2.87	9.906111	1.55	9.866564	4.42	0.133436	40
21	.772847	2.85	.906018	1.55	.866829	4.42	.133171	39
22	.773018	2.87	.905925	1.55	.867094	4.40	.132906	38
23	.773190	2.85	.905832	1.55	.867358	4.42	.132642	37
24	.773361	2.87	.905739	1.57	.867623	4.40	.132377	36
25	9.773533	2.85	9.905645	1.55	9.867887	4.42	0.132113	35
26	.773704	2.85	.905552	1.55	.868152	4.40	.131848	34
27	.773875	2.85	.905459	1.55	.868416	4.40	.131584	33
28	.774046	2.85	.905366	1.57	.868680	4.42	.131320	32
29	.774217	2.85	.905272	1.55	.868945	4.40	.131055	31
30	9.774388	2.83	9.905179	1.57	9.869209	4.40	0.130791	30
31	.774558	2.85	.905085	1.55	.869473	4.40	.130527	29
32	.774729	2.83	.904992	1.57	.869737	4.40	.130263	28
33	.774899	2.86	.904898	1.57	.870001	4.40	.129999	27
34	.775070	2.83	.904804	1.55	.870265	4.40	.129735	26
35	9.775240	2.83	9.904711	1.57	9.870529	4.40	0.129471	25
36	.775410	2.83	.904617	1.57	.870793	4.40	.129207	24
37	.775580	2.83	.904523	1.57	.871057	4.40	.128943	23
38	.775750	2.83	.904429	1.57	.871321	4.40	.128679	22
39	.775920	2.83	.904335	1.57	.871585	4.40	.128415	21
40	9.776090	2.82	9.904241	1.57	9.871849	4.38	0.128151	20
41	.776259	2.83	.904147	1.57	.872112	4.40	.127888	19
42	.776429	2.82	.904053	1.57	.872376	4.40	.127624	18
43	.776598	2.83	.903959	1.58	.872640	4.38	.127360	17
44	.776768	2.82	.903864	1.57	.872903	4.40	.127097	16
45	9.776937	2.82	9.903770	1.57	9.873167	4.38	0.126833	15
46	.777106	2.82	.903676	1.58	.873430	4.40	.126570	14
47	.777275	2.82	.903581	1.57	.873694	4.38	.126306	13
48	.777444	2.82	.903487	1.58	.873957	4.38	.126043	12
49	.777613	2.80	.903392	1.57	.874220	4.40	.125780	11
50	9.777781	2.82	9.903298	1.58	9.874484	4.38	0.125516	10
51	.777950	2.82	.903203	1.58	.874747	4.38	.125253	9
52	.778119	2.80	.903108	1.57	.875010	4.38	.124990	8
53	.778287	2.80	.903014	1.58	.875273	4.40	.124727	7
54	.778455	2.82	.902919	1.58	.875537	4.38	.124463	6
55	9.778624	2.80	9.902824	1.58	9.875800	4.38	0.124200	5
56	.778792	2.80	.902729	1.58	.876063	4.38	.123937	4
57	.778960	2.80	.902634	1.58	.876326	4.38	.123674	3
58	.779128	2.78	.902539	1.58	.876589	4.38	.123411	2
59	.779295	2.80	.902444	1.58	.876852	4.37	.123148	1
60	9.779463		9.902349		9.877114		0.122886	0
	Cos.	D. 1″.	Sin.	D. 1″.	Cot.	D. 1″.	Tan.	M.

TABLE IX. LOGARITHMIC SINES,

37°   142°

M.	Sin.	D. 1″.	Cos.	D. 1″.	Tan.	D. 1″.	Cot.	
0	9.779463		9.902349		9.877114		0.122886	60
1	.779631	2.80	.902253	1.60	.877377	4.38	.122623	59
2	.779798	2.78	.902158	1.58	.877640	4.38	.122360	58
3	.779966	2.80	.902063	1.58	.877903	4.38	.122097	57
4	.780133	2.78	.901967	1.60	.878165	4.37	.121835	56
5	9.780300	2.78	9.901872	1.58	9.878428	4.38	0.121572	55
6	.780467	2.78	.901776	1.60	.878691	4.38	.121309	54
7	.780634	2.78	.901681	1.58	.878953	4.37	.121047	53
8	.780801	2.78	.901585	1.60	.879216	4.38	.120784	52
9	.780968	2.78	.901490	1.58	.879478	4.37	.120522	51
10	9.781134	2.77	9.901394	1.60	9.879741	4.38	0.120259	50
11	.781301	2.78	.901298	1.60	.880003	4.37	.119997	49
12	.781468	2.78	.901202	1.60	.880265	4.37	.119735	48
13	.781634	2.77	.901106	1.60	.880528	4.38	.119472	47
14	.781800	2.77	.901010	1.60	.880790	4.37	.119210	46
15	9.781966	2.77	9.900914	1.60	9.881052	4.37	0.118948	45
16	.782132	2.77	.900818	1.60	.881314	4.38	.118686	44
17	.782298	2.77	.900722	1.60	.881577	4.37	.118423	43
18	.782464	2.77	.900626	1.60	.881839	4.37	.118161	42
19	.782630	2.77	.900529	1.62	.882101	4.37	.117899	41
20	9.782796	2.77	9.900433	1.60	9.882363	4.37	0.117637	40
21	.782961	2.75	.900337	1.60	.882625	4.37	.117375	39
22	.783127	2.77	.900240	1.62	.882887	4.37	.117113	38
23	.783292	2.75	.900144	1.60	.883148	4.35	.116852	37
24	.783458	2.77	.900047	1.62	.883410	4.37	.116590	36
25	9.783623	2.75	9.899951	1.60	9.883672	4.37	0.116328	35
26	.783788	2.75	.899854	1.62	.883934	4.37	.116066	34
27	.783953	2.75	.899757	1.62	.884196	4.37	.115804	33
28	.784118	2.75	.899660	1.62	.884457	4.35	.115543	32
29	.784282	2.73	.899564	1.60	.884719	4.37	.115281	31
30	9.784447	2.75	9.899467	1.62	9.884980	4.35	0.115020	30
31	.784612	2.75	.899370	1.62	.885242	4.37	.114758	29
32	.784776	2.73	.899273	1.62	.885504	4.37	.114496	28
33	.784941	2.75	.899176	1.62	.885765	4.35	.114235	27
34	.785105	2.73	.899078	1.63	.886026	4.35	.113974	26
35	9.785269	2.73	9.898981	1.62	9.886288	4.37	0.113712	25
36	.785433	2.73	.898884	1.62	.886549	4.35	.113451	24
37	.785597	2.73	.898787	1.62	.886811	4.35	.113189	23
38	.785761	2.73	.898689	1.63	.887072	4.35	.112928	22
39	.785925	2.73	.898592	1.62	.887333	4.35	.112667	21
40	9.786089	2.73	9.898494	1.63	9.887594	4.35	0.112406	20
41	.786252	2.72	.898397	1.62	.887855	4.35	.112145	19
42	.786416	2.73	.898299	1.63	.888116	4.37	.111884	18
43	.786579	2.72	.898202	1.62	.888378	4.35	.111622	17
44	.786742	2.72	.898104	1.63	.888639	4.35	.111361	16
45	9.786906	2.73	9.898006	1.63	9.888900	4.35	0.111100	15
46	.787069	2.72	.897908	1.63	.889161	4.33	.110839	14
47	.787232	2.72	.897810	1.63	.889421	4.35	.110579	13
48	.787395	2.72	.897712	1.63	.889682	4.35	.110318	12
49	.787557	2.70	.897614	1.63	.889943	4.35	.110057	11
50	9.787720	2.72	9.897516	1.63	9.890204	4.35	0.109796	10
51	.787883	2.72	.897418	1.63	.890465	4.35	.109535	9
52	.788045	2.70	.897320	1.63	.890725	4.33	.109275	8
53	.788208	2.72	.897222	1.63	.890986	4.35	.109014	7
54	.788370	2.70	.897123	1.65	.891247	4.33	.108753	6
55	9.788532	2.70	9.897025	1.63	9.891507	4.35	0.108493	5
56	.788694	2.70	.896926	1.65	.891768	4.33	.108232	4
57	.788856	2.70	.896828	1.63	.892028	4.35	.107972	3
58	.789018	2.70	.896729	1.65	.892289	4.33	.107711	2
59	.789180	2.70	.896631	1.63	.892549	4.35	.107451	1
60	9.789342	2.70	9.896532	1.65	9.892810		0.107190	0
	Cos.	D. 1″.	Sin.	D. 1″.	Cot.	D. 1″.	Tan.	M.

127°   52°

COSINES, TANGENTS, AND COTANGENTS

M.	Sin.	D. 1″.	Cos.	D. 1″.	Tan.	D. 1″.	Cot.	
0	9.789342	2.70	9.896532	1.65	9.892810	4.33	0.107190	60
1	.789504	2.68	.896433	1.63	.893070	4.35	.106930	59
2	.789665	2.70	.896335	1.65	.893331	4.33	.106669	58
3	.789827	2.68	.896236	1.65	.893591	4.33	.106409	57
4	.789988	2.68	.896137	1.65	.893851	4.33	.106149	56
5	9.790149	2.68	9.896038	1.65	9.894111	4.35	0.105889	55
6	.790310	2.68	.895939	1.65	.894372	4.33	.105628	54
7	.790471	2.68	.895840	1.65	.894632	4.33	.105368	53
8	.790632	2.68	.895741	1.67	.894892	4.33	.105108	52
9	.790793	2.68	.895641	1.65	.895152	4.33	.104848	51
10	9.790954	2.68	9.895542	1.65	9.895412	4.33	0.104588	50
11	.791115	2.67	.895443	1.67	.895672	4.33	.104328	49
12	.791275	2.68	.895343	1.67	.895932	4.33	.104068	48
13	.791436	2.67	.895244	1.65	.896192	4.33	.103808	47
14	.791596	2.68	.895145	1.65	.896452	4.33	.103548	46
15	9.791757	2.67	9.895015	1.67	9.896712	4.32	0.103288	45
16	.791917	2.67	.894945	1.67	.896971	4.33	.103029	44
17	.792077	2.67	.894846	1.65	.897231	4.33	.102769	43
18	.792237	2.67	.894746	1.67	.897491	4.33	.102509	42
19	.792397	2.67	.894646	1.67	.897751	4.32	.102249	41
20	9.792557	2.65	9.894546	1.67	9.898010	4.33	0.101990	40
21	.792716	2.67	.894446	1.67	.898270	4.33	.101730	39
22	.792876	2.65	.894346	1.67	.898530	4.32	.101470	38
23	.793035	2.67	.894246	1.67	.898789	4.33	.101211	37
24	.793195	2.65	.894146	1.67	.899049	4.32	.100951	36
25	9.793354	2.67	9.894046	1.67	9.899308	4.33	0.100692	35
26	.793514	2.65	.893946	1.67	.899568	4.32	.100432	34
27	.793673	2.65	.893846	1.68	.899827	4.33	.100173	33
28	.793832	2.65	.893745	1.67	.900087	4.32	.099913	32
29	.793991	2.65	.893645	1.68	.900346	4.32	.099654	31
30	9.794150	2.63	9.893544	1.67	9.900605	4.32	0.099395	30
31	.794308	2.65	.893444	1.68	.900864	4.33	.099136	29
32	.794467	2.65	.893343	1.67	.901124	4.32	.098876	28
33	.794626	2.63	.893243	1.68	.901383	4.32	.098617	27
34	.794784	2.63	.893142	1.68	.901642	4.32	.098358	26
35	9.794942	2.65	9.893041	1.68	9.901901	4.32	0.098099	25
36	.795101	2.63	.892940	1.68	.902160	4.33	.097840	24
37	.795259	2.63	.892839	1.68	.902420	4.32	.097580	23
38	.795417	2.63	.892739	1.67	.902679	4.32	.097321	22
39	.795575	2.63	.892638	1.70	.902938	4.32	.097062	21
40	9.795733	2.63	9.892536	1.68	9.903197	4.32	0.096803	20
41	.795891	2.63	.892435	1.68	.903456	4.30	.096544	19
42	.796049	2.62	.892334	1.68	.903714	4.32	.096286	18
43	.796206	2.63	.892233	1.68	.903973	4.32	.096027	17
44	.796364	2.62	.892132	1.70	.904232	4.32	.095768	16
45	9.796521	2.63	9.892030	1.68	9.904491	4.32	0.095509	15
46	.796679	2.62	.891929	1.70	.904750	4.30	.095250	14
47	.796836	2.62	.891827	1.70	.905008	4.32	.094992	13
48	.796993	2.62	.891726	1.68	.905267	4.32	.094733	12
49	.797150	2.62	.891624	1.70	.905526	4.32	.094474	11
50	9.797307	2.62	9.891523	1.68	9.905785	4.30	0.094215	10
51	.797464	2.62	.891421	1.70	.906043	4.32	.093957	9
52	.797621	2.60	.891319	1.70	.906302	4.30	.093698	8
53	.797777	2.62	.891217	1.70	.906560	4.32	.093440	7
54	.797934	2.62	.891115	1.70	.906819	4.30	.093181	6
55	9.798091	2.60	9.891013	1.70	9.907077	4.32	0.092923	5
56	.798247	2.60	.890911	1.70	.907336	4.30	.092664	4
57	.798403	2.62	.890809	1.70	.907594	4.32	.092406	3
58	.798560	2.60	.890707	1.70	.907853	4.30	.092147	2
59	.798716	2.60	.890605	1.70	.908111	4.30	.091889	1
60	9.798872		9.890503		9.908369		0.091631	0
	Cos.	D. 1″.	Sin.	D. 1″.	Cot.	D. 1″.	Tan.	M.

TABLE IX. LOGARITHMIC SINES,

39°   140°

M.	Sin.	D. 1″.	Cos.	D. 1″.	Tan.	D. 1″.	Cot.	
0	9.798872	2.60	9.890503	1.72	9.908369	4.32	0.091631	60
1	.799028	2.60	.890400	1.70	.908628	4.30	.091372	59
2	.799184	2.58	.890298	1.72	.908886	4.30	.091114	58
3	.799339	2.60	.890195	1.70	.909144	4.30	.090856	57
4	.799495	2.60	.890093	1.72	.909402	4.30	.090598	56
5	9.799651	2.58	9.889990	1.70	9.909660	4.30	0.090340	55
6	.799806	2.60	.889888	1.72	.909918	4.32	.090082	54
7	.799962	2.58	.889785	1.72	.910177	4.30	.089823	53
8	.800117	2.58	.889682	1.72	.910435	4.30	.039565	52
9	.800272	2.58	.889579	1.70	.910693	4.30	.089307	51
10	9.800427	2.58	9.889477	1.72	9.910951	4.30	0.089049	50
11	.800582	2.58	.889374	1.72	.911209	4.30	.088791	49
12	.800737	2.58	.889271	1.72	.911467	4.30	.088533	48
13	.800892	2.58	.889168	1.73	.911725	4.28	.088275	47
14	.801047	2.58	.889064	1.72	.911982	4.30	.038018	46
15	9.801201	2.57	9.888961	1.72	9.912240	4.30	0.087760	45
16	.801356	2.58	.888858	1.72	.912498	4.30	.087502	44
17	.801511	2.58	.888755	1.73	.912756	4.30	.087244	43
18	.801665	2.57	.888651	1.72	.913014	4.28	.086986	42
19	.801819	2.57	.888548	1.73	.913271	4.30	.086729	41
20	9.801973	2.58	9.888444	1.72	9.913529	4.30	0.086471	40
21	.802128	2.57	.888341	1.73	.913787	4.28	.086213	39
22	.802282	2.57	.888237	1.72	.914044	4.30	.085956	38
23	.802436	2.55	.888134	1.73	.914302	4.30	.085698	37
24	.802589	2.57	.888030	1.73	.914560	4.30	.085440	36
25	9.802743	2.57	9.887926	1.73	9.914817	4.28	0.085183	35
26	.802897	2.55	.887822	1.73	.915075	4.28	.084925	34
27	.803050	2.57	.887718	1.73	.915332	4.30	.084668	33
28	.803204	2.55	.887614	1.73	.915590	4.28	.084410	32
29	.803357	2.57	.887510	1.73	.915847	4.28	.084153	31
30	9.803511	2.55	9.887406	1.73	9.916104	4.30	0.083896	30
31	.803664	2.55	.887302	1.73	.916362	4.28	.083638	29
32	.803817	2.55	.887198	1.75	.916619	4.30	.083381	28
33	.803970	2.55	.887093	1.73	.916877	4.28	.083123	27
34	.804123	2.55	.886989	1.73	.917134	4.28	.082866	26
35	9.804276	2.53	9.886885	1.75	9.917391	4.28	0.082609	25
36	.804428	2.55	.886780	1.73	.917648	4.30	.082352	24
37	.804581	2.55	.886676	1.75	.917906	4.28	.082094	23
38	.804734	2.53	.886571	1.75	.918163	4.28	.081837	22
39	.804886	2.55	.886466	1.73	.918420	4.28	.081580	21
40	9.805039	2.53	9.886362	1.75	9.918677	4.28	0.081323	20
41	.805191	2.53	.886257	1.75	.918934	4.28	.081066	19
42	.805343	2.53	.886152	1.75	.919191	4.28	.080809	18
43	.805495	2.53	.886047	1.75	.919448	4.28	.080552	17
44	.805647	2.53	.885942	1.75	.919705	4.28	.080295	16
45	9.805799	2.53	9.885837	1.75	9.919962	4.28	0.080038	15
46	.805951	2.53	.885732	1.75	.920219	4.28	.079781	14
47	.806103	2.52	.885627	1.75	.920476	4.28	.079524	13
48	.806254	2.53	.885522	1.77	.920733	4.28	.079267	12
49	.806406	2.52	.885416	1.75	.920990	4.28	.079010	11
50	9.806557	2.53	9.885311	1.77	9.921247	4.27	0.078753	10
51	.806709	2.52	.885205	1.75	.921503	4.28	.078497	9
52	.806860	2.52	.885100	1.77	.921760	4.28	.078240	8
53	.807011	2.53	.884994	1.75	.922017	4.28	.077983	7
54	.807163	2.52	.884889	1.77	.922274	4.27	.077726	6
55	9.807314	2.52	9.884783	1.77	9.922530	4.28	0.077470	5
56	.807465	2.50	.884677	1.75	.922787	4.28	.077213	4
57	.807615	2.52	.884572	1.77	.923044	4.27	.076956	3
58	.807766	2.52	.884466	1.77	.923300	4.28	.076700	2
59	.807917	2.50	.884360	1.77	.923557	4.28	.076443	1
60	9.808067		9.884254		9.923814		0.076186	0
	Cos.	D. 1″.	Sin.	D. 1″.	Cot.	D. 1″.	Tan.	M.

COSINES, TANGENTS, AND COTANGENTS

40° 139°

M.	Sin.	D. 1".	Cos.	D. 1".	Tan.	D. 1".	Cot.	
0	9.808067	2.52	9.884254	1.77	9.923814	4.27	0.076186	60
1	.808218	2.50	.884148	1.77	.924070	4.28	.075930	59
2	.808368	2.52	.884042	1.77	.924327	4.27	.075673	58
3	.808519	2.50	.883936	1.78	.924583	4.28	.075417	57
4	.808669	2.50	.883829	1.77	.924840	4.27	.075160	56
5	9.808819	2.50	9.883723	1.77	9.925096	4.27	0.074904	55
6	.808969	2.50	.883617	1.78	.925352	4.28	.074648	54
7	.809119	2.50	.883510	1.77	.925609	4.27	.074391	53
8	.809269	2.50	.883404	1.78	.925865	4.28	.074135	52
9	.809419	2.50	.883297	1.77	.926122	4.27	.073878	51
10	9.809569	2.48	9.883191	1.78	9.926378	4.27	0.073622	50
11	.809718	2.50	.883084	1.78	.926634	4.27	.073366	49
12	.809868	2.48	.882977	1.78	.926890	4.28	.073110	48
13	.810017	2.50	.882871	1.77	.927147	4.27	.072853	47
14	.810167	2.48	.882764	1.78	.927403	4.27	.072597	46
15	9.810316	2.48	9.882657	1.78	9.927659	4.27	0.072341	45
16	.810465	2.48	.882550	1.78	.927915	4.27	.072085	44
17	.810614	2.48	.882443	1.78	.928171	4.27	.071829	43
18	.810763	2.48	.882336	1.78	.928427	4.28	.071573	42
19	.810912	2.48	.882229	1.80	.928684	4.27	.071316	41
20	9.811061	2.48	9.882121	1.78	9.928940	4.27	0.071060	40
21	.811210	2.47	.882014	1.78	.929196	4.27	.070804	39
22	.811358	2.48	.881907	1.80	.929452	4.27	.070548	38
23	.811507	2.47	.881799	1.78	.929708	4.27	.070292	37
24	.811655	2.48	.881692	1.80	.929964	4.27	.070036	36
25	9.811804	2.47	9.881584	1.80	9.930220	4.25	0.069780	35
26	.811952	2.47	.881477	1.78	.930475	4.27	.069525	34
27	.812100	2.47	.881369	1.80	.930731	4.27	.069269	33
28	.812248	2.47	.881261	1.80	.930987	4.27	.069013	32
29	.812396	2.47	.881153	1.80	.931243	4.27	.068757	31
30	9.812544	2.47	9.881046	1.78	9.931499	4.27	0.068501	30
31	.812692	2.47	.880938	1.80	.931755	4.25	.068245	29
32	.812840	2.47	.880830	1.80	.932010	4.27	.067990	28
33	.812988	2.45	.880722	1.80	.932266	4.27	.067734	27
34	.813135	2.47	.880613	1.82	.932522	4.27	.067478	26
35	9.813283	2.45	9.880505	1.80	9.932778	4.25	0.067222	25
36	.813430	2.47	.880397	1.80	.933033	4.27	.066967	24
37	.813578	2.45	.880289	1.80	.933289	4.27	.066711	23
38	.813725	2.45	.880180	1.82	.933545	4.25	.066455	22
39	.813872	2.45	.880072	1.80	.933800	4.27	.066200	21
40	9.814019	2.45	9.879963	1.82	9.934056	4.25	0.065944	20
41	.814166	2.45	.879855	1.80	.934311	4.27	.065689	19
42	.814313	2.45	.879746	1.82	.934567	4.25	.065433	18
43	.814460	2.45	.879637	1.82	.934822	4.27	.065178	17
44	.814607	2.43	.879529	1.80	.935078	4.25	.064922	16
45	9.814753	2.45	9.879420	1.82	9.935333	4.27	0.064667	15
46	.814900	2.43	.879311	1.82	.935589	4.25	.064411	14
47	.815046	2.45	.879202	1.82	.935844	4.27	.064156	13
48	.815193	2.43	.879093	1.82	.936100	4.25	.063900	12
49	.815339	2.43	.878984	1.82	.936355	4.27	.063645	11
50	9.815485	2.45	9.878875	1.82	9.936611	4.25	0.063389	10
51	.815632	2.43	.878766	1.83	.936866	4.25	.063134	9
52	.815778	2.43	.878656	1.82	.937121	4.27	.062879	8
53	.815924	2.42	.878547	1.82	.937377	4.25	.062623	7
54	.816069	2.43	.878438	1.83	.937632	4.25	.062368	6
55	9.816215	2.43	9.878328	1.82	9.937887	4.25	0.062113	5
56	.816361	2.43	.878219	1.83	.938142	4.27	.061858	4
57	.816507	2.42	.878109	1.83	.938398	4.25	.061602	3
58	.816652	2.43	.877999	1.83	.938653	4.25	.061347	2
59	.816798	2.42	.877890	1.82	.938908	4.25	.061092	1
60	9.816943		9.877780	1.83	9.939163		0.060837	0
	Cos.	D. 1".	Sin.	D. 1".	Cot.	D. 1".	Tan.	M.

130° 49°

APPENDIX B

TABLE IX. LOGARITHMIC SINES,

41°   138°

M.	Sin.	D. 1″.	Cos.	D. 1″.	Tan.	D. 1″.	Cot.	
0	9.816943	2.42	9.877780	1.83	9.939163	4.25	0.060837	60
1	.817088	2.42	.877670	1.83	.939418	4.25	.060582	59
2	.817233	2.43	.877560	1.83	.939673	4.25	.060327	58
3	.817379	2.42	.877450	1.83	.939928	4.25	.060072	57
4	.817524	2.40	.877340	1.83	.940183	4.27	.059817	56
5	9.817668	2.42	9.877230	1.83	9.940439	4.25	0.059561	55
6	.817813	2.42	.877120	1.83	.940694	4.25	.059306	54
7	.817958	2.42	.877010	1.85	.940949	4.25	.059051	53
8	.818103	2.40	.876899	1.83	.941204	4.25	.058796	52
9	.818247	2.42	.876789	1.85	.941459	4.23	.058541	51
10	9.818392	2.40	9.876678	1.83	9.941713	4.25	0.058287	50
11	.818536	2.42	.876568	1.85	.941968	4.25	.058032	49
12	.818681	2.40	.876457	1.83	.942223	4.25	.057777	48
13	.818825	2.40	.876347	1.85	.942478	4.25	.057522	47
14	.818969	2.40	.876236	1.85	.942733	4.25	.057267	46
15	9.819113	2.40	9.876125	1.85	9.942988	4.25	0.057012	45
16	.819257	2.40	.876014	1.83	.943243	4.25	.056757	44
17	.819401	2.40	.875904	1.85	.943498	4.23	.056502	43
18	.819545	2.40	.875793	1.85	.943752	4.25	.056248	42
19	.819689	2.38	.875682	1.85	.944007	4.25	.055993	41
20	9.819832	2.40	9.875571	1.87	9.944262	4.25	0.055738	40
21	.819976	2.40	.875459	1.85	.944517	4.23	.055483	39
22	.820120	2.38	.875348	1.85	.944771	4.25	.055229	38
23	.820263	2.38	.875237	1.85	.945026	4.25	.054974	37
24	.820406	2.40	.875126	1.87	.945281	4.23	.054719	36
25	9.820550	2.38	9.875014	1.85	9.945535	4.25	0.054465	35
26	.820693	2.38	.874903	1.87	.945790	4.25	.054210	34
27	.820836	2.38	.874791	1.87	.946045	4.23	.053955	33
28	.820979	2.38	.874680	1.85	.946299	4.25	.053701	32
29	.821122	2.38	.874568	1.87	.946554	4.23	.053446	31
30	9.821265	2.37	9.874456	1.87	9.946808	4.25	0.053192	30
31	.821407	2.38	.874344	1.87	.947063	4.25	.052937	29
32	.821550	2.38	.874232	1.87	.947318	4.23	.052682	28
33	.821693	2.37	.874121	1.85	.947572	4.25	.052428	27
34	.821835	2.37	.874009	1.87	.947827	4.23	.052173	26
35	9.821977	2.38	9.873896	1.88	9.948081	4.23	0.051919	25
36	.822120	2.37	.873784	1.87	.948335	4.25	.051665	24
37	.822262	2.37	.873672	1.87	.948590	4.23	.051410	23
38	.822404	2.37	.873560	1.87	.948844	4.25	.051156	22
39	.822546	2.37	.873448	1.88	.949099	4.23	.050901	21
40	9.822688	2.37	9.873335	1.87	9.949353	4.25	0.050647	20
41	.822830	2.37	.873223	1.88	.949608	4.23	.050392	19
42	.822972	2.37	.873110	1.87	.949862	4.23	.050138	18
43	.823114	2.35	.872998	1.88	950116	4.25	.049884	17
44	.823255	2.37	.872885	1.88	.950371	4.23	.049629	16
45	9.823397	2.37	9.872772	1.88	9.950625	4.23	0.049375	15
46	.823539	2.35	.872659	1.87	.950879	4.23	.049121	14
47	.823680	2.35	.872547	1.88	.951133	4.25	.048867	13
48	.823821	2.37	.872434	1.88	.951388	4.23	.048612	12
49	.823963	2.35	.872321	1.88	.951642	4.23	.048358	11
50	9.824104	2.35	9.872208	1.88	9.951896	4.23	0.048104	10
51	.824245	2.35	.872095	1.90	.952150	4.25	.047850	9
52	.824386	2.35	.871981	1.88	.952405	4.23	.047595	8
53	.824527	2.35	.871868	1.88	.952659	4.23	.047341	7
54	.824668	2.33	.871755	1.90	.952913	4.23	.047087	6
55	9.824808	2.35	9.871641	1.88	9.953167	4.23	0.046833	5
56	.824949	2.35	.871528	1.90	.953421	4.23	.046579	4
57	.825090	2.33	.871414	1.90	.953675	4.23	.046325	3
58	.825230	2.35	.871301	1.88	.953929	4.23	.046071	2
59	.825371	2.33	.871187	1.90	.954183	4.23	.045817	1
60	9.825511		9.871073	1.90	9.954437		0.045563	0
	Cos.	D. 1″.	Sin.	D. 1″.	Cot.	D. 1″.	Tan.	M.

131°   48°

COSINES, TANGENTS, AND COTANGENTS

42°   137°

M.	Sin.	D. 1″.	Cos.	D. 1″.	Tan.	D. 1″.	Cot.	
0	9.825511	2.33	9.871073	1.88	9.954437	4.23	0.045563	60
1	.825651	2.33	.870960	1.90	.954691	4.25	.045309	59
2	.825791	2.33	.870846	1.90	.954946	4.23	.045054	58
3	.825931	2.33	.870732	1.90	.955200	4.23	.044800	57
4	.826071	2.33	.870618	1.90	.955454	4.23	.044546	56
5	9.826211	2.33	9.870504	1.90	9.955708	4.22	0.044292	55
6	.826351	2.33	.870390	1.90	.955961	4.23	.044039	54
7	.826491	2.33	.870276	1.92	.956215	4.23	.043785	53
8	.826631	2.32	.870161	1.90	.956469	4.23	.043531	52
9	.826770	2.33	.870047	1.90	.956723	4.23	.043277	51
10	9.826910	2.32	9.869933	1.92	9.956977	4.23	0.043023	50
11	.827049	2.33	.869818	1.90	.957231	4.23	.042769	49
12	.827189	2.32	.869704	1.92	.957485	4.23	.042515	48
13	.827328	2.32	.869589	1.92	.957739	4.23	.042261	47
14	.827467	2.32	.869474	1.90	.957993	4.23	.042007	46
15	9.827606	2.32	9.869360	1.92	9.958247	4.22	0.041753	45
16	.827745	2.32	.869245	1.92	.958500	4.23	.041500	44
17	.827884	2.32	.869130	1.92	.958754	4.23	.041246	43
18	.828023	2.32	.869015	1.92	.959008	4.23	.040992	42
19	.828162	2.32	.868900	1.92	.959262	4.23	.040738	41
20	9.828301	2.30	9.868785	1.92	9.959516	4.22	0.040484	40
21	.828439	2.32	.868670	1.92	.959769	4.23	.040231	39
22	.828578	2.30	.868555	1.92	.960023	4.23	.039977	38
23	.828716	2.32	.868440	1.93	.960277	4.22	.039723	37
24	.828855	2.30	.868324	1.92	.960530	4.23	.039470	36
25	9.828993	2.30	9.868209	1.93	9.960784	4.23	0.039216	35
26	.829131	2.30	.868093	1.92	.961038	4.23	.038962	34
27	.829269	2.30	.867978	1.93	.961292	4.23	.038708	33
28	.829407	2.30	.867862	1.93	.961545	4.22	.038455	32
29	.829545	2.30	.867747	1.92	.961799	4.23	.038201	31
30	9.829683	2.30	9.867631	1.93	9.962052	4.22	0.037948	30
31	.829821	2.30	.867515	1.93	.962306	4.23	.037694	29
32	.829959	2.30	.867399	1.93	.962560	4.23	.037440	28
33	.830097	2.28	.867283	1.93	.962813	4.22	.037187	27
34	.830234	2.30	.867167	1.93	.963067	4.23	.036933	26
35	9.830372	2.28	9.867051	1.93	9.963320	4.22	0.036680	25
36	.830509	2.28	.866935	1.93	.963574	4.23	.036426	24
37	.830646	2.30	.866819	1.93	.963828	4.23	.036172	23
38	.830784	2.28	.866703	1.95	.964081	4.22	.035919	22
39	.830921	2.28	.866586	1.93	.964335	4.23	.035665	21
40	9.831058	2.28	9.866470	1.95	9.964588	4.23	0.035412	20
41	.831195	2.28	.866353	1.93	.964842	4.22	.035158	19
42	.831332	2.28	.866237	1.95	.965095	4.23	.034905	18
43	.831469	2.28	.866120	1.93	.965349	4.22	.034651	17
44	.831606	2.27	.866004	1.95	.965602	4.22	.034398	16
45	9.831742	2.28	9.865887	1.95	9.965855	4.23	0.034145	15
46	.831879	2.27	.865770	1.95	.966109	4.22	.033891	14
47	.832015	2.28	.865653	1.95	.966362	4.23	.033638	13
48	.832152	2.27	.865536	1.95	.966616	4.23	.033384	12
49	.832288	2.28	.865419	1.95	.966869	4.23	.033131	11
50	9.832425	2.27	9.865302	1.95	9.967123	4.22	0.032877	10
51	.832561	2.27	.865185	1.95	.967376	4.22	.032624	9
52	.832697	2.27	.865068	1.95	.967629	4.23	.032371	8
53	.832833	2.27	.864950	1.97	.967883	4.22	.032117	7
54	.832969	2.27	.864833	1.95	.968136	4.22	.031864	6
55	9.833105	2.27	9.864716	1.97	9.968389	4.23	0.031611	5
56	.833241	2.27	.864598	1.95	.968643	4.22	.031357	4
57	.833377	2.25	.864481	1.97	.968896	4.22	.031104	3
58	.833512	2.27	.864363	1.97	.969149	4.23	.030851	2
59	.833648	2.25	.864245	1.97	.969403	4.22	.030597	1
60	9.833783		9.864127	1.97	9.969656		0.030344	0
	Cos.	D. 1″.	Sin.	D. 1″.	Cot.	D. 1″.	Tan.	M.

132°   47°

TABLE IX. LOGARITHMIC SINES,

43°   136°

M.	Sin.	D. 1″.	Cos.	D. 1″.	Tan.	D. 1″.	Cot.	
0	9.833783		9.864127		9.969656		0.030344	60
1	.833919	2.27	.864010	1.95	.969909	4.22	.030091	59
2	.834054	2.25	.863892	1.97	.970162	4.22	.029838	58
3	.834189	2.25	.863774	1.97	.970416	4.23	.029584	57
4	.834325	2.27	.863656	1.97	.970669	4.22	.029331	56
5	9.834460	2.25	9.863538	1.97	9.970922	4.22	0.029078	55
6	.834595	2.25	.863419	1.98	.971175	4.22	.028825	54
7	.834730	2.25	.863301	1.97	.971429	4.23	.028571	53
8	.834865	2.25	.863183	1.97	.971682	4.22	.028318	52
9	.834999	2.23	.863064	1.98	.971935	4.22	.028065	51
		2.25		1.97		4.22		
10	9.835134	2.25	9.862946	1.98	9.972188	4.22	0.027812	50
11	.835269	2.23	.862827	1.97	.972441	4.23	.027559	49
12	.835403	2.25	.862709	1.98	.972695	4.22	.027305	48
13	.835538	2.23	.862590	1.98	.972948	4.22	.027052	47
14	.835672	2.25	.862471	1.97	.973201	4.22	.026799	46
15	9.835807	2.23	9.862353	1.98	9.973454	4.22	0.026546	45
16	.835941	2.23	.862234	1.98	.973707	4.22	.026293	44
17	.836075	2.23	.862115	1.98	.973960	4.22	.026040	43
18	.836209	2.23	.861996	1.98	.974213	4.22	.025787	42
19	.836343	2.23	.861877	1.98	.974466	4.23	.025534	41
20	9.836477	2.23	9.861758	2.00	9.974720	4.22	0.025280	40
21	.836611	2.23	.861638	1.98	.974973	4.22	.025027	39
22	.836745	2.22	.861519	1.98	.975226	4.22	.024774	38
23	.836878	2.23	.861400	2.00	.975479	4.22	.024521	37
24	.837012	2.23	.861280	1.98	.975732	4.22	.024268	36
25	9.837146	2.22	9.861161	2.00	9.975985	4.22	0.024015	35
26	.837279	2.22	.861041	1.98	.976238	4.22	.023762	34
27	.837412	2.23	.860922	2.00	.976491	4.22	.023509	33
28	.837546	2.22	.860802	2.00	.976744	4.22	.023256	32
29	.837679	2.22	.860682	2.00	.976997	4.22	.023003	31
30	9.837812	2.22	9.860562	2.00	9.977250	4.22	0.022750	30
31	.837945	2.22	.860442	2.00	.977503	4.22	.022497	29
32	.838078	2.22	.860322	2.00	.977756	4.22	.022244	28
33	.838211	2.22	.860202	2.00	.978009	4.22	.021991	27
34	.838344	2.22	.860082	2.00	.978262	4.22	.021738	26
35	9.838477	2.22	9.859962	2.00	9.978515	4.22	0.021485	25
36	.838610	2.20	.859842	2.00	.978768	4.22	.021232	24
37	.838742	2.22	.859721	2.02	.979021	4.22	.020979	23
38	.838875	2.20	.859601	2.00	.979274	4.22	.020726	22
39	.839007	2.22	.859480	2.02	.979527	4.22	.020473	21
40	9.839140	2.20	9.859360	2.00	9.979780	4.22	0.020220	20
41	.839272	2.20	.859239	2.02	.980033	4.22	.019967	19
42	.839404	2.20	.859119	2.00	.980286	4.20	.019714	18
43	.839536	2.20	.858998	2.02	.980538	4.22	.019462	17
44	.839668	2.20	.858877	2.02	.980791	4.22	.019209	16
45	9.839800	2.20	9.858756	2.02	9.981044	4.22	0.018956	15
46	.839932	2.20	.858635	2.02	.981297	4.22	.018703	14
47	.840064	2.20	.858514	2.02	.981550	4.22	.018450	13
48	.840196	2.20	.858393	2.02	.981803	4.22	.018197	12
49	.840328	2.18	.858272	2.02	.982056	4.22	.017944	11
50	9.840459	2.20	9.858151	2.03	9.982309	4.22	0.017691	10
51	.840591	2.18	.858029	2.02	.982562	4.20	.017438	9
52	.840722	2.20	.857908	2.03	.982814	4.22	.017186	8
53	.840854	2.18	.857786	2.02	.983067	4.22	.016933	7
54	.840985	2.18	.857665	2.03	.983320	4.22	.016680	6
55	9.841116	2.18	9.857543	2.02	9.983573	4.22	0.016427	5
56	.841247	2.18	.857422	2.03	.983826	4.22	.016174	4
57	.841378	2.18	.857300	2.03	.984079	4.22	.015921	3
58	.841509	2.18	.857178	2.03	.984332	4.20	.015668	2
59	.841640	2.18	.857056	2.03	.984584	4.22	.015416	1
60	9.841771		9.856934		9.984837		0.015163	0
	Cos.	D. 1″.	Sin.	D. 1″.	Cot.	D. 1″.	Tan.	M.

133°   46°

COSINES, TANGENTS, AND COTANGENTS

44°   135°

M.	Sin.	D. 1″.	Cos.	D. 1″.	Tan.	D. 1″.	Cot.	
0	9.841771	2.18	9.856934	2.03	9.984837	4.22	0.015163	60
1	.841902	2.18	.856812	2.03	.985090	4.22	.014910	59
2	.842033	2.17	.856690	2.03	.985343	4.22	.014657	58
3	.842163	2.18	.856568	2.03	.985596	4.20	.014404	57
4	.842294	2.17	.856446	2.05	.985848	4.22	.014152	56
5	9.842424	2.18	9.856323	2.03	9.986101	4.22	0.013899	55
6	.842555	2.17	.856201	2.05	.986354	4.22	.013646	54
7	.842685	2.17	.856078	2.03	.986607	4.22	.013393	53
8	.842815	2.18	.855956	2.05	.986860	4.20	.013140	52
9	.842946	2.17	.855833	2.03	.987112	4.22	.012888	51
10	9.843076	2.17	9.855711	2.05	9.987365	4.22	0.012635	50
11	.843206	2.17	.855588	2.05	.987618	4.22	.012382	49
12	.843336	2.17	.855465	2.05	.987871	4.20	.012129	48
13	.843466	2.15	.855342	2.05	.988123	4.22	.011877	47
14	.843595	2.17	.855219	2.05	.988376	4.22	.011624	46
15	9.843725	2.17	9.855096	2.05	9.988629	4.22	0.011371	45
16	.843855	2.15	.854973	2.05	.988882	4.20	.011118	44
17	.843984	2.17	.854850	2.05	.989134	4.22	.010866	43
18	.844114	2.15	.854727	2.07	.989387	4.22	.010613	42
19	.844243	2.15	.854603	2.05	.989640	4.22	.010360	41
20	9.844372	2.17	9.854480	2.07	9.989893	4.20	0.010107	40
21	.844502	2.15	.854356	2.05	.990145	4.22	.009855	39
22	.844631	2.15	.854233	2.07	.990398	4.22	.009602	38
23	.844760	2.15	.854109	2.05	.990651	4.22	.009349	37
24	.844889	2.15	.853986	2.07	.990903	4.20	.009097	36
25	9.845018	2.15	9.853862	2.07	9.991156	4.22	0.008844	35
26	.845147	2.15	.853738	2.07	.991409	4.22	.008591	34
27	.845276	2.15	.853614	2.07	.991662	4.20	.008338	33
28	.845405	2.13	.853490	2.07	.991914	4.22	.008086	32
29	.845533	2.15	.853366	2.07	.992167	4.22	.007833	31
30	9.845662	2.13	9.853242	2.07	9.992420	4.20	0.007580	30
31	.845790	2.15	.853118	2.07	.992672	4.22	.007328	29
32	.845919	2.13	.852994	2.08	.992925	4.22	.007075	28
33	.846047	2.13	.852869	2.07	.993178	4.22	.006822	27
34	.846175	2.15	.852745	2.07	.993431	4.20	.006569	26
35	9.846304	2.13	9.852620	2.08	9.993683	4.22	0.006317	25
36	.846432	2.13	.852496	2.07	.993936	4.22	.006064	24
37	.846560	2.13	.852371	2.07	.994189	4.20	.005811	23
38	.846688	2.13	.852247	2.08	.994441	4.22	.005559	22
39	.846816	2.13	.852122	2.08	.994694	4.22	.005306	21
40	9.846944	2.12	9.851997	2.08	9.994947	4.20	0.005053	20
41	.847071	2.13	.851872	2.08	.995199	4.22	.004801	19
42	.847199	2.13	.851747	2.08	.995452	4.22	.004548	18
43	.847327	2.12	.851622	2.08	.995705	4.20	.004295	17
44	.847454	2.13	.851497	2.08	.995957	4.22	.004043	16
45	9.847582	2.12	9.851372	2.08	9.996210	4.22	0.003790	15
46	.847709	2.12	.851246	2.10	.996463	4.20	.003537	14
47	.847836	2.13	.851121	2.08	.996715	4.22	.003285	13
48	.847964	2.12	.850996	2.10	.996968	4.22	.003032	12
49	.848091	2.12	.850870	2.08	.997221	4.20	.002779	11
50	9.848218	2.12	9.850745	2.10	9.997473	4.22	0.002527	10
51	.848345	2.12	.850619	2.10	.997726	4.22	.002274	9
52	.848472	2.12	.850493	2.08	.997979	4.20	.002021	8
53	.848599	2.12	.850368	2.10	.998231	4.22	.001769	7
54	.848726	2.10	.850242	2.10	.998484	4.22	.001516	6
55	9.848852	2.12	9.850116	2.10	9.998737	4.22	0.001263	5
56	.848979	2.12	.849990	2.10	.998989	4.20	.001011	4
57	.849106	2.10	.849864	2.10	.999242	4.22	.000758	3
58	.849232	2.12	.849738	2.12	.999495	4.22	.000505	2
59	.849359	2.10	.849611	2.10	.999747	4.20	.000253	1
60	9.849485		9.849485		0.000000	4.22	0.000000	0
	Cos.	D. 1″.	Sin.	D. 1″.	Cot.	D. 1″.	Tan.	M.

134°   45°

TABLE X. AUXILIARY TABLE FOR LOGARITHMIC SINES

	0°			1°			2°			
M.	S.	Sin.	Tan.	S.	Sin.	Tan.	S.	Sin.	Tan.	M.
		4.68			4.68			4.68		
0	0	5575	5575	3600	5553	5619	7200	5487	5751	0
1	60	5575	5575	3660	5552	5620	7260	5485	5754	1
2	120	5575	5575	3720	5551	5622	7320	5484	5757	2
3	180	5575	5575	3780	5551	5623	7380	5482	5760	3
4	240	5575	5575	3840	5550	5625	7440	5481	5763	4
5	300	5575	5575	3900	5549	5627	7500	5479	5766	5
6	360	5575	5575	3960	5548	5628	7560	5478	5769	6
7	420	5575	5575	4020	5547	5630	7620	5476	5773	7
8	480	5574	5576	4080	5547	5632	7680	5475	5776	8
9	540	5574	5576	4140	5546	5633	7740	5473	5779	9
10	600	5574	5576	4200	5545	5635	7800	5471	5782	10
11	660	5574	5576	4260	5544	5637	7860	5470	5785	11
12	720	5574	5577	4320	5543	5638	7920	5468	5788	12
13	780	5574	5577	4380	5542	5640	7980	5467	5792	13
14	840	5574	5577	4440	5541	5642	8040	5465	5795	14
15	900	5573	5578	4500	5540	5644	8100	5463	5798	15
16	960	5573	5578	4560	5539	5646	8160	5462	5802	16
17	1020	5573	5578	4620	5539	5648	8220	5460	5805	17
18	1080	5573	5579	4680	5538	5649	8280	5458	5808	18
19	1140	5573	5579	4740	5537	5651	8340	5457	5812	19
20	1200	5572	5580	4800	5536	5653	8400	5455	5815	20
21	1260	5572	5580	4860	5535	5655	8460	5453	5818	21
22	1320	5572	5581	4920	5534	5657	8520	5451	5822	22
23	1380	5572	5581	4980	5533	5659	8580	5450	5825	23
24	1440	5571	5582	5040	5532	5661	8640	5448	5829	24
25	1500	5571	5583	5100	5531	5663	8700	5446	5833	25
26	1560	5571	5583	5160	5530	5665	8760	5444	5836	26
27	1620	5570	5584	5220	5529	5668	8820	5443	5840	27
28	1680	5570	5584	5280	5527	5670	8880	5441	5843	28
29	1740	5570	5585	5340	5526	5672	8940	5439	5847	29
30	1800	5569	5586	5400	5525	5674	9000	5437	5851	30
31	1860	5569	5587	5460	5524	5676	9060	5435	5854	31
32	1920	5569	5587	5520	5523	5679	9120	5433	5858	32
33	1980	5568	5588	5580	5522	5681	9180	5431	5862	33
34	2040	5568	5589	5640	5521	5683	9240	5430	5866	34
35	2100	5567	5590	5700	5520	5685	9300	5428	5869	35
36	2160	5567	5591	5760	5518	5688	9360	5426	5873	36
37	2220	5566	5592	5820	5517	5690	9420	5424	5877	37
38	2280	5566	5593	5880	5516	5693	9480	5422	5881	38
39	2340	5566	5593	5940	5515	5695	9540	5420	5885	39
40	2400	5565	5594	6000	5514	5697	9600	5418	5889	40
41	2460	5565	5595	6060	5512	5700	9660	5416	5893	41
42	2520	5564	5596	6120	5511	5702	9720	5414	5897	42
43	2580	5564	5598	6180	5510	5705	9780	5412	5900	43
44	2640	5563	5599	6240	5509	5707	9840	5410	5905	44
45	2700	5562	5600	6300	5507	5710	9900	5408	5909	45
46	2760	5562	5601	6360	5506	5713	9960	5406	5913	46
47	2820	5561	5602	6420	5505	5715	10020	5404	5917	47
48	2880	5561	5603	6480	5503	5718	10080	5402	5921	48
49	2940	5560	5604	6540	5502	5720	10140	5400	5925	49
50	3000	5560	5605	6600	5501	5723	10200	5398	5929	50
51	3060	5559	5607	6660	5499	5726	10260	5396	5933	51
52	3120	5558	5608	6720	5498	5729	10320	5394	5937	52
53	3180	5558	5609	6780	5497	5731	10380	5392	5942	53
54	3240	5557	5611	6840	5495	5734	10440	5389	5946	54
55	3300	5556	5612	6900	5494	5737	10500	5387	5950	55
56	3360	5556	5613	6960	5492	5740	10560	5385	5955	56
57	3420	5555	5615	7020	5491	5743	10620	5383	5959	57
58	3480	5554	5616	7080	5490	5745	10680	5381	5963	58
59	3540	5554	5618	7140	5488	5748	10740	5379	5968	59
60	3600	5553	5619	7200	5487	5751	10800	5376	5972	60
M.	S.	Sin.	Tan.	S.	Sin.	Tan.	S.	Sin.	Tan.	M.

AND TANGENTS OF SMALL ANGLES

M.	S.	Sin.	Tan.	S.	Sin.	Tan.	S.	Sin.	Tan.	M.
	3°			4°			5°			
		4.68			4.68			4.68		
0	10800	5376	5972	14400	5222	6281	18000	5024	6679	0
1	10860	5374	5976	14460	5219	6287	18060	5020	6687	1
2	10920	5372	5981	14520	5216	6293	18120	5016	6694	2
3	10980	5370	5985	14580	5213	6299	18180	5012	6702	3
4	11040	5367	5990	14640	5210	6305	18240	5009	6709	4
5	11100	5365	5994	14700	5207	6311	18300	5005	6716	5
6	11160	5363	5999	14760	5204	6317	18360	5001	6724	6
7	11220	5361	6004	14820	5201	6323	18420	4997	6732	7
8	11280	5358	6008	14880	5198	6329	18480	4994	6739	8
9	11340	5356	6013	14940	5195	6335	18540	4990	6747	9
10	11400	5354	6017	15000	5192	6341	18600	4986	6754	10
11	11460	5351	6022	15060	5189	6348	18660	4982	6762	11
12	11520	5349	6027	15120	5186	6354	18720	4978	6770	12
13	11580	5347	6031	15180	5183	6360	18780	4975	6777	13
14	11640	5344	6036	15240	5180	6366	18840	4971	6785	14
15	11700	5342	6041	15300	5177	6372	18900	4967	6793	15
16	11760	5340	6046	15360	5173	6379	18960	4963	6800	16
17	11820	5337	6051	15420	5170	6385	19020	4959	6808	17
18	11880	5335	6055	15480	5167	6391	19080	4955	6816	18
19	11940	5332	6060	15540	5164	6398	19140	4951	6824	19
20	12000	5330	6065	15600	5161	6404	19200	4948	6832	20
21	12060	5327	6070	15660	5158	6410	19260	4944	6840	21
22	12120	5325	6075	15720	5154	6417	19320	4940	6848	22
23	12180	5322	6080	15780	5151	6423	19380	4936	6855	23
24	12240	5320	6085	15840	5148	6430	19440	4932	6863	24
25	12300	5317	6090	15900	5145	6436	19500	4928	6871	25
26	12360	5315	6095	15960	5141	6443	19560	4924	6879	26
27	12420	5312	6100	16020	5138	6449	19620	4920	6887	27
28	12480	5310	6105	16080	5135	6456	19680	4916	6896	28
29	12540	5307	6110	16140	5132	6463	19740	4912	6904	29
30	12600	5305	6116	16200	5128	6469	19800	4908	6912	30
31	12660	5302	6121	16260	5125	6476	19860	4904	6920	31
32	12720	5300	6126	16320	5122	6482	19920	4900	6928	32
33	12780	5297	6131	16380	5118	6489	19980	4895	6936	33
34	12840	5294	6136	16440	5115	6496	20040	4891	6944	34
35	12900	5292	6142	16500	5112	6503	20100	4887	6953	35
36	12960	5289	6147	16560	5108	6509	20160	4883	6961	36
37	13020	5286	6152	16620	5105	6516	20220	4880	6969	37
38	13080	5284	6158	16680	5101	6523	20280	4875	6977	38
39	13140	5281	6163	16740	5098	6530	20340	4871	6986	39
40	13200	5278	6168	16800	5095	6537	20400	4867	6994	40
41	13260	5276	6174	16860	5091	6544	20460	4862	7003	41
42	13320	5273	6179	16920	5088	6551	20520	4858	7011	42
43	13380	5270	6185	16980	5084	6558	20580	4854	7019	43
44	13440	5268	6190	17040	5081	6564	20640	4850	7028	44
45	13500	5265	6196	17100	5077	6571	20700	4846	7036	45
46	13560	5262	6201	17160	5074	6578	20760	4841	7045	46
47	13620	5259	6207	17220	5070	6585	20820	4837	7053	47
48	13680	5256	6212	17280	5067	6593	20880	4833	7062	48
49	13740	5254	6218	17340	5063	6600	20940	4829	7070	49
50	13800	5251	6224	17400	5060	6607	21000	4824	7079	50
51	13860	5248	6229	17460	5056	6614	21060	4820	7088	51
52	13920	5245	6235	17520	5053	6621	21120	4816	7096	52
53	13980	5242	6241	17580	5049	6628	21180	4811	7105	53
54	14040	5239	6246	17640	5045	6635	21240	4807	7114	54
55	14100	5237	6252	17700	5042	6643	21300	4803	7122	55
56	14160	5234	6258	17760	5038	6650	21360	4798	7131	56
57	14220	5231	6264	17820	5034	6657	21420	4794	7140	57
58	14280	5228	6269	17880	5031	6665	21480	4790	7149	58
59	14340	5225	6275	17940	5027	6672	21540	4785	7158	59
60	14400	5222	6281	18000	5024	6679	21600	4781	7166	60
M.	S.	Sin.	Tan.	S.	Sin.	Tan.	S.	Sin.	Tan.	M.

USE OF AUXILIARY TABLE X FOR LOGARITHMIC SINES AND TANGENTS OF SMALL ANGLES

Frequently the usual methods of interpolation are not sufficiently exact for determining the logarithmic sines, tangents, and cotangents of small angles. It is then necessary to apply a method based on the fact that the natural sines and tangents of small angles vary almost directly with the angles. Thus, $\dfrac{\sin\ 0°\ 15'\ 24''}{\sin\ 0°\ 15'\ 00''} = \dfrac{0°\ 15'\ 24''}{0°\ 15'\ 00''} = \dfrac{924''}{900''}$, and $\sin\ 0°\ 15'\ 24'' = 924 \times \dfrac{\sin\ 0°\ 15'\ 00''}{900}$. If logarithms of both sides of the equation are taken, log sin $0°\ 15'\ 24'' = $ log 924 + (log sin $0°\ 15'\ 00''$ − log 900).

In Table X (pages 508 and 509) the values of log sin $\propto$ − log $\propto$ (in seconds) and of log tan $\propto$ − log $\propto$ (in seconds) are given for various values of $\propto$ in the columns headed sin and tan, respectively. To obtain the logarithmic sine or the logarithmic tangent of a small angle, add the logarithm of the angle (expressed in seconds) to the value taken from the table for the nearest minute. When the logarithmic sine or tangent is known and the angle is required, first determine the approximate angle from Table IX. Subtract the value found in the auxiliary table from the given logarithmic sine or logarithmic tangent. The result is the logarithm of the required angle, expressed in seconds. Logarithmic cotangents of small angles may be obtained from the relation, log cot $\propto$ = 10 − log tan $\propto$.

EXAMPLES

To find log sin $0°\ 15'\ 24''$ ($=924''$). From Table X,	To find log tan $1°\ 12'\ 47''$ ($= 4367''$). From Table X,
$\log \left(\dfrac{\sin\ 0°\ 15'}{900}\right) = 4.685573$	$\log \left(\dfrac{\tan\ 1°\ 13'}{4380}\right) = 4.685640$
$\log 924 = 2.965672$	$\log 4367 = 3.640183$
$\log \sin\ 0°\ 15'\ 24'' = \overline{7.651245}$	$\log \tan\ 1°\ 12'\ 47'' = \overline{8.325823}$
To find angle when log sin $= 8.442414$. From Table IX the approximate angle is $1°\ 35'$,	To find angle when log tan $= 8.206747$. From Table IX the approximate angle is $0°\ 55'$,
$\log \sin\ \propto\ = 8.442414$	$\log \tan\ \propto\ = 8.206747$
From Table X,	From Table X,
$\log \left(\dfrac{\sin\ 1°\ 35'}{5700}\right) = 4.685520$	$\log \left(\dfrac{\tan\ 0°\ 55'}{3300}\right) = 4.685612$
$\log\ \propto'' = \overline{3.756894}$	$\log\ \propto'' = \overline{3.521135}$
$\propto\ = 5713'' = 1°\ 35'\ 13''$	$\propto\ = 3320'' = 0°\ 55'\ 20''$

TABLE XI. NATURAL SINES AND COSINES

′	0° Sine	0° Cosine	1° Sine	1° Cosine	2° Sine	2° Cosine	3° Sine	3° Cosine	4° Sine	4° Cosine	′
0	.00000	1.	.01745	.99985	.03490	.99939	.05234	.99863	.06976	.99756	60
1	.00029	1.	.01774	.99984	.03519	.99938	.05263	.99861	.07005	.99754	59
2	.00058	1.	.01803	.99984	.03548	.99937	.05292	.99860	.07034	.99752	58
3	.00087	1.	.01832	.99983	.03577	.99936	.05321	.99858	.07063	.99750	57
4	.00116	1.	.01862	.99983	.03606	.99935	.05350	.99857	.07092	.99748	56
5	.00145	1.	.01891	.99982	.03635	.99934	.05379	.99855	.07121	.99746	55
6	.00175	1.	.01920	.99982	.03664	.99933	.05408	.99854	.07150	.99744	54
7	.00204	1.	.01949	.99981	.03693	.99932	.05437	.99852	.07179	.99742	53
8	.00233	1.	.01978	.99980	.03723	.99931	.05466	.99851	.07208	.99740	52
9	.00262	1.	.02007	.99980	.03752	.99930	.05495	.99849	.07237	.99738	51
10	.00291	1.	.02036	.99979	.03781	.99929	.05524	.99847	.07266	.99736	50
11	.00320	.99999	.02065	.99979	.03810	.99927	.05553	.99846	.07295	.99734	49
12	.00349	.99999	.02094	.99978	.03839	.99926	.05582	.99844	.07324	.99731	48
13	.00378	.99999	.02123	.99977	.03868	.99925	.05611	.99842	.07353	.99729	47
14	.00407	.99999	.02152	.99977	.03897	.99924	.05640	.99841	.07382	.99727	46
15	.00436	.99999	.02181	.99976	.03926	.99923	.05669	.99839	.07411	.99725	45
16	.00465	.99999	.02211	.99976	.03955	.99922	.05698	.99838	.07440	.99723	44
17	.00495	.99999	.02240	.99975	.03984	.99921	.05727	.99836	.07469	.99721	43
18	.00524	.99999	.02269	.99974	.04013	.99919	.05756	.99834	.07498	.99719	42
19	.00553	.99998	.02298	.99974	.04042	.99918	.05785	.99833	.07527	.99716	41
20	.00582	.99998	.02327	.99973	.04071	.99917	.05814	.99831	.07556	.99714	40
21	.00611	.99998	.02356	.99972	.04100	.99916	.05844	.99829	.07585	.99712	39
22	.00640	.99998	.02385	.99972	.04129	.99915	.05873	.99827	.07614	.99710	38
23	.00669	.99998	.02414	.99971	.04159	.99913	.05902	.99826	.07643	.99708	37
24	.00698	.99998	.02443	.99970	.04188	.99912	.05931	.99824	.07672	.99705	36
25	.00727	.99997	.02472	.99969	.04217	.99911	.05960	.99822	.07701	.99703	35
26	.00756	.99997	.02501	.99969	.04246	.99910	.05989	.99821	.07730	.99701	34
27	.00785	.99997	.02530	.99968	.04275	.99909	.06018	.99819	.07759	.99699	33
28	.00814	.99997	.02560	.99967	.04304	.99907	.06047	.99817	.07788	.99696	32
29	.00844	.99996	.02589	.99966	.04333	.99906	.06076	.99815	.07817	.99694	31
30	.00873	.99996	.02618	.99966	.04362	.99905	.06105	.99813	.07846	.99692	30
31	.00902	.99996	.02647	.99965	.04391	.99904	.06134	.99812	.07875	.99689	29
32	.00931	.99996	.02676	.99964	.04420	.99902	.06163	.99810	.07904	.99687	28
33	.00960	.99995	.02705	.99963	.04449	.99901	.06192	.99808	.07933	.99685	27
34	.00989	.99995	.02734	.99963	.04478	.99900	.06221	.99806	.07962	.99683	26
35	.01018	.99995	.02763	.99962	.04507	.99898	.06250	.99804	.07991	.99680	25
36	.01047	.99995	.02792	.99961	.04536	.99897	.06279	.99803	.08020	.99678	24
37	.01076	.99994	.02821	.99960	.04565	.99896	.06308	.99801	.08049	.99676	23
38	.01105	.99994	.02850	.99959	.04594	.99894	.06337	.99799	.08078	.99673	22
39	.01134	.99994	.02879	.99959	.04623	.99893	.06366	.99797	.08107	.99671	21
40	.01164	.99993	.02908	.99958	.04653	.99892	.06395	.99795	.08136	.99668	20
41	.01193	.99993	.02938	.99957	.04682	.99890	.06424	.99793	.08165	.99666	19
42	.01222	.99993	.02967	.99956	.04711	.99889	.06453	.99792	.08194	.99664	18
43	.01251	.99992	.02996	.99955	.04740	.99888	.06482	.99790	.08223	.99661	17
44	.01280	.99992	.03025	.99954	.04769	.99886	.06511	.99788	.08252	.99659	16
45	.01309	.99991	.03054	.99953	.04798	.99885	.06540	.99786	.08281	.99657	15
46	.01338	.99991	.03083	.99952	.04827	.99883	.06569	.99784	.08310	.99654	14
47	.01367	.99991	.03112	.99952	.04856	.99882	.06598	.99782	.08339	.99652	13
48	.01396	.99990	.03141	.99951	.04885	.99881	.06627	.99780	.08368	.99649	12
49	.01425	.99990	.03170	.99950	.04914	.99879	.06656	.99778	.08397	.99647	11
50	.01454	.99989	.03199	.99949	.04943	.99878	.06685	.99776	.08426	.99644	10
51	.01483	.99989	.03228	.99948	.04972	.99876	.06714	.99774	.08455	.99642	9
52	.01513	.99989	.03257	.99947	.05001	.99875	.06743	.99772	.08484	.99639	8
53	.01542	.99988	.03286	.99946	.05030	.99873	.06773	.99770	.08513	.99637	7
54	.01571	.99988	.03316	.99945	.05059	.99872	.06802	.99768	.08542	.99635	6
55	.01600	.99987	.03345	.99944	.05088	.99870	.06831	.99766	.08571	.99632	5
56	.01629	.99987	.03374	.99943	.05117	.99869	.06860	.99764	.08600	.99630	4
57	.01658	.99986	.03403	.99942	.05146	.99867	.06889	.99762	.08629	.99627	3
58	.01687	.99986	.03432	.99941	.05175	.99866	.06918	.99760	.08658	.99625	2
59	.01716	.99985	.03461	.99940	.05205	.99864	.06947	.99758	.08687	.99622	1
60	.01745	.99985	.03490	.99939	.05234	.99863	.06976	.99756	.08716	.99619	0
′	Cosine	Sine	Cosine	Sine	Cosine	Sine	Cosine	Sine	Cosine	Sine	′
	89°		88°		87°		86°		85°		

TABLE XI. NATURAL SINES AND COSINES

′	5° Sine	5° Cosine	6° Sine	6° Cosine	7° Sine	7° Cosine	8° Sine	8° Cosine	9° Sine	9° Cosine	′
0	.08716	.99619	.10453	.99452	.12187	.99255	.13917	.99027	.15643	.98769	60
1	.08745	.99617	.10482	.99449	.12216	.99251	.13946	.99023	.15672	.98764	59
2	.08774	.99614	.10511	.99446	.12245	.99248	.13975	.99019	.15701	.98760	58
3	.08803	.99612	.10540	.99443	.12274	.99244	.14004	.99015	.15730	.98755	57
4	.08831	.99609	.10569	.99440	.12302	.99240	.14033	.99011	.15758	.98751	56
5	.08860	.99607	.10597	.99437	.12331	.99237	.14061	.99006	.15787	.98746	55
6	.08889	.99604	.10626	.99434	.12360	.99233	.14090	.99002	.15816	.98741	54
7	.08918	.99602	.10655	.99431	.12389	.99230	.14119	.98998	.15845	.98737	53
8	.08947	.99599	.10684	.99428	.12418	.99226	.14148	.98994	.15873	.98732	52
9	.08976	.99596	.10713	.99424	.12447	.99222	.14177	.98990	.15902	.98728	51
10	.09005	.99594	.10742	.99421	.12476	.99219	.14205	.98986	.15931	.98723	50
11	.09034	.99591	.10771	.99418	.12504	.99215	.14234	.98982	.15959	.98718	49
12	.09063	.99588	.10800	.99415	.12533	.99211	.14263	.98978	.15988	.98714	48
13	.09092	.99586	.10829	.99412	.12562	.99208	.14292	.98973	.16017	.98709	47
14	.09121	.99583	.10858	.99409	.12591	.99204	.14320	.98969	.16046	.98704	46
15	.09150	.99580	.10887	.99406	.12620	.99200	.14349	.98965	.16074	.98700	45
16	.09179	.99578	.10916	.99402	.12649	.99197	.14378	.98961	.16103	.98695	44
17	.09208	.99575	.10945	.99399	.12678	.99193	.14407	.98957	.16132	.98690	43
18	.09237	.99572	.10973	.99396	.12706	.99189	.14436	.98953	.16160	.98686	42
19	.09266	.99570	.11002	.99393	.12735	.99186	.14464	.98948	.16189	.98681	41
20	.09295	.99567	.11031	.99390	.12764	.99182	.14493	.98944	.16218	.98676	40
21	.09324	.99564	.11060	.99386	.12793	.99178	.14522	.98940	.16246	.98671	39
22	.09353	.99562	.11089	.99383	.12822	.99175	.14551	.98936	.16275	.98667	38
23	.09382	.99559	.11118	.99380	.12851	.99171	.14580	.98931	.16304	.98662	37
24	.09411	.99556	.11147	.99377	.12880	.99167	.14608	.98927	.16333	.98657	36
25	.09440	.99553	.11176	.99374	.12908	.99163	.14637	.98923	.16361	.98652	35
26	.09469	.99551	.11205	.99370	.12937	.99160	.14666	.98919	.16390	.98648	34
27	.09498	.99548	.11234	.99367	.12966	.99156	.14695	.98914	.16419	98643	33
28	.09527	.99545	.11263	.99364	.12995	.99152	.14723	.98910	.16447	.98638	32
29	.09556	.99542	.11291	.99360	.13024	.99148	.14752	.98906	.16476	.98633	31
30	.09585	.99540	.11320	.99357	.13053	.99144	.14781	.98902	.16505	.98629	30
31	.09614	.99537	.11349	.99354	.13081	.99141	.14810	.98897	.16533	.98624	29
32	.09642	.99534	.11378	.99351	.13110	.99137	.14838	.98893	.16562	.98619	28
33	.09671	99531	.11407	.99347	.13139	.99133	.14867	.98889	.16591	.98614	27
34	.09700	.99528	.11436	.99344	.13168	.99129	.14896	.98884	.16620	.98609	26
35	.09729	.99526	.11465	.99341	.13197	.99125	.14925	.98880	.16648	.98604	25
36	.09758	.99523	.11494	.99337	.13226	.99122	.14954	.98876	.16677	.98600	24
37	.09787	.99520	.11523	.99334	.13254	.99118	.14982	.98871	.16706	.98595	23
38	.09816	.99517	.11552	.99331	.13283	.99114	.15011	.98867	.16734	.98590	22
39	.09845	.99514	.11580	.99327	.13312	.99110	.15040	.98863	.16763	.98585	21
40	.09874	.99511	.11609	.99324	.13341	.99106	.15069	.98858	.16792	.98580	20
41	.09903	.99508	.11638	.99320	.13370	.99102	.15097	.98854	.16820	.98575	19
42	.09932	.99506	.11667	.99317	.13399	.99098	.15126	.98849	.16849	.98570	18
43	.09961	.99503	.11696	.99314	.13427	.99094	.15155	.98845	.16878	.98565	17
44	.09990	.99500	.11725	.99310	.13456	.99091	.15184	.98841	.16906	.98561	16
45	.10019	.99497	.11754	.99307	.13485	.99087	.15212	.98836	.16935	.98556	15
46	.10048	.99494	.11783	.99303	.13514	.99083	.15241	.98832	.16964	.98551	14
47	.10077	.99491	.11812	.99300	.13543	.99079	.15270	.98827	.16992	.98546	13
48	.10106	.99488	.11840	.99297	.13572	.99075	.15299	.98823	.17021	.98541	12
49	.10135	.99485	.11869	.99293	.13600	.99071	.15327	.98818	.17050	.98536	11
50	.10164	.99482	.11898	.99290	.13629	.99067	.15356	.98814	.17078	.98531	10
51	.10192	.99479	.11927	.99286	.13658	.99063	.15385	.98809	.17107	.98526	9
52	.10221	.99476	.11956	.99283	.13687	.99059	.15414	.98805	.17136	.98521	8
53	.10250	.99473	.11985	.99279	.13716	.99055	.15442	.98800	.17164	.98516	7
54	.10279	.99470	.12014	.99276	.13744	.99051	.15471	.98796	.17193	.98511	6
55	.10308	.99467	.12043	.99272	.13773	.99047	.15500	.98791	.17222	.98506	5
56	.10337	.99464	.12071	.99269	.13802	.99043	.15529	.98787	.17250	.98501	4
57	.10366	.99461	.12100	.99265	.13831	.99039	.15557	.98782	.17279	.98496	3
58	.10395	.99458	.12129	.99262	.13860	.99035	.15586	.98778	.17308	.98491	2
59	.10424	.99455	.12158	.99258	.13889	.99031	.15615	.98773	.17336	.98486	1
60	.10453	.99452	.12187	.99255	.13917	.99027	.15643	.98769	.17365	.98481	0
′	Cosine	Sine	Cosine	Sine	Cosine	Sine	Cosine	Sine	Cosine	Sine	′
	84°		83°		82°		81°		80°		

TABLE XI. NATURAL SINES AND COSINES

′	10° Sine	10° Cosine	11° Sine	11° Cosine	12° Sine	12° Cosine	13° Sine	13° Cosine	14° Sine	14° Cosine	′
0	.17365	.98481	.19081	.98163	.20791	.97815	.22495	.97437	.24192	.97030	60
1	.17393	.98476	.19109	.98157	.20820	.97809	.22523	.97430	.24220	.97023	59
2	.17422	.98471	.19138	.98152	.20848	.97803	.22552	.97424	.24249	.97015	58
3	.17451	.98466	.19167	.98146	.20877	.97797	.22580	.97417	.24277	.97008	57
4	.17479	.98461	.19195	.98140	.20905	.97791	.22608	.97411	.24305	.97001	56
5	.17508	.98455	.19224	.98135	.20933	.97784	.22637	.97404	.24333	.96994	55
6	.17537	.98450	.19252	.98129	.20962	.97778	.22665	.97398	.24362	.96987	54
7	.17565	.98445	.19281	.98124	.20990	.97772	.22693	.97391	.24390	.96980	53
8	.17594	.98440	.19309	.98118	.21019	.97766	.22722	.97384	.24418	.96973	52
9	.17623	.98435	.19338	.98112	.21047	.97760	.22750	.97378	.24446	.96966	51
10	.17651	.98430	.19366	.98107	.21076	.97754	.22778	.97371	.24474	.96959	50
11	.17680	.98425	.19395	.98101	.21104	.97748	.22807	.97365	.24503	.96952	49
12	.17708	.98420	.19423	.98096	.21132	.97742	.22835	.97358	.24531	.96945	48
13	.17737	.98414	.19452	.98090	.21161	.97735	.22863	.97351	.24559	.96937	47
14	.17766	.98409	.19481	.98084	.21189	.97729	.22892	.97345	.24587	.96930	46
15	.17794	.98404	.19509	.98079	.21218	.97723	.22920	.97338	.24615	.96923	45
16	.17823	.98399	.19538	.98073	.21246	.97717	.22948	.97331	.24644	.96916	44
17	.17852	.98394	.19566	.98067	.21275	.97711	.22977	.97325	.24672	.96909	43
18	.17880	.98389	.19595	.98061	.21303	.97705	.23005	.97318	.24700	.96902	42
19	.17909	.98383	.19623	.98056	.21331	.97698	.23033	.97311	.24728	.96894	41
20	.17937	.98378	.19652	.98050	.21360	.97692	.23062	.97304	.24756	.96887	40
21	.17966	.98373	.19680	.98044	.21388	.97686	.23090	.97298	.24784	.96880	39
22	.17995	.98368	.19709	.98039	.21417	.97680	.23118	.97291	.24813	.96873	38
23	.18023	.98362	.19737	.98033	.21445	.97673	.23146	.97284	.24841	.96866	37
24	.18052	.98357	.19766	.98027	.21474	.97667	.23175	.97278	.24869	.96858	36
25	.18081	.98352	.19794	.98021	.21502	.97661	.23203	.97271	.24897	.96851	35
26	.18109	.98347	.19823	.98016	.21530	.97655	.23231	.97264	.24925	.96844	34
27	.18138	.98341	.19851	.98010	.21559	.97648	.23260	.97257	.24954	.96837	33
28	.18166	.98336	.19880	.98004	.21587	.97642	.23288	.97251	.24982	.96829	32
29	.18195	.98331	.19908	.97998	.21616	.97636	.23316	.97244	.25010	.96822	31
30	.18224	.98325	.19937	.97992	.21644	.97630	.23345	.97237	.25038	.96815	30
31	.18252	.98320	.19965	.97987	.21672	.97623	.23373	.97230	.25066	.96807	29
32	.18281	.98315	.19994	.97981	.21701	.97617	.23401	.97223	.25094	.96800	28
33	.18309	.98310	.20022	.97975	.21729	.97611	.23429	.97217	.25122	.96793	27
34	.18338	.98304	.20051	.97969	.21758	.97604	.23458	.97210	.25151	.96786	26
35	.18367	.98299	.20079	.97963	.21786	.97598	.23486	.97203	.25179	.96778	25
36	.18395	.98294	.20108	.97958	.21814	.97592	.23514	.97196	.25207	.96771	24
37	.18424	.98288	.20136	.97952	.21843	.97585	.23542	.97189	.25235	.96764	23
38	.18452	.98283	.20165	.97946	.21871	.97579	.23571	.97182	.25263	.96756	22
39	.18481	.98277	.20193	.97940	.21899	.97573	.23599	.97176	.25291	.96749	21
40	.18509	.98272	.20222	.97934	.21928	.97566	.23627	.97169	.25320	.96742	20
41	.18538	.98267	.20250	.97928	.21956	.97560	.23656	.97162	.25348	.96734	19
42	.18567	.98261	.20279	.97922	.21985	.97553	.23684	.97155	.25376	.96727	18
43	.18595	.98256	.20307	.97916	.22013	.97547	.23712	.97148	.25404	.96719	17
44	.18624	.98250	.20336	.97910	.22041	.97541	.23740	.97141	.25432	.96712	16
45	.18652	.98245	.20364	.97905	.22070	.97534	.23769	.97134	.25460	.96705	15
46	.18681	.98240	.20393	.97899	.22098	.97528	.23797	.97127	.25488	.96697	14
47	.18710	.98234	.20421	.97893	.22126	.97521	.23825	.97120	.25516	.96690	13
48	.18738	.98229	.20450	.97887	.22155	.97515	.23853	.97113	.25545	.96682	12
49	.18767	.98223	.20478	.97881	.22183	.97508	.23882	.97106	.25573	.96675	11
50	.18795	.98218	.20507	.97875	.22212	.97502	.23910	.97100	.25601	.96667	10
51	.18824	.98212	.20535	.97869	.22240	.97496	.23938	.97093	.25629	.96660	9
52	.18852	.98207	.20563	.97863	.22268	.97489	.23966	.97086	.25657	.96653	8
53	.18881	.98201	.20592	.97857	.22297	.97483	.23995	.97079	.25685	.96645	7
54	.18910	.98196	.20620	.97851	.22325	.97476	.24023	.97072	.25713	.96638	6
55	.18938	.98190	.20649	.97845	.22353	.97470	.24051	.97065	.25741	.96630	5
56	.18967	.98185	.20677	.97839	.22382	.97463	.24079	.97058	.25769	.96623	4
57	.18995	.98179	.20706	.97833	.22410	.97457	.24108	.97051	.25798	.96615	3
58	.19024	.98174	.20734	.97827	.22438	.97450	.24136	.97044	.25826	.96608	2
59	.19052	.98168	.20763	.97821	.22467	.97444	.24164	.97037	.25854	.96600	1
60	.19081	.98163	.20791	.97815	.22495	.97437	.24192	.97030	.25882	.96593	0
′	Cosine	Sine	Cosine	Sine	Cosine	Sine	Cosine	Sine	Cosine	Sine	′
	79°		78°		77°		76°		75°		

APPENDIX B

TABLE XI.   NATURAL SINES AND COSINES

′	15° Sine	15° Cosine	16° Sine	16° Cosine	17° Sine	17° Cosine	18° Sine	18° Cosine	19° Sine	19° Cosine	′
0	.25882	.96593	.27564	.96126	.29237	.95630	.30902	.95106	.32557	.94552	60
1	.25910	.96585	.27592	.96118	.29265	.95622	.30929	.95097	.32584	.94542	59
2	.25938	.96578	.27620	.96110	.29293	.95613	.30957	.95088	.32612	.94533	58
3	.25966	.96570	.27648	.96102	.29321	.95605	.30985	.95079	.32639	.94523	57
4	.25994	.96562	.27676	.96094	.29348	.95596	.31012	.95070	.32667	.94514	56
5	.26022	.96555	.27704	.96086	.29376	.95588	.31040	.95061	.32694	.94504	55
6	.26050	.96547	.27731	.96078	.29404	.95579	.31068	.95052	.32722	.94495	54
7	.25079	.96540	.27759	.96070	.29432	.95571	.31095	.95043	.32749	.94485	53
8	.26107	.96532	.27787	.96062	.29460	.95562	.31123	.95033	.32777	.94476	52
9	.26135	.96524	.27815	.96054	.29487	.95554	.31151	.95024	.32804	.94466	51
10	.26163	.96517	.27843	.96046	.29515	.95545	.31178	.95015	.32832	.94457	50
11	.26191	.96509	.27871	.96037	.29543	.95536	.31206	.95006	.32859	.94447	49
12	.26219	.96502	.27899	.96029	.29571	.95528	.31233	.94997	.32887	.94438	48
13	.26247	.96494	.27927	.96021	.29599	.95519	.31261	.94988	.32914	.94428	47
14	.26275	.96486	.27955	.96013	.29626	.95511	.31289	.94979	.32942	.94418	46
15	.26303	.96479	.27983	.96005	.29654	.95502	.31316	.94970	.32969	.94409	45
16	.26331	.96471	.28011	.95997	.29682	.95493	.31344	.94961	.32997	.94399	44
17	.26359	.96463	.28039	.95989	.29710	.95485	.31372	.94952	.33024	.94390	43
18	.26387	.96456	.28067	.95981	.29737	.95476	.31399	.94943	.33051	.94380	42
19	.26415	.96448	.28095	.95972	.29765	.95467	.31427	.94933	.33079	.94370	41
20	.26443	.96440	.28123	.95964	.29793	.95459	.31454	.94924	.33106	.94361	40
21	.26471	.96433	.28150	.95956	.29821	.95450	.31482	.94915	.33134	.94351	39
22	.26500	.96425	.28178	.95948	.29849	.95441	.31510	.94906	.33161	.94342	38
23	.26528	.96417	.28206	.95940	.29876	.95433	.31537	.94897	.33189	.94332	37
24	.26556	.96410	.28234	.95931	.29904	.95424	.31565	.94888	.33216	.94322	36
25	.26584	.96402	.28262	.95923	.29932	.95415	.31593	.94878	.33244	.94313	35
26	.26612	.96394	.28290	.95915	.29960	.95407	.31620	.94869	.33271	.94303	34
27	.26640	.96386	.28318	.95907	.29987	.95398	.31648	.94860	.33298	.94293	33
28	.26668	.96379	.28346	.95898	.30015	.95389	.31675	.94851	.33326	.94284	32
29	.26696	.96371	.28374	.95890	.30043	.95380	.31703	.94842	.33353	.94274	31
30	.26724	.96363	.28402	.95882	.30071	.95372	.31730	.94832	.33381	.94264	30
31	.26752	.96355	.28429	.95874	.30098	.95363	.31758	.94823	.33408	.94254	29
32	.26780	.96347	.28457	.95865	.30126	.95354	.31786	.94814	.33436	.94245	28
33	.26808	.96340	.28485	.95857	.30154	.95345	.31813	.94805	.33463	.94235	27
34	.26836	.96332	.28513	.95849	.30182	.95337	.31841	.94795	.33490	.94225	26
35	.26864	.96324	.28541	.95841	.30209	.95328	.31868	.94786	.33518	.94215	25
36	.26892	.96316	.28569	.95832	.30237	.95319	.31896	.94777	.33545	.94206	24
37	.26920	.96308	.28597	.95824	.30265	.95310	.31923	.94768	.33573	.94196	23
38	.26948	.96301	.28625	.95816	.30292	.95301	.31951	.94758	.33600	.94186	22
39	.26976	.96293	.28652	.95807	.30320	.95293	.31979	.94749	.33627	.94176	21
40	.27004	.96285	.28680	.95799	.30348	.95284	.32006	.94740	.33655	.94167	20
41	.27032	.96277	.28708	.95791	.30376	.95275	.32034	.94730	.33682	.94157	19
42	.27060	.96269	.28736	.95782	.30403	.95266	.32061	.94721	.33710	.94147	18
43	.27088	.96261	.28764	.95774	.30431	.95257	.32089	.94712	.33737	.94137	17
44	.27116	.96253	.28792	.95766	.30459	.95248	.32116	.94702	.33764	.94127	16
45	.27144	.96246	.28820	.95757	.30486	.95240	.32144	.94693	.33792	.94118	15
46	.27172	.96238	.28847	.95749	.30514	.95231	.32171	.94684	.33819	.94108	14
47	.27200	.96230	.28875	.95740	.30542	.95222	.32199	.94674	.33846	.94098	13
48	.27228	.96222	.28903	.95732	.30570	.95213	.32227	.94665	.33874	.94088	12
49	.27256	.96214	.28931	.95724	.30597	.95204	.32254	.94656	.33901	.94078	11
50	.27284	.96206	.28959	.95715	.30625	.95195	.32282	.94646	.33929	.94068	10
51	.27312	.96198	.28987	.95707	.30653	.95186	.32309	.94637	.33956	.94058	9
52	.27340	.96190	.29015	.95698	.30680	.95177	.32337	.94627	.33983	.94049	8
53	.27368	.96182	.29042	.95690	.30708	.95168	.32364	.94618	.34011	.94039	7
54	.27396	.96174	.29070	.95681	.30736	.95159	.32392	.94609	.34038	.94029	6
55	.27424	.96166	.29098	.95673	.30763	.95150	.32419	.94599	.34065	.94019	5
56	.27452	.96158	.29126	.95664	.30791	.95142	.32447	.94590	.34093	.94009	4
57	.27480	.96150	.29154	.95656	.30819	.95133	.32474	.94580	.34120	.93999	3
58	.27508	.96142	.29182	.95647	.30846	.95124	.32502	.94571	.34147	.93989	2
59	.27536	.96134	.29209	.95639	.30874	.95115	.32529	.94561	.34175	.93979	1
60	.27564	.96126	.29237	.95630	.30902	.95106	.32557	.94552	.34202	.93969	0
′	Cosine	Sine	Cosine	Sine	Cosine	Sine	Cosine	Sine	Cosine	Sine	′
	74°		73°		72°		71°		70°		

TABLE XI. NATURAL SINES AND COSINES

′	20° Sine	20° Cosine	21° Sine	21° Cosine	22° Sine	22° Cosine	23° Sine	23° Cosine	24° Sine	24° Cosine	′
0	.34202	.93969	.35837	.93358	.37461	.92718	.39073	.92050	.40674	.91355	60
1	.34229	.93959	.35864	.93348	.37488	.92707	.39100	.92039	.40700	.91343	59
2	.34257	.93949	.35891	.93337	.37515	.92697	.39127	.92028	.40727	.91331	58
3	.34284	.93939	.35918	.93327	.37542	.92686	.39153	.92016	.40753	.91319	57
4	.34311	.93929	.35945	.93316	.37569	.92675	.39180	.92005	.40780	.91307	56
5	.34339	.93919	.35973	.93306	.37595	.92664	.39207	.91994	.40806	.91295	55
6	.34366	.93909	.36000	.93295	.37622	.92653	.39234	.91982	.40833	.91283	54
7	.34393	.93899	.36027	.93285	.37649	.92642	.39260	.91971	.40860	.91272	53
8	.34421	.93889	.36054	.93274	.37676	.92631	.39287	.91959	.40886	.91260	52
9	.34448	.93879	.36081	.93264	.37703	.92620	.39314	.91948	.40913	.91248	51
10	.34475	.93869	.36108	.93253	.37730	.92609	.39341	.91936	.40939	.91236	50
11	.34503	.93859	.36135	.93243	.37757	.92598	.39367	.91925	.40966	.91224	49
12	.34530	.93849	.36162	.93232	.37784	.92587	.39394	.91914	.40992	.91212	48
13	.34557	.93839	.36190	.93222	.37811	.92576	.39421	.91902	.41019	.91200	47
14	.34584	.93829	.36217	.93211	.37838	.92565	.39448	.91891	.41045	.91188	46
15	.34612	.93819	.36244	.93201	.37865	.92554	.39474	.91879	.41072	.91176	45
16	.34639	.93809	.36271	.93190	.37892	.92543	.39501	.91868	.41098	.91164	44
17	.34666	.93799	.36298	.93180	.37919	.92532	.39528	.91856	.41125	.91152	43
18	.34694	.93789	.36325	.93169	.37946	.92521	.39555	.91845	.41151	.91140	42
19	.34721	.93779	.36352	.93159	.37973	.92510	.39581	.91833	.41178	.91128	41
20	.34748	.93769	.36379	.93148	.37999	.92499	.39608	.91822	.41204	.91116	40
21	.34775	.93759	.36406	.93137	.38026	.92488	.39635	.91810	.41231	.91104	39
22	.34803	.93748	.36434	.93127	.38053	.92477	.39661	.91799	.41257	.91092	38
23	.34830	.93738	.36461	.93116	.38080	.92466	.39688	.91787	.41284	.91080	37
24	.34857	.93728	.36488	.93106	.38107	.92455	.39715	.91775	.41310	.91068	36
25	.34884	.93718	.36515	.93095	.38134	.92444	.39741	.91764	.41337	.91056	35
26	.34912	.93708	.36542	.93084	.38161	.92432	.39768	.91752	.41363	.91044	34
27	.34939	.93698	.36569	.93074	.38188	.92421	.39795	.91741	.41390	.91032	33
28	.34966	.93688	.36596	.93063	.38215	.92410	.39822	.91729	.41416	.91020	32
29	.34993	.93677	.36623	.93052	.38241	.92399	.39848	.91718	.41443	.91008	31
30	.35021	.93667	.36650	.93042	.38268	.92388	.39875	.91706	.41469	.90996	30
31	.35048	.93657	.36677	.93031	.38295	.92377	.39902	.91694	.41496	.90984	29
32	.35075	.93647	.36704	.93020	.38322	.92366	.39928	.91683	.41522	.90972	28
33	.35102	.93637	.36731	.93010	.38349	.92355	.39955	.91671	.41549	.90960	27
34	.35130	.93626	.36758	.92999	.38376	.92343	.39982	.91660	.41575	.90948	26
35	.35157	.93616	.36785	.92988	.38403	.92332	.40008	.91648	.41602	.90936	25
36	.35184	.93606	.36812	.92978	.38430	.92321	.40035	.91636	.41628	.90924	24
37	.35211	.93596	.36839	.92967	.38456	.92310	.40062	.91625	.41655	.90911	23
38	.35239	.93585	.36867	.92956	.38483	.92299	.40088	.91613	.41681	.90899	22
39	.35266	.93575	.36894	.92945	.38510	.92287	.40115	.91601	.41707	.90887	21
40	.35293	.93565	.36921	.92935	.38537	.92276	.40141	.91590	.41734	.90875	20
41	.35320	.93555	.36948	.92924	.38564	.92265	.40168	.91578	.41760	.90863	19
42	.35347	.93544	.36975	.92913	.38591	.92254	.40195	.91566	.41787	.90851	18
43	.35375	.93534	.37002	.92902	.38617	.92243	.40221	.91555	.41813	.90839	17
44	.35402	.93524	.37029	.92892	.38644	.92231	.40248	.91543	.41840	.90826	16
45	.35429	.93514	.37056	.92881	.38671	.92220	.40275	.91531	.41866	.90814	15
46	.35456	.93503	.37083	.92870	.38698	.92209	.40301	.91519	.41892	.90802	14
47	.35484	.93493	.37110	.92859	.38725	.92198	.40328	.91508	.41919	.90790	13
48	.35511	.93483	.37137	.92849	.38752	.92186	.40355	.91496	.41945	.90778	12
49	.35538	.93472	.37164	.92838	.38778	.92175	.40381	.91484	.41972	.90766	11
50	.35565	.93462	.37191	.92827	.38805	.92164	.40408	.91472	.41998	.90753	10
51	.35592	.93452	.37218	.92816	.38832	.92152	.40434	.91461	.42024	.90741	9
52	.35619	.93441	.37245	.92805	.38859	.92141	.40461	.91449	.42051	.90729	8
53	.35647	.93431	.37272	.92794	.38886	.92130	.40488	.91437	.42077	.90717	7
54	.35674	.93420	.37299	.92784	.38912	.92119	.40514	.91425	.42104	.90704	6
55	.35701	.93410	.37326	.92773	.38939	.92107	.40541	.91414	.42130	.90692	5
56	.35728	.93400	.37353	.92762	.38966	.92096	.40567	.91402	.42156	.90680	4
57	.35755	.93389	.37380	.92751	.38993	.92085	.40594	.91390	.42183	.90668	3
58	.35782	.93379	.37407	.92740	.39020	.92073	.40621	.91378	.42209	.90655	2
59	.35810	.93368	.37434	.92729	.39046	.92062	.40647	.91366	.42235	.90643	1
60	.35837	.93358	.37461	.92718	.39073	.92050	.40674	.91355	.42262	.90631	0
′	Cosine	Sine	Cosine	Sine	Cosine	Sine	Cosine	Sine	Cosine	Sine	′
	69°		68°		67°		66°		65°		

TABLE XI. NATURAL SINES AND COSINES

,	25° Sine	25° Cosine	26° Sine	26° Cosine	27° Sine	27° Cosine	28° Sine	28° Cosine	29° Sine	29° Cosine	,
0	.42262	.90631	.43837	.89879	.45399	.89101	.46947	.88295	.48481	.87462	60
1	.42288	.90618	.43863	.89867	.45425	.89087	.46973	.88281	.48506	.87448	59
2	.42315	.90606	.43889	.89854	.45451	.89074	.46999	.88267	.48532	.87434	58
3	.42341	.90594	.43916	.89841	.45477	.89061	.47024	.88254	.48557	.87420	57
4	.42367	.90582	.43942	.89828	.45503	.89048	.47050	.88240	.48583	.87406	56
5	.42394	.90569	.43968	.89816	.45529	.89035	.47076	.88226	.48608	.87391	55
6	.42420	.90557	.43994	.89803	.45554	.89021	.47101	.88213	.48634	.87377	54
7	.42446	.90545	.44020	.89790	.45580	.89008	.47127	.88199	.48659	.87363	53
8	.42473	.90532	.44046	.89777	.45606	.88995	.47153	.88185	.48684	.87349	52
9	.42499	.90520	.44072	.89764	.45632	.88981	.47178	.88172	.48710	.87335	51
10	.42525	.90507	.44098	.89752	.45658	.88968	.47204	.88158	.48735	.87321	50
11	.42552	.90495	.44124	.89739	.45684	.88955	.47229	.88144	.48761	.87306	49
12	.42578	.90483	.44151	.89726	.45710	.88942	.47255	.88130	.48786	.87292	48
13	.42604	.90470	.44177	.89713	.45736	.88928	.47281	.88117	.48811	.87278	47
14	.42631	.90458	.44203	.89700	.45762	.88915	.47306	.88103	.48837	.87264	46
15	.42657	.90446	.44229	.89687	.45787	.88902	.47332	.88089	.48862	.87250	45
16	.42683	.90433	.44255	.89674	.45813	.88888	.47358	.88075	.48888	.87235	44
17	.42709	.90421	.44281	.89662	.45839	.88875	.47383	.88062	.48913	.87221	43
18	.42736	.90408	.44307	.89649	.45865	.88862	.47409	.88048	.48938	.87207	42
19	.42762	.90396	.44333	.89636	.45891	.88848	.47434	.88034	.48964	.87193	41
20	.42788	.90383	.44359	.89623	.45917	.88835	.47460	.88020	.48989	.87178	40
21	.42815	.90371	.44385	.89610	.45942	.88822	.47486	.88006	.49014	.87164	39
22	.42841	.90358	.44411	.89597	.45968	.88808	.47511	.87993	.49040	.87150	38
23	.42867	.90346	.44437	.89584	.45994	.88795	.47537	.87979	.49065	.87136	37
24	.42894	.90334	.44464	.89571	.46020	.88782	.47562	.87965	.49090	.87121	36
25	.42920	.90321	.44490	.89558	.46046	.88768	.47588	.87951	.49116	.87107	35
26	.42946	.90309	.44516	.89545	.46072	.88755	.47614	.87937	.49141	.87093	34
27	.42972	.90296	.44542	.89532	.46097	.88741	.47639	.87923	.49166	.87079	33
28	.42999	.90284	.44568	.89519	.46123	.88728	.47665	.87909	.49192	.87064	32
29	.43025	.90271	.44594	.89506	.46149	.88715	.47690	.87896	.49217	.87050	31
30	.43051	.90259	.44620	.89493	.46175	.88701	.47716	.87882	.49242	.87036	30
31	.43077	.90246	.44646	.89480	.46201	.88688	.47741	.87868	.49268	.87021	29
32	.43104	.90233	.44672	.89467	.46226	.88674	.47767	.87854	.49293	.87007	28
33	.43130	.90221	.44698	.89454	.46252	.88661	.47793	.87840	.49318	.86993	27
34	.43156	.90208	.44724	.89441	.46278	.88647	.47818	.87826	.49344	.86978	26
35	.43182	.90196	.44750	.89428	.46304	.88634	.47844	.87812	.49369	.86964	25
36	.43209	.90183	.44776	.89415	.46330	.88620	.47869	.87798	.49394	.86949	24
37	.43235	.90171	.44802	.89402	.46355	.88607	.47895	.87784	.49419	.86935	23
38	.43261	.90158	.44828	.89389	.46381	.88593	.47920	.87770	.49445	.86921	22
39	.43287	.90146	.44854	.89376	.46407	.88580	.47946	.87756	.49470	.86906	21
40	.43313	.90133	.44880	.89363	.46433	.88566	.47971	.87743	.49495	.86892	20
41	.43340	.90120	.44906	.89350	.46458	.88553	.47997	.87729	.49521	.86878	19
42	.43366	.90108	.44932	.89337	.46484	.88539	.48022	.87715	.49546	.86863	18
43	.43392	.90095	.44958	.89324	.46510	.88526	.48048	.87701	.49571	.86849	17
44	.43418	.90082	.44984	.89311	.46536	.88512	.48073	.87687	.49596	.86834	16
45	.43445	.90070	.45010	.89298	.46561	.88499	.48099	.87673	.49622	.86820	15
46	.43471	.90057	.45036	.89285	.46587	.88485	.48124	.87659	.49647	.86805	14
47	.43497	.90045	.45062	.89272	.46613	.88472	.48150	.87645	.49672	.86791	13
48	.43523	.90032	.45088	.89259	.46639	.88458	.48175	.87631	.49697	.86777	12
49	.43549	.90019	.45114	.89245	.46664	.88445	.48201	.87617	.49723	.86762	11
50	.43575	.90007	.45140	.89232	.46690	.88431	.48226	.87603	.49748	.86748	10
51	.43602	.89994	.45166	.89219	.46716	.88417	.48252	.87589	.49773	.86733	9
52	.43628	.89981	.45192	.89206	.46742	.88404	.48277	.87575	.49798	.86719	8
53	.43654	.89968	.45218	.89193	.46767	.88390	.48303	.87561	.49824	.86704	7
54	.43680	.89956	.45243	.89180	.46793	.88377	.48328	.87546	.49849	.86690	6
55	.43706	.89943	.45269	.89167	.46819	.88363	.48354	.87532	.49874	.86675	5
56	.43733	.89930	.45295	.89153	.46844	.88349	.48379	.87518	.49899	.86661	4
57	.43759	.89918	.45321	.89140	.46870	.88336	.48405	.87504	.49924	.86646	3
58	.43785	.89905	.45347	.89127	.46896	.88322	.48430	.87490	.49950	.86632	2
59	.43811	.89892	.45373	.89114	.46921	.88308	.48456	.87476	.49975	.86617	1
60	.43837	.89879	.45399	.89101	.46947	.88295	.48481	.87462	.50000	.86603	0
,	64° Cosine	64° Sine	63° Cosine	63° Sine	62° Cosine	62° Sine	61° Cosine	61° Sine	60° Cosine	60° Sine	,

TABLE XI. NATURAL SINES AND COSINES

′	30° Sine	30° Cosine	31° Sine	31° Cosine	32° Sine	32° Cosine	33° Sine	33° Cosine	34° Sine	34° Cosine	′
0	.50000	.86603	.51504	.85717	.52992	.84805	.54464	.83867	.55919	.82904	60
1	.50025	.86588	.51529	.85702	.53017	.84789	.54488	.83851	.55943	.82887	59
2	.50050	.86573	.51554	.85687	.53041	.84774	.54513	.83835	.55968	.82871	58
3	.50076	.86559	.51579	.85672	.53066	.84759	.54537	.83819	.55992	.82855	57
4	.50101	.86544	.51604	.85657	.53091	.84743	.54561	.83804	.56016	.82839	56
5	.50126	.86530	.51628	.85642	.53115	.84728	.54586	.83788	.56040	.82822	55
6	.50151	.86515	.51653	.85627	.53140	.84712	.54610	.83772	.56064	.82806	54
7	.50176	.86501	.51678	.85612	.53164	.84697	.54635	.83756	.56088	.82790	53
8	.50201	.86486	.51703	.85597	.53189	.84681	.54659	.83740	.56112	.82773	52
9	.50227	.86471	.51728	.85582	.53214	.84666	.54683	.83724	.56136	.82757	51
10	.50252	.86457	.51753	.85567	.53238	.84650	.54708	.83708	.56160	.82741	50
11	.50277	.86442	.51778	.85551	.53263	.84635	.54732	.83692	.56184	.82724	49
12	.50302	.86427	.51803	.85536	.53288	.84619	.54756	.83676	.56208	.82708	48
13	.50327	.86413	.51828	.85521	.53312	.84604	.54781	.83660	.56232	.82692	47
14	.50352	.86398	.51852	.85506	.53337	.84588	.54805	.83645	.56256	.82675	46
15	.50377	.86384	.51877	.85491	.53361	.84573	.54829	.83629	.56280	.82659	45
16	.50403	.86369	.51902	.85476	.53386	.84557	.54854	.83613	.56305	.82643	44
17	.50428	.86354	.51927	.85461	.53411	.84542	.54878	.83597	.56329	.82626	43
18	.50453	.86340	.51952	.85446	.53435	.84526	.54902	.83581	.56353	.82610	42
19	.50478	.86325	.51977	.85431	.53460	.84511	.54927	.83565	.56377	.82593	41
20	.50503	.86310	.52002	.85416	.53484	.84495	.54951	.83549	.56401	.82577	40
21	.50528	.86295	.52026	.85401	.53509	.84480	.54975	.83533	.56425	.82561	39
22	.50553	.86281	.52051	.85385	.53534	.84464	.54999	.83517	.56449	.82544	38
23	.50578	.86266	.52076	.85370	.53558	.84448	.55024	.83501	.56473	.82528	37
24	.50603	.86251	.52101	.85355	.53583	.84433	.55048	.83485	.56497	.82511	36
25	.50628	.86237	.52126	.85340	.53607	.84417	.55072	.83469	.56521	.82495	35
26	.50654	.86222	.52151	.85325	.53632	.84402	.55097	.83453	.56545	.82478	34
27	.50679	.86207	.52175	.85310	.53656	.84386	.55121	.83437	.56569	.82462	33
28	.50704	.86192	.52200	.85294	.53681	.84370	.55145	.83421	.56593	.82446	32
29	.50729	.86178	.52225	.85279	.53705	.84355	.55169	.83405	.56617	.82429	31
30	.50754	.86163	.52250	.85264	.53730	.84339	.55194	.83389	.56641	.82413	30
31	.50779	.86148	.52275	.85249	.53754	.84324	.55218	.83373	.56665	.82396	29
32	.50804	.86133	.52299	.85234	.53779	.84308	.55242	.83356	.56689	.82380	28
33	.50829	.86119	.52324	.85218	.53804	.84292	.55266	.83340	.56713	.82363	27
34	.50854	.86104	.52349	.85203	.53828	.84277	.55291	.83324	.56736	.82347	26
35	.50879	.86089	.52374	.85188	.53853	.84261	.55315	.83308	.56760	.82330	25
36	.50904	.86074	.52399	.85173	.53877	.84245	.55339	.83292	.56784	.82314	24
37	.50929	.86059	.52423	.85157	.53902	.84230	.55363	.83276	.56808	.82297	23
38	.50954	.86045	.52448	.85142	.53926	.84214	.55388	.83260	.56832	.82281	22
39	.50979	.86030	.52473	.85127	.53951	.84198	.55412	.83244	.56856	.82264	21
40	.51004	.86015	.52498	.85112	.53975	.84182	.55436	.83228	.56880	.82248	20
41	.51029	.86000	.52522	.85096	.54000	.84167	.55460	.83212	.56904	.82231	19
42	.51054	.85985	.52547	.85081	.54024	.84151	.55484	.83195	.56928	.82214	18
43	.51079	.85970	.52572	.85066	.54049	.84135	.55509	.83179	.56952	.82198	17
44	.51104	.85956	.52597	.85051	.54073	.84120	.55533	.83163	.56976	.82181	16
45	.51129	.85941	.52621	.85035	.54097	.84104	.55557	.83147	.57000	.82165	15
46	.51154	.85926	.52646	.85020	.54122	.84088	.55581	.83131	.57024	.82148	14
47	.51179	.85911	.52671	.85005	.54146	.84072	.55605	.83115	.57047	.82132	13
48	.51204	.85896	.52696	.84989	.54171	.84057	.55630	.83098	.57071	.82115	12
49	.51229	.85881	.52720	.84974	.54195	.84041	.55654	.83082	.57095	.82098	11
50	.51254	.85866	.52745	.84959	.54220	.84025	.55678	.83066	.57119	.82082	10
51	.51279	.85851	.52770	.84943	.54244	.84009	.55702	.83050	.57143	.82065	9
52	.51304	.85836	.52794	.84928	.54269	.83994	.55726	.83034	.57167	.82048	8
53	.51329	.85821	.52819	.84913	.54293	.83978	.55750	.83017	.57191	.82032	7
54	.51354	.85806	.52844	.84897	.54317	.83962	.55775	.83001	.57215	.82015	6
55	.51379	.85792	.52869	.84882	.54342	.83946	.55799	.82985	.57238	.81999	5
56	.51404	.85777	.52893	.84866	.54366	.83930	.55823	.82969	.57262	.81982	4
57	.51429	.85762	.52918	.84851	.54391	.83915	.55847	.82953	.57286	.81965	3
58	.51454	.85747	.52943	.84836	.54415	.83899	.55871	.82936	.57310	.81949	2
59	.51479	.85732	.52967	.84820	.54440	.83883	.55895	.82920	.57334	.81932	1
60	.51504	.85717	.52992	.84805	.54464	.83867	.55919	.82904	.57358	.81915	0
′	Cosine	Sine	Cosine	Sine	Cosine	Sine	Cosine	Sine	Cosine	Sine	′
	59°		58°		57°		56°		55°		

TABLE XI. NATURAL SINES AND COSINES

′	35° Sine	35° Cosine	36° Sine	36° Cosine	37° Sine	37° Cosine	38° Sine	38° Cosine	39° Sine	39° Cosine	′
0	.57358	.81915	.58779	.80902	.60182	.79864	.61566	.78801	.62932	.77715	60
1	.57381	.81899	.58802	.80885	.60205	.79846	.61589	.78783	.62955	.77696	59
2	.57405	.81882	.58826	.80867	.60228	.79829	.61612	.78765	.62977	.77678	58
3	.57429	.81865	.58849	.80850	.60251	.79811	.61635	.78747	.63000	.77660	57
4	.57453	.81848	.58873	.80833	.60274	.79793	.61658	.78729	.63022	.77641	56
5	.57477	.81832	.58896	.80816	.60298	.79776	.61681	.78711	.63045	.77623	55
6	.57501	.81815	.58920	.80799	.60321	.79758	.61704	.78694	.63068	.77605	54
7	.57524	.81798	.58943	.80782	.60344	.79741	.61726	.78676	.63090	.77586	53
8	.57548	.81782	.58967	.80765	.60367	.79723	.61749	.78658	.63113	.77568	52
9	.57572	.81765	.58990	.80748	.60390	.79706	.61772	.78640	.63135	.77550	51
10	.57596	.81748	.59014	.80730	.60414	.79688	.61795	.78622	.63158	.77531	50
11	.57619	.81731	.59037	.80713	.60437	.79671	.61818	.78604	.63180	.77513	49
12	.57643	.81714	.59061	.80696	.60460	.79653	.61841	.78586	.63203	.77494	48
13	.57667	.81698	.59084	.80679	.60483	.79635	.61864	.78568	.63225	.77476	47
14	.57691	.81681	.59108	.80662	.60506	.79618	.61887	.78550	.63248	.77458	46
15	.57715	.81664	.59131	.80644	.60529	.79600	.61909	.78532	.63271	.77439	45
16	.57738	.81647	.59154	.80627	.60553	.79583	.61932	.78514	.63293	.77421	44
17	.57762	.81631	.59178	.80610	.60576	.79565	.61955	.78496	.63316	.77402	43
18	.57786	.81614	.59201	.80593	.60599	.79547	.61978	.78478	.63338	.77384	42
19	.57810	.81597	.59225	.80576	.60622	.79530	.62001	.78460	.63361	.77366	41
20	.57833	.81580	.59248	.80558	.60645	.79512	.62024	.78442	.63383	.77347	40
21	.57857	.81563	.59272	.80541	.60668	.79494	.62046	.78424	.63406	.77329	39
22	.57881	.81546	.59295	.80524	.60691	.79477	.62069	.78405	.63428	.77310	38
23	.57904	.81530	.59318	.80507	.60714	.79459	.62092	.78387	.63451	.77292	37
24	.57928	.81513	.59342	.80489	.60738	.79441	.62115	.78369	.63473	.77273	36
25	.57952	.81496	.59365	.80472	.60761	.79424	.62138	.78351	.63496	.77255	35
26	.57976	.81479	.59389	.80455	.60784	.79406	.62160	.78333	.63518	.77236	34
27	.57999	.81462	.59412	.80438	.60807	.79388	.62183	.78315	.63540	.77218	33
28	.58023	.81445	.59436	.80420	.60830	.79371	.62206	.78297	.63563	.77199	32
29	.58047	.81428	.59459	.80403	.60853	.79353	.62229	.78279	.63585	.77181	31
30	.58070	.81412	.59482	.80386	.60876	.79335	.62251	.78261	.63608	.77162	30
31	.58094	.81395	.59506	.80368	.60899	.79318	.62274	.78243	.63630	.77144	29
32	.58118	.81378	.59529	.80351	.60922	.79300	.62297	.78225	.63653	.77125	28
33	.58141	.81361	.59552	.80334	.60945	.79282	.62320	.78206	.63675	.77107	27
34	.58165	.81344	.59576	.80316	.60968	.79264	.62342	.78188	.63698	.77088	26
35	.58189	.81327	.59599	.80299	.60991	.79247	.62365	.78170	.63720	.77070	25
36	.58212	.81310	.59622	.80282	.61015	.79229	.62388	.78152	.63742	.77051	24
37	.58236	.81293	.59646	.80264	.61038	.79211	.62411	.78134	.63765	.77033	23
38	.58260	.81276	.59669	.80247	.61061	.79193	.62433	.78116	.63787	.77014	22
39	.58283	.81259	.59693	.80230	.61084	.79176	.62456	.78098	.63810	.76996	21
40	.58307	.81242	.59716	.80212	.61107	.79158	.62479	.78079	.63832	.76977	20
41	.58330	.81225	.59739	.80195	.61130	.79140	.62502	.78061	.63854	.76959	19
42	.58354	.81208	.59763	.80178	.61153	.79122	.62524	.78043	.63877	.76940	18
43	.58378	.81191	.59786	.80160	.61176	.79105	.62547	.78025	.63899	.76921	17
44	.58401	.81174	.59809	.80143	.61199	.79087	.62570	.78007	.63922	.76903	16
45	.58425	.81157	.59832	.80125	.61222	.79069	.62592	.77988	.63944	.76884	15
46	.58449	.81140	.59856	.80108	.61245	.79051	.62615	.77970	.63966	.76866	14
47	.58472	.81123	.59879	.80091	.61268	.79033	.62638	.77952	.63989	.76847	13
48	.58496	.81106	.59902	.80073	.61291	.79016	.62660	.77934	.64011	.76828	12
49	.58519	.81089	.59926	.80056	.61314	.78998	.62683	.77916	.64033	.76810	11
50	.58543	.81072	.59949	.80038	.61337	.78980	.62706	.77897	.64056	.76791	10
51	.58567	.81055	.59972	.80021	.61360	.78962	.62728	.77879	.64078	.76772	9
52	.58590	.81038	.59995	.80003	.61383	.78944	.62751	.77861	.64100	.76754	8
53	.58614	.81021	.60019	.79986	.61406	.78926	.62774	.77843	.64123	.76735	7
54	.58637	.81004	.60042	.79968	.61429	.78908	.62796	.77824	.64145	.76717	6
55	.58661	.80987	.60065	.79951	.61451	.78891	.62819	.77806	.64167	.76698	5
56	.58684	.80970	.60089	.79934	.61474	.78873	.62842	.77788	.64190	.76679	4
57	.58708	.80953	.60112	.79916	.61497	.78855	.62864	.77769	.64212	.76661	3
58	.58731	.80936	.60135	.79899	.61520	.78837	.62887	.77751	.64234	.76642	2
59	.58755	.80919	.60158	.79881	.61543	.78819	.62909	.77733	.64256	.76623	1
60	.58779	.80902	.60182	.79864	.61566	.78801	.62932	.77715	.64279	.76604	0
′	Cosine	Sine	Cosine	Sine	Cosine	Sine	Cosine	Sine	Cosine	Sine	′
	54°		53°		52°		51°		50°		

TABLE XI. NATURAL SINES AND COSINES

′	40° Sine	40° Cosine	41° Sine	41° Cosine	42° Sine	42° Cosine	43° Sine	43° Cosine	44° Sine	44° Cosine	′
0	.64279	.76604	.65606	.75471	.66913	.74314	.68200	.73135	.69466	.71934	60
1	.64301	.76586	.65628	.75452	.66935	.74295	.68221	.73116	.69487	.71914	59
2	.64323	.76567	.65650	.75433	.66956	.74276	.68242	.73096	.69508	.71894	58
3	.64346	.76548	.65672	.75414	.66978	.74256	.68264	.73076	.69529	.71873	57
4	.64368	.76530	.65694	.75395	.66999	.74237	.68285	.73056	.69549	.71853	56
5	.64390	.76511	.65716	.75375	.67021	.74217	.68306	.73036	.69570	.71833	55
6	.64412	.76492	.65738	.75356	.67043	.74198	.68327	.73016	.69591	.71813	54
7	.64435	.76473	.65759	.75337	.67064	.74178	.68349	.72996	.69612	.71792	53
8	.64457	.76455	.65781	.75318	.67086	.74159	.68370	.72976	.69633	.71772	52
9	.64479	.76436	.65803	.75299	.67107	.74139	.68391	.72957	.69654	.71752	51
10	.64501	.76417	.65825	.75280	.67129	.74120	.68412	.72937	.69675	.71732	50
11	.64524	.76398	.65847	.75261	.67151	.74100	.68434	.72917	.69696	.71711	49
12	.64546	.76380	.65869	.75241	.67172	.74080	.68455	.72897	.69717	.71691	48
13	.64568	.76361	.65891	.75222	.67194	.74061	.68476	.72877	.69737	.71671	47
14	.64590	.76342	.65913	.75203	.67215	.74041	.68497	.72857	.69758	.71650	46
15	.64612	.76323	.65935	.75184	.67237	.74022	.68518	.72837	.69779	.71630	45
16	.64635	.76304	.65956	.75165	.67258	.74002	.68539	.72817	.69800	.71610	44
17	.64657	.76286	.65978	.75146	.67280	.73983	.68561	.72797	.69821	.71590	43
18	.64679	.76267	.66000	.75126	.67301	.73963	.68582	.72777	.69842	.71569	42
19	.64701	.76248	.66022	.75107	.67323	.73944	.68603	.72757	.69862	.71549	41
20	.64723	.76229	.66044	.75088	.67344	.73924	.68624	.72737	.69883	.71529	40
21	.64746	.76210	.66066	.75069	.67366	.73904	.68645	.72717	.69904	.71508	39
22	.64768	.76192	.66088	.75050	.67387	.73885	.68666	.72697	.69925	.71488	38
23	.64790	.76173	.66109	.75030	.67409	.73865	.68688	.72677	.69946	.71468	37
24	.64812	.76154	.66131	.75011	.67430	.73846	.68709	.72657	.69966	.71447	36
25	.64834	.76135	.66153	.74992	.67452	.73826	.68730	.72637	.69987	.71427	35
26	.64856	.76116	.66175	.74973	.67473	.73806	.68751	.72617	.70008	.71407	34
27	.64878	.76097	.66197	.74953	.67495	.73787	.68772	.72597	.70029	.71386	33
28	.64901	.76078	.66218	.74934	.67516	.73767	.68793	.72577	.70049	.71366	32
29	.64923	.76059	.66240	.74915	.67538	.73747	.68814	.72557	.70070	.71345	31
30	.64945	.76041	.66262	.74896	.67559	.73728	.68835	.72537	.70091	.71325	30
31	.64967	.76022	.66284	.74876	.67580	.73708	.68857	.72517	.70112	.71305	29
32	.64989	.76003	.66306	.74857	.67602	.73688	.68878	.72497	.70132	.71284	28
33	.65011	.75984	.66327	.74838	.67623	.73669	.68899	.72477	.70153	.71264	27
34	.65033	.75965	.66349	.74818	.67645	.73649	.68920	.72457	.70174	.71243	26
35	.65055	.75946	.66371	.74799	.67666	.73629	.68941	.72437	.70195	.71223	25
36	.65077	.75927	.66393	.74780	.67688	.73610	.68962	.72417	.70215	.71203	24
37	.65100	.75908	.66414	.74760	.67709	.73590	.68983	.72397	.70236	.71182	23
38	.65122	.75889	.66436	.74741	.67730	.73570	.69004	.72377	.70257	.71162	22
39	.65144	.75870	.66458	.74722	.67752	.73551	.69025	.72357	.70277	.71141	21
40	.65166	.75851	.66480	.74703	.67773	.73531	.69046	.72337	.70298	.71121	20
41	.65188	.75832	.66501	.74683	.67795	.73511	.69067	.72317	.70319	.71100	19
42	.65210	.75813	.66523	.74664	.67816	.73491	.69088	.72297	.70339	.71080	18
43	.65232	.75794	.66545	.74644	.67837	.73472	.69109	.72277	.70360	.71059	17
44	.65254	.75775	.66566	.74625	.67859	.73452	.69130	.72257	.70381	.71039	16
45	.65276	.75756	.66588	.74606	.67880	.73432	.69151	.72236	.70401	.71019	15
46	.65298	.75738	.66610	.74586	.67901	.73413	.69172	.72216	.70422	.70998	14
47	.65320	.75719	.66632	.74567	.67923	.73393	.69193	.72196	.70443	.70978	13
48	.65342	.75700	.66653	.74548	.67944	.73373	.69214	.72176	.70463	.70957	12
49	.65364	.75680	.66675	.74528	.67965	.73353	.69235	.72156	.70484	.70937	11
50	.65386	.75661	.66697	.74509	.67987	.73333	.69256	.72136	.70505	.70916	10
51	.65408	.75642	.66718	.74489	.68008	.73314	.69277	.72116	.70525	.70896	9
52	.65430	.75623	.66740	.74470	.68029	.73294	.69298	.72095	.70546	.70875	8
53	.65452	.75604	.66762	.74451	.68051	.73274	.69319	.72075	.70567	.70855	7
54	.65474	.75585	.66783	.74431	.68072	.73254	.69340	.72055	.70587	.70834	6
55	.65496	.75566	.66805	.74412	.68093	.73234	.69361	.72035	.70608	.70813	5
56	.65518	.75547	.66827	.74392	.68115	.73215	.69382	.72015	.70628	.70793	4
57	.65540	.75528	.66848	.74373	.68136	.73195	.69403	.71995	.70649	.70772	3
58	.65562	.75509	.66870	.74353	.68157	.73175	.69424	.71974	.70670	.70752	2
59	.65584	.75490	.66891	.74334	.68179	.73155	.69445	.71954	.70690	.70731	1
60	.65606	.75471	.66913	.74314	.68200	.73135	.69466	.71934	.70711	.70711	0
′	Cosine	Sine	Cosine	Sine	Cosine	Sine	Cosine	Sine	Cosine	Sine	′
	49°		48°		47°		46°		45°		

520 APPENDIX B

TABLE XII. NATURAL TANGENTS AND COTANGENTS

′	0° Tang	0° Cotang	1° Tang	1° Cotang	2° Tang	2° Cotang	3° Tang	3° Cotang	4° Tang	4° Cotang	′
0	.00000	Infinite	.01746	57.2900	.03492	28.6363	.05241	19.0811	.06993	14.3007	60
1	.00029	3437.75	.01775	56.3506	.03521	28.3994	.05270	18.9755	.07022	14.2411	59
2	.00058	1718.87	.01804	55.4415	.03550	28.1664	.05299	18.8711	.07051	14.1821	58
3	.00087	1145.92	.01833	54.5613	.03579	27.9372	.05328	18.7678	.07080	14.1235	57
4	.00116	859.436	.01862	53.7086	.03609	27.7117	.05357	18.6656	.07110	14.0655	56
5	.00145	687.549	.01891	52.8821	.03638	27.4899	.05387	18.5645	.07139	14.0079	55
6	.00175	572.957	.01920	52.0807	.03667	27.2715	.05416	18.4645	.07168	13.9507	54
7	.00204	491.106	.01949	51.3032	.03696	27.0566	.05445	18.3655	.07197	13.8940	53
8	.00233	429.718	.01978	50.5485	.03725	26.8450	.05474	18.2677	.07227	13.8378	52
9	.00262	381.971	.02007	49.8157	.03754	26.6367	.05503	18.1708	.07256	13.7821	51
10	.00291	343.774	.02036	49.1039	.03783	26.4316	.05533	18.0750	.07285	13.7267	50
11	.00320	312.521	.02066	48.4121	.03812	26.2296	.05562	17.9802	.07314	13.6719	49
12	.00349	286.478	.02095	47.7395	.03842	26.0307	.05591	17.8863	.07344	13.6174	48
13	.00378	264.441	.02124	47.0853	.03871	25.8348	.05620	17.7934	.07373	13.5634	47
14	.00407	245.552	.02153	46.4489	.03900	25.6418	.05649	17.7015	.07402	13.5098	46
15	.00436	229.182	.02182	45.8294	.03929	25.4517	.05678	17.6106	.07431	13.4566	45
16	.00465	214.858	.02211	45.2261	.03958	25.2644	.05708	17.5205	.07461	13.4039	44
17	.00495	202.219	.02240	44.6386	.03987	25.0798	.05737	17.4314	.07490	13.3515	43
18	.00524	190.984	.02269	44.0661	.04016	24.8978	.05766	17.3432	.07519	13.2996	42
19	.00553	180.932	.02298	43.5081	.04046	24.7185	.05795	17.2558	.07548	13.2480	41
20	.00582	171.885	.02328	42.9641	.04075	24.5418	.05824	17.1693	.07578	13.1969	40
21	.00611	163.700	.02357	42.4335	.04104	24.3675	.05854	17.0837	.07607	13.1461	39
22	.00640	156.259	.02386	41.9158	.04133	24.1957	.05883	16.9990	.07636	13.0958	38
23	.00669	149.465	.02415	41.4106	.04162	24.0263	.05912	16.9150	.07665	13.0458	37
24	.00698	143.237	.02444	40.9174	.04191	23.8593	.05941	16.8319	.07695	12.9962	36
25	.00727	137.507	.02473	40.4358	.04220	23.6945	.05970	16.7496	.07724	12.9469	35
26	.00756	132.219	.02502	39.9655	.04250	23.5321	.05999	16.6681	.07753	12.8981	34
27	.00785	127.321	.02531	39.5059	.04279	23.3718	.06029	16.5874	.07782	12.8496	33
28	.00815	122.774	.02560	39.0568	.04308	23.2137	.06058	16.5075	.07812	12.8014	32
29	.00844	118.540	.02589	38.6177	.04337	23.0577	.06087	16.4283	.07841	12.7536	31
30	.00873	114.589	.02619	38.1885	.04366	22.9038	.06116	16.3499	.07870	12.7062	30
31	.00902	110.892	.02648	37.7686	.04395	22.7519	.06145	16.2722	.07899	12.6591	29
32	.00931	107.426	.02677	37.3579	.04424	22.6020	.06175	16.1952	.07929	12.6124	28
33	.00960	104.171	.02706	36.9560	.04454	22.4541	.06204	16.1190	.07958	12.5660	27
34	.00989	101.107	.02735	36.5627	.04483	22.3081	.06233	16.0435	.07987	12.5199	26
35	.01018	98.2179	.02764	36.1776	.04512	22.1640	.06262	15.9687	.08017	12.4742	25
36	.01047	95.4895	.02793	35.8006	.04541	22.0217	.06291	15.8945	.08046	12.4288	24
37	.01076	92.9085	.02822	35.4313	.04570	21.8813	.06321	15.8211	.08075	12.3838	23
38	.01105	90.4633	.02851	35.0695	.04599	21.7426	.06350	15.7483	.08104	12.3390	22
39	.01135	88.1436	.02881	34.7151	.04628	21.6056	.06379	15.6762	.08134	12.2946	21
40	.01164	85.9398	.02910	34.3678	.04658	21.4704	.06408	15.6048	.08163	12.2505	20
41	.01193	83.8435	.02939	34.0273	.04687	21.3369	.06437	15.5340	.08192	12.2067	19
42	.01222	81.8470	.02968	33.6935	.04716	21.2049	.06467	15.4638	.08221	12.1632	18
43	.01251	79.9434	.02997	33.3662	.04745	21.0747	.06496	15.3943	.08251	12.1201	17
44	.01280	78.1263	.03026	33.0452	.04774	20.9460	.06525	15.3254	.08280	12.0772	16
45	.01309	76.3900	.03055	32.7303	.04803	20.8188	.06554	15.2571	.08309	12.0346	15
46	.01338	74.7292	.03084	32.4213	.04833	20.6932	.06584	15.1893	.08339	11.9923	14
47	.01367	73.1390	.03114	32.1181	.04862	20.5691	.06613	15.1222	.08368	11.9504	13
48	.01396	71.6151	.03143	31.8205	.04891	20.4465	.06642	15.0557	.08397	11.9087	12
49	.01425	70.1533	.03172	31.5284	.04920	20.3253	.06671	14.9898	.08427	11.8673	11
50	.01455	68.7501	.03201	31.2416	.04949	20.2056	.06700	14.9244	.08456	11.8262	10
51	.01484	67.4019	.03230	30.9599	.04978	20.0872	.06730	14.8596	.08485	11.7853	9
52	.01513	66.1055	.03259	30.6833	.05007	19.9702	.06759	14.7954	.08514	11.7448	8
53	.01542	64.8580	.03288	30.4116	.05037	19.8546	.06788	14.7317	.08544	11.7045	7
54	.01571	63.6567	.03317	30.1446	.05066	19.7403	.06817	14.6685	.08573	11.6645	6
55	.01600	62.4992	.03346	29.8823	.05095	19.6273	.06847	14.6059	.08602	11.6248	5
56	.01629	61.3829	.03376	29.6245	.05124	19.5156	.06876	14.5438	.08632	11.5853	4
57	.01658	60.3058	.03405	29.3711	.05153	19.4051	.06905	14.4823	.08661	11.5461	3
58	.01687	59.2659	.03434	29.1220	.05182	19.2959	.06934	14.4212	.08690	11.5072	2
59	.01716	58.2612	.03463	28.8771	.05212	19.1879	.06963	14.3607	.08720	11.4685	1
60	.01746	57.2900	.03492	28.6363	.05241	19.0811	.06993	14.3007	.08749	11.4301	0
′	Cotang	Tang	Cotang	Tang	Cotang	Tang	Cotang	Tang	Cotang	Tang	′
	89°		88°		87°		86°		85°		

TABLE XII. NATURAL TANGENTS AND COTANGENTS

′	5° Tang	Cotang	6° Tang	Cotang	7° Tang	Cotang	8° Tang	Cotang	9° Tang	Cotang	′
0	.08749	11.4301	.10510	9.51436	.12278	8.14435	.14054	7.11537	.15838	6.31375	60
1	.08778	11.3919	.10540	9.48781	.12308	8.12481	.14084	7.10038	.15868	6.30189	59
2	.08807	11.3540	.10569	9.46141	.12338	8.10536	.14113	7.08546	.15898	6.29007	58
3	.08837	11.3163	.10599	9.43515	.12367	8.08600	.14143	7.07059	.15928	6.27829	57
4	.08866	11.2789	.10628	9.40904	.12397	8.06674	.14173	7.05579	.15958	6.26655	56
5	.08895	11.2417	.10657	9.38307	.12426	8.04756	.14202	7.04105	.15988	6.25486	55
6	.08925	11.2048	.10687	9.35724	.12456	8.02848	.14232	7.02637	.16017	6.24321	54
7	.08954	11.1681	.10716	9.33155	.12485	8.00948	.14262	7.01174	.16047	6.23160	53
8	.08983	11.1316	.10746	9.30599	.12515	7.99058	.14291	6.99718	.16077	6.22003	52
9	.09013	11.0954	.10775	9.28058	.12544	7.97176	.14321	6.98268	.16107	6.20851	51
10	.09042	11.0594	.10805	9.25530	.12574	7.95302	.14351	6.96823	.16137	6.19703	50
11	.09071	11.0237	.10834	9.23016	.12603	7.93438	.14381	6.95385	.16167	6.18559	49
12	.09101	10.9882	.10863	9.20516	.12633	7.91582	.14410	6.93952	.16196	6.17419	48
13	.09130	10.9529	.10893	9.18028	.12662	7.89734	.14440	6.92525	.16226	6.16283	47
14	.09159	10.9178	.10922	9.15554	.12692	7.87895	.14470	6.91104	.16256	6.15151	46
15	.09189	10.8829	.10952	9.13093	.12722	7.86064	.14499	6.89688	.16286	6.14023	45
16	.09218	10.8483	.10981	9.10646	.12751	7.84242	.14529	6.88278	.16316	6.12899	44
17	.09247	10.8139	.11011	9.08211	.12781	7.82428	.14559	6.86874	.16346	6.11779	43
18	.09277	10.7797	.11040	9.05789	.12810	7.80622	.14588	6.85475	.16376	6.10664	42
19	.09306	10.7457	.11070	9.03379	.12840	7.78825	.14618	6.84082	.16405	6.09552	41
20	.09335	10.7119	.11099	9.00983	.12869	7.77035	.14648	6.82694	.16435	6.08444	40
21	.09365	10.6783	.11128	8.98598	.12899	7.75254	.14678	6.81312	.16465	6.07340	39
22	.09394	10.6450	.11158	8.96227	.12929	7.73480	.14707	6.79936	.16495	6.06240	38
23	.09423	10.6118	.11187	8.93867	.12958	7.71715	.14737	6.78564	.16525	6.05143	37
24	.09453	10.5789	.11217	8.91520	.12988	7.69957	.14767	6.77199	.16555	6.04051	36
25	.09482	10.5462	.11246	8.89185	.13017	7.68208	.14796	6.75838	.16585	6.02962	35
26	.09511	10.5136	.11276	8.86862	.13047	7.66466	.14826	6.74483	.16615	6.01878	34
27	.09541	10.4813	.11305	8.84551	.13076	7.64732	.14856	6.73133	.16645	6.00797	33
28	.09570	10.4491	.11335	8.82252	.13106	7.63005	.14886	6.71789	.16674	5.99720	32
29	.09600	10.4172	.11364	8.79964	.13136	7.61287	.14915	6.70450	.16704	5.98646	31
30	.09629	10.3854	.11394	8.77689	.13165	7.59575	.14945	6.69116	.16734	5.97576	30
31	.09658	10.3538	.11423	8.75425	.13195	7.57872	.14975	6.67787	.16764	5.96510	29
32	.09688	10.3224	.11452	8.73172	.13224	7.56176	.15005	6.66463	.16794	5.95448	28
33	.09717	10.2913	.11482	8.70931	.13254	7.54487	.15034	6.65144	.16824	5.94390	27
34	.09746	10.2602	.11511	8.68701	.13284	7.52806	.15064	6.63831	.16854	5.93335	26
35	.09776	10.2294	.11541	8.66482	.13313	7.51132	.15094	6.62523	.16884	5.92283	25
36	.09805	10.1988	.11570	8.64275	.13343	7.49465	.15124	6.61219	.16914	5.91236	24
37	.09834	10.1683	.11600	8.62078	.13372	7.47806	.15153	6.59921	.16944	5.90191	23
38	.09864	10.1381	.11629	8.59893	.13402	7.46154	.15183	6.58627	.16974	5.89151	22
39	.09893	10.1080	.11659	8.57718	.13432	7.44509	.15213	6.57339	.17004	5.88114	21
40	.09923	10.0780	.11688	8.55555	.13461	7.42871	.15243	6.56055	.17033	5.87080	20
41	.09952	10.0483	.11718	8.53402	.13491	7.41240	.15272	6.54777	.17063	5.86051	19
42	.09981	10.0187	.11747	8.51259	.13521	7.39616	.15302	6.53503	.17093	5.85024	18
43	.10011	9.98931	.11777	8.49128	.13550	7.37999	.15332	6.52234	.17123	5.84001	17
44	.10040	9.96007	.11806	8.47007	.13580	7.36389	.15362	6.50970	.17153	5.82982	16
45	.10069	9.93101	.11836	8.44896	.13609	7.34786	.15391	6.49710	.17183	5.81966	15
46	.10099	9.90211	.11865	8.42795	.13639	7.33190	.15421	6.48456	.17213	5.80953	14
47	.10128	9.87338	.11895	8.40705	.13669	7.31600	.15451	6.47206	.17243	5.79944	13
48	.10158	9.84482	.11924	8.38625	.13698	7.30018	.15481	6.45961	.17273	5.78938	12
49	.10187	9.81641	.11954	8.36555	.13728	7.28442	.15511	6.44720	.17303	5.77936	11
50	.10216	9.78817	.11983	8.34496	.13758	7.26873	.15540	6.43484	.17333	5.76937	10
51	.10246	9.76009	.12013	8.32446	.13787	7.25310	.15570	6.42253	.17363	5.75941	9
52	.10275	9.73217	.12042	8.30406	.13817	7.23754	.15600	6.41026	.17393	5.74949	8
53	.10305	9.70441	.12072	8.28376	.13846	7.22204	.15630	6.39804	.17423	5.73960	7
54	.10334	9.67680	.12101	8.26355	.13876	7.20661	.15660	6.38587	.17453	5.72974	6
55	.10363	9.64935	.12131	8.24345	.13906	7.19125	.15689	6.37374	.17483	5.71992	5
56	.10393	9.62205	.12160	8.22344	.13935	7.17594	.15719	6.36165	.17513	5.71013	4
57	.10422	9.59490	.12190	8.20352	.13965	7.16071	.15749	6.34961	.17543	5.70037	3
58	.10452	9.56791	.12219	8.18370	.13995	7.14553	.15779	6.33761	.17573	5.69064	2
59	.10481	9.54106	.12249	8.16398	.14024	7.13042	.15809	6.32566	.17603	5.68094	1
60	.10510	9.51436	.12278	8.14435	.14054	7.11537	.15838	6.31375	.17633	5.67128	0
′	Cotang	Tang	Cotang	Tang	Cotang	Tang	Cotang	Tang	Cotang	Tang	′
	84°		83°		82°		81°		80°		

TABLE XII.   NATURAL TANGENTS AND COTANGENTS

′	10° Tang	10° Cotang	11° Tang	11° Cotang	12° Tang	12° Cotang	13° Tang	13° Cotang	14° Tang	14° Cotang	′
0	.17633	5.67128	.19438	5.14455	.21256	4.70463	.23087	4.33148	.24933	4.01078	60
1	.17663	5.66165	.19468	5.13658	.21286	4.69791	.23117	4.32573	.24964	4.00582	59
2	.17693	5.65205	.19498	5.12862	.21316	4.69121	.23148	4.32001	.24995	4.00086	58
3	.17723	5.64248	.19529	5.12069	.21347	4.68452	.23179	4.31430	.25026	3.99592	57
4	.17753	5.63295	.19559	5.11279	.21377	4.67786	.23209	4.30860	.25056	3.99099	56
5	.17783	5.62344	.19589	5.10490	.21408	4.67121	.23240	4.30291	.25087	3.98607	55
6	.17813	5.61397	.19619	5.09704	.21438	4.66458	.23271	4.29724	.25118	3.98117	54
7	.17843	5.60452	.19649	5.08921	.21469	4.65797	.23301	4.29159	.25149	3.97627	53
8	.17873	5.59511	.19680	5.08139	.21499	4.65138	.23332	4.28595	.25180	3.97139	52
9	.17903	5.58573	.19710	5.07360	.21529	4.64480	.23363	4.28032	.25211	3.96651	51
10	.17933	5.57638	.19740	5.06584	.21560	4.63825	.23393	4.27471	.25242	3.96165	50
11	.17963	5.56706	.19770	5.05809	.21590	4.63171	.23424	4.26911	.25273	3.95680	49
12	.17993	5.55777	.19801	5.05037	.21621	4.62518	.23455	4.26352	.25304	3.95196	48
13	.18023	5.54851	.19831	5.04267	.21651	4.61868	.23485	4.25795	.25335	3.94713	47
14	.18053	5.53927	.19861	5.03499	.21682	4.61219	.23516	4.25239	.25366	3.94232	46
15	.18083	5.53007	.19891	5.02734	.21712	4.60572	.23547	4.24685	.25397	3.93751	45
16	.18113	5.52090	.19921	5.01971	.21743	4.59927	.23578	4.24132	.25428	3.93271	44
17	.18143	5.51176	.19952	5.01210	.21773	4.59283	.23608	4.23580	.25459	3.92793	43
18	.18173	5.50264	.19982	5.00451	.21804	4.58641	.23639	4.23030	.25490	3.92316	42
19	.18203	5.49356	.20012	4.99695	.21834	4.58001	.23670	4.22481	.25521	3.91839	41
20	.18233	5.48451	.20042	4.98940	.21864	4.57363	.23700	4.21933	.25552	3.91364	40
21	.18263	5.47548	.20073	4.98188	.21895	4.56726	.23731	4.21387	.25583	3.90890	39
22	.18293	5.46648	.20103	4.97438	.21925	4.56091	.23762	4.20842	.25614	3.90417	38
23	.18323	5.45751	.20133	4.96690	.21956	4.55458	.23793	4.20298	.25645	3.89945	37
24	.18353	5.44857	.20164	4.95945	.21986	4.54826	.23823	4.19756	.25676	3.89474	36
25	.18384	5.43966	.20194	4.95201	.22017	4.54196	.23854	4.19215	.25707	3.89004	35
26	.18414	5.43077	.20224	4.94460	.22047	4.53568	.23885	4.18675	.25738	3.88536	34
27	.18444	5.42192	.20254	4.93721	.22078	4.52941	.23916	4.18137	.25769	3.88068	33
28	.18474	5.41309	.20285	4.92984	.22108	4.52316	.23946	4.17600	.25800	3.87601	32
29	.18504	5.40429	.20315	4.92249	.22139	4.51693	.23977	4.17064	.25831	3.87136	31
30	.18534	5.39552	.20345	4.91516	.22169	4.51071	.24008	4.16530	.25862	3.86671	30
31	.18564	5.38677	.20376	4.90785	.22200	4.50451	.24039	4.15997	.25893	3.86208	29
32	.18594	5.37805	.20406	4.90056	.22231	4.49832	.24069	4.15465	.25924	3.85745	28
33	.18624	5.36936	.20436	4.89330	.22261	4.49215	.24100	4.14934	.25955	3.85284	27
34	.18654	5.36070	.20466	4.88605	.22292	4.48600	.24131	4.14405	.25986	3.84824	26
35	.18684	5.35206	.20497	4.87882	.22322	4.47986	.24162	4.13877	.26017	3.84364	25
36	.18714	5.34345	.20527	4.87162	.22353	4.47374	.24193	4.13350	.26048	3.83906	24
37	.18745	5.33487	.20557	4.86444	.22383	4.46764	.24223	4.12825	.26079	3.83449	23
38	.18775	5.32631	.20588	4.85727	.22414	4.46155	.24254	4.12301	.26110	3.82992	22
39	.18805	5.31778	.20618	4.85013	.22444	4.45548	.24285	4.11778	.26141	3.82537	21
40	.18835	5.30928	.20648	4.84300	.22475	4.44942	.24316	4.11256	.26172	3.82083	20
41	.18865	5.30080	.20679	4.83590	.22505	4.44338	.24347	4.10736	.26203	3.81630	19
42	.18895	5.29235	.20709	4.82882	.22536	4.43735	.24377	4.10216	.26235	3.81177	18
43	.18925	5.28393	.20739	4.82175	.22567	4.43134	.24408	4.09699	.26266	3.80726	17
44	.18955	5.27553	.20770	4.81471	.22597	4.42534	.24439	4.09182	.26297	3.80276	16
45	.18986	5.26715	.20800	4.80769	.22628	4.41936	.24470	4.08666	.26328	3.79827	15
46	.19016	5.25880	.20830	4.80068	.22658	4.41340	.24501	4.08152	.26359	3.79378	14
47	.19046	5.25048	.20861	4.79370	.22689	4.40745	.24532	4.07639	.26390	3.78931	13
48	.19076	5.24218	.20891	4.78673	.22719	4.40152	.24562	4.07127	.26421	3.78485	12
49	.19106	5.23391	.20921	4.77978	.22750	4.39560	.24593	4.06616	.26452	3.78040	11
50	.19136	5.22566	.20952	4.77286	.22781	4.38969	.24624	4.06107	.26483	3.77595	10
51	.19166	5.21744	.20982	4.76595	.22811	4.38381	.24655	4.05599	.26515	3.77152	9
52	.19197	5.20925	.21013	4.75906	.22842	4.37793	.24686	4.05092	.26546	3.76709	8
53	.19227	5.20107	.21043	4.75219	.22872	4.37207	.24717	4.04586	.26577	3.76268	7
54	.19257	5.19293	.21073	4.74534	.22903	4.36623	.24747	4.04081	.26608	3.75828	6
55	.19287	5.18480	.21104	4.73851	.22934	4.36040	.24778	4.03578	.26639	3.75388	5
56	.19317	5.17671	.21134	4.73170	.22964	4.35459	.24809	4.03076	.26670	3.74950	4
57	.19347	5.16863	.21164	4.72490	.22995	4.34879	.24840	4.02574	.26701	3.74512	3
58	.19378	5.16058	.21195	4.71813	.23026	4.34300	.24871	4.02074	.26733	3.74075	2
59	.19408	5.15256	.21225	4.71137	.23056	4.33723	.24902	4.01576	.26764	3.73640	1
60	.19438	5.14455	.21256	4.70463	.23087	4.33148	.24933	4.01078	.26795	3.73205	0
′	Cotang	Tang	Cotang	Tang	Cotang	Tang	Cotang	Tang	Cotang	Tang	′
	79°		78°		77°		76°		75°		

TABLE XII.　NATURAL TANGENTS AND COTANGENTS

′	15° Tang	15° Cotang	16° Tang	16° Cotang	17° Tang	17° Cotang	18° Tang	18° Cotang	19° Tang	19° Cotang	′
0	.26795	3.73205	.28675	3.48741	.30573	3.27085	.32492	3.07768	.34433	2.90421	60
1	.26826	3.72771	.28706	3.48359	.30605	3.26745	.32524	3.07464	.34465	2.90147	59
2	.26857	3.72338	.28738	3.47977	.30637	3.26406	.32556	3.07160	.34498	2.89873	58
3	.26888	3.71907	.28769	3.47596	.30669	3.26067	.32588	3.06857	.34530	2.89600	57
4	.26920	3.71476	.28800	3.47216	.30700	3.25729	.32621	3.06554	.34563	2.89327	56
5	.26951	3.71046	.28832	3.46837	.30732	3.25392	.32653	3.06252	.34596	2.89055	55
6	.26982	3.70616	.28864	3.46458	.30764	3.25055	.32685	3.05950	.34628	2.88783	54
7	.27013	3.70188	.28895	3.46080	.30796	3.24719	.32717	3.05649	.34661	2.88511	53
8	.27044	3.69761	.28927	3.45703	.30828	3.24383	.32749	3.05349	.34693	2.88240	52
9	.27076	3.69335	.28958	3.45327	.30860	3.24049	.32782	3.05049	.34726	2.87970	51
10	.27107	3.68909	.28990	3.44951	.30891	3.23714	.32814	3.04749	.34758	2.87700	50
11	.27138	3.68485	.29021	3.44576	.30923	3.23381	.32846	3.04450	.34791	2.87430	49
12	.27169	3.68061	.29053	3.44202	.30955	3.23048	.32878	3.04152	.34824	2.87161	48
13	.27201	3.67638	.29084	3.43829	.30987	3.22715	.32911	3.03854	.34856	2.86892	47
14	.27232	3.67217	.29116	3.43456	.31019	3.22384	.32943	3.03556	.34889	2.86624	46
15	.27263	3.66796	.29147	3.43084	.31051	3.22053	.32975	3.03260	.34922	2.86356	45
16	.27294	3.66376	.29179	3.42713	.31083	3.21722	.33007	3.02963	.34954	2.86089	44
17	.27326	3.65957	.29210	3.42343	.31115	3.21392	.33040	3.02667	.34987	2.85822	43
18	.27357	3.65538	.29242	3.41973	.31147	3.21063	.33072	3.02372	.35020	2.85555	42
19	.27388	3.65121	.29274	3.41604	.31178	3.20734	.33104	3.02077	.35052	2.85289	41
20	.27419	3.64705	.29305	3.41236	.31210	3.20406	.33136	3.01783	.35085	2.85023	40
21	.27451	3.64289	.29337	3.40869	.31242	3.20079	.33169	3.01489	.35118	2.84758	39
22	.27482	3.63874	.29368	3.40502	.31274	3.19752	.33201	3.01196	.35150	2.84494	38
23	.27513	3.63461	.29400	3.40136	.31306	3.19426	.33233	3.00903	.35183	2.84229	37
24	.27545	3.63048	.29432	3.39771	.31338	3.19100	.33266	3.00611	.35216	2.83965	36
25	.27576	3.62636	.29463	3.39406	.31370	3.18775	.33298	3.00319	.35248	2.83702	35
26	.27607	3.62224	.29495	3.39042	.31402	3.18451	.33330	3.00028	.35281	2.83439	34
27	.27638	3.61814	.29526	3.38679	.31434	3.18127	.33363	2.99738	.35314	2.83176	33
28	.27670	3.61405	.29558	3.38317	.31466	3.17804	.33395	2.99447	.35346	2.82914	32
29	.27701	3.60996	.29590	3.37955	.31498	3.17481	.33427	2.99158	.35379	2.82653	31
30	.27732	3.60588	.29621	3.37594	.31530	3.17159	.33460	2.98868	.35412	2.82391	30
31	.27764	3.60181	.29653	3.37234	.31562	3.16838	.33492	2.98580	.35445	2.82130	29
32	.27795	3.59775	.29685	3.36875	.31594	3.16517	.33524	2.98292	.35477	2.81870	28
33	.27826	3.59370	.29716	3.36516	.31626	3.16197	.33557	2.98004	.35510	2.81610	27
34	.27858	3.58966	.29748	3.36158	.31658	3.15877	.33589	2.97717	.35543	2.81350	26
35	.27889	3.58562	.29780	3.35800	.31690	3.15558	.33621	2.97430	.35576	2.81091	25
36	.27921	3.58160	.29811	3.35443	.31722	3.15240	.33654	2.97144	.35608	2.80833	24
37	.27952	3.57758	.29843	3.35087	.31754	3.14922	.33686	2.96858	.35641	2.80574	23
38	.27983	3.57357	.29875	3.34732	.31786	3.14605	.33718	2.96573	.35674	2.80316	22
39	.28015	3.56957	.29906	3.34377	.31818	3.14288	.33751	2.96288	.35707	2.80059	21
40	.28046	3.56557	.29938	3.34023	.31850	3.13972	.33783	2.96004	.35740	2:79802	20
41	.28077	3.56159	.29970	3.33670	.31882	3.13656	.33816	2.95721	.35772	2.79545	19
42	.28109	3.55761	.30001	3.33317	.31914	3.13341	.33848	2.95437	.35805	2.79289	18
43	.28140	3.55364	.30033	3.32965	.31946	3.13027	.33881	2.95155	.35838	2.79033	17
44	.28172	3.54968	.30065	3.32614	.31978	3.12713	.33913	2.94872	.35871	2.78778	16
45	.28203	3.54573	.30097	3.32264	.32010	3.12400	.33945	2.94591	.35904	2.78523	15
46	.28234	3.54179	.30128	3.31914	.32042	3.12087	.33978	2.94309	.35937	2.78269	14
47	.28266	3.53785	.30160	3.31565	.32074	3.11775	.34010	2.94028	.35969	2.78014	13
48	.28297	3.53393	.30192	3.31216	.32106	3.11464	.34043	2.93748	.36002	2.77761	12
49	.28329	3.53001	.30224	3.30868	.32139	3.11153	.34075	2.93468	.36035	2.77507	11
50	.28360	3.52609	.30255	3.30521	.32171	3.10842	.34108	2.93189	.36068	2.77254	10
51	.28391	3.52219	.30287	3.30174	.32203	3.10532	.34140	2.92910	.36101	2.77002	9
52	.28423	3.51829	.30319	3.29829	.32235	3.10223	.34173	2.92632	.36134	2.76750	8
53	.28454	3.51441	.30351	3.29483	.32267	3.09914	.34205	2.92354	.36167	2.76498	7
54	.28486	3.51053	.30382	3.29139	.32299	3.09606	.34238	2.92076	.36199	2.76247	6
55	.28517	3.50666	.30414	3.28795	.32331	3.09298	.34270	2.91799	.36232	2.75996	5
56	.28549	3.50279	.30446	3.28452	.32363	3.08991	.34303	2.91523	.36265	2.75746	4
57	.28580	3.49894	.30478	3.28109	.32396	3.08685	.34335	2.91246	.36298	2.75496	3
58	.28612	3.49509	.30509	3.27767	.32428	3.08379	.34368	2.90971	.36331	2.75246	2
59	.28643	3.49125	.30541	3.27426	.32460	3.08073	.34400	2.90696	.36364	2.74997	1
60	.28675	3.48741	.30573	3.27085	.32492	3.07768	.34433	2.90421	.36397	2.74748	0
′	Cotang	Tang	Cotang	Tang	Cotang	Tang	Cotang	Tang	Cotang	Tang	′
	74°		73°		72°		71°		70°		

TABLE XII. NATURAL TANGENTS AND COTANGENTS

′	20°		21°		22°		23°		24°		′
	Tang	Cotang	Tang	Cotang	Tang	Cotang	Tang	Cotang	Tang	Cotang	
0	.36397	2.74748	.38386	2.60509	.40403	2.47509	.42447	2.35585	.44523	2.24604	60
1	.36430	2.74499	.38420	2.60283	.40436	2.47302	.42482	2.35395	.44558	2.24428	59
2	.36463	2.74251	.38453	2.60057	.40470	2.47095	.42516	2.35205	.44593	2.24252	58
3	.36496	2.74004	.38487	2.59831	.40504	2.46888	.42551	2.35015	.44627	2.24077	57
4	.36529	2.73756	.38520	2.59606	.40538	2.46682	.42585	2.34825	.44662	2.23902	56
5	.36562	2.73509	.38553	2.59381	.40572	2.46476	.42619	2.34636	.44697	2.23727	55
6	.36595	2.73263	.38587	2.59156	.40606	2.46270	.42654	2.34447	.44732	2.23553	54
7	.36628	2.73017	.38620	2.58932	.40640	2.46065	.42688	2.34258	.44767	2.23378	53
8	.36661	2.72771	.38654	2.58708	.40674	2.45860	.42722	2.34069	.44802	2.23204	52
9	.36694	2.72526	.38687	2.58484	.40707	2.45655	.42757	2.33881	.44837	2.23030	51
10	.36727	2.72281	.38721	2.58261	.40741	2.45451	.42791	2.33693	.44872	2.22857	50
11	.36760	2.72036	.38754	2.58038	.40775	2.45246	.42826	2.33505	.44907	2.22683	49
12	.36793	2.71792	.38787	2.57815	.40809	2.45043	.42860	2.33317	.44942	2.22510	48
13	.36826	2.71548	.38821	2.57593	.40843	2.44839	.42894	2.33130	.44977	2.22337	47
14	.36859	2.71305	.38854	2.57371	.40877	2.44636	.42929	2.32943	.45012	2.22164	46
15	.36892	2.71062	.38888	2.57150	.40911	2.44433	.42963	2.32756	.45047	2.21992	45
16	.36925	2.70819	.38921	2.56928	.40945	2.44230	.42998	2.32570	.45082	2.21819	44
17	.36958	2.70577	.38955	2.56707	.40979	2.44027	.43032	2.32383	.45117	2.21647	43
18	.36991	2.70335	.38988	2.56487	.41013	2.43825	.43067	2.32197	.45152	2.21475	42
19	.37024	2.70094	.39022	2.56266	.41047	2.43623	.43101	2.32012	.45187	2.21304	41
20	.37057	2.69853	.39055	2.56046	.41081	2.43422	.43136	2.31826	.45222	2.21132	40
21	.37090	2.69612	.39089	2.55827	.41115	2.43220	.43170	2.31641	.45257	2.20961	39
22	.37123	2.69371	.39122	2.55608	.41149	2.43019	.43205	2.31456	.45292	2.20790	38
23	.37157	2.69131	.39156	2.55389	.41183	2.42819	.43230	2.31271	.45327	2.20619	37
24	.37190	2.68892	.39190	2.55170	.41217	2.42618	.43274	2.31086	.45362	2.20449	36
25	.37223	2.68653	.39223	2.54952	.41251	2.42418	.43308	2.30902	.45397	2.20278	35
26	.37256	2.68414	.39257	2.54734	.41285	2.42218	.43343	2.30718	.45432	2.20108	34
27	.37289	2.68175	.39290	2.54516	.41319	2.42019	.43378	2.30534	.45467	2.19938	33
28	.37322	2.67937	.39324	2.54299	.41353	2.41819	.43412	2.30351	.45502	2.19769	32
29	.37355	2.67700	.39357	2.54082	.41387	2.41620	.43447	2.30167	.45538	2.19599	31
30	.37388	2.67462	.39391	2.53865	.41421	2.41421	.43481	2.29984	.45573	2.19430	30
31	.37422	2.67225	.39425	2.53648	.41455	2.41223	.43516	2.29801	.45608	2.19261	29
32	.37455	2.66989	.39458	2.53432	.41490	2.41025	.43550	2.29619	.45643	2.19092	28
33	.37488	2.66752	.39492	2.53217	.41524	2.40827	.43585	2.29437	.45678	2.18923	27
34	.37521	2.66516	.39526	2.53001	.41558	2.40629	.43620	2.29254	.45713	2.18755	26
35	.37554	2.66281	.39559	2.52786	.41592	2.40432	.43654	2.29073	.45748	2.18587	25
36	.37588	2.66046	.39593	2.52571	.41626	2.40235	.43689	2.28891	.45784	2.18419	24
37	.37621	2.65811	.39626	2.52357	.41660	2.40038	.43724	2.28710	.45819	2.18251	23
38	.37654	2.65576	.39660	2.52142	.41694	2.39841	.43758	2.28528	.45854	2.18084	22
39	.37687	2.65342	.39694	2.51929	.41728	2.39645	.43793	2.28348	.45889	2.17916	21
40	.37720	2.65109	.39727	2.51715	.41763	2.39449	.43828	2.28167	.45924	2.17749	20
41	.37754	2.64875	.39761	2.51502	.41797	2.39253	.43862	2.27987	.45960	2.17582	19
42	.37787	2.64642	.39795	2.51289	.41831	2.39058	.43897	2.27806	.45995	2.17416	18
43	.37820	2.64410	.39829	2.51076	.41865	2.38863	.43932	2.27626	.46030	2.17249	17
44	.37853	2.64177	.39862	2.50864	.41899	2.38668	.43966	2.27447	.46065	2.17083	16
45	.37887	2.63945	.39896	2.50652	.41933	2.38473	.44001	2.27267	.46101	2.16917	15
46	.37920	2.63714	.39930	2.50440	.41968	2.38279	.44036	2.27088	.46136	2.16751	14
47	.37953	2.63483	.39963	2.50229	.42002	2.38084	.44071	2.26909	.46171	2.16585	13
48	.37986	2.63252	.39997	2.50018	.42036	2.37891	.44105	2.26730	.46206	2.16420	12
49	.38020	2.63021	.40031	2.49807	.42070	2.37697	.44140	2.26552	.46242	2.16255	11
50	.38053	2.62791	.40065	2.49597	.42105	2.37504	.44175	2.26374	.46277	2.16090	10
51	.38086	2.62561	.40098	2.49386	.42139	2.37311	.44210	2.26196	.46312	2.15925	9
52	.38120	2.62332	.40132	2.49177	.42173	2.37118	.44244	2.26018	.46348	2.15760	8
53	.38153	2.62103	.40166	2.48967	.42207	2.36925	.44279	2.25840	.46383	2.15596	7
54	.38186	2.61874	.40200	2.48758	.42242	2.36733	.44314	2.25663	.46418	2.15432	6
55	.38220	2.61646	.40234	2.48549	.42276	2.36541	.44349	2.25486	.46454	2.15268	5
56	.38253	2.61418	.40267	2.48340	.42310	2.36349	.44384	2.25309	.46489	2.15104	4
57	.38286	2.61190	.40301	2.48132	.42345	2.36158	.44418	2.25132	.46525	2.14940	3
58	.38320	2.60963	.40335	2.47924	.42379	2.35967	.44453	2.24956	.46560	2.14777	2
59	.38353	2.60736	.40369	2.47716	.42413	2.35776	.44488	2.24780	.46595	2.14614	1
60	.38386	2.60509	.40403	2.47509	.42447	2.35585	.44523	2.24604	.46631	2.14451	0
′	Cotang	Tang	Cotang	Tang	Cotang	Tang	Cotang	Tang	Cotang	Tang	′
	69°		68°		67°		66°		65°		

TABLE XII. NATURAL TANGENTS AND COTANGENTS

′	25° Tang	25° Cotang	26° Tang	26° Cotang	27° Tang	27° Cotang	28° Tang	28° Cotang	29° Tang	29° Cotang	′
0	.46631	2.14451	.48773	2.05030	.50953	1.96261	.53171	1.88073	.55431	1.80405	60
1	.46666	2.14288	.48809	2.04879	.50989	1.96120	.53208	1.87941	.55469	1.80281	59
2	.46702	2.14125	.48845	2.04728	.51026	1.95979	.53246	1.87809	.55507	1.80158	58
3	.46737	2.13963	.48881	2.04577	.51063	1.95838	.53283	1.87677	.55545	1.80034	57
4	.46772	2.13801	.48917	2.04426	.51099	1.95698	.53320	1.87546	.55583	1.79911	56
5	.46808	2.13639	.48953	2.04276	.51136	1.95557	.53358	1.87415	.55621	1.79788	55
6	.46843	2.13477	.48989	2.04125	.51173	1.95417	.53395	1.87283	.55659	1.79665	54
7	.46879	2.13316	.49026	2.03975	.51209	1.95277	.53432	1.87152	.55697	1.79542	53
8	.46914	2.13154	.49062	2.03825	.51246	1.95137	.53470	1.87021	.55736	1.79419	52
9	.46950	2.12993	.49098	2.03675	.51283	1.94997	.53507	1.86891	.55774	1.79296	51
10	.46985	2.12832	.49134	2.03526	.51319	1.94858	.53545	1.86760	.55812	1.79174	50
11	.47021	2.12671	.49170	2.03376	.51356	1.94718	.53582	1.86630	.55850	1.79051	49
12	.47056	2.12511	.49206	2.03227	.51393	1.94579	.53620	1.86499	.55888	1.78929	48
13	.47092	2.12350	.49242	2.03078	.51430	1.94440	.53657	1.86369	.55926	1.78807	47
14	.47128	2.12190	.49278	2.02929	.51467	1.94301	.53694	1.86239	.55964	1.78685	46
15	.47163	2.12030	.49315	2.02780	.51503	1.94162	.53732	1.86109	.56003	1.78563	45
16	.47199	2.11871	.49351	2.02631	.51540	1.94023	.53769	1.85979	.56041	1.78441	44
17	.47234	2.11711	.49387	2.02483	.51577	1.93885	.53807	1.85850	.56079	1.78319	43
18	.47270	2.11552	.49423	2.02335	.51614	1.93746	.53844	1.85720	.56117	1.78198	42
19	.47305	2.11392	.49459	2.02187	.51651	1.93608	.53882	1.85591	.56156	1.78077	41
20	.47341	2.11233	.49495	2.02039	.51688	1.93470	.53920	1.85462	.56194	1.77955	40
21	.47377	2.11075	.49532	2.01891	.51724	1.93332	.53957	1.85333	.56232	1.77834	39
22	.47412	2.10916	.49568	2.01743	.51761	1.93195	.53995	1.85204	.56270	1.77713	38
23	.47448	2.10758	.49604	2.01596	.51798	1.93057	.54032	1.85075	.56309	1.77592	37
24	.47483	2.10600	.49640	2.01449	.51835	1.92920	.54070	1.84946	.56347	1.77471	36
25	.47519	2.10442	.49677	2.01302	.51872	1.92782	.54107	1.84818	.56385	1.77351	35
26	.47555	2.10284	.49713	2.01155	.51909	1.92645	.54145	1.84689	.56424	1.77230	34
27	.47590	2.10126	.49749	2.01008	.51946	1.92508	.54183	1.84561	.56462	1.77110	33
28	.47626	2.09969	.49786	2.00862	.51983	1.92371	.54220	1.84433	.56501	1.76990	32
29	.47662	2.09811	.49822	2.00715	.52020	1.92235	.54258	1.84305	.56539	1.76869	31
30	.47698	2.09654	.49858	2.00569	.52057	1.92098	.54296	1.84177	.56577	1.76749	30
31	.47733	2.09498	.49894	2.00423	.52094	1.91962	.54333	1.84049	.56616	1.76629	29
32	.47769	2.09341	.49931	2.00277	.52131	1.91826	.54371	1.83922	.56654	1.76510	28
33	.47805	2.09184	.49967	2.00131	.52168	1.91690	.54409	1.83794	.56693	1.76390	27
34	.47840	2.09028	.50004	1.99986	.52205	1.91554	.54446	1.83667	.56731	1.76271	26
35	.47876	2.08872	.50040	1.99841	.52242	1.91418	.54484	1.83540	.56769	1.76151	25
36	.47912	2.08716	.50076	1.99695	.52279	1.91282	.54522	1.83413	.56808	1.76032	24
37	.47948	2.08560	.50113	1.99550	.52316	1.91147	.54560	1.83286	.56846	1.75913	23
38	.47984	2.08405	.50149	1.99406	.52353	1.91012	.54597	1.83159	.56885	1.75794	22
39	.48019	2.08250	.50185	1.99261	.52390	1.90876	.54635	1.83033	.56923	1.75675	21
40	.48055	2.08094	.50222	1.99116	.52427	1.90741	.54673	1.82906	.56962	1.75556	20
41	.48091	2.07939	.50258	1.98972	.52464	1.90607	.54711	1.82780	.57000	1.75437	19
42	.48127	2.07785	.50295	1.98828	.52501	1.90472	.54748	1.82654	.57039	1.75319	18
43	.48163	2.07630	.50331	1.98684	.52538	1.90337	.54786	1.82528	.57078	1.75200	17
44	.48198	2.07476	.50368	1.98540	.52575	1.90203	.54824	1.82402	.57116	1.75082	16
45	.48234	2.07321	.50404	1.98396	.52613	1.90069	.54862	1.82276	.57155	1.74964	15
46	.48270	2.07167	.50441	1.98253	.52650	1.89935	.54900	1.82150	.57193	1.74846	14
47	.48306	2.07014	.50477	1.98110	.52687	1.89801	.54938	1.82025	.57232	1.74728	13
48	.48342	2.06860	.50514	1.97966	.52724	1.89667	.54975	1.81899	.57271	1.74610	12
49	.48378	2.06706	.50550	1.97823	.52761	1.89533	.55013	1.81774	.57309	1.74492	11
50	.48414	2.06553	.50587	1.97681	.52798	1.89400	.55051	1.81649	.57348	1.74375	10
51	.48450	2.06400	.50623	1.97538	.52836	1.89266	.55089	1.81524	.57386	1.74257	9
52	.48486	2.06247	.50660	1.97395	.52873	1.89133	.55127	1.81399	.57425	1.74140	8
53	.48521	2.06094	.50696	1.97253	.52910	1.89000	.55165	1.81274	.57464	1.74022	7
54	.48557	2.05942	.50733	1.97111	.52947	1.88867	.55203	1.81150	.57503	1.73905	6
55	.48593	2.05790	.50769	1.96969	.52985	1.88734	.55241	1.81025	.57541	1.73788	5
56	.48629	2.05637	.50806	1.96827	.53022	1.88602	.55279	1.80901	.57580	1.73671	4
57	.48665	2.05485	.50843	1.96685	.53059	1.88469	.55317	1.80777	.57619	1.73555	3
58	.48701	2.05333	.50879	1.96544	.53096	1.88337	.55355	1.80653	.57657	1.73438	2
59	.48737	2.05182	.50916	1.96402	.53134	1.88205	.55393	1.80529	.57696	1.73321	1
60	.48773	2.05030	.50953	1.96261	.53171	1.88073	.55431	1.80405	.57735	1.73205	0
′	Cotang 64°	Tang	Cotang 63°	Tang	Cotang 62°	Tang	Cotang 61°	Tang	Cotang 60°	Tang	′

TABLE XII. NATURAL TANGENTS AND COTANGENTS

′	30° Tang	30° Cotang	31° Tang	31° Cotang	32° Tang	32° Cotang	33° Tang	33° Cotang	34° Tang	34° Cotang	′
0	.57735	1.73205	.60086	1.66428	.62487	1.60033	.64941	1.53986	.67451	1.48256	60
1	.57774	1.73089	.60126	1.66318	.62527	1.59930	.64982	1.53888	.67493	1.48163	59
2	.57813	1.72973	.60165	1.66209	.62568	1.59826	.65024	1.53791	.67536	1.48070	58
3	.57851	1.72857	.60205	1.66099	.62608	1.59723	.65065	1.53693	.67578	1.47977	57
4	.57890	1.72741	.60245	1.65990	.62649	1.59620	.65106	1.53595	.67620	1.47885	56
5	.57929	1.72625	.60284	1.65881	.62689	1.59517	.65148	1.53497	.67663	1.47792	55
6	.57968	1.72509	.60324	1.65772	.62730	1.59414	.65189	1.53400	.67705	1.47699	54
7	.58007	1.72393	.60364	1.65663	.62770	1.59311	.65231	1.53302	.67748	1.47607	53
8	.58046	1.72278	.60403	1.65554	.62811	1.59208	.65272	1.53205	.67790	1.47514	52
9	.58085	1.72163	.60443	1.65445	.62852	1.59105	.65314	1.53107	.67832	1.47422	51
10	.58124	1.72047	.60483	1.65337	.62892	1.59002	.65355	1.53010	.67875	1.47330	50
11	.58162	1.71932	.60522	1.65228	.62933	1.58900	.65397	1.52913	.67917	1.47238	49
12	.58201	1.71817	.60562	1.65120	.62973	1.58797	.65438	1.52816	.67960	1.47146	48
13	.58240	1.71702	.60602	1.65011	.63014	1.58695	.65480	1.52719	.68002	1.47053	47
14	.58279	1.71588	.60642	1.64903	.63055	1.58593	.65521	1.52622	.68045	1.46962	46
15	.58318	1.71473	.60681	1.64795	.63095	1.58490	.65563	1.52525	.68088	1.46870	45
16	.58357	1.71358	.60721	1.64687	.63136	1.58388	.65604	1.52429	.68130	1.46778	44
17	.58396	1.71244	.60761	1.64579	.63177	1.58286	.65646	1.52332	.68173	1.46686	43
18	.58435	1.71129	.60801	1.64471	.63217	1.58184	.65688	1.52235	.68215	1.46595	42
19	.58474	1.71015	.60841	1.64363	.63258	1.58083	.65729	1.52139	.68258	1.46503	41
20	.58513	1.70901	.60881	1.64256	.63299	1.57981	.65771	1.52043	.68301	1.46411	40
21	.58552	1.70787	.60921	1.64148	.63340	1.57879	.65813	1.51946	.68343	1.46320	39
22	.58591	1.70673	.60960	1.64041	.63380	1.57778	.65854	1.51850	.68386	1.46229	38
23	.58631	1.70560	.61000	1.63934	.63421	1.57676	.65896	1.51754	.68429	1.46137	37
24	.58670	1.70446	.61040	1.63826	.63462	1.57575	.65938	1.51658	.68471	1.46046	36
25	.58709	1.70332	.61080	1.63719	.63503	1.57474	.65980	1.51562	.68514	1.45955	35
26	.58748	1.70219	.61120	1.63612	.63544	1.57372	.66021	1.51466	.68557	1.45864	34
27	.58787	1.70106	.61160	1.63505	.63584	1.57271	.66063	1.51370	.68600	1.45773	33
28	.58826	1.69992	.61200	1.63398	.63625	1.57170	.66105	1.51275	.68642	1.45682	32
29	.58865	1.69879	.61240	1.63292	.63666	1.57069	.66147	1.51179	.68685	1.45592	31
30	.58905	1.69766	.61280	1.63185	.63707	1.56969	.66189	1.51084	.68728	1.45501	30
31	.58944	1.69653	.61320	1.63079	.63748	1.56868	.66230	1.50988	.68771	1.45410	29
32	.58983	1.69541	.61360	1.62972	.63789	1.56767	.66272	1.50893	.68814	1.45320	28
33	.59022	1.69428	.61400	1.62866	.63830	1.56667	.66314	1.50797	.68857	1.45229	27
34	.59061	1.69316	.61440	1.62760	.63871	1.56566	.66356	1.50702	.68900	1.45139	26
35	.59101	1.69203	.61480	1.62654	.63912	1.56466	.66398	1.50607	.68942	1.45049	25
36	.59140	1.69091	.61520	1.62548	.63953	1.56366	.66440	1.50512	.68985	1.44958	24
37	.59179	1.68979	.61561	1.62442	.63994	1.56265	.66482	1.50417	.69028	1.44868	23
38	.59218	1.68866	.61601	1.62336	.64035	1.56165	.66524	1.50322	.69071	1.44778	22
39	.59258	1.68754	.61641	1.62230	.64076	1.56065	.66566	1.50228	.69114	1.44688	21
40	.59297	1.68643	.61681	1.62125	.64117	1.55966	.66608	1.50133	.69157	1.44598	20
41	.59336	1.68531	.61721	1.62019	.64158	1.55866	.66650	1.50038	.69200	1.44508	19
42	.59376	1.68419	.61761	1.61914	.64199	1.55766	.66692	1.49944	.69243	1.44418	18
43	.59415	1.68308	.61801	1.61808	.64240	1.55666	.66734	1.49849	.69286	1.44329	17
44	.59454	1.68196	.61842	1.61703	.64281	1.55567	.66776	1.49755	.69329	1.44239	16
45	.59494	1.68085	.61882	1.61598	.64322	1.55467	.66818	1.49661	.69372	1.44149	15
46	.59533	1.67974	.61922	1.61493	.64363	1.55368	.66860	1.49566	.69416	1.44060	14
47	.59573	1.67863	.61962	1.61388	.64404	1.55269	.66902	1.49472	.69459	1.43970	13
48	.59612	1.67752	.62003	1.61283	.64446	1.55170	.66944	1.49378	.69502	1.43881	12
49	.59651	1.67641	.62043	1.61179	.64487	1.55071	.66986	1.49284	.69545	1.43792	11
50	.59691	1.67530	.62083	1.61074	.64528	1.54972	.67028	1.49190	.69588	1.43703	10
51	.59730	1.67419	.62124	1.60970	.64569	1.54873	.67071	1.49097	.69631	1.43614	9
52	.59770	1.67309	.62164	1.60865	.64610	1.54774	.67113	1.49003	.69675	1.43525	8
53	.59809	1.67198	.62204	1.60761	.64652	1.54675	.67155	1.48909	.69718	1.43436	7
54	.59849	1.67088	.62245	1.60657	.64693	1.54576	.67197	1.48816	.69761	1.43347	6
55	.59888	1.66978	.62285	1.60553	.64734	1.54478	.67239	1.48722	.69804	1.43258	5
56	.59928	1.66867	.62325	1.60449	.64775	1.54379	.67282	1.48629	.69847	1.43169	4
57	.59967	1.66757	.62366	1.60345	.64817	1.54281	.67324	1.48536	.69891	1.43080	3
58	.60007	1.66647	.62406	1.60241	.64858	1.54183	.67366	1.48442	.69934	1.42992	2
59	.60046	1.66538	.62446	1.60137	.64899	1.54085	.67409	1.48349	.69977	1.42903	1
60	.60086	1.66428	.62487	1.60033	.64941	1.53986	.67451	1.48256	.70021	1.42815	0
′	Cotang	Tang	Cotang	Tang	Cotang	Tang	Cotang	Tang	Cotang	Tang	′
	59°		58°		57°		56°		55°		

TABLE XII. NATURAL TANGENTS AND COTANGENTS

′	35° Tang	Cotang	36° Tang	Cotang	37° Tang	Cotang	38° Tang	Cotang	39° Tang	Cotang	′
0	.70021	1.42815	.72654	1.37638	.75355	1.32704	.78129	1.27994	.80978	1.23490	60
1	.70064	1.42726	.72699	1.37554	.75401	1.32624	.78175	1.27917	.81027	1.23416	59
2	.70107	1.42638	.72743	1.37470	.75447	1.32544	.78222	1.27841	.81075	1.23343	58
3	.70151	1.42550	.72788	1.37386	.75492	1.32464	.78269	1.27764	.81123	1.23270	57
4	.70194	1.42462	.72832	1.37302	.75538	1.32384	.78316	1.27688	.81171	1.23196	56
5	.70238	1.42374	.72877	1.37218	.75584	1.32304	.78363	1.27611	.81220	1.23123	55
6	.70281	1.42286	.72921	1.37134	.75629	1.32224	.78410	1.27535	.81268	1.23050	54
7	.70325	1.42198	.72966	1.37050	.75675	1.32144	.78457	1.27458	.81316	1.22977	53
8	.70368	1.42110	.73010	1.36967	.75721	1.32064	.78504	1.27382	.81364	1.22904	52
9	.70412	1.42022	.73055	1.36883	.75767	1.31984	.78551	1.27306	.81413	1.22831	51
10	.70455	1.41934	.73100	1.36800	.75812	1.31904	.78598	1.27230	.81461	1.22758	50
11	.70499	1.41847	.73144	1.36716	.75858	1.31825	.78645	1.27153	.81510	1.22685	49
12	.70542	1.41759	.73189	1.36633	.75904	1.31745	.78692	1.27077	.81558	1.22612	48
13	.70586	1.41672	.73234	1.36549	.75950	1.31666	.78739	1.27001	.81606	1.22539	47
14	.70629	1.41584	.73278	1.36466	.75996	1.31586	.78786	1.26925	.81655	1.22467	46
15	.70673	1.41497	.73323	1.36383	.76042	1.31507	.78834	1.26849	.81703	1.22394	45
16	.70717	1.41409	.73368	1.36300	.76088	1.31427	.78881	1.26774	.81752	1.22321	44
17	.70760	1.41322	.73413	1.36217	.76134	1.31348	.78928	1.26698	.81800	1.22249	43
18	.70804	1.41235	.73457	1.36134	.76180	1.31269	.78975	1.26622	.81849	1.22176	42
19	.70848	1.41148	.73502	1.36051	.76226	1.31190	.79022	1.26546	.81898	1.22104	41
20	.70891	1.41061	.73547	1.35968	.76272	1.31110	.79070	1.26471	.81946	1.22031	40
21	.70935	1.40974	.73592	1.35885	.76318	1.31031	.79117	1.26395	.81995	1.21959	39
22	.70979	1.40887	.73637	1.35802	.76364	1.30952	.79164	1.26319	.82044	1.21886	38
23	.71023	1.40800	.73681	1.35719	.76410	1.30873	.79212	1.26244	.82092	1.21814	37
24	.71066	1.40714	.73726	1.35637	.76456	1.30795	.79259	1.26169	.82141	1.21742	36
25	.71110	1.40627	.73771	1.35554	.76502	1.30716	.79306	1.26093	.82190	1.21670	35
26	.71154	1.40540	.73816	1.35472	.76548	1.30637	.79354	1.26018	.82238	1.21598	34
27	.71198	1.40454	.73861	1.35389	.76594	1.30558	.79401	1.25943	.82287	1.21526	33
28	.71242	1.40367	.73906	1.35307	.76640	1.30480	.79449	1.25867	.82336	1.21454	32
29	.71285	1.40281	.73951	1.35224	.76686	1.30401	.79496	1.25792	.82385	1.21382	31
30	.71329	1.40195	.73996	1.35142	.76733	1.30323	.79544	1.25717	.82434	1.21310	30
31	.71373	1.40109	.74041	1.35060	.76779	1.30244	.79591	1.25642	.82483	1.21238	29
32	.71417	1.40022	.74086	1.34978	.76825	1.30166	.79639	1.25567	.82531	1.21166	28
33	.71461	1.39936	.74131	1.34896	.76871	1.30087	.79686	1.25492	.82580	1.21094	27
34	.71505	1.39850	.74176	1.34814	.76918	1.30009	.79734	1.25417	.82629	1.21023	26
35	.71549	1.39764	.74221	1.34732	.76964	1.29931	.79781	1.25343	.82678	1.20951	25
36	.71593	1.39679	.74267	1.34650	.77010	1.29853	.79829	1.25268	.82727	1.20879	24
37	.71637	1.39593	.74312	1.34568	.77057	1.29775	.79877	1.25193	.82776	1.20808	23
38	.71681	1.39507	.74357	1.34487	.77103	1.29696	.79924	1.25118	.82825	1.20736	22
39	.71725	1.39421	.74402	1.34405	.77149	1.29618	.79972	1.25044	.82874	1.20665	21
40	.71769	1.39336	.74447	1.34323	.77196	1.29541	.80020	1.24969	.82923	1.20593	20
41	.71813	1.39250	.74492	1.34242	.77242	1.29463	.80067	1.24895	.82972	1.20522	19
42	.71857	1.39165	.74538	1.34160	.77289	1.29385	.80115	1.24820	.83022	1.20451	18
43	.71901	1.39079	.74583	1.34079	.77335	1.29307	.80163	1.24746	.83071	1.20379	17
44	.71946	1.38994	.74628	1.33998	.77382	1.29229	.80211	1.24672	.83120	1.20308	16
45	.71990	1.38909	.74674	1.33916	.77428	1.29152	.80258	1.24597	.83169	1.20237	15
46	.72034	1.38824	.74719	1.33835	.77475	1.29074	.80306	1.24523	.83218	1.20166	14
47	.72078	1.38738	.74764	1.33754	.77521	1.28997	.80354	1.24449	.83268	1.20095	13
48	.72122	1.38653	.74810	1.33673	.77568	1.28919	.80402	1.24375	.83317	1.20024	12
49	.72167	1.38568	.74855	1.33592	.77615	1.28842	.80450	1.24301	.83366	1.19953	11
50	.72211	1.38484	.74900	1.33511	.77661	1.28764	.80498	1.24227	.83415	1.19882	10
51	.72255	1.38399	.74946	1.33430	.77708	1.28687	.80546	1.24153	.83465	1.19811	9
52	.72299	1.38314	.74991	1.33349	.77754	1.28610	.80594	1.24079	.83514	1.19740	8
53	.72344	1.38229	.75037	1.33268	.77801	1.28533	.80642	1.24005	.83564	1.19669	7
54	.72388	1.38145	.75082	1.33187	.77848	1.28456	.80690	1.23931	.83613	1.19599	6
55	.72432	1.38060	.75128	1.33107	.77895	1.28379	.80738	1.23858	.83662	1.19528	5
56	.72477	1.37976	.75173	1.33026	.77941	1.28302	.80786	1.23784	.83712	1.19457	4
57	.72521	1.37891	.75219	1.32946	.77988	1.28225	.80834	1.23710	.83761	1.19387	3
58	.72565	1.37807	.75264	1.32865	.78035	1.28148	.80882	1.23637	.83811	1.19316	2
59	.72610	1.37722	.75310	1.32785	.78082	1.28071	.80930	1.23563	.83860	1.19246	1
60	.72654	1.37638	.75355	1.32704	.78129	1.27994	.80978	1.23490	.83910	1.19175	0
′	Cotang	Tang	Cotang	Tang	Cotang	Tang	Cotang	Tang	Cotang	Tang	′
	54°		53°		52°		51°		50°		

TABLE XII. NATURAL TANGENTS AND COTANGENTS

′	40° Tang	40° Cotang	41° Tang	41° Cotang	42° Tang	42° Cotang	43° Tang	43° Cotang	44° Tang	44° Cotang	′
0	.83910	1.19175	.86929	1.15037	.90040	1.11061	.93252	1.07237	.96569	1.03553	60
1	.83960	1.19105	.86980	1.14969	.90093	1.10996	.93306	1.07174	.96625	1.03493	59
2	.84009	1.19035	.87031	1.14902	.90146	1.10931	.93360	1.07112	.96681	1.03433	58
3	.84059	1.18964	.87082	1.14834	.90199	1.10867	.93415	1.07049	.96738	1.03372	57
4	.84108	1.18894	.87133	1.14767	.90251	1.10802	.93469	1.06987	.96794	1.03312	56
5	.84158	1.18824	.87184	1.14699	.90304	1.10737	.93524	1.06925	.96850	1.03252	55
6	.84208	1.18754	.87236	1.14632	.90357	1.10672	.93578	1.06862	.96907	1.03192	54
7	.84258	1.18684	.87287	1.14565	.90410	1.10607	.93633	1.06800	.96963	1.03132	53
8	.84307	1.18614	.87338	1.14498	.90463	1.10543	.93688	1.06738	.97020	1.03072	52
9	.84357	1.18544	.87389	1.14430	.90516	1.10478	.93742	1.06676	.97076	1.03012	51
10	.84407	1.18474	.87441	1.14363	.90569	1.10414	.93797	1.06613	.97133	1.02952	50
11	.84457	1.18404	.87492	1.14296	.90621	1.10349	.93852	1.06551	.97189	1.02892	49
12	.84507	1.18334	.87543	1.14229	.90674	1.10285	.93906	1.06489	.97246	1.02832	48
13	.84556	1.18264	.87595	1.14162	.90727	1.10220	.93961	1.06427	.97302	1.02772	47
14	.84606	1.18194	.87646	1.14095	.90781	1.10156	.94016	1.06365	.97359	1.02713	46
15	.84656	1.18125	.87698	1.14028	.90834	1.10091	.94071	1.06303	.97416	1.02653	45
16	.84706	1.18055	.87749	1.13961	.90887	1.10027	.94125	1.06241	.97472	1.02593	44
17	.84756	1.17986	.87801	1.13894	.90940	1.09963	.94180	1.06179	.97529	1.02533	43
18	.84806	1.17916	.87852	1.13828	.90993	1.09899	.94235	1.06117	.97586	1.02474	42
19	.84856	1.17846	.87904	1.13761	.91046	1.09834	.94290	1.06056	.97643	1.02414	41
20	.84906	1.17777	.87955	1.13694	.91099	1.09770	.94345	1.05994	.97700	1.02355	40
21	.84956	1.17708	.88007	1.13627	.91153	1.09706	.94400	1.05932	.97756	1.02295	39
22	.85006	1.17638	.88059	1.13561	.91206	1.09642	.94455	1.05870	.97813	1.02236	38
23	.85057	1.17569	.88110	1.13494	.91259	1.09578	.94510	1.05809	.97870	1.02176	37
24	.85107	1.17500	.88162	1.13428	.91313	1.09514	.94565	1.05747	.97927	1.02117	36
25	.85157	1.17430	.88214	1.13361	.91366	1.09450	.94620	1.05685	.97984	1.02057	35
26	.85207	1.17361	.88265	1.13295	.91419	1.09386	.94676	1.05624	.98041	1.01998	34
27	.85257	1.17292	.88317	1.13228	.91473	1.09322	.94731	1.05562	.98098	1.01939	33
28	.85308	1.17223	.88369	1.13162	.91526	1.09258	.94786	1.05501	.98155	1.01879	32
29	.85358	1.17154	.88421	1.13096	.91580	1.09195	.94841	1.05439	.98213	1.01820	31
30	.85408	1.17085	.88473	1.13029	.91633	1.09131	.94896	1.05378	.98270	1.01761	30
31	.85458	1.17016	.88524	1.12963	.91687	1.09067	.94952	1.05317	.98327	1.01702	29
32	.85509	1.16947	.88576	1.12897	.91740	1.09003	.95007	1.05255	.98384	1.01642	28
33	.85559	1.16878	.88628	1.12831	.91794	1.08940	.95062	1.05194	.98441	1.01583	27
34	.85609	1.16809	.88680	1.12765	.91847	1.08876	.95118	1.05133	.98499	1.01524	26
35	.85660	1.16741	.88732	1.12699	.91901	1.08813	.95173	1.05072	.98556	1.01465	25
36	.85710	1.16672	.88784	1.12633	.91955	1.08749	.95229	1.05010	.98613	1.01406	24
37	.85761	1.16603	.88836	1.12567	.92008	1.08686	.95284	1.04949	.98671	1.01347	23
38	.85811	1.16535	.88888	1.12501	.92062	1.08622	.95340	1.04888	.98728	1.01288	22
39	.85862	1.16466	.88940	1.12435	.92116	1.08559	.95395	1.04827	.98786	1.01229	21
40	.85912	1.16398	.88992	1.12369	.92170⌋	1.08496	.95451	1.04766	.98843	1.01170	20
41	.85963	1.16329	.89045	1.12303	92224	1.08432	.95506	1.04705	.98901	1.01112	19
42	.86014	1.16261	.89097	1.12238	.92277	1.08369	.95562	1.04644	.98958	1.01053	18
43	.86064	1.16192	.89149	1.12172	.92331	1.08306	.95618	1.04583	.99016	1.00994	17
44	.86115	1.16124	.89201	1.12106	.92385	1.08243	.95673	1.04522	.99073	1.00935	16
45	.86166	1.16056	.89253	1.12041	.92439	1.08179	.95729	1.04461	.99131	1.00876	15
46	.86216	1.15987	.89306	1.11975	.92493	1.08116	.95785	1.04401	.99189	1.00818	14
47	.86267	1.15919	.89358	1.11909	.92547	1.08053	.95841	1.04340	.99247	1.00759	13
48	.86318	1.15851	.89410	1.11844	.92601	1.07990	.95897	1.04279	.99304	1.00701	12
49	.86368	1.15783	.89463	1.11778	.92655	1.07927	.95952	1.04218	.99362	1.00642	11
50	.86419	1.15715	.89515	1.11713	.92709	1.07864	.96008	1.04158	.99420	1.00583	10
51	.86470	1.15647	.89567	1.11648	.92763	1.07801	.96064	1.04097	.99478	1.00525	9
52	.86521	1.15579	.89620	1.11582	.92817	1.07738	.96120	1.04036	.99536	1.00467	8
53	.86572	1.15511	.89672	1.11517	.92872	1.07676	.96176	1.03976	.99594	1.00408	7
54	.86623	1.15443	.89725	1.11452	.92926	1.07613	.96232	1.03915	.99652	1.00350	6
55	.86674	1.15375	.89777	1.11387	.92980	1.07550	.96288	1.03855	.99710	1.00291	5
56	.86725	1.15308	.89830	1.11321	.93034	1.07487	.96344	1.03794	.99768	1.00233	4
57	.86776	1.15240	.89883	1.11256	.93088	1.07425	.96400	1.03734	.99826	1.00175	3
58	.86827	1.15172	.89935	1.11191	.93143	1.07362	.96457	1.03674	.99884	1.00116	2
59	.86878	1.15104	.89988	1.11126	.93197	1.07299	.96513	1.03613	.99942	1.00058	1
60	.86929	1.15037	.90040	1.11061	.93252	1.07237	.96569	1.03553	1.00000	1.00000	0
′	Cotang 49°	Tang	Cotang 48°	Tang	Cotang 47°	Tang	Cotang 46°	Tang	Cotang 45°	Tang	′

TABLE XIII. LENGTHS OF CIRCULAR ARCS FOR RADIUS = 1

Deg.	Length	Deg.	Length	Min.	Length	Sec.	Length
1	0.017 45 329	61	1.064 65 084	1	.000 29 089	1	.000 00 485
2	.034 90 659	62	.082 10 414	2	0 58 178	2	00 970
3	.052 35 988	63	.099 55 743	3	0 87 266	3	01 454
4	.069 81 317	64	.117 01 072	4	1 16 355	4	01 939
5	0.087 26 646	65	1.134 46 401	5	.001 45 444	5	.000 02 424
6	.104 71 976	66	.151 91 731	6	1 74 533	6	02 909
7	.122 17 305	67	.169 37 060	7	2 03 622	7	03 394
8	.139 62 634	68	.186 82 389	8	2 32 711	8	03 879
9	.157 07 963	69	.204 27 718	9	2 61 799	9	04 363
10	0.174 53 293	70	1.221 73 048	10	.002 90 888	10	.000 04 848
11	.191 98 622	71	.239 18 377	11	3 19 977	11	05 333
12	.209 43 951	72	.256 63 706	12	3 49 066	12	05 818
13	.226 89 280	73	.274 09 035	13	3 78 155	13	06 303
14	.244 34 610	74	.291 54 365	14	4 07 243	14	06 787
15	0.261 79 939	75	1.308 99 694	15	.004 36 332	15	.000 07 272
16	.279 25 268	76	.326 45 023	16	4 65 421	16	07 757
17	.296 70 597	77	.343 90 352	17	4 94 510	17	08 242
18	.314 15 927	78	.361 35 682	18	5 23 599	18	08 727
19	.331 61 256	79	.378 81 011	19	5 52 688	19	09 211
20	0.349 06 585	80	1.396 26 340	20	.005 81 776	20	.000 09 696
21	.366 51 914	81	.413 71 669	21	6 10 865	21	10 181
22	.383 97 244	82	.431 16 999	22	6 39 954	22	10 666
23	.401 42 573	83	.448 62 328	23	6 69 043	23	11 151
24	.418 87 902	84	.466 07 657	24	6 98 132	24	11 636
25	0.436 33 231	85	1.483 52 986	25	.007 27 221	25	.000 12 120
26	.453 78 561	86	.500 98 316	26	7 56 309	26	12 605
27	.471 23 890	87	.518 43 645	27	7 85 398	27	13 090
28	.488 69 219	88	.535 88 974	28	8 14 487	28	13 575
29	.506 14 548	89	.553 34 303	29	8 43 576	29	14 060
30	0.523 59 878	90	1.570 79 633	30	.008 72 665	30	.000 14 544
31	.541 05 207	91	.588 24 962	31	9 01 753	31	15 029
32	.558 50 536	92	.605 70 291	32	9 30 842	32	15 514
33	.575 95 865	93	.623 15 620	33	9 59 931	33	15 999
34	.593 41 195	94	.640 60 950	34	9 89 020	34	16 484
35	0.610 86 524	95	1.658 06 279	35	.010 18 109	35	.000 16 969
36	.628 31 853	96	.675 51 608	36	10 47 199	36	17 453
37	.645 77 182	97	.692 96 937	37	10 76 286	37	17 938
38	.663 22 512	98	.710 42 267	38	11 05 375	38	18 423
39	.680 67 841	99	.727 87 596	39	11 34 464	39	18 908
40	0.698 13 170	100	1.745 32 925	40	.011 63 553	40	.000 19 393
41	.715 58 499	101	.762 78 254	41	11 92 642	41	19 877
42	.733 03 829	102	.780 23 584	42	12 21 730	42	20 362
43	.750 49 158	103	.797 68 913	43	12 50 819	43	20 847
44	.767 94 487	104	.815 14 242	44	12 79 908	44	21 332
45	0.785 39 816	105	1.832 59 571	45	.013 08 997	45	.000 21 817
46	.802 85 146	106	.850 04 901	46	13 38 086	46	22 301
47	.820 30 475	107	.867 50 230	47	13 67 175	47	22 786
48	.837 75 804	108	.884 95 559	48	13 96 263	48	23 271
49	.855 21 133	109	.902 40 888	49	14 25 352	49	23 756
50	0.872 66 463	110	1.919 86 218	50	.014 54 441	50	.000 24 241
51	.890 11 792	111	.937 31 547	51	14 83 530	51	24 726
52	.907 57 121	112	.954 76 876	52	15 12 619	52	25 210
53	.925 02 450	113	.972 22 205	53	15 41 708	53	25 695
54	.942 47 780	114	.989 67 535	54	15 70 796	54	26 180
55	0.959 93 109	115	2.007 12 864	55	.015 99 885	55	.000 26 665
56	0.977 38 438	116	.024 58 193	56	16 28 974	56	27 150
57	0.994 83 767	117	.042 03 522	57	16 58 063	57	27 634
58	1.012 29 097	118	.059 48 852	58	16 87 152	58	28 119
59	1.029 74 426	119	.076 94 181	59	17 16 240	59	28 604
60	1.047 19 755	120	.094 39 510	60	17 45 329	60	29 089

TABLE XIV. TRIGONOMETRIC FORMULAS FOR THE SOLUTION OF RIGHT TRIANGLES

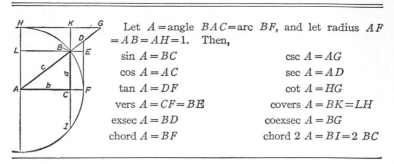

Let A = angle BAC = arc BF, and let radius AF = AB = AH = 1. Then,

$\sin A = BC$ $\csc A = AG$

$\cos A = AC$ $\sec A = AD$

$\tan A = DF$ $\cot A = HG$

vers $A = CF = BE$ covers $A = BK = LH$

exsec $A = BD$ coexsec $A = BG$

chord $A = BF$ chord 2 $A = BI = 2\ BC$

In the right-angled triangle ABC, let $AB = c$, $BC = a$, $CA = b$. Then,

1. $\sin A = \dfrac{a}{c}$

2. $\cos A = \dfrac{b}{c}$

3. $\tan A = \dfrac{a}{b}$

4. $\cot A = \dfrac{b}{a}$

5. $\sec A = \dfrac{c}{b}$

6. $\csc A = \dfrac{c}{a}$

7. vers $A = 1 - \cos A = \dfrac{c-b}{c} =$ covers B

8. exsec $A = \sec A - 1 = \dfrac{c-b}{b} =$ coexsec B

9. covers $A = \dfrac{c-a}{c} =$ vers B

10. coexsec $A = \dfrac{c-a}{a} =$ exsec B

11. $a = c \sin A = b \tan A$

12. $b = c \cos A = a \cot A$

13. $c = \dfrac{a}{\sin A} = \dfrac{b}{\cos A}$

14. $a = c \cos B = b \cot B$

15. $b = c \sin B = a \tan B$

16. $c = \dfrac{a}{\cos B} = \dfrac{b}{\sin B}$

17. $a = \sqrt{c^2 - b^2} = \sqrt{(c-b)(c+b)}$

18. $b = \sqrt{c^2 - a^2} = \sqrt{(c-a)(c+a)}$

19. $c = \sqrt{a^2 + b^2}$

20. $C = 90° = A + B$

21. Area $= \frac{1}{2}ab$

TABLE XIV. TRIGONOMETRIC FORMULAS FOR THE SOLUTION OF OBLIQUE TRIANGLES

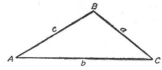

No.	Given	Sought	Formula
22	A, B, a	C, b, c	$C = 180° - (A+B)$ $b = \dfrac{a}{\sin A} \times \sin B$ $c = \dfrac{a}{\sin A} \times \sin (A+B) = \dfrac{a}{\sin A} \times \sin C$
		Area	$\text{Area} = \tfrac{1}{2}ab \sin C = \dfrac{a^2 \sin B \sin C}{2 \sin A}$
23	A, a, b	B, C, c	$\sin B = \dfrac{\sin A}{a} \times b$ $C = 180° - (A+B)$ $c = \dfrac{a}{\sin A} \times \sin C$
		Area	$\text{Area} = \tfrac{1}{2}ab \sin C$
24	$C, a, b,$	c	$c = \sqrt{a^2 + b^2 - 2ab \cos C}$
25		$\tfrac{1}{2}(A+B)$	$\tfrac{1}{2}(A+B) = 90° - \tfrac{1}{2}C$
26		$\tfrac{1}{2}(A-B)$	$\tan \tfrac{1}{2}(A-B) = \dfrac{a-b}{a+b} \times \tan \tfrac{1}{2}(A+B)$
27		A, B	$A = \tfrac{1}{2}(A+B) + \tfrac{1}{2}(A-B)$ $B = \tfrac{1}{2}(A+B) - \tfrac{1}{2}(A-B)$
28		c	$c = (a+b) \times \dfrac{\cos \tfrac{1}{2}(A+B)}{\cos \tfrac{1}{2}(A-B)} = (a-b) \times \dfrac{\sin \tfrac{1}{2}(A+B)}{\sin \tfrac{1}{2}(A-B)}$
29		Area	$\text{Area} = \tfrac{1}{2}ab \sin C$
30	a, b, c	A	$\text{Let } s = \dfrac{a+b+c}{2}$
31			$\sin \tfrac{1}{2} A = \sqrt{\dfrac{(s-b)(s-c)}{bc}}$ $\cos \tfrac{1}{2} A = \sqrt{\dfrac{s(s-a)}{bc}}$ $\tan \tfrac{1}{2} A = \sqrt{\dfrac{(s-b)(s-c)}{s(s-a)}}$
32			$\sin A = \dfrac{2\sqrt{s(s-a)(s-b)(s-c)}}{bc}$ $\cos A = \dfrac{b^2 + c^2 - a^2}{2bc}$
33		Area	$\text{Area} = \sqrt{s(s-a)(s-b)(s-c)}$

REFERENCES

REFERENCES

AMERICAN SOCIETY OF CIVIL ENGINEERS, Committee of the Surveying and Mapping Division on Definition of Surveying Terms. *Definitions of Surveying, Mapping, and Related Terms.* Manual No. 34, 1954.

BOUCHARD, HARRY. *Surveying,* 3d ed. Scranton: International Textbook Company, 1947.

BRINKER, RUSSELL C. *2222 Review Questions for Surveyors,* 4th ed. Published by the author, Blacksburg, Virginia, 1954.

BRINKER, RUSSELL C., and DONALD F. GRIFFIN. *Surveying Field Notes,* 2d ed. Published by the authors, Blacksburg, Virginia, 1951.

BROWN, CURTIS M. *Boundary Control for Surveyors in California.* Published by the author, San Diego, 1954.

CLARK, FRANK E. *Law of Surveying and Boundaries.* Indianapolis: The Bobbs-Merrill Company, 1939.

DAVIS, RAYMOND E., and FRANCIS S. FOOTE. *Surveying,* 4th ed. New York: McGraw-Hill Book Company, Inc., 1953.

EICHLER, JOHN O., and HARRY TUBIS. *Photogrammetry Laboratory Kit,* 1953.

Ephemeris. (Ephemerides are published annually by W. & L. E. Gurley, by Keuffel and Esser Company, and by C. L. Berger and Sons, Inc.]

MEYER, CARL F. *Route Surveying.* Scranton: International Textbook Company, 1949.

Optical Tooling Equipment. Keuffel and Esser Company, 1953.

RICE, PAUL P., and CHARLES O. ROTH. *Engineer's Field Notes.* Published by the authors, Phillipsburg, New Jersey, 1940.

RUBEY, HARRY. *Route Surveys,* 2d ed. New York: The Macmillan Company, 1951.

RUBEY, HARRY, GEORGE E. LOMMEL, and MARION W. TODD. *Engineering Surveys: Elementary and Applied,* 2d ed. New York: The Macmillan Company, 1950.

SKELTON, RAY H. *Legal Elements of Boundaries and Adjacent Properties.* Indianapolis: The Bobbs-Merrill Company, 1930.

SKELTON, RUSSELL R. *Route Surveys.* New York: McGraw-Hill Book Company, Inc., 1949.

STEWART, LOWELL O. *Public Land Surveys.* Ames, Iowa: Collegiate Press, Inc., 1935.

Surveying and Mapping. [The quarterly journal of the American Congress on Surveying and Mapping.]

TRACY, JOHN C. *Surveying Theory and Practice.* New York: John Wiley & Sons, Inc., 1947.

UNITED STATES BUREAU OF LAND MANAGEMENT. *Manual of Instructions for the Survey of the Public Lands of the United States.* Washington, D.C.: Government Printing Office, 1947.

UNITED STATES GENERAL LAND OFFICE. *Standard Field Tables.* Washington, D.C.: Government Printing Office, 1942.

WATTLES, WILLIAM C. *Description and Survey in Title, California Land Titles.* Los Angeles: Title Insurance and Trust Company, 1952.

WHITMORE, GEORGE D. *Advanced Surveying and Mapping.* Scranton: International Textbook Company, 1949.

535

INDEX

INDEX